Life's Little Secrets & Shortcuts

FOR

DUMMIES®

Edited by Dummies Press

Hungry Minds™

Best-Selling Books • Digital Downloads • e-Books • Answer Networks
e-Newsletters • Branded Web Sites • e-Learning

New York, NY ◆ Cleveland, OH ◆ Indianapolis, IN

Life's Little Secrets & Shortcuts For Dummies®

Published by:
Hungry Minds, Inc.
909 Third Avenue
New York, NY 10022
www.hungryminds.com
www.dummies.com

Library of Congress Control Number: 2001099014

ISBN: 0-7645-8303-4

Printed in the United States of America

10 9 8 7 6 5 4 3 2

1OX/RY/QR/QS/IN

Distributed in the United States by Hungry Minds, Inc.

Distributed by CDG Books Canada Inc. for Canada; by Transworld Publishers Limited in the United Kingdom; by IDG Norge Books for Norway; by IDG Sweden Books for Sweden; by IDG Books Australia Publishing Corporation Pty. Ltd. for Australia and New Zealand; by TransQuest Publishers Pte Ltd. for Singapore, Malaysia, Thailand, Indonesia, and Hong Kong; by Gotop Information Inc. for Taiwan; by ICG Muse, Inc. for Japan; by Intersoft for South Africa; by Eyrolles for France; by International Thomson Publishing for Germany, Austria and Switzerland; by Distribuidora Cuspide for Argentina; by LR International for Brazil; by Galileo Libros for Chile; by Ediciones ZETA S.C.R. Ltda. for Peru; by WS Computer Publishing Corporation, Inc., for the Philippines; by Contemporanea de Ediciones for Venezuela; by Express Computer Distributors for the Caribbean and West Indies; by Micronesia Media Distributor, Inc. for Micronesia; by Chips Computadoras S.A. de C.V. for Mexico; by Editorial Norma de Panama S.A. for Panama; by American Bookshops for Finland.

For general information on Hungry Minds' products and services please contact our Customer Care department; within the U.S. at 800-762-2974, outside the U.S. at 317-572-3993 or fax 317-572-4002.

For sales inquiries and resellers information, including discounts, premium and bulk quantity sales and foreign language translations please contact our Customer Care department at 800-434-3422, fax 317-572-4002 or write to Hungry Minds, Inc., Attn: Customer Care department, 10475 Crosspoint Boulevard, Indianapolis, IN 46256.

For information on licensing foreign or domestic rights, please contact our Sub-Rights Customer Care department at 212-884-5000.

For information on using Hungry Minds' products and services in the classroom or for ordering examination copies, please contact our Educational Sales department at 800-434-2086 or fax 317-572-4005.

Please contact our Public Relations department at 212-884-5163 for press review copies or 212-884-5000 for author interviews and other publicity information or fax 212-884-5400.

For authorization to photocopy items for corporate, personal, or educational use, please contact Copyright Clearance Center, 222 Rosewood Drive, Danvers, MA 01923, or fax 978-750-4470.

Hungry Minds is a trademark of Hungry Minds, Inc.

About the Authors

Kathleen Allen (*The Complete MBA For Dummies*) is an authority on entrepreneurship and small business technology. She has authored several books on entrepreneurship, as well as written articles for publications such as *Inc.* and *The New York Times*.

Carol Baroudi (*Internet For Dummies*) writes for and speaks to a variety of audiences — academic, business, and general users — about the impact of technology on society.

William E. Berger, M.D., M.B.A. (*Allergies and Asthma For Dummies*) is a member of the Joint Task Force on Practice Parameters that writes the national treatment guidelines for asthma and allergies.

Marcy Blum (*Weddings For Dummies*) has been planning weddings, parties, and events of all kinds for nearly 20 years. Her company, Marcy Blum Associates, Inc., was started in 1985.

Stephen Bodian (*Meditation For Dummies*) practices as a psychotherapist at the San Francisco Center for Meditation and Psychotherapy, where he uses meditative techniques for inner exploration and healing.

Reid Bramblett (*Europe For Dummies*) splits his time between his native Philadelphia and Rome, Italy, while researching and writing such guides as *Frommer's Italy from $70 A Day* and *Frommer's Tuscany & Umbria*.

Marty Brounstein (*Coaching & Mentoring For Dummies* and *Communicating Effectively For Dummies*) has served as a consultant, speaker, and trainer for a variety of companies, from high tech to government.

Ray Brown (*Home Buying For Dummies*) is a veteran real estate broker with more than two decades of hands-on experience. Ray is currently a writer, radio talk show host, and public speaker on residential real estate topics

Joy Browne (*Dating For Dummies*) is a licensed clinical psychologist who has been on the radio for more than a decade, reaching more than 8 million listeners and making her the fourth most popular talk show host in the U.S.

Gene Busnar (*Making Marriage Work For Dummies*) is an author and collaborative writer. His books include *Loving and Leaving: Winning at the Business of Divorce* and *Conquering Corporate Codependence*.

Steve Capellini, L.M.T. (*Massage For Dummies*) has worked as a spa trainer, hiring staff and overseeing openings of spas around the world. He's written three books on massage.

James and **Morris Carey** (*Home Remodeling For Dummies*) share their 40 combined years of experience as award-winning, licensed contractors with millions nationwide through their syndicated radio and newspaper feature *On the House*. The pair continue to operate a successful remodeling and construction firm.

Perrin Cunningham (*Business Etiquette For Dummies*) is founder and CEO of Ethologie, a professional services firm providing discreet one-on-one behavioral coaching for top executives.

Karan Davis Cutler (*Herb Gardening For Dummies*) publishes regularly in horticultural magazines and is an eight-time winner of the Quill & Trowel Award from the Garden Writers Association of America.

James Dillard, M.D., D.C., C.A.C. (*Alternative Medicine For Dummies*) is the Medical Director for Oxford Health Plan's Alternative Medicine program and the chairman of the Oxford Chiropractic Advisory Board.

Michael C. Donaldson (*Negotiating For Dummies*) is a founding partner of Berton & Donaldson, a firm specializing in entertainment and copyright law with an emphasis in the representation of independent film producers.

Mimi Donaldson (*Negotiating For Dummies*) is an international management consultant specializing in communications training. She has been training managers and employees to negotiate with each other for more than 20 years.

Peter Economy (*Managing For Dummies* and *The Complete MBA For Dummies*) is a business consultant and freelance business writer who has authored numerous books and articles on a wide variety of business topics.

The Editors of the National Gardening Association (*Flowering Bulbs For Dummies, Gardening For Dummies, Herb Gardening For Dummies, Lawn Care For Dummies,* and *Vegetable Gardening For Dummies*) is the largest member-based, nonprofit organization of home gardeners in the U.S. NGA is best known for its bimonthly publication, *National Gardening* magazine.

Paul and **Sarah Edwards** (*Cool Careers For Dummies*) have written career and self-employment books, selling more than a million copies. Their weekly column is syndicated by the *Los Angeles Times.*

Susan Feniger (*Mexican Cooking For Dummies*) and her counterpart Mary Sue Milliken own three restaurants, have authored four cookbooks, and are heard regularly on Southern California Radio.

Lynn Fischer (*Quick & Healthy Cooking For Dummies*) founded the National Women's Health Awareness Forum and hosts the popular cooking series *Healthy Indulgences* on PBS.

Kathleen Fisher (*Herb Gardening For Dummies*) is former editor of *The American Gardener,* published by the American Horticultural Society.

Barry Fox, Ph.D. (*Arthritis For Dummies*) co-authored the best-selling book *The Arthritis Cure* and wrote the best-selling *Beverly Hills Medical Diet* and *End Chronic Pain and Depression.*

Sue Fox (*Business Etiquette For Dummies* and *Etiquette For Dummies*) is founder and President of Etiquette Survival, Inc. As a former event manager at Apple Computer, Inc., she has ten years experience in business protocol.

Echo Montgomery Garrett (*Caribbean For Dummies*) was a founding editor at the award-winning Web site BizTravel.com, and is the co-author of numerous island guides and destination articles.

Kevin Garrett (*Caribbean For Dummies*) is a photographer and journalist. His work has appeared in books, magazines, and Web sites galore.

Judy Glattstein (*Flowering Bulbs For Dummies*) is an instructor in bulb identification for School of Professional Horticulture Students at the New York Botanical Gardens and a leader of international gardening tours.

Dan Gookin (*Parenting For Dummies*) is the author and creator of the *For Dummies* book that started the best-selling series, *DOS For Dummies*. A computer writer and "guru," he enjoys writing on non-technical topics, too.

Sandra Hardin Gookin (*Parenting For Dummies*) works with her husband Dan to make computer terms easy to understand.

Elson Haas, M.D. (*Vitamins For Dummies*) has been in medical practice for more than 25 years and founded the Preventative Medical Center of Marin, an integrated healthcare facility specializing in nutritional medicine and detoxification.

Gene and **Katie Hamilton** (*Home Improvement For Dummies*) are the popular husband-and-wife team that has authored the witty syndicated newspaper column *Do It Yourself . . . or Not?* and more than a dozen best-selling books on home improvement.

Maddy Hargrove (*Aquariums For Dummies*) is a contributing writer and columnist for *Tropical Fish Hobbyist* and *Marine Fish Monthly*.

Mic Hargrove (*Aquariums For Dummies*) is a contributing writer for several tropical fish magazines. He is an expert advisor on aquarium equipment and water chemistry.

Christopher Hobbs (*Herbal Remedies For Dummies* and *Vitamins For Dummies*) is a fourth-generation herbalist and botanist. He co-founded the American Herbalists Guild, the only U.S. organization for professional herbalists.

Michael Hodgson (*Camping For Dummies*) is an editor with *Planet Outdoors* and is a founding partner in GearTrends LLC, the premier information Web site for products and trends in the outdoor sport market.

Sarah Hodgson (*Dog Tricks For Dummies* and *Puppies For Dummies*) has trained dogs for more than a decade and has appeared on TV shows such as *Today* and *The Rosie O'Donnell Show*. She is the author of several dog books.

Greg Holden (*Internet Auctions For Dummies*) is founder and President of Stylus Media, a group of editorial, design, and computer professionals who produce both print and electronic publications.

Thomas Hoving (*Art For Dummies*) was the director of the Metropolitan Museum of Art in New York for ten years. During his tenure, he renovated more than 50 galleries and doubled the size of the museum.

Jack Hungelmann, CPCU, CIC (*Insurance For Dummies*) has taught professional continuing education classes for both the CPCU and CIC societies and has been published numerous times in *American Agent & Broker* magazine.

Therese Iknoian (*Mind-Body Fitness For Dummies*) is an American College of Sports Medicine-certified Health/Fitness instructor and a nationally ranked race walker.

Charles B. Inlander (*Family Health For Dummies, First Aid & Safety For Dummies,* and *Men's Health For Dummies*) serves as President of the People's Medical Society and is a highly acclaimed health commentator on National Public Radio's *Marketplace.*

Laura Fisher Kaiser (*Weddings For Dummies*) is a senior editor at *This Old House* magazine. The former editor-in-chief of *Avenue* magazine, she has written extensively about the fashion world and cultural trends.

David Daniel Kennedy (*Feng Shui For Dummies*) is a professional Feng Shui consultant, teacher, and speaker, as well as a columnist for *Feng Shui*, a journal devoted to the art, and a contributor to *Natural Health* magazine.

Joyce Lain Kennedy (*Job Interviews For Dummies* and *Resumes For Dummies*) is the author of the *Los Angeles Times Syndicate's* column *Careers,* which has been running for nearly 30 years and appears in more than 100 newspapers.

Kathi Keville (*Aromatherapy For Dummies*) is a nationally known herbalist, aromatherapist, and masseuse with more than 30 years experience. She's Director of the American Herb Association.

Jane Kirby, R.D. (*Dieting For Dummies*) is President of Kirby-O'Brien and Company, a nutrition and food communications firm. She is the former editor of *Eating Well* magazine and the food and nutrition editor for *Glamour.*

Malcolm Kushner (*Public Speaking For Dummies*) is an internationally acclaimed expert on humor and communication. He has trained thousands of managers, executives, and professionals on using humor.

Pierre Lehu (*Rekindling Romance For Dummies*) works with Dr. Ruth Westheimer acting as her "Minister of Communications." He's assisted in writing several of her books including *Dr. Ruth's Guide to College Life.*

John R. Levine (*Internet For Dummies*) writes books and does public speaking. He holds a Ph.D. in computer science from Yale University, but please don't hold that against him.

Bill Marken (*Gardening For Dummies*) is the editor of *Rebecca's Garden Magazine,* a publication based on the popular television show.

Michael MacCaskey (*Gardening For Dummies*) is a prolific gardening writer who has been honored by both the Western Magazine Publishers Association and the Garden Writers of America.

Gary McCord (*Golf For Dummies*) is a 25-year PGA Tour veteran and popular CBS broadcaster.

Katherine Kaye McMillan (*Home Decorating For Dummies*) is a writer who has contributed to numerous design and decorating magazines. She's a contributing editor to *Design: The Magazine of Luxurious Living.*

Patricia Hart McMillan (*Home Decorating For Dummies*) is a nationally recognized interior designer, writer, and magazine editor. She has co-authored three books on interior design and has taught dozens of college courses.

Pamela Maraldo, Ph.D. R.N. (*Women's Health For Dummies*) is a professor of nursing at the Columbia School of Nursing and has appeared on numerous radio and television programs.

Jeffery J. Mayer (*Time Management For Dummies*) is one of the country's foremost authorities on time management. His "Clean Desk" approach to organization earned him the title of "Mr. Neat, the Clutterbuster" from *USA Today*.

Max Messmer (*Job Hunting For Dummies, Managing Your Career For Dummies,* and *Motivating Employees For Dummies*) serves as chairman and CEO of Robert Half International Inc., the world's largest specialized staffing firm.

Elizabeth Miles (*Organizing For Dummies*) is a Los Angeles author who specializes in making the good life easier for busy people.

Bryan Miller (*Cooking For Dummies*) is a former restaurant critic and feature writer for *The New York Times*. He currently serves as a culinary consultant and instructor at The Culinary Institute of America.

Mary Sue Milliken (*Mexican Cooking For Dummies*) and her counterpart Susan Feniger own three restaurants, have authored four cookbooks, and host the popular Television Food Network series, *Two Hot Tamales*.

Kara Morales (*Family Health For Dummies*) is Vice President of Editorial Services and Communications for the People's Medical Society and has co-authored several best-selling books.

Charlie Nardozzi (*Vegetable Gardening For Dummies*) writes for *National Gardening* magazine, hosts a call-in gardening radio show, and is often seen on TV as the gardening expert on such shows as HGTV's *Today at Home*.

Bob Nelson (*Managing For Dummies*) is founder of Nelson Motivation and Vice President of Blanchard Training and Development. He's published 17 books on business and management.

Marty Nemko (*Cool Careers For Dummies*) writes a column that appears in the *Los Angeles Times and* the *San Francisco Examiner/Chronicle*. He's the producer and host of the public radio show, *Work with Marty Nemko*.

Liz Neporent (*Fitness For Dummies, Fitness Walking For Dummies,* and *Weight Training For Dummies*) is a certified trainer and President of Plus One Health Management, a fitness consulting company in New York City. She is co-author of *Abs of Steel* and *Buns of Steel: Total Body Workout*.

Janet Worsley Norwood (*First Aid & Safety For Dummies*) is a health writer and researcher who has co-authored several books. She served previously as an editor for the People's Medical Society.

Pat Ordovensky (*College Planning For Dummies*) was an education writer with *USA Today* and founded the annual USA Today College Admission/Financial Aid Hotline.

Paul D. Pion, D.V.M. (*Cats For Dummies*) is the co-founder, President, and CEO of the Veterinary Information Network, Inc., and has taught at the veterinary school at the University of California, Davis.

Marie Rama (*Cooking For Dummies*) has worked as a professional pastry chef and recipe developer for numerous food companies and associations, including The United Fresh Fruit and Vegetable Association.

Carol Ann Rinzler (*Nutrition For Dummies*) is the author of *The Complete Book of Food*, as well as articles that have appeared in numerous publications including *The New York Times, Family Circle*, and *Ladies' Home Journal*.

Eileen Roth (*Organizing For Dummies*) is a professional organizer who owns the Phoenix-based company, *Everything in Its Place*. She has appeared on the *Oprah* and *Today* shows and conducts workshops across the country.

James. M. Rippe, M.D. (*Healthy Heart For Dummies*) is one of the leading authorities on preventive cardiology, health and fitness, and healthy weight loss in the U.S. He is the founder and Director of the Center for Clinical and Lifestyle Research.

Alan L. Rubin M.D. (*Diabetes For Dummies*) is one of the nation's foremost experts on diabetes. He is a regular speaker on radio and television programs, advocating for the awareness, prevention, and treatment of diabetes.

Suzanne Schlosberg (*Fitness For Dummies* and *Weight Training For Dummies*) is a magazine writer known for her humorous approach to health and fitness. She is a contributing editor to *Shape* and *Health* magazines.

Deana Sclar (*Auto Repair For Dummies*) is an internationally best-selling author and former contributing editor to *Family Circle, Boys' Life,* and *Exploring*.

Deborah Shouse (*Antiquing For Dummies*) has given workshops and creative expression seminars for businesses, colleges, and organizations. She provides creativity coaching services for authors, business professionals, and other visionary souls.

Helene Siegel (*Mexican Cooking For Dummies*) is the author of *The Ethnic Kitchen* series and 32 cookbooks in the *Totally Cookbook* series. She is also the co-author *Cooking with the Two Hot Tamales* with Mary Sue Millikin and Susan Feniger.

Steven Simring, M.D., M.P.H. (*Making Marriage Work For Dummies*) is Associate Professor and Vice Chair of the Department of Psychiatry at New Jersey Medical School.

Sue Klavans Simring, D.S.W. (*Making Marriage Work For Dummies*) is a practicing psychotherapist who specializes in working with couples and families. She is a lecturer at the Columbia University School of Social Work.

Molly Siple, M.S. R.D. (*Healing Foods For Dummies*) is a member of the International Association of Culinary Professionals.

Julian Smith (*Travel Planning Online For Dummies*) is the author of *On Your Own in El Salvador* as well as *Ecuador Handbook*.

Linda Smith (*Entertaining For Dummies*) is a freelance writer for regional and national publications with a focus on entertaining and party planning.

Janet Sobesky (*Household Hints For Dummies*) is the Home Design and Lifestyle Editor for *Woman's Day* magazine, where she also edits the popular "Tip Talk" feature.

Gina Spadafori (*Birds For Dummies, Cats For Dummies,* and *Dogs For Dummies*) is an award-winning author whose weekly *Pet Connection* column appears in major U.S. newspapers, as well as in the Pet Care Forum of America Online.

Brian L. Speer, D.V.M. (*Birds For Dummies*) is one of only a handful of veterinarians certified as an avian specialist in both the United States and Europe. He consults on cases worldwide from his specialty practice, The Medical Center for Birds.

Nadine Taylor-Fox (*Arthritis For Dummies*) is a published health writer and registered dietician. She also edited the best-selling book *The Arthritis Cure*.

Eric Tyson (*Home Buying For Dummies, Investing For Dummies, Mutual Funds For Dummies,* and *Personal Finance For Dummies*) is a syndicated personal financial writer, lecturer, and counselor. He's authored five nationally best-selling *For Dummies* books and has been featured in hundreds of national publications.

Michel Van Welden, P.T. N.T. (*Massage For Dummies*) is acting Director of Research for two clinical projects at Vanderbilt University.

Jack Volhard (*Dog Training For Dummies*) has taught classes, lectures, seminars, and training camps in the U.S., Canada, and England, enabling countless dog owners to communicate more effectively with their pets.

Wendy Volhard (*Dog Training For Dummies*) is the recipient of four awards from the Dog Writers' Association of America and has authored more than 100 articles for various dog publications.

Lance Walheim (*Lawn Care For Dummies*) has written and contributed to more than 40 gardening books on subjects ranging from roses to landscaping.

Dr. Ruth K. Westheimer (*Rekindling Romance For Dummies* and *Sex For Dummies*) is a psychosexual therapist known to most people as America's foremost expert on sex. She is an Adjunct Professor at NYU and a fellow of the New York Academy of Medicine.

Suzanne Williamson (*Entertaining For Dummies*) has spent the past decade speaking about entertaining. Her audiences have totaled more than 10,000 people from all over the world.

Martin Yan (*Chinese Cooking For Dummies*) is the founder of the Yan Can International Cooking School in the San Francisco Bay Area. He has hosted more than 1,500 cooking shows and written 24 best-selling cookbooks.

Margaret Levine Young (*Internet For Dummies*) has co-authored more than 20 computer books on Internet and technology topics. She runs Great Tapes for Kids with her husband from their home in the middle of Vermont.

Zig Ziglar (*Success For Dummies*) is a nationally known speaker, author, and authority on high-level performance.

Terra Diane Ziporyn, Ph.D. (*Alternative Medicine For Dummies*) is a writer and historian specializing in making science and medicine accessible to the public. She is the co-author of the *The Harvard Guide to Women's Health*.

Ron Zoglin (*Antiquing For Dummies*) studies antiques and teaches about them in colleges and universities. His shop, *Brookside Antiques,* in Kansas City, specializes in European antiques and Oriental furnishings.

Publisher's Acknowledgments

We're proud of this book; please send us your comments through our Online Registration Form located at www.hungryminds.com

Some of the people who helped bring this book to market include the following:

Acquisitions, Editorial, and Media Development

Project Editor: Brian Kramer

Contributing Editors: Jena Brandt, Kathy Cox, Michelle Fernung, Stephanie Koutek, Patricia Pan, Linda Stark, Janet Withers, Zoë Wykes

Editorial Manager: Stephanie Corby

Production

Project Coordinator: Cindy Phipps

Layout and Graphics: Jacque Schneider, Lissa Auciello-Brogan, Kristine Leonardo, Janet Seib

Proofreader: Brian Massey

Indexer: Sherry Massey

Hungry Minds Consumer Reference Group

Business: Kathleen Nebenhaus, Vice President and Publisher; Kevin Thornton, Acquisitions Manager

Cooking/Gardening: Jennifer Feldman, Associate Vice President and Publisher; Anne Ficklen, Executive Editor; Kristi Hart, Managing Editor

Education/Reference: Diane Graves Steele, Vice President and Publisher

Lifestyles: Kathleen Nebenhaus, Vice President and Publisher; Tracy Boggier, Managing Editor

Pets: Kathleen Nebenhaus, Vice President and Publisher; Tracy Boggier, Managing Editor

Travel: Michael Spring, Vice President and Publisher; Brice Gosnell, Publishing Director; Suzanne Jannetta, Editorial Director

Hungry Minds Consumer Editorial Services: Kathleen Nebenhaus, Vice President and Publisher; Kristin A. Cocks, Editorial Director; Cindy Kitchel, Editorial Director

Hungry Minds Consumer Production: Debbie Stailey, Production Director

Contents at a Glance

Cartoons at a Glance

By Rich Tennant

"You know, I liked you a whole lot more on the Internet."

page 531

"The lost art of conversation isn't lost at all. It's been kidnapped and held hostage by your sister-in-law."

page 439

Popeye's Weight Training Video

PHEW! THAT'S ENOUGH FOREARM WORK. LET'S GET BACK TO THOSE CALF MUSCLES BEFORE WE FINISH UP WITH—YOU GUESSED IT—MORE FOREARM WORK.

page 137

"My portfolio's gonna take a hit for this."

page 383

"I heard it was good to use humor when you're having an argument."

page 305

"QUIT MOPING—YOU WON FIRST PLACE IN THE MEATLOAF CATEGORY, AND THAT'S GOOD. I'M THE ONLY ONE WHO KNOWS IT WAS A CARROT CAKE YOU ENTERED"

page 553

IT WAS WORSE THAN SARAH THOUGHT—HER GARDEN HAD BECOME INFESTED WITH WORMS, MAGGOTS, AND PERSONAL INJURY ATTORNEYS.

page 5

"Very good answer! Now, let me ask you another question..."

page 345

Cartoon Information:
Fax: 978-546-7747
E-Mail: richtennant@the5thwave.com
World Wide Web: www.the5thwave.com

Table of Contents

Introduction

*I*f you're the type of person who's always in search of quick answers to your most pressing questions, then *Life's Little Secrets & Shortcuts For Dummies* is the perfect reference book for you!

This book covers a lot of ground — everything from changing a flat tire to giving a relaxing massage to hosting a fantastic birthday party. And while we can't guarantee that *Life's Little Secrets & Shortcuts For Dummies* answers *every* question under the sun, we do promise that it can answer many (if not most) of the questions that you have in your day-to-day doings.

About This Book

To create *Life's Little Secrets & Shortcuts For Dummies,* we read through hundreds of titles in the best-selling *For Dummies* series of reference books and selected the best, most usable, most interesting bits of information. We then combined all these goodies into one organized book (what a value!) that's perfect for quick answers or leisurely reading. Think of this book as the *For Dummies Greatest Hits Collection, Volume 1.*

Rather than wading through several hundred pages on gardening, the Internet, or rekindling romance, you can turn to this book for a simple solution or a fast answer to your burning questions. And rest assured that the trademark *For Dummies* irreverence and humor is with you every step of the way.

How to Use This Book

Like all *For Dummies* books, you can jump in to any portion of this book that interests you most. If the stuff you want is in Chapter 10, you don't have to worry about reading Chapters 1 through 9, just dive in to Chapter 10, and you're on your way!

Also, you don't have to read an entire chapter — you don't have to read even an entire section — to find helpful hints and great ideas. The handy table of contents in the front of the book, the gray parts pages sprinkled throughout the book, and the index in the back of the book, can all guide you to the information that you want.

Of course, you can always read this book from cover to cover. We've done it ourselves and had a great time! But how you use the book is totally up to you.

How This Book Is Organized

We organized this book into eight parts that cover the topics and areas of interest that matter most to you: your home, your health, your relationships, your career, your money, and your free time. The following info gives you the highlights of each part in this book.

Part 1: Homespun Help

In this part, we touch on literally hundreds of easy things you can start doing today to make your home a happier, healthier, and, well, homier, place. You find great tips on cleaning, decorating, cooking, gardening, raising pets, and even maintaining your car.

Part 11: Staying Healthy and Fit

Your health is key to your happiness in life. This part offers hints for eating better, getting (and staying) in shape, dealing with injuries and illness, and exploring alternative medical treatments.

Part 111: Relationships: Living with the Ones You Love, Like, and Loathe

If you need to relight the fire in your marriage or just figure out how to communicate better with your kids or in-laws, this part gives you great ideas that can make all of your relationships joyful, enriching elements of your life.

Part IV: Satisfying Careers in Today's Business World

From figuring out your ideal career to creating a fantastic resume to dazzling potential employers in interviews, this part shows you how to get a great job — as well as how to keep it — by using good communication and organization skills.

Part V: Getting Personal: Personal Finance

Do you love getting more for your money? Well, check out this part for financial-savvy advice on everyday ways to save money, budget your hard-earned dollars, invest in safe and profitable places, get loans, and protect your family and possessions.

Part VI: Fun, Fun, Fun: Hobbies and Entertainment

Have a great time exploring your favorite pastimes with this part — or get started on a new hobby you've been meaning to find out more about. This part is jam-packed with cool stuff on antiquing, collecting, traveling, enjoying nature, and entertaining.

Part VII: Connecting to the World with Technology

Joining the Internet revolution can be easy, fascinating, and — most importantly — fun! This part offers totally painless ways to get online, find the cool stuff you want, buy great gifts safely and cheaply, keep in touch with loved ones, and make some new cyber-friends.

Part VIII: The Part of Tens

The Part of Tens is a classic feature of all *For Dummies* books. In this part, you get handy lists of ten (or so) tips on your favorite topics: successful living, managing your money, improving your health, and spicing up your romantic life!

Icons Used in This Book

The little graphic symbols that you see sprinkled throughout the margins of this book are a staple of the *For Dummies* experience. These symbols — or *icons* — highlight the following points:

Get on target with this handy shortcut that can save you time, money, or effort — or perhaps all three!

Don't forget to remember this important point.

Watch out and proceed with care whenever you see this icon.

Nerd alert! Read this in-depth, technical information only when you're looking for more details and explanation. If you just want the facts, skip ahead.

Where to Go from Here

Where you start reading this book is totally based on your needs. For example:

- ✔ If you want to start making your home a more comfortable place to live, head for Chapter 1.
- ✔ If need to know how to bandage a cut, check out Chapter 11.
- ✔ Don't know how to set the table for a formal dinner? Chapter 25 has the answer for you.
- ✔ If you're looking for fun and fast information, make tracks to Chapters 28 through 31 for our Part of Tens lists.

You can also just hop around from icon to icon or sidebar to sidebar. Whatever way you use this book, you'll find loads of information and have a good time in the process!

Part I
Homespun Help

The 5th Wave · By Rich Tennant

IT WAS WORSE THAN SARAH THOUGHT — HER GARDEN HAD BECOME INFESTED WITH WORMS, MAGGOTS, AND PERSONAL INJURY ATTORNEYS.

In this part . . .

No word makes you feel quite as safe, secure, and welcome as *home*. Regardless of whether you live in the tiniest of apartments or a grand mansion, you want your home to be the place you and your family and friends are most comfortable.

If home is where your heart is, then you need the fun ideas and practical solutions you'll find in the following chapters to clean your home, decorate it with style, prepare delicious dishes, harvest a bountiful garden, raise fabulous feline (or canine) friends, and even tune up that old jalopy in the garage.

Chapter 1

All the Comforts of Home

*I*f you're like most people, you want a spic-and-span home but somehow can't seem to find the time, the tools, or the inclination to get it done. This chapter is packed with simple tools and techniques to get (and keep) your home looking great.

Housekeeping brings order out of chaos and gives relatively instant gratification. You may never get to the point where you think that cleaning is fun, but at least you can get a kick out of finding the fastest, easiest, and cheapest ways to solve your nagging little household problems.

Cleaning Up and Out

You want the pleasures of a clean house, but you also want them quickly and with minimal effort. Well, you *can* have your house and clean it, too, but you need to acquire a few simple techniques and find some practical cleaning products so that you spend less time cleaning your place and more time having fun in it.

Mixing up homemade cleaners

Plenty of good cleaners on the market can attack a myriad of stains and dirt, but you can make cheaper and more eco-friendly cleaners at home.

Labels save lives

Make sure that you clearly label your homemade cleaners. Don't put them in recognizable food containers where folks may mistake the cleaner for water or lemonade. List the names and amounts of ingredients as well as directions for use. Add a skull and crossbones or some other symbol to warn users.

- **All-purpose cleaner:** Mix ½ cup ammonia, ½ cup white vinegar, ¼ cup baking soda, and 1 gallon water.

  Or mix ½ cup baking soda and 2 quarts water.

- **Mirror cleaner:** Mix 2 cups isopropyl rubbing alcohol, 2 table-spoons liquid dishwashing detergent, and 2 cups water. Pour into a spray bottle.

- **Toilet bowl cleaner:** Pour ½ cup chlorine bleach into bowl and let stand for 10 minutes. Scrub with toilet brush and flush.

- **Oven cleaner:** Put 1 cup ammonia in a glass or ceramic bowl. Put the bowl on the bottom of a cold oven and leave it in the closed oven overnight. The next morning, pour the ammonia into a pail of warm water and use this solution and a sponge to wipe away the loosened grime. Wear rubber gloves. Be careful of the fumes. They're very strong when you first open the oven.

- **Bathtub and tile cleaner:** Mix 1 cup vinegar in 1 gallon warm water. Spray a small area. Leave spray on for 1 minute and then wipe off with clear water.

  Or mix ½ cup vinegar, 1 cup clear ammonia, ¼ cup baking soda, and 1 gallon water.

- **Plastic laminate and appliance scrubber:** Sprinkle baking soda on a damp sponge, rub the stain, and wipe off the surface with a damp cloth.

- **Floor cleaner:** Mix ½ cup vinegar and 1 gallon warm water. Wear rubber gloves.

Keeping dust in check

The following list of hints can help make your dusting duties as swift and painless as possible:

- ✔ **Place a doormat by all entrances.** Most professional cleaners claim that most household dirt and dust is carried in through the front door on the soles of your feet. You can keep the problem in check by putting mats in front of all the exterior entrances. You can forget about the crocheted mat your Aunt Doris gave you — mats need solid rubber backing (to prevent slippage when you're rubbing shoes on them) and should be stiff enough to scrape off dirt.

- ✔ **Check all filters.** Change or clean the filters in your air conditioner and furnace every month or two depending on how serious your dust problems are. Don't forget to vacuum the dust and lint from the heating vents and registers often. Vents are the main source of air to your home, and if they're dusty, they're just transmitting dust to the rest of the room.

- ✔ **Become a dirt detective.** Look for hidden dust in forgotten places that you can't see at first glance like beneath your refrigerator, behind the sofa, under beds, on the floor of your closets, and on window sills and moldings.

- ✔ **Make your house airtight.** Keep your windows closed. Check caulking and weather stripping around your home. If windows and doors aren't sealed tightly enough, dust seeps in continuously, and your dusting won't be able to keep up with it.

- ✔ **Remove the dust catchers.** Sift through plants, knickknacks, books, silk flowers, for starters — all major places where dust collects. If you can't bear to part with your collections, keep them in cabinets with glass front doors.

Removing stains on carpet

Table 1-1 lists common spots and suggested removal strategies. Follow the strategies in order, starting with the first suggested spot removal solution and continue as long as you see improvement. If that doesn't work, go on to the next step. If the stain remains, call a professional.

Weather (or not) to dust

Dust and vacuum on rainy or humid days. The dampness keeps the dust from rising and floating. Also, if you're sweeping dust into a dustpan, moisten the pan slightly to keep the dust from floating out of the dustpan and into the air.

Table 1-1	Spot Removal Chart for Carpets				
Spill			**Solutions**		
	Step 1	**Step 2**	**Step 3**	**Step 4**	**Step 5**
Alcohol	Detergent	Ammonia	White vinegar	Warm water rinse	Call a pro
Candy	Detergent	Ammonia	White vinegar	Warm water rinse	Call a pro
Chocolate	Dry-cleaning fluid	Detergent	Ammonia	White vinegar	Warm water rinse
Coffee with cream and sugar	Dry-cleaning fluid	Detergent	White vinegar	Warm water rinse	Spot removal kit
Crayon	Dry-cleaning fluid	Detergent	Call a pro		
Egg	Detergent	Ammonia	White vinegar	Warm water rinse	Call a pro
Glue, household	Detergent	White vinegar	Warm water rinse	Spot removal kit	Call a pro
Grape juice	Detergent	White vinegar	Warm water rinse	Spot removal kit	Call a pro
Greasy food	Dry-cleaning fluid	Detergent	Warm water rinse	Call a pro	
Markers, felt tip	Detergent	Warm water rinse	Call a pro		
Salad dressing	Dry-cleaning fluid	Detergent	Spot removal kit	Warm water rinse	Call a pro
Spaghetti sauce	Detergent	Ammonia	Warm water rinse	Call a pro	
Wine	Detergent	White vinegar	Ammonia	Warm water rinse	Spot removal kit

The following three stains are really tough (but not impossible) to remove:

- ✔ **Animal messes:** Blot liquid messes with a towel and scrape off solids with a spoon. Flush with lukewarm water and then apply a mixture of equal parts white vinegar and water. Again, blot the liquid until it's dry. If the spot remains, apply a solution of ¼ teaspoon dishwashing liquid and 1 cup water. Blot again. Reapply the vinegar solution and let it sit for 5 minutes. Then blot the excess liquid with several towels, replacing the towels until all the moisture is removed. For several pet messes, use an enzymatic cleaner from a pet store. Follow the label instructions and test on a hidden area first.

- ✔ **Chewing gum:** Put an ice cube in a plastic bag and hold it on top of the gum to harden it. Pick at the gum and pull off as much as you can very carefully so that you don't pull up any carpet fibers. Dot with methyl salicylate (use an analgesic muscle rub) and gently pull the rest off. After the gum is removed, clean the area with a detergent solution, followed by a warm water rinse.

- ✔ **Ink:** Pour a small amount of rubbing alcohol (90 percent isopropyl) on a cloth. Dot the stain carefully and then blot. Don't pour alcohol directly on the stain or rub the stain — that can cause the ink to spread.

Getting scuff marks off floors

Get an art gum eraser (one of those grayish-tan ones you used in school) or borrow a Pink Pearl eraser from your kid's school supplies. Just rub the mark and — voilà! — the mark disappears.

For tougher scuffs, use a little paint thinner on a rag to rub the spot clean. Be careful not to go nuts with the thinner — you can remove the no-wax finish. Then stop wearing scuff-makers, like cheap plastic-soled shoes, hiking boots, and running shoes, in the house.

Cleaning the inside of vases

Vases can be one of the most frustrating things to clean because getting down inside them is difficult. Try this: Fill the vase half full with a solution of dishwashing liquid and water or a teaspoon of ammonia and water. Add some uncooked rice or beans and shake. The rice scrapes the dirt off. You can also try a teaspoon of automatic dishwasher detergent and water or a denture tablet and water. Rinse out thoroughly after any of these treatments.

Cleaning out a junk drawer

Here's a good task to do while talking on the phone because it only takes about ten minutes. Put a box on a counter or desktop next to the junk drawer to hold things that need to be moved. Then dump everything out of the drawer onto the counter or desktop and ruthlessly go through the stuff. Throw away any old batteries, no-name keys, dried up glue, and other unneeded junk. Anything that belongs elsewhere, put in the box.

After you finish, you still have a junk drawer, just one with a lot less junk. When you have another free ten minutes, put the stuff in the box back where it belongs.

Cleaning up mildew

Credit for this mildew-zapping formula goes to the U.S. Department of Agriculture's Forest Products Laboratory. Use it on any (non-colorfast) painted or washable surface — inside or outside. You need the following items:

- ⅓ cup powdered laundry detergent
- 1 quart liquid chlorine bleach
- 3 quarts warm water
- 1 mixing bucket
- Safety goggles
- Rubber gloves
- 1 stiff bristle broom
- 1 garden hose and running water

Then follow these steps:

1. **Add the bleach to the water first, then the detergent.**

   Even though this solution is mild, make certain to wear safety goggles and rubber gloves and have plenty of ventilation.

   Never mix bleach with ammonia because the combination of the two creates a lethal gas similar to mustard gas.

2. **Apply the solution to the affected areas using the broom.**

   Leave the mixture on long enough for the stains to turn white, but don't allow it to dry — 15 minutes is probably long enough.

3. **Rinse the entire area with fresh water.**

Malicious mildew

In addition to mildew's unsightly appearance and its often fierce odor, recent medical studies show that mildew can cause a variety of physical ailments as well. In 1989, the *British Medical Journal* reported that "Scottish doctors who surveyed 597 families in London, Edinburgh, and Glasgow found that those who lived in damp, moldy houses — about half the number studied — suffered a much higher incidence of respiratory problems, headaches, nausea, fevers, backaches, high blood pressure, and fatigue."

Cleaning power for shower curtains

Wash a pliable plastic curtain in cold water on the delicate cycle. Put ½ cup detergent and ½ cup baking soda in the machine along with a couple of large bath towels. The towels rub against the curtain during the cycle and scrub the dirt off. Add 1 cup vinegar to the rinse cycle to cut down on wrinkling. Remove the curtain immediately and hang it over the shower rod to dry.

If you have a stiff plastic curtain, wash it in the bathtub. Lay the curtain flat in the tub and pour over it a mixture of ¼ cup vinegar, ½ cup clear ammonia, ⅛ cup baking soda, and 2 quarts water. Open doors and windows to ventilate the bathroom well. Let the curtain soak for a few minutes to allow the cleaner to do the work. Then scrub the curtain with a sponge or nylon scouring pad, if necessary. Drain the tub and rinse the curtain with warm water. Add a few drops of mineral oil to the water to keep the curtain flexible.

Pre-treating and soaking clothes

Pre-treat any dirty cuffs, collars, and any noticeable soil by rubbing liquid detergent, pre-wash stain remover, or a paste of granular detergent and water onto the stain. If the clothes are heavily soiled, soak them in a pre-soak solution or a detergent solution. Sort the clothes according to color before soaking. Then follow these steps:

1. **Mix the detergent or pre-soak with water in a sink or in a washer with a pre-soak cycle.**

2. **Follow the manufacturer's instructions for the length of time that you should soak an item — usually about 30 minutes.**

3. **Spin or wring out garments before starting to wash.**

Avoid pre-soaking fabrics like silk or wool. Soak elasticized clothes for only a few minutes.

Storing cleaning products safely

Under the sink may seem like the most convenient place to store your cleaning supplies, but *don't* store cleaning products there. First of all, they're within the reach of the exploring hands of small children. In addition, the moist environment doesn't do good things to powdered dishwasher detergent. Moisture can cause the powder to get lumpy so that it doesn't dissolve when you put it in the dishwasher. A cool dry spot works better. Try storing your cleaning supplies within arm's reach in an upper cabinet or in a nearby closet.

Shopping for greener cleaners

Many companies offer safe, nonpolluting cleaning products. In stores, look for a nonchlorinated scouring powder that also is nonabrasive, such as Bon Ami Polishing Cleanser. If you have hard water, stick to vegetable-oil detergents, such as Murphy's Oil Soap and Ecover. Get to know brands that offer full lines of nontoxic household cleaning products, such as Seventh Generation and Planet (visit their Web sites at www.seventhgen.com and www.planetinc.com, respectively). The Earthrite line of cleaning products is also widely available, sold in natural-foods stores and grocery store chains. And that's just the tip of the iceberg.

Avoid cleaning products that display these warnings on the labels: DANGER, POISON, WARNING, TOXIC, FLAMMABLE, or CORROSIVE.

Organizing Your Personal Spaces

The power of putting everything in its place is that doing so improves all aspects of your life, from work to play, professional reputation to personal relationships. Why get organized? How about recovering the 15 minutes a day you spend looking for your car keys? Getting dinner on the table with ease? Inviting guests into your home without embarrassment? Getting organized helps you achieve your peak potential and enjoy lifelong peace.

Storing kitchen items creatively

A well-organized kitchen is a thing of beauty. Try the following hints to discover extra space in your kitchen.

On the wall

Walls can add an extra dimension to your storage options. Everything else may be full, but you usually have a bare spot that you can grab for storage on the wall. Use some of these ideas to find new places to put things:

- **Pegboard:** Cheap and easy to find, pegboard can easily hold kitchen gadgets or pots and pans of different sizes and shapes. Paint the pegboard to match your cabinets or other kitchen surfaces. To keep the pegboard organized, trace the outline of the spoon, whisk, bowl, or any other gadget on the board, and write the name underneath.

- **Grid storage systems:** Made of criss-crossed metal or plastic, grids are a clean look that come in many different sizes and configurations for wall-mounting. Cookware and gadgets can hang from S-hooks.

- **Homemade storage racks:** You can make a storage rack from something as simple as a 2 x 4 piece of lumber. Hang it either vertically or horizontally and attach it securely to the wall studs. Paint or stain, and then screw in hooks the length of the board. Because this rack is so narrow, it can fit into tight spots in a corner or above a shelf.

- **Wooden shaker peg racks:** Available by the foot in home centers or through catalogs, most shaker peg racks are unfinished and can be painted or stained to suit your needs. Use racks to hold aprons, towels, oven mitts, and so on.

- **Magnetic steel bars:** Get knives out of a drawer (which isn't good for knives anyway) and display them where you can reach them easily. You can also use magnetic bars for hanging metal utensils such as spatulas or scissors.

If you have small children in the house, hang knives and such out of their reach.

On the ceiling

Stand in your kitchen and look up. See anything? If not, you just found some more storage space. Hang things high or within arm's reach, depending on how often you use them. Make sure that you have adequate clearance for cabinet doors and the head of the tallest person in your home.

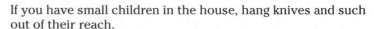

- Sturdy metal racks come in all sizes and shapes to hold pots and pans. They make an attractive display as well.

✔ Convert a small ladder into a ceiling rack. Attach it to the studs with lengths of chain, and hang items from S-hooks looped around the rungs.

✔ Hang a collection of baskets from the rafters for a rustic look. They give the kitchen ceiling a rich texture while acting as hidden storage bins for items that you don't use often.

Inside or on doors

All those flat vertical surfaces inside the cabinet doors present a wealth of storage space. Attach hooks or clips to hold placemats, napkins, or utensils. Or tack up a small bulletin board as a handy catch-all for kids' artwork or messages. Hang a clipboard to hold grocery lists or recipes while you're cooking. Narrow shelves and wire racks are available to mount inside the cabinet doors.

Measure the space before you install anything to be sure that you have enough room to shut the door without interfering with the contents on the shelves inside.

Other great kitchen storage spaces

Keep the following in mind as other places to store things in your kitchen:

✔ **On top of the cabinets:** The space between the top cabinet and the ceiling often goes unused. Make a shelf by nailing a board that's sized to fit on top of the cabinets. You now have a great place to store cookbooks or platters that you want out of the way but still within sight. Or make an attractive arrangement of baskets, boxes, or pieces of pottery, and store things you rarely use inside such as turkey laces or cake decorating supplies.

✔ **Inside cabinets:** Most upper cabinets have 12 inches of vertical space between shelves. That usually makes for wasted space because you can't really stack anything that high. You risk accidents and breakage. Put in some plastic-coated wire racks with legs on each shelf to create a new storage area about 5 inches high — literally doubling the available space in cabinets. Dishes, cups, cans, and bottles can be stacked to a reasonable height on these racks.

✔ **Between the cabinets:** Many manufacturers have noticed that the area between the top cabinets and the countertop is often underutilized and have created all sorts of nifty products to take advantage of that space. Baskets, cookbook racks, towel holders, radios, microwaves, toasters, can openers, clocks, and even TV sets can be mounted in this space.

Special places for odd-sized items

Kitchen supplies come in all sorts of shapes and sizes. Try the following tricks for those hard-to-fit-in items:

- ✔ **Large platters:** Store these vertically in a cabinet. Dish racks or even office file folder racks can hold them upright in a small space. You can create a narrow display shelf with strip molding and lean the platters against the wall. Put a piece of putty behind the platters to keep them from slipping.

- ✔ **Pan lids:** Depending on the number and size of lids, several workable options are available. If you have a large number of lids or are the "piler not filer" kind of person, buy a plastic dishpan to throw them in. If you need a lid, you can just yank out the whole container and look inside. Or you can store lids vertically in a dish rack.

- ✔ **Cookie sheets:** Slip them inside a large plastic bag and slide them into the space between the refrigerator and the lower cabinet.

- ✔ **Sponges and scrubbers:** Install a plastic or metal tilt-out tray in the cabinet panel in front of the sink. (The panel looks like a drawer but actually nothing is behind it.) Tilt-out trays come in various lengths and are available at home centers.

- ✔ **Plastic grocery bags:** Stuff them inside an empty paper towel tube or tissue box. You'd be surprised how many fit inside.

- ✔ **Spices:** Store the bottles by category in those little plastic see-through berry boxes that you get at the grocery store. Herbs (rosemary, thyme, oregano, and so on) go in one, peppers (black, white, and red) go in another.

- ✔ **Garbage bags:** Store the full roll in the bottom of the trash basket. When you throw the top one out, just reach into the bottom for the replacement.

- ✔ **Cookie cutters:** Tie them together with a ribbon and hang them on a hook for a look both decorative and organized.

Shoe-bagging stuff everywhere

Here's an ideal all-purpose, ready-made multiple storage unit: The shoe bag. Shoe bags come in different sizes, containing from 4 to 16 pockets. You can hang them over a door or nail them to a wall in every room of the house:

- ✔ **In the bathroom:** Cosmetics, hairdryers, nontoxic medicines, combs, brushes, hair curlers, scrunchies, brushes

✔ **In the front closet:** Hats, gloves, keys, messages, small items you take out the door each day

✔ **In the kitchen:** Utensils such as peelers, zesters, garlic presses, wooden spoons, packets of dry soup or salad dressing, meat thermometers, small bags of spices you don't use often

✔ **In the workshop:** Screwdrivers, sandpaper, nails, nuts, bolts, bottles of glue, tape measures, duct or electrical tape

✔ **In the craft or sewing room:** Needles, thread, scissors, buttons, soft tape measures, yarn, knitting needles, bobbins, bottles of glue, sewing machine accessories

✔ **In the kids' room:** Small toys, socks, hair ribbons, rolled T-shirts, books, crayons, pens and pencils, rulers

✔ **In the bedroom:** Pantyhose, underpants, lingerie, necklaces, bracelets, rings, earrings, bulky socks

✔ **In the home office:** Envelopes, stamps, scissors, bills, tape, staplers, push pins

Straightening up the medicine cabinet

This task is easy and fast. Look at the expiration dates of all your medicines and throw out any medicine that's outdated. Get rid of rusty razor blades, makeup more than six months old, dried-up perfume, used-up lipstick . . . you know the drill. Wipe off the shelves with a damp paper towel. Put plastic lids under the shaving cream or any other metal container to prevent rust rings.

Creating a return and repair center

Making returns and taking things to be repaired are rarely at the top of anyone's fun list. Handle the rejects in your life by establishing a return and repair center in a basket or container kept in the front hall closet. If the volume of items exceeds your closet space, try a spot near the back door instead. Under a sink is another idea, but being out of sight may put your errand out of mind.

Keep the original receipt in the bag with return items so you don't have to search the house when you decide to hit the store.

Power-coordinating clothes closets

Your bedroom closet can get a spruce up by using the following simple organizing techniques:

- ✔ **Dress down your wardrobe.** Fashion changes each year, so go through every item in your closet, from shoes to suits and everything in between, and purge anything you haven't worn in the last 12 months or can't squeeze into soon. This is a great opportunity to figure out what flatters you and ditch the dead weight. Grab a couple of friends and put on a fashion show, asking their honest but kindly couched opinions regarding what looks good on you and fits the current style.

- ✔ **Move your off-season duds offsite.** Even if you live in a warm climate, you probably have at least a spring/summer and fall/winter wardrobe. Relocate your off-season clothes to a closet in the guest bedroom, attic, or basement, or into storage boxes.

- ✔ **Double tier.** If you have one closet rod and many short garments such as shirts, blouses, jackets, and skirts, adding a second rod underneath can double your storage space. Home improvement people can install rod number two directly into closet walls; those less inclined can opt for an add-a-rod that simply hangs from the existing rod. Figure 1-1 shows how easy double-tiering can be.

- ✔ **Try layering.** Hang a bar with holes for additional hangers from the rod. Keep a single color of garment on a bar so you know just where to look for what. See Figure 1-1.

- ✔ **Organize like with like.** Think occasion first and then type of garment. Dressing for work is always a time-sensitive affair, so put all your professional clothes in the place most accessible when you open the door. You can delve deeper for casual clothes, when you have more time. If you're sharing a closet and have two double-tiered sections, each spouse takes one for short clothes, and you can split the remaining space. If you only have one tiered section, the taller person gets the higher rod. Devote this section to shirts — dress, and then casual. Within your work and casual categories, divide by garment type, and then style.

- ✔ **Have light fade into dark.** Within each section, work from the lightest to darkest color for easy matching — white at one end, black at the other. *Helpful hint:* Putting navy blue and black together invites chromatic confusion, so separate these two colors with the red/pink family or put multicolored garments in between them.

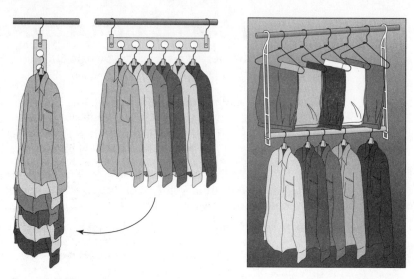

Figure 1-1: Second rods and layering can double your closet space in a snap.

If your closet lacks good lighting, install a battery-operated light so you can spare yourself the squint and get the right garment the first time.

✔ **Stock the shelves.** The more shelves the merrier (or at least the more organized you can be), so if you have a walk-in closet short on shelves with room to spare, build them in! Shelves are great for sweaters, t-shirts, shoes, purses, scarves, blankets, pillows, and hats.

Creating a tool center

An avid carpenter or handyperson may prefer a workshop in the garage, where air and sunshine are plentiful and messes aren't a problem, to a basement location. If you're one of these and live in a moderate climate, set up your main workbench here. Otherwise, you can move your tools and supplies out to the garage during the summer, and then back into the basement as the temperature drops.

Part-timers can get by with a pegboard in the garage to hold tools for cars, bikes, and outdoor equipment, as well as a very long extension cord and an extra flashlight for everything from poking around under the hood to finding your way in a power outage. Keep a ladder or two in the garage for high-level jobs. A stepladder can cover most household tasks, while you may need an extension ladder for rooftop adventures. Both can hang on wall-mounted hooks, the stepladder vertically and the tall extension ladder horizontally.

> ## Two times the tools
>
> Stock duplicates of tools you use in the garage and other parts of the house, so you don't have to go for a hike every time you need a screwdriver.

Decorating Your Home

Having trouble finding your own personal style? Can't mix and match colors and patterns? Face it: Comfort, convenience, and good looks matter. If you want a house that truly feels like a home but are unsure how to achieve it, you need the valuable hints in this section that can help you make beautiful decorating decisions.

Creating a focal point

There is no "right" or "wrong" object or item to use as a focal point. A focal point just needs to be prominent. A focal point can be anything that you want to focus attention on. Just be sure that all other furniture and furnishings help make the focal point stand out.

Following are some tips for figuring out where to focus a room:

✔ **Look first for architectural focus points.** If you have two or more architectural focal points in a room, then give one element or object special status and have all other objects and furnishings play supporting roles. That is, don't make secondary areas more interesting by adding stronger colors and patterns that compete with the focal point. Some possible focal points:

  • *Fireplaces:* Fires are visually interesting, even captivating. And with mantels to decorate, most fireplaces easily steal the show. Drawing seating around the fireplace plays up the fireplace and designates it as the star of the room.

  • *Large windows:* Beautiful moldings and trims make them even more interesting. And if you have a gorgeous view, the window can really shine. The sofa often fits in naturally on the wall opposite the window.

✔ **If you don't have an architectural focal point, use a large piece of furniture.** An attractive armoire, bookcase, wall unit, secretary, or highboy can fill the focal point bill. A lovely sofa, accented with pillows and a large painting hanging above it also works nicely as a focal point in any living room.

Change your luck with a new door color

Door colors on most houses are white or a color that matches the house. These color choices are generally fine. However, you can boost your front door energy by using *Feng Shui* (the ancient Chinese art of harmonious design) to pick your door paint color. The colors with the strongest effects include:

✔ **Bright red:** This classic Feng Shui door color confers power, protection, luck, and a sense of royalty to the house and its occupants. A great all-around choice for boosting your home's energy.

✔ **Green:** This color is another excellent choice, symbolizing life, health, and money.

✔ **Black:** Black is a fine color for a front door and is especially good if your front door is in the center, which represents your career. Black also symbolizes money in Feng Shui. Enough said.

Making rooms look cozy with color

Whenever you're picking colors for a room, keep the following two basic principles in mind:

✔ *Warm colors* **(those on the red side of the color wheel) communicate warmth, relaxation, informality, closeness, and intimacy.** Warm colors seem to advance toward you. Intense, highly saturated warm or hot colors such as red and orange stimulate and excite.

✔ *Cool colors* **(those on the blue side of the color wheel) connote alertness, formality, coolness, reserve, and emotional distance.** Cool colors seem to recede away from you. Mildly cool colors soothe; intensely cool or cold colors depress.

Color to suit every mood

The following list suggests the power of various decorating colors:

✔ **Black:** Traditionally, black represents darkness, despair, sorrow, mourning, formality, and solemnity. The modern idea about black is that it is the epitome of mystery and style. Use black in restricted amounts — as accents or accessories — and in rooms that you don't use frequently or for long periods of time.

✔ **White:** Traditionally, white stands for peace, purity, faith, joy, and cleanliness. You can use white, unlike black, in large amounts without it seeming overwhelming. Predominately white color schemes look modern and fresh. A white room seems brighter (and larger) than it does if it were decorated in a color.

✔ **Gray:** Gray, a non-color, is a somber shade that suggests humility and penance. Gray is a cerebral shade and emphasizes spiritual and intellectual values over sensual ones. Too much gray can look monotonously boring and dull instead of chic. Avoid dullness by adding extra textural interest. On the positive side, gray is an easy-to-live-with neutral that makes a good backdrop for most accent colors.

✔ **Red:** Red stimulates and energizes. Various reds symbolize passion, anger, warmth, gaiety, martyrdom, and revolution. Red increases desire, excitability, domination, and sexuality by increasing circulation and raising the heart rate. A welcome counterbalance to neutrals, red adds life and sparkle.

✔ **Orange:** Orange has some of the effects of red, but to a lesser degree. Orange stands for force of will and is considered an active and competitive color. Widely used in fast food restaurants, orange tends to make people eat fast and leave quickly. Softer oranges are welcoming and pleasing, adding warmth and energy to a neutral or cool decor.

✔ **Yellow:** Yellow, the subtlest of the warm colors, stimulates and energizes in a positive, non-aggressive way. Yellow conjures feelings of warmth, cheerfulness, and fruitfulness. Traditionally, yellow represents spontaneity and is active, expansive, and aspiring. Tints based on yellow (such as cream and beige) are safe neutrals. With yellow, use colors nearby on the color wheel, such as oranges and reds, or *complementary* (opposites on the color wheel) violets and blues for balance.

✔ **Green:** Green suggests hope, restfulness, and calm and is the color of defense and flight. Green has even been known to slow down heart rate and circulation. Green is a favorite for creating calm and restful balanced color schemes. Used as a counterbalance to hot colors like orange or red, green can add relief. Yellow-greens (bright and light) and blue-greens (cool and jewel-toned) are a great balance for strong red.

✔ **Blue:** Blue, the coolest of the cool colors, depresses the nervous system and makes the body ready for nodding off to sleep. This hue has come to stand for depth of feeling and is associated with sensitivity, perception, and unification. Used as an accent, blue can counterbalance warm and warm-neutral color schemes. But blues that are too dark can generate depression or zap all the pep out of a person or room.

✔ **Purple:** Violets and purples, the cool colors closest to warm, are associated with justice and royalty, and, interestingly enough, depression and suffering. Considered unsafe or risky colors, violets tend to convey uncertainty and ambiguity. These delicate and difficult shades of purple can add a surprising twist to drab or overheated color schemes.

Correcting decorating problems with color

Color is a powerful tool, and when you use it artfully, you can work magic:

- ✔ **To make a room look bigger:** Use monochromatic, light, cool color schemes to create a receding atmospheric look. Paint all surfaces the same color and match the upholstery to the floor.

- ✔ **To make a room look cozier:** Use darker, warm neutrals. Use decorative wall features like *wainscoting* (less than full wall height wood paneling) or paneling as accents. Use contrasting paint for paneling, and either match or contrast the molding.

- ✔ **To make a ceiling look higher:** Use white paint or the same color as the walls, and keep floors relatively light.

- ✔ **To square off a long, rectangular room:** Paint or paper the long narrow wall in light, cool colors to make these walls recede. To make the ends of the room advance, use a dark, warm color on the short walls.

Improving and Maintaining Your Home

Your home is probably the largest investment that you'll make in your lifetime. Doing everything you can to protect your investment from deteriorating forces of nature, insects, and good, old-fashioned wear and tear just makes sense. Besides all that, regular maintenance and improvements can increase the resale value of your house, save on energy costs, make your home safer and more accessible, improve your quality of life, and fix small problems before they become costly disasters.

Ten tools you can't live without

Stock your toolbox with the following must-have tools:

- ✔ **⅜-inch variable speed reversible drill:** This tool, available as plug-in or cordless, uses steel blades called *bits* to drive in or remove screws, drill holes, sand wood, and do other important home improvement tasks.

- ✔ **Claw hammer:** Look for a 16-ounce hammer with a fiberglass handle to cushion the blow to your hand.

- ✔ **Pliers:** Slip-joint pliers have toothed jaws that enable you to grip various sized objects, like a water pipe, the top of a gallon of mineral spirits, or the tape measure you accidentally dropped into the toilet. Because its jaws are adjustable, pliers give you leverage to open and firmly grip objects.

- ✔ **Toolbox saw:** A small, easy-to-use handsaw is useful for cutting such materials as paneling or shelving.

- ✔ **Assorted pack of screwdrivers:** Be sure that you have both slotted (flat-head) and Phillips screwdrivers in a variety of sizes. The slotted type has a straight, flat blade; the Phillips blade has a cross or plus-sign.

- ✔ **Utility knife:** Choose a compact knife with replaceable blades that's strong enough to open heavy cardboard boxes and precise enough for trimming wallpaper.

Buy a knife with a retractable blade — this feature comes in handy the first time you squat down with the knife in your pocket. (Ouch!)

- ✔ **Staple gun:** You can use this tool for a variety of jobs, like securing insulation, ceiling tile, plastic sheeting, and fabrics.

- ✔ **Carpenter's level:** A straight-edge tool that has a series of glass tubes containing liquid with a bubble of air. When the bubble in a single tube is framed between marks on the glass, it shows that the surface is *level* (horizontal) or *plumb* (vertical).

- ✔ **Metal file:** Metal files are useful for sharpening the edges of scrapers, putty knives, and even shovels and garden trowels.

- ✔ **Allen wrench:** These L-shaped metal bars, often sold in sets, are designed for turning screws or bolts that have hexagonal sockets in their heads. This tool also goes by the name hex-key or set-screw wrench. You reach for Allen wrenches to assemble everything from knock-down furniture to bicycles to gas grills.

The prime way to save paint

Instead of two coats of regular expensive paint, most professionals use a primer for the first coat over hard-to-cover surfaces. Primer paint is designed to cover well, but because it is an undercoat, it doesn't need to be washable like standard paint, making it less expensive. When painting a dark color, pros often add a color tint to the white primer. Tints for both latex or alkyd paints are available at most paint stores. For best results, choose a tint shade that's close to the top coat color.

Calculating the right amount of paint

Use the following process to figure out how much paint to buy for your next paint project:

1. **Add together the length of all the walls and then multiply the number by the height of the room, from floor to ceiling. The total you come up with is in square feet.**

2. **Determine how much of that square footage is paintable surface area.**

   If you're not painting the doors and windows, subtract those areas from the room total. Subtract 20 square feet for each door and 15 square feet for each average-sized window in the room. You end up with a number that is close to the actual wall area you have to cover with paint.

3. **Divide the paintable wall area by 350 (the average square-foot coverage for a gallon can of paint) to find the number of gallons of paint you need for the walls.**

   You need slightly more than a gallon if the walls are unpainted drywall, which absorbs more paint. You also need to consider whether to paint more than one coat.

   If you're painting walls that are unfinished, heavily patched, or dark in color, plan on applying two coats of paint.

You can round uneven numbers; if the remainder is less than .5, order a couple of quarts of wall paint to go with the gallons; if the remainder is more than .5, order an extra gallon. Of course, buying in bulk is usually more economical, so you may discover that 3 quarts of paint cost as much as a gallon.

Turning off water supply faucets

For many plumbing repair projects, you need to turn off the water supply. The *main water shutoff valve* is usually located in the basement, close to where the water main enters the house. You can also turn off the water at *shutoff valves* located under each individual fixture.

✔ The *main valve* (see Figure 1-2) is usually a gate valve that allows a full flow of water through the pipe when it's open. This valve is located near the water meter (or pressure tank, if you rely on well water). Turning this valve clockwise cuts off the water supply to the entire house.

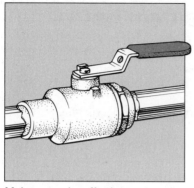
Main water shutoff valve.

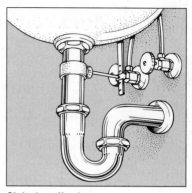
Sink shutoff valve.

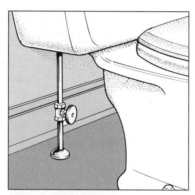
Toilet shutoff valve.

Figure 1-2: Common types of water shutoff valves.

✔ Most houses have *fixture shutoff valves* at the toilet and at each sink. These valves enable you to shut off the water supply to one fixture without halting water service to other fixtures.

The water shutoff valves to the kitchen sink are inside the cabinets beneath the sink; the bath lavatory valves are usually concealed in the vanity cabinet beneath the lavatory. For the toilet, the water shutoff valve may be on either side, or beneath the water closet or tank.

Picking the right plunger for the problem

Before you attempt to unclog a toilet, clean up any overflow so that you can work in clean, dry surroundings. Be careful when you handle toilet water and waste; it's laced with bacteria. Thoroughly wash the area, your hands, and your clothing with a disinfectant soap.

The toilet plunger

A ball, or cup-type, plunger is designed specifically for toilets. The rounded lower surface nests tightly in the bowl, giving the plunger greater suction to dislodge the blockage. The trick to using this baby is properly positioning it completely over the hole in the bottom of the toilet bowl, as shown in Figure 1-3. With the plunger in place, push down gently and pull up quickly to create suction that pulls the blockage back a bit and dislodges it.

Another advantage of the ball plunger is that it doesn't splash as much water around as regular plungers because the ball of the plunger covers the entire hole. However, if all you have is a small sink-type plunger, try using it. It can't hurt, and it just may work.

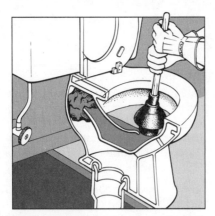

Figure 1-3: Push the plunger down gently and then pull it up quickly to loosen the clog.

The toilet auger

A more aggressive solution is to use a toilet auger. A *toilet auger* is a short, manually turned clean-out tool designed specifically to fit in a toilet bowl and clean out clogged toilet traps. Insert the rigid, hollow rod all the way in the bowl. Turn the crank while slowly pushing the flexible shaft through the hollow rod until it hits the blockage, as shown in Figure 1-4.

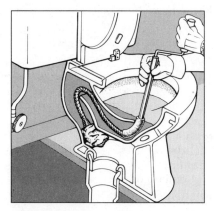

Figure 1-4: Crank the toilet auger into the toilet until it snags the blockage.

The heavy artillery

If the toilet auger doesn't do the trick, your last hope for repairing the problem yourself is to rent a *snake*. Make sure that the snake's small head fits past the tight curve in the toilet trap. Feed the flexible snake into the toilet until you feel it engage the clog — when the cable becomes harder to turn or refuses to move another inch into the toilet. When this happens, pull the snake back a bit to dislodge the clog. The water level going down signals that the clog is loose. Then flush the toilet to push the clog down the drain line and, hopefully, out to the sewer or septic system. If the clog is a diaper, rubber ducky, or something else substantial, you may have to pull the offending item all the way out of the toilet to clear the line.

Using water meters to detect leaks

If you're on a public water system, you have a water meter somewhere on or near your property. Besides telling you how much water you're using, it can also help you detect leaks. You can use your water meter to detect a hidden leak. Take a meter reading, and then turn off every plumbing fixture in your house for a couple of hours. (Don't forget to turn off the built-in icemaker or other water-consuming appliances.) After everything is off, take another meter reading. If the reading changes, you have a leak.

Finding a wall stud

Where possible, anchor hardware and pictures into the wall studs, not the space between them.

To find the stud locations, you can go the high-tech route and use an electronic stud finder — a gadget that locates studs in the wall by measuring the density of various points in the wall. When you pass the stud finder over a wall stud, a light signals the stud location.

For low-tech solutions:

✔ Remove the shade from a lamp and set the lamp with bare bulb about a foot away from the wall. This *side-lighting* technique highlights the nail locations.

✔ Get down on your hands and knees and look at where the base-board molding has nailheads showing. Wherever you see a nail-head, especially if they appear to be 16 inches apart, you're likely to find a stud.

Caulking your tub

Caulking is a necessary sealant around many bathroom and kitchen fixtures. The following covers your caulking bases.

Preparing to caulk

Removing caulk isn't as hard as it appears. Check your local home improvement store for products that are specially formulated to soften caulk for easy removal. After the caulk softens (it may take a few hours), remove it with a plastic putty knife. Clean the joint with paint thinner and wipe the area dry with a clean rag.

Then clean the joint with a mildew cleaner. Check out the section "Cleaning up mildew" for more info.

Immediately after eradicating the mildew, use a hair dryer or a hot air gun to thoroughly dry out the area. You can now recaulk the joint.

Now you're caulking

Use a roll of blue painter's masking tape for a professional-looking job. Apply the tape to the tub ⅛ inch from the joint. Next, apply another strip of tape along the wall, ⅛ inch from the joint. The caulk-ing can go between the two pieces of tape, making straight, smooth lines.

Ten household tasks to address every month

Each month, be sure to:

- ✓ Check the furnace and air-conditioner filters.
- ✓ Check water filters and softeners.
- ✓ Clean the dryer duct and filter.
- ✓ Clean and freshen sink drains.
- ✓ Test smoke detectors.
- ✓ Test CO detectors.
- ✓ Check the PTR valve on the water heater.
- ✓ Flush the water heater.
- ✓ Clean and/or lubricate at least one major appliance.
- ✓ Test the GFCI receptacles.

Apply tub and tile caulk into the joint and smooth the goo with your finger, an old teaspoon, or a caulking spreader. Immediately remove the tape by pulling it out and away from the freshly caulked joint. Be careful not to touch the caulk. Let it dry.

Getting rid of roaches

If you suspect that you may have a roach problem — but aren't sure where they're coming from — you need to find out where the little critters are hiding. Remember the following:

- ✓ **Use light.** Outsmart roaches by turning off the lights and shining a flashlight on the areas where you think they may be lurking. You'll see them go scattering about.

- ✓ **Use "roach motels."** When the bugs step into these inexpensive traps, their feet stick to tacky material inside, and they can't move. Put roach motels around the baseboards and walls in the kitchen, bathroom, and any other place you think roaches hang out. Check the motels frequently and keep track of how many you catch in the trap. You can see which areas of your home need more serious help.

✔ **Check out narrow cracks and crevices.** Refrigerators, stoves, hot water heaters, and dryers are some of roaches' favorites hiding places. Periodically, give appliances a thorough check by pulling them out and cleaning the area behind and underneath. If you see signs of roaches, vacuum up droppings from the floor and wash the area thoroughly with a strong household cleanser. Throw away the vacuum cleaner bag afterwards.

The best roach eradicator

The best thing to use to get rid of roaches is *boric acid*. It's very effective, and it's better for the environment than more toxic pesticides because it doesn't evaporate into the air and isn't absorbed through the skin. Be sure to get the kind that's rated 99 percent pure acid, which is more effective than other kinds.

You still have to be cautious, however, because boric acid can be toxic if ingested. Always keep it out of the reach of small children and pets. When you apply it to infested areas, don't let it get on your skin or breathe it in. Put on a mask and gloves, and wear a long-sleeved shirt and long pants to avoid exposing any skin.

Apply boric acid in one of the following ways:

✔ **Sprinkle:** When you sprinkle boric acid around, the roaches walk in it and ingest it when they clean themselves. Put it along the edges of baseboards, in corners, and under appliances. Use a bulb duster or turkey baster to gently blow it into small crevices, baseboards, and under walls and sinks.

✔ **Spray:** Mix a very light solution of 1 teaspoon boric acid to 1 quart water and shake well. Spray it in the crevices, baseboards, or dark corners where roaches lurk. Reapply as necessary. Be careful not to spray it where kids or pets can get into it.

✔ **Make a bait:** If you'd rather make up a yummy bait for the roaches to eat, mix together ½ cup borax (another form of boric acid), ¼ cup flour, ¼ cup cornmeal, ⅛ cup powdered sugar. Sprinkle the mixture onto plastic lids or paper plates and let it sit for about 10 days. Repeat if roaches are still around.

Natural repellents

Here are some natural methods of roach control:

✔ **Bay leaves:** Spread around some crushed bay leaves on kitchen shelves and under the sink.

✔ **Garlic:** Cockroaches hate the smell of garlic. Some people like to cut up garlic cloves and sprinkle them around drawers and baseboards. As long as the odor lasts, the roaches stay away. However, in a couple of weeks, you have to put out fresh garlic slices again. Unfortunately, many people feel that living with the smell of garlic is worse than living with the cockroaches.

Dealing with dust mites

Your bed and bedding is the favorite breeding ground for dust mites — it's moist and hot. Here are some tips for dealing with these critters:

✔ Wash off all bedding in the hottest water possible every week (at least 130 degrees). If you can't wash your comforter weekly, try buying allergen-proof covers for it. You can also buy allergen-proof coverings for the mattress, box springs, and pillows. And don't forget to wash off any pillows or stuffed toys that you keep on the bed that can contain dust mites.

✔ Periodically vacuum the mattress and box spring.

✔ Vacuum religiously to get dust mites up and away from one of their other prime breeding grounds — your carpet. If you're really allergic, don't use a conventional vacuum that vents dust out the exhaust hatch, which results in tossing dust mites back into the air again. Best to use a central vacuum system or one that has a special high efficiency particulate air (HEPA) filter.

✔ Put on a dust mask while vacuuming.

✔ Use a silicone-treated cloth when dusting so the dust isn't dispersed into the air.

✔ If you're really allergic, consider switching to wood floors.

Safe ways to rid your home of lead paint

To ensure that your home is safe from potentially toxic levels of lead, have a professional lead-testing lab perform paint inspection and/or risk assessment. Home test kits for lead are widely available, but, according to the EPA, recent studies suggest that they are not always accurate. Trained professionals use a range of methods to check your home, including visual inspection of paint condition and location, lab tests of paint samples, surface dust test, and a portable x-ray fluorescence machine.

Reasons to get the lead out

Public health officials rank lead as the number one environmental threat to children under the age of six — whether they live in public housing or suburban homes. Lead from paint chips and dust can pose serious health hazards if not taken care of properly. The good news is that lead-based paint in good condition is usually not a hazard.

According to the U.S. Department of Housing and Urban Development, 74 percent of all private housing built before 1980 contains some lead paint. As if that weren't enough, one in nine children under age six has enough lead in his blood to place him at risk. Moreover, children with high lead levels are six times more likely to have reading disabilities. The fetus of a pregnant woman who ingests lead is especially vulnerable to brain damage.

To permanently remove lead hazards you must hire a *lead abatement contractor.* Abatement methods include removing, sealing, or enclosing lead-based paints with special materials. Simply painting over the hazard is not enough.

Always hire a person with special training for correcting lead problems — someone who knows how to do this work safely and has the proper equipment to clean up thoroughly. If possible, hire a *certified lead abatement contractor.* Certified contractors employ qualified workers and follow strict safety rules as set by their state or by the federal government. Your best bet for finding a certified lead abatement contractor is via the Yellow Pages in your local telephone directory or by obtaining a list of referrals from a testing lab.

Picking plants to purify the air

Plants have always been good for your indoor environment, not only because they look beautiful, but also because they absorb carbon dioxide and give off oxygen. Studies show that plants actually freshen the air by absorbing toxic organic pollutants, such as benzene and formaldehyde, around the home. Peace lily, English ivy, Boston fern, and chrysanthemum are good all-around pollution fighters.

Chapter 2

Now You're Cooking!

*T*he phone lines are down, and you have no way to reach your favorite restaurant for a delivery order! You don't need to panic if you know the basics of cooking, from tools to techniques to time-savers. In this chapter, you find out about essential kitchen equipment, tricks that can make foods go from simple to scrumptious, and valuable inside information that can make you look (and sound) like a pro.

Outfitting Your Kitchen

Modern kitchens often boast conveniences such as granite counter-tops and six-burner ranges, but you don't need such luxuries to cook a great meal. This section covers all you need to get by.

Ten must-have tools

The bare-bones-all-I-can-spend-now kitchen includes:

- ✔ **10-inch chef's knife:** You can perform more than 80 percent of all cutting and slicing chores with this one knife.

- ✔ **Paring knife:** For peeling, coring, and carving garnishes from vegetables and fruits.

Microwaving your food

When microwaving, use ovenproof glass or ceramic containers rather than plastic. Many studies show that toxic chemicals from plastics migrate into food, so never microwave in containers like yogurt cups or margarine tubs. In addition, don't allow plastic film to touch food while cooking.

Not all ceramics are microwave safe, however. Vintage ceramic dinnerware made before 1950 contains dangerously high levels of lead, a toxic mineral that can leach out and enter your food.

- **10-inch nonstick frying pan:** The all-around pan for sautéing, making egg dishes, braising small quantities of food, and more.

- **3-quart saucepan:** For cooking vegetables, rice, soups, sauces, and small quantities of pasta.

- **Expandable steamer (to fit the 3-quart saucepan):** For steaming vegetables, fish, and shellfish.

- **10-quart stock pot with lid:** For making stocks or large quantities of soup, pasta, and vegetables. You'll be surprised by how often you use this pot.

- **Heavy-duty roasting pan:** For all kinds of roasting.

- **Liquid and dry measuring cups:** So you don't botch up recipes by using too much or too little of something.

- **Strainer:** Essential for certain sauces, pastas, salads, and soups.

- **Meat thermometer, vegetable peeler, rubber spatula, and wooden spoons:** Don't go off the deep end buying complicated kitchen gizmos; stick with the simple versions.

Kitchen layout 101

A large, eat-in kitchen is great, but the design of the cooking area needs to be practical. Moving from your working counter space to the stove and the refrigerator should be smooth and unobstructed. This working space actually has a name: the *kitchen triangle* (see Figure 2-1). If a table, plant, or small child is blocking the way, move it.

Kitchen islands are extremely efficient in that they can have considerable storage space below. Moreover, they can double as a kitchen table. If you don't have an island (and you have the space), consider buying a butcher-block table with shelving underneath.

Figure 2-1: An efficient kitchen triangle.

Cookware for good health

The kind of cookware you use to prepare food can make a difference in a meal's nutritional value. Some cookware leaches nutrients from foods, while others retain or even add vitamins and minerals. And some tools can be havens for bacteria if you're not careful.

- ✔ Build up a collection of pots and pans that are stainless steel-lined aluminum or copper and include some cast-iron sauté pans.

- ✔ Avoid all-aluminum cookware to limit your exposure to this mineral, which can interfere with kidney function and possibly the composition of bone.

- ✔ The plastic and chemicals that make up non-stick surfaces in pots and pans don't react with food as long as the surface is unscratched and intact. Use wood or plastic utensils with these pots and pans. Don't worry if you swallow tiny pieces of the nonstick coating; they can pass through your body undigested.

- ✔ Buy a fold-up steamer that adjusts to different sizes of pots.

- ✔ Invest in a juicer, a blender, and possibly a spice mill. A slow cooker can also be useful.

- ✔ Culinary experts once thought that plastic cutting boards were more sanitary than ones made of wood. Now, new research shows that wooden ones are far safer. A plastic surface harbors germs, even after you wash it, but a wood cutting board after you wash it shows no sign of bacteria — even after being left overnight.

Demystifying Cooking Techniques

Those TV chefs make cooking look so easy, as they banter while turning out scrumptious dishes. You can do it, too, by understanding that basic cooking techniques are pretty simple. Poaching, grilling, broiling, roasting, braising, and steaming have the added bonus of being healthful ways of cooking because they minimize fat content.

Boiling, simmering, and poaching

Boiling is bringing water to 212 degrees Fahrenheit for cooking. You don't need a thermometer. Let the water come to a *full rolling boil* (when the bubbles are rapidly breaking the surface). Speed up the heating process by covering the pot to trap surface heat. And no one knows why, but watching the pot indeed slows down the boiling process.

In *simmering,* tiny bubbles break the surface gently. Simmering occurs at a lower temperature — just below a boil — and is used for long, slow cooking and braising.

Poaching and simmering are virtually identical. Cookbook writers use the terms interchangeably.

Blanching and parboiling

You can easily remove skins from tomatoes, peaches, and nectarines by briefly plunging vegetables or fruits into boiling water for a few seconds and then into cold water to stop the cooking process. This technique is called *blanching.* Blanch vegetables like green beans and asparagus before you freeze or can them to help retain color and flavor.

Parboil (cook briefly in boiling water) foods such as dense vegetables (carrots, potatoes, turnips) or meaty ribs to cook them slightly before another cooking method finishes cooking them. (Parboil green peppers before you stuff and bake them, or parboil ribs before grilling.) This technique guarantees that all the ingredients in the dish finish cooking at the same time.

Steaming made simple

Steaming is the gentlest way to cook and is better than boiling or poaching for retaining a food's color, flavor, texture, and shape. It is also one of the most healthful methods because you don't lose nutrients in the cooking liquids.

- ✔ You can steam in two ways: in a perforated steamer set over simmering water (and covered) or in a deep, covered pot or saucepan holding about 1 to 2 inches of water. The latter method works especially well for large vegetables like broccoli and asparagus.

- ✔ If you steam foods often, you may want to invest in some sort of steamer. The conventional steamer model is a pair of pots, the top one having a perforated bottom and a lid.

- ✔ Fresh vegetables have more flavor and retain their nutrients better if you cook them only until *crisp-tender,* or firm to the bite. (The B vitamins and vitamin C are water soluble and leach into the cooking water as the vegetables cook.) Save the vitamin-packed cooking liquid to fortify soups and stews.

Going with the grains

Most grains cook quickly in boiling water or flavored boiling liquid such as beef stock or chicken stock. Grains usually don't need to be soaked before cooking, but rinsing them to remove any surface grit is usually a good idea.

Rice

You can store white rice almost indefinitely, but brown rice should be consumed within six months of purchase. Store all uncooked rice in a tightly sealed container in a cool, dry place.

Rice absorbs its cooking water while simmering, so getting your proportions right is important — always measure the amounts of rice and liquid. Keep the lid on tightly to trap steam.

The more flavor in the cooking liquid, the better the rice tastes because the flavors permeate the grains. Use chicken or vegetable stock, seasoned herbs, saffron, lemon zest or juice, or any combination of herbs and spices you like to flavor the liquid. If adding fresh herbs, do so in the last 10 minutes of cooking; any longer, and the flavors of the herbs fade.

Other whole grains

Barley is a great substitute for rice in soups and side dishes. It is commonly sold as "pearl" barley, with its outer hull and bran removed. It cooks relatively quickly — about 25 minutes in boiling water or stock. Season with butter, salt, and pepper.

What kind of rice is that?

The world is home to thousands of strains of rice, but you can get away with remembering just five types:

- ✔ **Converted or parboiled rice:** Basic white rice used for home cooking in much of the Western world. *Converted* refers to a precooking process that makes milling easier, removes some of the starch, and conserves nutrients.

- ✔ **Long-grain rice:** Rice that has been polished to remove the hull, bran, and germ. Includes the aromatic Indian basmati and Thai jasmine varieties.

- ✔ **Short-grain rice:** Polished rice that has a higher starch content (and is therefore stickier) than long-grain rice. Includes Arborio rice; also used in sushi.

- ✔ **"Wild rice":** A remote relative of white rice — actually a long-grain, aquatic grass — that grows almost exclusively in the Great Lakes region of the United States. Complements robust meat dishes, game, and smoked foods.

- ✔ **Brown rice:** Rice that has not been "polished"; that is, nothing but the tough, outer husk has been removed. The intact bran layer makes brown rice more nutritious than polished rice and is also a little more expensive. It has a faintly nutty flavor and a shorter shelf life than white rice.

Bulgur consists of wheat grains that are steamed then hulled, dried, and cracked. Bulgur cooks very quickly. In fact, in some recipes, like tabbouleh, you don't have to cook it at all (although you do soak it in water to soften it).

Quinoa (KEEN-wah) — a small grain that is power-packed with nutrients — is available in most health food stores, Middle Eastern shops, and quality supermarkets. You must rinse quinoa a few times before cooking. Use about 2 parts liquid to 1 part quinoa; it cooks in about 15 minutes.

Although not really a grain, you treat buckwheat like one. *Buckwheat* is really a grass and a cousin of the rhubarb plant. It has an earthy, almost nut-like flavor and tastes more like brown rice than other grains — an acquired taste. *Kasha*, also called buckwheat groats, is simply buckwheat that has been roasted.

Five tips on creating perfect pasta

Following are some no-fail tips for cooking this popular side or main dish:

✔ **Use a lot of water and an 8-quart pot (5 to 6 quarts of water for a pound of pasta).** Pasta needs room to move as it cooks. If you don't have a pot large enough to hold that much water and still be three-fourths full or less, splitting pasta into two pots of boiling water is better than overloading one pot.

✔ **Stir the pasta immediately and thoroughly for one minute after you add it to the water to avoid sticking.** Continue to stir occasionally as it cooks.

✔ **Check pasta for doneness by scooping out a piece or two with a fork and then tasting it.** The pasta should be *al dente*, an Italian term that means "to the tooth" or "to the bite." The cooked pasta should feel slightly firm to the bite. When pasta cooks too long, it absorbs more water and becomes mushy.

✔ **Do not rinse pasta.** When the pasta is *al dente,* pour it gradually into a colander. Do not rinse! You want starch on the pasta to help the sauce adhere to it. The only exception is if you're making a cold pasta salad.

✔ **Add sauce to cooked pasta immediately after the pasta drains, or it will become stiff and gluey.** Always have the sauce ready and waiting before the pasta is cooked. Then all you need to do is drain the pasta, add the sauce, toss well, and serve.

Is that fish done or just resting?

One traditional guideline for cooking fish is the so-called *Canadian Fish Rule.* Measure the whole fish steak or fillet at its thickest point and cook it (whether you're boiling, steaming, baking, broiling, or poaching) for precisely 10 minutes per inch. You may find that 8 to 9 minutes per inch is more like it; then check for doneness.

To check a whole fish, gently pull the dorsal fin. If it comes out easily, the fish is done; if not, the fish needs more cooking. Scallops turn opaque when done, and shrimp, which takes only a couple of minutes to cook, turns pink. Salmon and tuna are darkish pink at the center when medium. Cooked white fish glistens and appears wet only at the innermost core. Unless the recipe instructs you to do otherwise, remove all cooked fish from the heat or the poaching liquid immediately.

The shells of mussels, clams, and oysters open up when they're done, no matter how you cook them. Discard the ones that have closed shells.

> # Pork paranoia
>
> Cooks used to believe that if you ate pork cooked under 185 degrees Fahrenheit, you could contract *trichinosis.* The average person didn't know what trichinosis was, but it sure sounded unpleasant. Thus, for years, everyone ate overcooked pork. About a decade ago, scientists discovered that harmful trichinae bacteria die at 135 degrees. Cooking pork to 155 degrees is considered plenty safe and yields a much juicier result than the 185 degrees of the past.

Braising and stewing

Braising and *stewing* involve long, slow cooking in liquid. Braised foods lie in a few inches of liquid, not quite submerged, so that they stew and steam at the same time. Stewing involves submerging ingredients in a liquid and simmering the mixture for a long time.

Use the less expensive front cuts of beef: the chuck, brisket, shank, and plate. (Braise the larger cuts of meat and the very toughest; stew cut-up meat.) These more muscular cuts don't make much of a steak, but when you braise them for hours, their fibers break down, and they become succulent. These cuts are often more flavorful than expensive tenderloin.

Braised and stewed dishes take a lot of time to cook, so you're best off preparing them the day before and reheating them at serving time — the flavors are actually more pronounced this way. Braising and stewing is also great for parties because you can easily and inexpensively make large batches.

Grilling and broiling

Grilling and broiling are healthy ways to cook some vegetables and small cuts of meat, poultry, and seafood quickly. These methods let the fat and juices drain off for better health.

- ✔ Brush the grill or broiler pan with a few drops of oil or lightly coat the food with nonstick spray before cooking.
- ✔ To add flavor to lowfat cuts, marinate or coat the food with defatted stock, barbecue sauce, and marinades of lime juice, herbs, spices, garlic, and whatever else you like.

✔ To grill small pieces of seafood or vegetables, place them on a special cooking rack, perforated with small holes, that sits right on top the grill rack. Or create your own perforated surface by punching holes in a double thickness of heavy-duty foil.

Roasting food

Remove a roast when its internal temperature is 5 to 10 degrees *less* than the recipe's final internal temperature, and then let it rest on a counter for about 15 minutes. During the resting time, the roast cooks 5 to 10 degrees more. Always use a meat thermometer for accuracy.

Salt is a flavor enhancer that brings out the best in many foods. For that reason, salting meat, fish, poultry, and vegetables before roasting is important. However, because some people are advised to limit salt in their diets, ask guests ahead of time.

✔ **Chicken:** Before you roast a chicken, remove the packaged giblets (the neck, heart, gizzard, and liver) inside the cavity and save them. Rinse the bird thoroughly, inside and out, under cold running water. Then pat the skin dry with paper towels and season.

✔ **Pork:** Roasted pork tenderloin is great with a touch of sweetness — apple sauce is a traditional accompaniment. Another way to sweeten the dish is by applying a simple glaze toward the end of cooking: apricot jam, ginger marmalade, or even brown sugar melted with orange juice.

✔ **Beef:** When roasting a side of beef, scatter a variety of root vegetables (such as cut up carrots, onions, and peeled potatoes) in the roasting pan. Turn them every so often in the pan drippings so they cook evenly. A beef roast makes for a great presentation at the table.

What's your beef?

If you want a great hamburger — juicy, moist, and not fatty — you have to start with the right meat. Many people think that if they buy the "best" meat, like ground sirloin or ground round, they will have a superior burger. The flavor may be good, but those cuts are so lean that they tend to be dry.

The best all-around meat for hamburgers is ground chuck, which has about 15 to 20 percent fat, just enough to keep burgers moist. Supermarkets usually list the percentage of fat on the label. Also look for coarsely ground meat, which yields a looser patty.

The most flavorful and tender rib roasts come from the small end of the cow, which some butchers identify as the 12th through 9th ribs, or "first cut." Ask your butcher for this. Have the roast trimmed and cut to order, which means the butcher removes the short ribs (if not already removed) and the chinebone (for easier carving). The butcher can also partly separate the ribs to ease carving — once loosened you need to tie them back and together with twine for roasting.

✔ **Vegetables:** Take a large roasting pan and scatter chopped vegetables in it. Drizzle with olive oil, toss to coat well, and season generously with salt and pepper. Add any fresh or dried herbs of your choice: tarragon, rosemary, basil, marjoram, and so on. Roast the vegetables in a 400- to 425-degree oven until they're tender, turning them over in the oil every so often.

If you combine different vegetables on the same roasting pan, be sure to choose those that cook in about the same amount of time — for example, tomatoes cook much faster than carrots. Another way to achieve even cooking is to cut the hardest vegetables (carrots, parsnips, potatoes) into smaller pieces than the soft vegetables (celery, bell peppers, eggplant, and so on).

If you have leftover roasted vegetables, use them the next day in a salad, rolled in a tortilla with hot sauce, or in an omelet. If you want to make them crisp again, before serving, place them in a 400-degree oven for about 5 minutes.

Cooking methods for your sweet tooth

Desserts are crowd-pleasers, so if you want to make a good impression on your family and friends, try your hand at creating a delicious sweet treat.

✔ **When *poaching* fruit, use a basic poaching syrup made of one part sugar to three parts water.**

- Enhance the poaching syrup with flavors like vanilla bean, orange and lemon zest, honey, white or red wine, fresh ginger, whole cloves, star anise, fresh herb sprigs (rosemary is especially good with pears), and even whole black peppercorns.

- Fruit for poaching should be ripe but still a little firm. Underripe fruit has little sweetness. Overly ripe fruit, on the other hand, may fall apart and become soggy.

✔ **Use pure unsalted butter (also known as *sweet butter*) in all of your baked goods.** Salt (in salted butter) can affect the delicate sweetness of many baked goods. Avoid margarine, which just doesn't taste as good. Sometimes, however, margarine is used in combination with butter to add a light and flaky quality to pie crusts.

✔ **Bring the butter to room temperature quickly by grating it.** Just grate the butter on the largest holes of a box grater. It softens quickly.

✔ **When grating citrus peel, be sure to remove only the colored portion of the skin called the *zest*.** The white portion underneath, called the *pith*, is bitter. And who needs bitterness?

✔ **Use a plastic knife to slice up a cold pan of brownies.** No sticking!

✔ **Bring out the full flavor of nuts by toasting them slightly before adding to doughs or batters.** Simply spread out the nuts (whole or in pieces) on a baking sheet and toast in a 350-degree oven for about 10 minutes or until lightly browned. You can also place the nuts in a single layer in a heavy frying pan and toast over medium-high heat for 2 to 3 minutes. Stir the nuts or shake the pan occasionally, and watch carefully to avoid burning the nuts.

✔ **When a recipe calls for fresh lemon juice, never use the bottled reconstituted liquid kind.** It tastes more like furniture polish than lemon juice.

Sweet things in your pantry

Use the following tips to stock your dessert-ready pantry:

✔ **To keep a box of brown sugar from hardening after opening, put the whole box in a resealble, airtight plastic bag.** If the sugar hardens, place half an apple in the bag for several hours or overnight and then remove the apple.

✔ **If possible, don't use imitation vanilla.** Imitation vanilla consists of chemically treated wood by-products. Pure extracts, although more expensive, make a big difference in flavor.

✔ **Smell herbs and spices that have been sitting on your shelf for months or years.** If they've lost their enticing fragrance, throw them out and treat yourself to new ones.

✔ **Don't store nuts on a shelf if you're not going to eat them right away.** Most kinds of nuts quickly go stale or rancid if left exposed to air at room temperature. To prevent this, wrap them well in foil or plastic wrap (or place in a tightly sealed container or resealable bag) and store in the freezer. You don't need to defrost them before using.

Which apples are best for baking?

Tart, crisp apples that hold their shape are best for pie-making. Fall or early winter is the ideal time to bake an apple pie because the apple crop is fresh. With the exception of Granny Smiths (tart, green apples that are available all year), apples you buy in markets in the spring and summer have been stored since the fall harvest and don't have the same taste or texture as fresh apples.

The following varieties are among the best for baking in pies: Baldwin, Cortland, Granny Smith, Gravenstein, Jonathan, Macoun, Newtown Pippin, Northern Spy, Rhode Island Greening, Rome Beauty, and Winesap.

Taking a cake walk

For perfect cakes:

- ✓ **Avoid a bulge on the top of your cake from uneven cooking.** Use "cake strips," which are strips of aluminum-coated cloth that you wet and place around the outside of the cake pan (they come with pins to secure them in place). You can also use strips of old denim to accomplish the same thing. The wet strips slow the heat transfer around the perimeter and prevent the bulging.

- ✓ **Always measure dry and wet ingredients precisely.** Level off the tops of dry measuring cups with the flat edge of a knife. Also do this when using measuring spoons to measure dry ingredients like baking powder, flour, or baking soda.

- ✓ **Decorate a layer cake without using frosting by sprinkling it with a layer of confectioners' sugar.** Place the sugar in a fine mesh sieve, hold the sieve over the top of the cake, and tap it lightly with your hand, distributing the sugar evenly over the cake. You can also place a decorative stencil or paper doily on the cake. Sprinkle the confectioners' sugar over the stencil, and then carefully lift it straight up off the cake to reveal the design. Powdered semisweet cocoa also works nicely for light-colored cakes.

- ✓ **Always check the temperature of your oven when baking.** If a cake looks soupy when the timer goes off, your oven may not be working correctly. Buy an oven thermometer (the mercury type is best) to determine whether your oven is accurate.

Invaluable Insider Info (of the Cooking Variety)

The French term *mise en place* ("meeze-on-PLAHS") means to have "everything in its place." Get the peeling, chopping, mincing, deboning, and washing chores out of the way in order to create an even, efficient flow of cooking steps. The following sections offer some great suggestions.

A recipe-reading checklist

Go through the following steps before you dive into any recipe:

- ✔ Read through the recipe at least twice to make sure that you understand the directions.
- ✔ Make sure that you can perform all the techniques.
- ✔ Check that you have all the necessary equipment and ingredients.
- ✔ Make sure that you have enough time before serving to prepare and cook the recipe.
- ✔ Check whether you can (or need to) make any part of the recipe ahead of time.

Six timesaving tips

Here are six goodies that can save you a bundle of time in the kitchen:

- ✔ For easy-to-peel hard-cooked eggs, use eggs that have been refrigerated for a week to 10 days. The fresher the egg, the more difficult it is to peel.
- ✔ Take meats out of the refrigerator about 15 minutes before cooking so that they warm to room temperature. They cook faster and more evenly.
- ✔ Line the broiler pan with aluminum foil to ease cleanup.
- ✔ Make salad dressings and other dishes that contain onion, garlic, fresh herbs, and the like in a food processor or blender to save chopping time.
- ✔ Place a garlic clove on a cutting board and whack it with the flat side of a heavy knife or a cleaver to make removing the skin easier.
- ✔ Roll a lemon or orange under the palm of your hand on the countertop to make extracting the juice easier.

✔ Read through the ingredients to see whether you like them all (sea slugs anyone?), as well as whether the recipe has too much fat, sugar, or salt for your dietary needs.

✔ Check whether you need to use an ingredient, such as butter or oil, at different stages in the recipe so that you don't make the mistake of using that ingredient all at once.

✔ Find out whether you need to preheat the oven.

✔ Check the yield of the recipe. Double or half the recipe as appropriate.

Recovering from cooking blunders

Everybody goofs up in the kitchen once in a while. Here are a few common calamities and some easy solutions:

✔ **Beef, overcooked roast:** Make roast beef hash, beef pot pie, barbeque, soups, stews, shredded beef tacos, or Beef Stroganoff.

✔ **Bread, burned:** Scrape off the black part with a grater.

✔ **Butter, blackened in a pan:** Pour off and discard the burned butter and wipe the pan. Use equal amounts of butter and vegetable oil, which don't burn as easily.

✔ **Cake, burned:** Cut away the black part and fill any holes with frosting. Scrape surface burns with a grater.

✔ **Cake, stuck in a pan:** Let sit for 5 minutes and then try again.

✔ **Chicken, browning too fast:** Cover the browned parts with foil, shiny side out, and continue roasting until all the chicken is cooked.

✔ **Eggshells, crack while hard-cooking:** Add a teaspoon of salt or a few drops of lemon juice to the cooking liquid to prevent the white from running out of the shell.

✔ **Egg whites, won't whip:** Try again with whites at room temperature. Use a clean, dry copper bowl or add a pinch of cream of tartar before whipping.

✔ **Fat, spattering in pan:** Add pinch of salt or cornstarch to the hot fat. Pour off the fat as soon as possible — or cover the pan.

✔ **Fruits, discolored:** If cut fruits such as bananas and apples start turning brown, sprinkle them with lemon juice and cover with plastic wrap.

✔ **Gravy, lumpy:** Whisk vigorously or whirl in a food processor.

- **Gravy, too thin:** Raise heat and reduce, whisking until the gravy thickens. Or add a creamy paste of 1½ teaspoons cornstarch mixed with ½ cup stock or water for every 1 cup of gravy. Stir and cook for about 2 minutes over medium heat.

- **Gravy, too salty:** Add a little brown sugar or currant jelly.

- **Puddings, thick skin forms on top:** Let cool to room temperature, cover with plastic wrap, and refrigerate.

- **Rice, crunchy:** Add a little water and continue cooking.

- **Soufflé, doesn't rise:** Salvage as an alternative dessert (fallen soufflés are very chic in restaurants) by placing it as attractively as you can on a serving dish. Garnish with ice cream and a sprig of mint.

- **Soup, too salty:** Add water. Or add slices of potato, which soak up salt. Just be sure to remove the potato slices before serving.

- **Soup, too thin:** Make *beurre manié* (a 1-to-1 ratio of softened butter and flour mashed into a paste). Add to soup and stir well over medium heat until it thickens. Arrowroot and cornstarch are other thickeners. Blend with a little water before serving soup.

- **Soup or stew, lacks flavor:** Add one of the following: freshly grated lemon peel, salt, fresh or dried herbs, a little dry sherry, a bouillon cube, or a pinch of sugar.

- **Vegetables, overcooked:** Puree in a blender, adding a little cream (or half-and-half) and seasonings to taste.

Filling your pantry with exotic herbs and spices

Herbs and spices energize virtually every type of cooking. Change the herb or spice, and the dish takes on entirely different tastes and aromas.

Herb 'n' matters

Purchase dried herbs and spices in small quantities, keep them in tightly sealed containers away from heat and light, and try to use them within 10 to 12 months. The flavor of dried herbs fades over time. The following covers which foods marry well with particular herbs.

- **Basil:** Pungent, sweet flavor. Available as fresh sprigs or crumbled dry. Essential to Mediterranean cooking, especially Italian and French cuisine. Excellent with tomatoes, eggs, pasta, poultry, fish, and green salads, and in vinaigrettes.

✔ **Bay leaf:** Strong, herbaceous taste. Sold as a whole, dried leaf. Excellent in long-cooking dishes like soups, stews, poaching liquid, marinades, pot roasts, rice casseroles, stuffings, and barbecue sauces. Remove the leaf before serving the dish.

✔ **Chervil:** Aromatic, with delicate licorice-like flavor. Available as fresh sprigs or crumbled dry. Use with fish and shellfish, eggs, chicken, tomatoes, asparagus, summer squash, eggplant, herb butters, sauces, green salads, and soups.

✔ **Chives:** Delicate, mild-onion flavor. Sold in thin, fresh stalks, chopped, or dried. Wonderful in cream sauces or soups, with chicken, eggs, shellfish, or marinated salads, or as a garnish.

✔ **Cilantro or Chinese parsley:** Extremely pungent and aromatic. Sold in fresh, curly-leafed bunches. Found in Mexican and Asian dishes and works well with rice, fish, pork, ham, salsa, avocado, and tomato.

✔ **Dill:** Delicate caraway flavor. Sold in feathery, fresh bunches or as dried seeds. Use seeds in pickling recipes; use fresh leaves with fish and shellfish, omelets, chicken, turkey, dressings and vinaigrettes, cold salads and marinades, fish mousses, and pâtés.

✔ **Marjoram:** A little like oregano in taste, but much milder and sweeter. Sold fresh or crumbled dry. Extremely versatile. Add to almost any vegetable dish, especially good with sweet potatoes, squash, tomatoes, corn, stuffings, stews, omelets, soups, rice, pork, lamb, beef, poultry, or fish.

✔ **Mint:** Fresh scent and a sweet, pungent flavor. Most common varieties are standard peppermint and spearmint. Sold in fresh bunches or crumbled dry. Terrific in cold grain and rice salads, with fresh fruit, in cold fruit soups and sauces, and with marinated vegetable salads of cucumber or tomato; also good with grilled chicken, pork, lamb, and shellfish, and in cold drinks like iced tea.

✔ **Oregano:** Intense flavor. Sold fresh or crumbled dry. An essential ingredient in Italian and Greek cooking. A little goes far with poultry, tomato sauces, egg dishes, vegetable stews, and stir-fries.

✔ **Parsley:** Fresh-flavored and slightly tart. Available year-round in fresh bunches or crumbled dry. Two common fresh varieties are the stronger-flavored Italian flat leaf and the curly leaf. An all-purpose herb; use in savory soups or stocks in bouquet garni, stews, dressings, stuffings, and frittatas, with fish, poultry, beef, pork, lamb, veal, game, and all vegetables. Also a pretty plate garnish.

- **Rosemary:** Quite aromatic, needle-shaped leaves smell a little like lemon and pine. Sold as fresh sprigs or dried. Use sparingly with vegetables and in stuffings, rice dishes, and stews. Excellent with game, meats (especially grilled), chicken, halibut, salmon, tuna; in herb breads; or to flavor oils and marinades. Pull the needles or leaves off the stem, and mince the leaves finely before using. Discard the tough stem.

- **Sage:** Green-gray or purple oval leaves with a slightly bitter mint taste. Available in fresh sprigs, crumbled dry, and ground. Use sparingly. Excellent in poultry stuffings, pâtés, fish and chicken stews, chicken salads, meat loaves, and herb butters, with halibut and salmon, and for seasoning meat and poultry roasts.

- **Savory:** Full-bodied herb that some people say tastes like a cross between mint and thyme. Crumbled dry available year-round. Excellent with fresh or dried bean salads, most fish and shellfish dishes, omelets, soufflés, rice dishes, stuffings, meat and poultry, tomatoes, potatoes, artichokes, and onions.

- **Tarragon:** Aromatic herb with assertive, licorice-like flavor. Sold as fresh whole sprigs, crumbled dry, and whole dried leaves. Fresh tarragon, widely available in the summer months, has the most subtle flavor. Use with chicken, pork, lamb, veal, fish, shellfish, omelets and other egg dishes, dips and dressings, mayonnaise, vegetable casseroles and salads, herb butters, and as flavoring for white vinegar and hot or cold potato dishes.

- **Thyme:** Tiny leaves with minty aroma and tea-like taste. Sold as fresh sprigs and crumbled dry. Fresh varieties include lemon, orange, and French (the common variety). Add to vegetables, meat, poultry, fish, egg dishes, soups, stews, cream sauces, meat loaf, pâtés, chowders, and stuffings.

TIP

Making and storing dressings

To save the time and effort of making vinaigrette every time you need it, make a large batch and store it in empty wine bottles. In a mixing bowl, combine 1 tablespoon or more of Dijon-style mustard with lots of salt and freshly ground black pepper. Add about ½ cup olive oil in a slow stream while whisking. Gradually whisk in vinegar (roughly a 5-to-2 ratio of oil to vinegar). Taste constantly. When you like the results, pour the dressing into the bottle with a funnel. If you like, add fresh herbs or minced garlic to the bottle. Shake, seal with a cork, and refrigerate.

Spicing up your life

Dried spices are generally more concentrated than fresh, so use them carefully. For example, if a recipe calls for 1 tablespoon of fresh oregano, you need only use ½ teaspoon dry oregano. After you become familiar with the qualities of different spices, your cooking repertoire expands exponentially.

- ✔ **Allspice:** Spice berries of the evergreen pimiento tree with tastes of cinnamon, nutmeg, and cloves. Sold as whole, dried berries or ground. Excellent in both sweet and savory dishes — pâtés, stews, chilies, poached fish, meat loaf and meatballs, pumpkin and fruit pie fillings, barbecue sauce, stuffed cabbage, winter squash, chutneys and preserves, and gingerbread.

- ✔ **Caraway:** Has a nutty, faint anise flavor and is commonly used in German cooking. Sold as dried seeds. Found in rye bread and also in cakes, stews, and some European cheeses.

- ✔ **Cardamom:** Pungent, spicy-sweet flavor. Sold as whole dried seeds and ground. Excellent in baked goods, fruit salads, pumpkin pie, and Indian curries, one of the main ingredients in *barain masala,* an essential spice mixture in Indian cooking.

- ✔ **Cayenne or ground red pepper:** A hot, powdered mixture of several chili peppers. Sold ground. Use sparingly. Especially good in dishes with egg, cheese, rice, fish, chicken, or ground beef.

- ✔ **Chili powder:** A hot and spicy mixture of dried chilies, cumin, oregano, garlic, coriander, and cloves. Sold ground. A multipurpose hot seasoning; use sparingly in stews, soups, chili, egg dishes, dressings, guacamole and bean dips, barbecue sauces, and rice and bean casseroles.

- ✔ **Cinnamon:** Sweet and aromatic spice from the bark of a tropical tree. Sold whole, in dry sticks or ground. Primarily a baking spice in cakes, cookies, and pies, but also adds a savory touch to stews, curries, baked sweet potatoes, and yellow squash.

- ✔ **Clove:** Sharp and deeply fragrant. Sold as whole dried buds or ground. Use much like cinnamon, but more judiciously. Excellent in stocks, vegetable soups, and glazes.

- ✔ **Coriander:** Similar in flavor to caraway. Sold as whole dried seeds and ground. Seeds used for pickling; powder used for curries, lamb, pork, sausage, and baked goods.

- ✔ **Cumin:** Slightly acidic aroma; nutty-flavored seed. Sold as whole dried seeds and ground. Essential to Middle Eastern and Asian cooking. Use in curries, chili, and bean dips and with fish, lamb, poultry, and beef.

- **Curry powder:** A spice blend that can include more than a dozen different herbs and spices, often with cinnamon, cloves, cardamom, chilies, fenugreek seeds, mustard seeds, turmeric (which gives curry its distinctive golden color), and red and black pepper. Commercial blends tend to lose their flavor fast, so use them within 2 months of purchase. Use to season lamb, pork, chicken, rice, stuffings, and sautéed vegetables like onions, cabbage, and baked squash.

- **Ginger:** Sharp and faintly sweet flavor; intensely aromatic. Sold dried ground, crystallized, preserved, and fresh. Use ground sparingly in curries, spice cakes, and marinades and with pork, chicken, and seafood. Use crystallized (candied) in fruit syrups and glazes and with pies and cakes. Grate fresh ginger into stir-fries of pork, chicken, beef, and fresh vegetables.

- **Nutmeg:** Pleasing aroma; slightly sweet and nutty taste. Sold as whole seeds and ground. Delicious in white sauces, sweet sauces, and glazes, pureed vegetables and soups, eggnog, fruit pies, spice cakes, and pumpkin pie. Best freshly grated. Use very sparingly.

- **Paprika:** Beautiful red powder; varieties range from sweet to hot. Sold ground (the Hungarian variety is considered the best). Accents dips, creamy salads, dressings, stews (like goulash), sautéed meats, chicken, and fish. Imparts rusty red color to creamed dishes and sauces.

- **Peppercorns:** Black peppercorns are intense, hot, and aromatic. Sold cracked, finely ground, or as whole peppercorns in black and white, with black being the strongest. (All are berries from the same vine, picked at various stages of maturity.) Black pepper is perhaps the world's most popular spice, used to accent nearly every savory dish. Use freshly ground peppercorns for best effect — ground pepper quickly loses its intensity. Use white pepper to enrich cream sauces and white dishes if you don't want the pepper specks to show.

- **Saffron:** The world's most expensive spice. Made from dried stigmas hand-picked from a special variety of purple crocus flowers. Available as powder or whole red threads (which are of better quality). A little goes a long way. Essential to classic dishes like bouillabaisse and paella, but also delicious in rice casseroles, creamed dishes, risotto, and with seafood. Imparts a pale yellow color to cream sauces and rice dishes.

- **Turmeric:** Yellow-orange powder that is intensely aromatic and has a bitter, pungent flavor; gives American-style mustard its color. Sold as a powder. Essential ingredient in curries; use in rice and chili and with lamb and winter squash.

Picking poultry by age, weight, and sex

The tenderness and flavor of fresh poultry vary somewhat from one commercial producer to the next, so buy and taste a few different brands to determine which you like. The following are some popular types:

- **Broiler/fryer:** A 7- to 9-week-old bird weighing between 2 and 4 pounds. Flavorful meat that is best for broiling, frying, sautéing, or roasting. A whole broiler/fryer is always less expensive than a precut one.

- **Roaster or pullet:** From 3 to 7 months old and between 3 and 7 pounds. Very meaty, with high fat content under the skin, which makes for excellent roasting.

- **Capon:** A 6- to 9-pound castrated male chicken. Excellent as a roasting chicken because of its abundance of fat. Just to be sure, pour off or scoop out excess melted fat as the chicken roasts — especially if you don't have an exhaust fan. Not widely available in supermarkets (it usually needs to be special-ordered).

- **Stewing chicken:** From 3 to 7 pounds and at least 1 year old. Needs slow, moist cooking to tenderize. Makes the best soups and stews.

- **Rock Cornish game hen:** A smaller breed of chicken weighing 1 to 2 pounds. Meaty, moist, and flavorful for roasting.

What to look for

USDA Grade A poultry is the most economical because it has the most meat in proportion to bone.

Skin color is not an indication of quality or fat content. A chicken's skin ranges from white to deep yellow, depending on its diet. However, dry, bruised skin or depressions and dimpling in the meat are signs that the bird isn't fresh and has been mishandled.

Check the "sell-by" date. These dates generally indicate when two weeks have passed by since the processor butchered and packaged the bird. The closer you are to that stamped date, the closer you are to eating a 2-week-old chicken. Dig through the poultry case to find a package with a sell-by date as far in the future as possible.

Storing and preparing

Consume whole or cut-up poultry within 1 to 2 days of purchase. You can wrap and freeze a whole, raw chicken for up to 12 months; you can freeze parts for up to 9 months. Defrost in the refrigerator, never at room temperature. Be sure to place the thawing package in a pan or on a plate to catch any dripping juices. A 4-pound chicken takes 24 hours to thaw in the refrigerator; cut-up parts between 3 and 6 hours. If you use your microwave to defrost poultry, do so on a very low setting and be sure to cook the poultry immediately after thawing it.

Remove the package of giblets (the neck, heart, gizzard, and liver) in the cavity of a whole bird and then rinse under running cold water before cooking the bird. Also trim away excess fat. After preparing poultry, wash your hands and work surfaces (counters and cutting boards) with soap and water to avoid bacteria contamination.

Converting cooking measurements

Use the following equivalents for quick and easy conversion between measurements:

Liquid volume equivalents

1 cup = 8 fluid ounces

2 cups = 1 pint or 16 fluid ounces

2 pints = 1 quart or 32 fluid ounces

4 quarts = 1 gallon

½ tablespoon = 1½ teaspoons

1 tablespoon = 3 teaspoons

2 tablespoons = 1 fluid ounce

Dry equivalents

¼ cup = 4 tablespoons

⅓ cup = 5 tablespoons plus 1 teaspoon

½ cup = 8 tablespoons or 4 ounces

¾ cup = 12 tablespoons

1 cup = 16 tablespoons

2 cups = 1 pint

4 cups = 1 quart

Baking equivalents

1 cup sifted cake flour = 1 cup minus 2 tablespoons sifted all-purpose flour

1 cup sifted all-purpose flour = 1 cup plus 2 tablespoons sifted cake flour

1 teaspoon double-acting baking powder = ¼ teaspoon baking soda plus ½ teaspoon cream of tartar

Miscellaneous equivalents

1 tablespoon prepared mustard = 1 teaspoon dried mustard

1 cup stock or broth = 1 bouillon cube dissolved in 1 cup boiling water

1 square (1 ounce) unsweetened baking chocolate = 3 tablespoons cocoa powder plus 1 tablespoon butter

1 ounce semisweet chocolate = 3 tablespoons cocoa powder plus 2 tablespoons butter plus 3 tablespoons sugar

Food equivalents

2 slices bread = 1 cup fresh bread crumbs

1 stick butter = 8 tablespoons butter

1 pound butter = 4 sticks butter

1 pound confectioners' sugar = about 4½ cups confectioners' sugar, sifted

1 pound granulated sugar = 2 cups granulated sugar

½ pound hard cheese = about 2 cups grated cheese

1 cup heavy whipping cream = 2 cups whipped cream

Wining and dining

Red wines are normally served at room temperature, and white wines are chilled so that the flavor and aroma are at their peak. If the day is a very warm one, a slightly chilled red wine may be more desirable.

Pairing up food and wine

Choose a wine that doesn't overpower the food or isn't overpowered by it:

✔ Light meat dishes (such as pork), poultry, or full-flavored fish (such as salmon) go well with a red wine such as Pinot Noir or French Burgundy.

✔ Lighter fish and shellfish dishes are fine with a light-bodied white wine, such as Chenin Blanc, Sancerre, Pinot Grigio, or German Riesling.

✔ Lobster or richer fish dishes are complemented by a full-bodied Chardonnay, Sémillon, or Viognier.

✔ Chicken and pasta can go with either red or white wine, depending on the sauce. A heavy meat sauce is better complemented by a medium-bodied red wine, such as Merlot or Cabernet Franc, while a light vegetable or cream sauce goes well with a white or sparkling wine.

✔ Stews, roasts, game, duck, and other full-flavored dishes go best with full-bodied red wines, such as Cabernet Sauvignon, Petite Syrah, or Zinfandel.

What to serve with international foods

Some international foods were not designed to go with wine, so be creative and experiment with different varieties. Chefs across the country pour Champagne with everything from Asian-influenced main courses to Indian curries. The effervescence of Champagne can refresh the palate so that the spices don't overwhelm the wine.

Some other combinations you can try include:

✔ **Cajun**: Alsatian white wines, Champagne

✔ **Mexican and Indian:** Chardonnay, beer

✔ **Sushi:** Sauvignon Blanc

✔ **Chinese:** White Zinfandel

Uncorking a bottle of wine

The one indispensable corkscrew for every household is the screwpull (see Figure 2-2). To use a screwpull:

1. **Remove the metal or plastic capsule that covers the cork.**

2. **Position the plastic part of the corkscrew over the bottle top until a lip on the plastic is resting on the top of the bottle.**

3. **Hold on to the plastic firmly while turning the lever atop the worm clockwise. The worm descends into the cork.**

4. **Simply keep turning the lever in the same clockwise direction, and the cork emerges from the bottle.**

5. **Remove the cork from the screwpull, by turning the lever counterclockwise while holding on to the cork.**

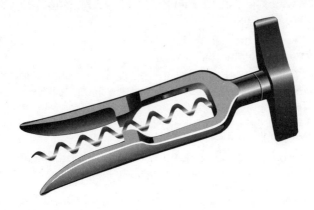

Figure 2-2: Uncork wine with ease.

Chapter 3

Getting the Dirt on Gardening

*I*n times past, gardens were purely practical, plain, and utilitarian — a rectangular patch of ground "out back" where vegetables and flowers grew. Now, the word "gardening" signifies so much more. Gardening is all about a process that delights the eyes and fuels the soul with a connection to the earth. As countless educators and community volunteers know, gardening is one of the quicker (and cheaper!) ways to reduce vandalism and crime and to increase community pride — so dig in!

Fostering Healthy Flowers and Plants

Of all the wonderful benefits that flowers bring to a garden, their vibrant and beautiful colors mean the most to many. Although you may get excited just thinking about mixing and matching flowers of different colors to create striking effects, actually seeing the finished product is the real payoff.

Choosing bulbs

Bulbs are a dream come true for many people, especially for those who have never had much luck growing plants. Think of bulbs as flowering powerhouses: Plants that pack most of what they need for a season's worth of growth into some type of underground storage device, the bulb. Plant a bulb at the right time of year and at the proper depth, and you're almost guaranteed a spectacular bloom — true, you have to wait a few months, but your patience is almost always rewarded.

Figure 3-1 shows you how to easily figure out what depth to plant various bulbs at.

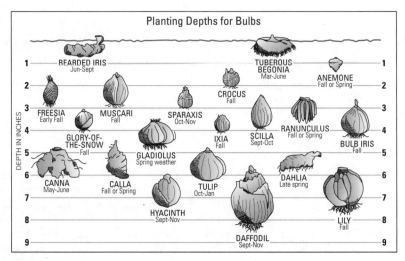

Figure 3-1: Use this bulb-planting depth chart as a guide when you plant your own bulbs.

Picking the right roses

You can choose from literally thousands of kinds of roses, short to tall, big to little flowers, fragrant or not — you name it. But most of the roses you find in garden and home centers, and available by mail-order, are "modern roses," which means they're one of the following:

✔ **Hybrid teas:** The blossoms of hybrid tea roses look like the roses that come from a florist, yet usually smell much better. The plants are upright and rather angular, and their distinctive flowers and buds on long stems have come to typify what a rose is for most people. The hybrid tea is the latest development in the history of the rose and is by far the most popular rose today. The big plus of hybrid teas is that they're *ever-blooming,* meaning they bloom all summer. (Actually, that's a bit optimistic. Although some varieties come close to being in bloom all season, most bloom in waves every six weeks or so beginning in spring and peaking again in fall.)

You can use hybrid teas as stand-out plants in mixed flower beds or group them in a special rose bed. Some varieties are relatively hardy. Most varieties, however, require special attention to keep the plants vigorous where winters are severe.

✔ **Floribundas:** These crosses of polyantha roses (cluster-flowering roses) with hybrid teas were developed in an attempt to bring larger flowers and repeat bloom (bloom early in the season, stop, and then bloom again later) to winter-hardy roses. Roses in the floribunda class have blossoms shaped like those of hybrid teas, but the flowers are usually smaller and often are grouped in loose clusters. Floribundas are comparatively rugged and make great specimen shrubs or hedges.

✔ **Grandiflora:** These flowers have the size and form of hybrid teas but are more freely produced, singly or in clusters, on taller, exceptionally vigorous plants. "Queen Victoria" and "Gold Medal" are two popular and beautiful grandifloras.

✔ **Climbing roses:** You can tie these long-branched roses onto (or weave them into) a support structure so that the roses look as though they're climbing. Climbing roses can be old-fashioned roses, hybrids, or chance variants of hybrid teas. The supporting structure can be anything from a chain-link fence to a fancy iron archway. Tie climbing roses gently with pieces of stretchy cloth or old pantyhose.

✔ **Miniature roses:** These have small leaves, short stems, and small flowers; they usually grow less than 2 feet tall (61 cm). Miniatures fit easily into small beds and make great edging plants. You can also grow them in containers.

✔ **Rose trees:** A fun trick rosarians have played on the hapless rose is turning it into a tree. These trees are called *standards,* and you can buy almost any kind of popular rose this way. Standards cost more because it takes more time and effort to create one, but they're worth it. The secret? Growers graft desired roses on top of a tall trunk. Standards raise the flowers to nose height. So-called *patio roses* are the same idea, but smaller.

✔ **Shrub roses:** While growing roses for their charm alone has many rewards, hundreds of kinds of roses serve as colorful landscape shrubs, ground covers, and vines. Shrub roses as a group combine some of the best traits of the toughest roses with the most beautiful. Ideal features of shrub roses are profuse and nearly continuous bloom, pest and disease resistance, cold and heat hardiness, minimal pruning requirements, and attractive plant shape.

✔ **Ground-cover roses:** These produce long, wide spreading canes, but grow no higher than about 2 feet. They make good covers for slopes. Plant about 4 or 5 feet apart. Also use them in containers where they can spill over sides, or plant them wherever you want to have a trespass-preventing barrier. All are vigorous, very cold hardy, and produce many flowers.

Mixing up high-powered rose fertilizer

If you want to grow prize-winning roses, try this recipe for success:

1. **A week after plants leaf out, use a 20-20-20 soluble fertilizer at the rate of 1 tablespoon per gallon and 2 gallons per rose plant.**

2. **One week later, scatter ½ cup of Epsom salts around each plant and water it in.**

3. **The third week, apply fish emulsion, also at the rate of 1 tablespoon per gallon and 2 gallons per plant.**

4. **Week four, apply a liquid fertilizer with an approximate 16-4-2 ratio and which also includes a soil penetrant and chelated micronutrients, again at 1 tablespoon per gallon, 2 gallons per plant.**

5. **Week five, start all over again.**

Choosing a healthy tree

The easiest way to have tree problems down the road is to purchase and plant one that's unhealthy to begin with. Here are some tips for buying a healthy tree:

✔ Avoid trees that have been in a nursery container for too long or are unhealthy and growing poorly — they're most often disappointing once in the ground.

Examine the top of the root ball. Avoid specimens that have large, circling roots near the surface, a sign the tree has been in the container too long.

✔ Avoid trees that are the smallest or largest of a group. Select ones that are well proportioned from top to bottom.

✔ Select trees that can stand on their own without being tightly tied to a stake. (Tightly tied stakes can be like crutches, preventing a tree from developing a strong trunk).

 ✔ Pick a tree that has an evenly tapered trunk from bottom to top.

 ✔ Look for healthy, even-colored foliage.

 ✔ Pick a tree that's free of insects and disease.

Knowing when to work the soil

Have you ever grown your own mouth-watering melon, checking it daily to see whether it's perfectly ripe? Preparing the soil is similar. You need to wait until the soil is in the right condition — lightly moist, but not wet. If too wet, clay soil can dry into brick. If too dry, soil can turn into dust and blow away, leaving beneficial soil life to perish. If your soil tends to be wet and clammy in spring when you're ready to plant annual flowers, you can avoid this frustration by preparing your beds in the fall, when dry conditions often prevail.

Fortunately, the right soil condition is easy to evaluate. Take a handful of soil and squeeze it in your fist. Tap the resulting ball with your finger. If it breaks up easily, the soil is ready. If it stays in a sodden clump, the soil needs to dry out more. If it doesn't cling at all, the soil is dry: Water the area, wait a day, and try again.

Using old newspapers as mulch material

Newspapers provide the ultimate organic "herbicide," a simple and cost-effective way to mulch out weeds. A thin layer of five to ten sheets of newspaper suppresses all sprouting weed seeds, stops some resprouting taproots, and makes life difficult for runner roots. Use newsprint that is plain black and white or that has colored pictures. (Glossy, color paper can contain toxic chemicals, such as cadmium and lead.) Newspapers work best around woody perennials, shrubs, and trees, but after you get familiar with the process, you can use them around flowers or vegetables.

To apply the newspaper, moisten the sheets so that they don't blow around as you lay them out among the plants. Cover the papers with a thin layer of a weed-free, attractive mulch. The mulch helps the newspaper last for 6 to 18 months, depending on whether you have wet or dry summers, respectively.

Cardboard works even better than newspaper for the really tough weeds.

Deadheading

Deadheading is the process of pinching or cutting off faded flowers while the plant is in bloom. Deadheading forces the plant to spend its energy on developing more flowers instead of creating seed. The result of deadheading is usually a longer bloom cycle.

Many perennials benefit from being cut back at various times during their growth cycles. To stimulate branching on lower stems and to make the plant bushier, for example, pinch out new growth at the top of the plant.

Some perennials, such as coreopsis, delphinium, and gaillardia, rebloom if cut back by about one-third after the initial bloom cycle.

At the end of the growing season, cut back most perennials (some shrubbier types are an exception) to a height of 6 to 8 inches. Cutting back growth rejuvenates the plant and results in a better bloom next season. Where the ground freezes in winter, mulch plants with at least 6 inches of organic matter such as straw or loose leaves. If you use leaves, start with an 8- to 12-inch layer because over the course of winter the leaves pack down substantially.

Taller perennials, such as delphiniums, and bushy types, such as peonies, may need staking to prevent the flowers from falling over. You can opt for thin metal wire loops (for bushy plants) or bamboo stake ties (for taller perennials).

If older plants become overcrowded or bloom poorly, rejuvenate them by *dividing*. In fact, division is a good way to increase plant numbers.

Knowing when to prune

As a general rule, don't prune unless you must. Always consider whether you really need to prune the plant. Many native or naturalized trees grow perfectly fine without pruning. But roses and fruit trees, among others, need thoughtful pruning for maximum production of flowers and fruit. Table 3-1 shows you the what and when of foliage trimming.

Table 3-1	Pruning Timetable
Type of plant	*When*
Shrubs that bloom in spring	Just after flowers fade
Shrubs that bloom in summer or fall	Early spring

Type of plant	When
Rhododendrons and azalea	Just after flowers fade
Pine trees	Late spring
Formal hedges	Late spring and, if necessary, fall
Most trees, shrubs, and vines	Late winter or early spring

Basic rules of tree and shrub pruning

A few "rules of limb" apply when pruning all trees and shrubs:

- ✔ Remove dead or diseased wood as soon as possible. (Be sure not to spread certain diseases, like fireblight, with the pruning tools: Clean the blade with a 10 percent dilution of bleach after every cut.)
- ✔ Cut out one or two branches or shoots if they run against each other.
- ✔ Prune in the winter to encourage new shoots and leafy growth in the spring.
- ✔ To remove unwanted shoots or limbs without stimulating too many new shoots, prune in the summer.

Boosting plants' natural defenses with homemade tea

Compost tea is a genetic cocktail teeming with microorganisms that appear to boost a plant's natural defenses and suppress the growth of some fungi. It can help reduce the spread of some molds, blights, and mildews by 50 to 90 percent. Make the tea by mixing one part mature compost that contains some manure with five parts water in a bucket. Let the mixture sit in the shade for about 10 days. Then filter the solution through cheesecloth, dilute the tea to half strength if you want, and spray it or dribble it on the leaves. Try to coat both sides. Reapply after two to three weeks. You can also spread the left-over residue on the ground around your plants. Avoid spraying any products containing manures directly on leafy vegetables such as lettuce and spinach that you may soon harvest.

When you use any disease-control remedies on food crops, be sure to wash your harvest well before eating it.

Outwitting animals

If you've ever had a newly planted garden decimated by a ground-hog, then you know that driving to the store, buying fencing, rushing home, and installing it takes a great deal of time and money. Whether you're dealing with greedy groundhogs, nibbling rabbits, browsing deer, or gophers and moles tunneling throughout your yard, animals can be a nemesis to gardeners.

When trying to coexist with wild animals, the first priority is to keep your sense of humor. Beyond that, you can use a few techniques to protect some of that garden produce for you to enjoy. If you don't succeed with one method, try another:

- **Deer:** Deer are creatures of habit. They often travel along the same routes day after day, moving between two locations. Build a deer-excluding fence about 8 feet high (deer have been known to jump 10-foot fences). Before you invest in a fence, you may want to try surrounding your garden with a heavy fishing line attached to posts at about 3 feet high. This can startle deer because they don't see the fishing line, and they may retreat. Don't try this method if you have young children around who may injure themselves on the line.

    Deer avoid some plants, although they're notorious for changing their minds about what they want for dinner. In general, pungent or fuzzy-leafed plants are safe.

- **Gophers:** Each of these burrowing, antisocial rodents can carve out 700 square yards of elaborate underground tunnels. While they tunnel, they work up quite an appetite, and any plant roots that happen to be in the way turn into lunch.

    Underground barriers made of hardware cloth are effective. Install barriers at least 2 feet deep to block further borrowing.

    Various traps are available to catch gophers dead or alive, and traps are the only method that orchardists and others who are serious about limiting gopher damage use. Traps work best when set inside the tunnels.

- **Groundhogs (Woodchucks):** The easiest way to eliminate groundhogs is a fence, one that extends 3 to 4 feet above ground and 18 inches below ground. Traps are next best. Groundhogs are one of the easier garden raiders to trap alive with a Havahart trap. Check with local and state ordinances about any restrictions on live trapping, and take care when releasing any wild animal so that it doesn't turn on you.

If you're at wit's end dealing with marauding deer or gophers, or woodchucks, consult your local animal control officer. Normally, you can find these folks listed under the city, county, or state listings in the telephone book.

Keeping pesky birds at bay

The pleasing sounds and movements that birds bring to your garden sometimes come at a cost. If you plan to grow fruits, you must take precautions to keep birds from devouring them. Birds especially love berries, and some eat corn and tomatoes. Effective deterrents include:

- ✔ **Polyester bird netting:** Sold at most garden centers, this barrier is by far the most reliable way to protect fruits and vegetables. Drape the netting over fruit-bearing plants as soon as fruits begin to ripen.

- ✔ **Birdscare flash tape:** This tape looks like metallic ribbon. Decorate the tops of plants with the stuff and trick birds into thinking the plant is on fire.

- ✔ **Fake predators:** These fool-the-eye figures include artificial snakes, and owls, and good old scarecrows. Rearrange these phony spooks often to keep the birds baffled.

- ✔ **Noisemakers:** The devices include wind chimes, bells, rattling aluminum pie pans, and other items that make sounds when bumped by birds or jostled by the wind (just use your imagination).

Dealing with almost any garden pest

Think of garden pest management as a staircase. On the first step you can find the least disruptive, innocuous actions, and on the top step are the most toxic and most potentially harmful measures. The best way to control pests is to start at the bottom and move up the stairs only when absolutely necessary. This strategy is called *integrated pest management,* or IPM. This approach takes advantage of the complex interrelationships between insects and plants to find the least toxic ways to reduce damage to crops.

The following list outlines the actions you can take in your garden to keep a pest from getting the upper hand. The measures move from the least aggressive and potentially harmful to the most aggressive.

✔ Strong blast from a hose that knocks small pests such as aphids and spider mites off your plants. Spraying daily can provide good control.

✔ Barriers such as floating row covers (translucent, lightweight fabrics that cover plants) that keep flying insects from reaching plants; cutworm collars placed around seedlings; and copper strips that encircle plants and give slugs an electric shock. Make cutworm collars with 4-inch-high rings pushed 2 inches into the soil or use toilet tissue rolls or rolled newspaper.

✔ Insect traps that use chemical attractants and colors to lure pests, such as sticky, red balls for apple maggots.

✔ Bacterial insecticides, such as *Bacillus thuringiensis* (Bt) for caterpillars, and milky spore disease for soil-dwelling grubs.

✔ Least toxic controls, such as insecticidal soaps, horticultural oils, and rotenone insecticides, which kill pests but cause minimal impact on the environment.

✔ Botanical insecticides, such as neem.

Top ten garden pests and how to deal with them

Do borers drive you buggy? Don't know the difference between a cutworm and a caterpillar? Here's a quick course in the nature of some creepy, crawly characters . . . and some tips on taming the bothersome beasts.

✔ **Aphids:** These tiny, soft-bodied, pear-shaped pests suck plant sap with their needlelike noses. Colors vary: They may be black, green, red, or even translucent. Aphids leave behind sticky sap droppings that may turn black if covered with sooty mold. Aphids can proliferate quickly on weakened plants. Blast them off with a hose, control with beneficial insects or sticky yellow traps, or spray with insecticidal soap. The beneficial insects green lacewings and ladybird beetles are also excellent controls.

✔ **Borers:** Several kinds of beetle and caterpillar larvae (they look like small worms and are usually less than 1 inch long) tunnel into the wood or stems of fruit trees, white birches, dogwoods, shade trees, rhododendrons, German irises, and squash vines. The boring weakens the plant and makes it more susceptible to diseases. The holes can also cut off nutrient flow to the affected limb or vine. Choose species that are less susceptible to borers. Keep susceptible plants growing vigorously and watch for signs of borer damage — dead bark, sawdust piles, and poor performance. When you find borers, cut off and destroy severely infested limbs. Inject parasitic nematodes into the remaining borer holes.

✔ **Cutworms:** These ½-inch-long, grayish caterpillars emerge on spring and early summer nights to eat the base of young seedling stems, cutting the tops off from the roots. To control, surround seedlings with a barrier that prevents the cutworms from crawling close and feeding. These devices can be as simple as an empty cardboard toilet paper roll or a collar made from aluminum foil — just make sure that the collar encircles the stem completely and set 1 inch deep in the soil.

✔ **Gypsy moths:** These 2-inch-long, gray (with brown hairs), foliage-eating caterpillars or their egg clusters hitchhike across the country on cars, campers, and trains. They eat foliage on a number of shade trees, including oaks, and can defoliate trees when their population gets large enough. Monitor population sizes with pheromone traps. Catch caterpillars as they attempt to crawl up tree trunks by using duct tape treated with a sticky barrier. Spray with Bt or neem.

Sticky pest barriers are just that — bands of goop that a crawling insect cannot navigate. Buy this stuff at garden centers or from a mail-order supplier.

✔ **Japanese beetles:** These beetles are ½ inch long, and are metallic blue-green with coppery wing covers. They eat almost any plant with gusto. Their fat, white, C-shaped, ¾-inch-long larvae consume turf roots. To control, treat your lawn with milky spore disease, which takes several years to spread through the lawn, or with parasitic nematodes, a quicker-acting helper. Inspect your garden in the evening or after dark for the beetles, knocking them off plants into a can or bucket of soapy water. You can also spray with neem.

Avoid using the Japanese beetle traps that you can hang. The pheromones in these traps attract beetles not only from your yard, but from your neighbors' yards as well. You end up with more beetles than you had without the traps.

✔ **Mealybugs:** These small sucking insects cover their bodies with a white, cottony substance that makes them easy to identify. Plus, they usually feed in groups. Mealybugs are common on houseplants. You can wash off small numbers with cotton dipped in rubbing alcohol. Spray indoor plants with an oil-based "leaf shine" product and use horticultural oil for landscape plants. Insecticidal soap and neem are also effective remedies.

✔ **Scale:** Looking like bumps on plant stems and leaves, these tiny sucking insects cling to plant branches, hiding under an outer shell that serves as a shield. These pests suck plant sap and can kill plants if present in large numbers. Look for sticky, honeylike sap droppings, one clue that scale may be present. Remove and destroy badly infested stems. Indoors or on small plants, clean off light infestations with a cotton ball soaked in rubbing alcohol. Spray larger plants with horticultural oil in early spring or summer.

✔ **Snails and slugs:** These soft-bodied mollusks feed on tender leaves during the cool of night or in rainy weather. Sometimes they're hard to spot: All you see is the slime trail they leave behind. They proliferate in damp areas, hiding and breeding under rocks, mulch, and other garden debris. Clean up dark, damp hiding spots to relocate slugs elsewhere. Catch the ones that remain by setting a saucer with the rim at ground level. Fill the saucer with beer. Slugs crawl in and can't get out. Refill regularly. Or surround plants with copper barriers — metal strips that seem to shock slugs if they attempt to crawl across. Set out traps, commercial or homemade. Look for nontoxic baits that contain iron phosphate.

Make your own slug trap by placing a few boards or rolled-up newspaper in the garden. In the early morning, lift the board and destroy the slugs. Toss out the newspaper if it has slugs.

✔ **Spider mites:** These tiny arachnids are almost microscopic, but when they appear in large numbers, you can begin to see the fine webs that they weave. They suck plant sap, causing leaves to discolor and plants to lose vigor. They're especially active in arid conditions. You find spider mites on fruit trees, miniature roses, potted begonias, and many houseplants. Indoors, wash houseplants often and spray with insecticidal soap. Outdoors, wash plants with a strong blast of water, or use dormant oil in early spring or light horticultural oil in summer.

✔ **Tent caterpillars:** These caterpillars form tentlike webs full of teeming caterpillars on trees and shrubs. In large numbers, they can defoliate an entire tree. Knock caterpillars off severely infested branches with a broom or pole.

Making cut flowers last

If you're cutting flowers for arrangements, care in harvesting and handling helps them last. Remember the following tips:

✔ Use sharp shears and cut the flowers in the early morning (before too much moisture has transpired from the plant).

✔ As you cut, put stems directly into water — carry a water-filled bucket into the garden with you.

- ✔ As soon as you bring the flowers indoors, remove the lower leaves that are below the water in your vase. Submerged leaves rot, cloud the water, and can give off an unpleasant odor.

- ✔ Recut stems under water before placing them in the vase.

- ✔ Adding floral preservative to the vase water provides nutrients, acidifies the water, and slows respiration — all of which serve to lengthen the life of the flower.

- ✔ Change the vase water every couple of days.

- ✔ Place your bouquet in a cool spot, out of direct sunlight, and away from heating vents.

Some large flowers with hollow stems, such as delphiniums and amaryllis, last longer if you first hold the stems upside down and pour water into them. Then plug the base of the stem with cotton.

Certain flowers, including Iceland poppies, euphorbias, and hollyhocks, need to have their stems sealed by searing to prevent them from drooping. Immediately after cutting, hold each stem over a flame for a few seconds or dip the stems in boiling water for 1 or 1 ½ minutes.

For roses, fill a clean sink or large baking dish with lukewarm water and lay the roses in flat. Soak the roses for 10 to 20 minutes before arranging or to revive fading flowers. The process may even restore drooping flower heads.

Plants with woody stems, such as lilacs, forsythias, and pussy willows, require a slightly different treatment. You need to split or smash the stems to help with the uptake of water. One way to accomplish this is to pound the bottom few inches of each stem with a hammer. Alternatively, use a sharp knife or clippers to cut several times into the stem.

Caring for Your Lawn

A lawn is so much more than just a patch of grass; it's the soft spot in your yard where you play, entertain, or lie down to relax. A well-kept lawn is also a source of pride that tells the world that this is *my* house, and I take care of my house and the people who live in it. Grass lawns also buffer some of the harsher edges of the environment, reducing dust, producing oxygen, cooling the air, and cutting down on glare and reflected heat.

Knowing some lawn lingo

Cool-season grasses are the grasses of the north. They can withstand cold winters, grow most vigorously in spring and fall, and grow slowly in warm summer weather. Cool-season grasses include

- ✔ Bent grasses
- ✔ Kentucky bluegrass
- ✔ Fescues
- ✔ Ryegrass

Warm-season grasses are the grasses of the south. They thrive in hot summer, mild winter areas and go dormant in cool winters or die in very cold winters. Warm-season grasses include

- ✔ Bahia grass
- ✔ Bermuda grass
- ✔ Buffalo grass
- ✔ Centipede grass
- ✔ St. Augustine grass
- ✔ Zoysia grass

Unbelievable lawn factoids

A lawn is a dynamic place, filled with stems, microorganisms, tillers, deep roots, shallow roots, rhizomes (sprigs), wide leaves, thin leaves, and more. Just to show you how incredible the lawn environment is, a team of brave research-types crawled across every inch of a healthy, 10,000-square foot lawn and took it apart piece by piece.

Above ground:

- ✔ Six grass plants per square inch
- ✔ 850 plants per square foot (we told you it was crowded)
- ✔ 8.5 million total grass plants!

Below ground:

- ✔ 387 miles of root per grass plant
- ✔ 329,000 miles of root per square foot
- ✔ 3 billion miles of total root!

Thatch is a spongy layer of grass stems and debris that forms between grass blades and roots. It's bad stuff that prevents water, air, and nutrients from reaching grass roots, while providing a perfect home for insects and diseases.

Aerating is the process of removing small cores of soil from a lawn. It helps reduce thatch.

Eight keys to a happy, healthy lawn

Here's a handful of tips that can help you nurture the nicest grounds:

- ✔ Plant grasses that are well-adapted to your climate and the growing conditions in your yard (sun, shade, lots of foot traffic, and so on).
- ✔ Prepare the soil properly before planting.
- ✔ Plant at the right time: early fall or spring for cool-season grasses; late spring or early summer for warm-season grasses.
- ✔ Water deeply and only when your lawn really needs it.
- ✔ Fertilize at the appropriate times: spring and especially fall for cool-season grasses; late spring through summer for warm-season grasses.
- ✔ Mow at the appropriate height. Cut the grass when it reaches one-third higher than its recommended mowing height.
- ✔ Leave the clippings on the lawn. They add free nutrients and organic matter and don't cause thatch.
- ✔ Reduce thatch. Aerate or power rake to keep thatch at a minimum.

Determining your soil type

Soil comes in three main types with a lot of variations in between: Hard clay soil is at one end of the soil spectrum, soft sandy soil is at the other end, and loam soil is in the middle.

In a nutshell, following are the characteristics of the three basic types of soil:

- ✔ **Sandy soils** are composed of mostly large mineral particles. Water moves through these soils quickly and, as it does, takes nutrients with it. Sandy soils are well-aerated, quick to dry out, and often lack the nutrients that grass plants need.

✔ **Clay soils** consist mostly of small mineral particles that cling tightly together and hang on to water. Clay soils are slow to dry out and have poor aeration.

✔ **Loamy soils** are a happy mixture of large and small mineral particles, and they usually contain an abundance of organic matter. Loamy soil is well-aerated and drains properly, while still being able to hold water and nutrients.

Grass grows best in loam soil. Loam soil provides the right mixture of moisture, nutrient-holding capacity, and aeration that roots love.

The worst thing you can do is add sand to change your clay soil or add clay to change your sandy soil. Doing so changes either one to something more akin to concrete than soil. The best way to amend your soil is with organic matter.

When you have your soil tested and as you go about the process of amending or improving soil, you need to know your soil type. You can get a pretty good idea by grabbing a moist handful of soil and squeezing. When you let go, sandy soil falls apart and doesn't hold together in a ball. Clay soil oozes through your fingers as you squeeze and stays in a slippery wad when you let go. Loamy soil usually stays together after squeezing but falls apart easily if you poke it with your finger.

Knowing how much grass seed to sow

To determine how much seed you need to purchase, start with a pretty close estimate of the size of the area you aim to plant. For example, a rectangular lawn that is 20 x 50 feet is 1,000 square feet in area. Most lawns aren't so convenient to measure, and if yours is one of these, don't worry. For one thing, your measurement needn't be precise. You can also measure the area by dividing it into separate, discrete shapes and then add them all together at the end.

Measure with your stride: An adult stride is usually around 3 feet. Measure yours with a yardstick until you know what a 3-foot stride feels like before heading out onto your lawn. If your lawn measures in acres rather than feet, consider renting one of the distance-measuring tools available at local rental yards.

If you buy a seed mix for home lawns, the package label most likely specifies how much area the seed in the package covers. If you aren't buying packaged seed, use the size of your area and Table 3-2 to figure out how much seed to buy.

Table 3-2	How Much Seed to Sow
Grass Name	*Pounds of Seed/1,000 sq. ft.*
Bahia	8 to 10
Bermuda grass	2 to 3
Buffalo grass	2 to 3
Centipede	1 to 2
Fine fescue	4 to 5
Kentucky bluegrass	1 to 2
Perennial ryegrass	4 to 5
Turf-type Tall fescue	6 to 10

Sharpening your rotary mower blades

Although you need to take reel mowers to a lawn mower shop for a professional sharpening, you can sharpen rotary mower blades yourself. Of course, you need to check the owner's manual for specifics, but basically, the procedure is as follows:

1. **Turn the mower off and disconnect the spark plug.**

2. **Remove the blade with a wrench, secure the blade in a vise, and sharpen the beveled edge with a file.**

3. **Maintain the existing angle on the blade and sharpen with a smooth, easy pass with the file.**

4. **After sharpening, check the balance of the blade by centering the blade (not the sharp side!) on top of your finger or a dowel.**

5. **Reinstall the blade, making sure that it's right side up. Secure locking nut.**

If the blade doesn't balance, file a little more off the heavy end until it does. Or, forget the whole thing and buy a brand new blade. You can usually get one for less than $10.

Nine things to do with your lawn during draught

Sooner or later, Mother Nature wreaks havoc on your life with drought or limited water supplies. Such conditions are common in the western United States but can happen almost anywhere. Obviously, during such times, conserving water is critical. If the situation is severe enough, you may need to follow mandatory watering restrictions or even water rationing. In some dry summer areas like California, city water districts estimate that outdoor watering makes up about half of an average family's water consumption, and much of that goes on lawns. Naturally, the lawn is a major target for water conservation.

Following are ten ways of handling your lawn to conserve water.

✔ **Fertilize less**. Cutting back on the nitrogen you apply causes grass to grow slower and need less water. You may want to limit your fertilizer application prior to or during a period of drought or quit fertilizing altogether.

✔ **Mow higher**. Set your mower at the high end of the your particular grass type's ideal mowing height. (If you don't know what type of grass you have, dig up or pull up a little piece near an unseen edge and take it to your local nursery. They can identify it for you.) Grass that grows on the tall side develops deeper roots within weeks and helps shade the soil, keeping it cooler and reducing the loss of water due to evaporation. This simple mowing adjustment helps lawns withstand drought better.

✔ **Water less frequently.** Don't cut back on how much you apply at each irrigation, just how often you water. If you water every three days, cut back to once every four or five days. The lawn doesn't look as good, but it springs back faster when things get back to normal.

✔ **Let the lawn go brown**. Just stop watering altogether. Many grasses can go dormant for two or three weeks or longer and come back when the rains return. If not, renovate and reseed with a more drought-tolerant grass.

✔ **Let the lawn go brown and then paint it green.** That's right — you *can* find such a thing as lawn paint. Ask your nursery person about it.

✔ **Use gray water.** *Gray water* is the water left over after you take a bath or wash clothes. Where droughts are common, gray water has saved many a plant and lawn. However, using gray water properly, getting it out to the lawn, and then coping with any problems that it causes are a bit tricky.

✔ **Reduce the size of the lawn**. Maybe all you really need is a small green spot in the backyard where the kids can play. So water only that area. When the rains return, you can water the whole lawn again or tear out part of it and replant with ground covers or some other less thirsty plants.

✔ **Put in AstroTurf.** Your days of going barefoot on the lawn may end, but the yard is at least green.

✔ **Pave the whole thing.** You can always use more places to park, right?

Growing a Bountiful Garden

Gardening is part of an age-old cycle that goes back to ancient peoples. The process is rewarding and fulfilling in a way that connects you to your roots (no pun intended) as a human being.

Stretching your garden season

If you live in a cooler climate, you have to deal with a short growing season. If you want to increase your garden bounty, you need to squeeze in a few extra weeks of plant growth earlier and later in the year. By using some of the techniques in this section, you can enjoy the advantages that gardeners have in milder climate zones.

Planting earlier in the year

Gardeners are master manipulators and have devised all sorts of ways to get a jump on spring. The first simply is to plant early. Here's how to get away with fooling Mother Nature:

✔ **Start plants indoors.** Cool-season plants, such as snapdragons or lettuce, tolerate light frosts. Start them indoors, timed so that they're ready for transplanting about three to four weeks before the average last frost date.

You can start frost-tender plants — such as marigolds — early, too. Plan to transplant them under protective cover about two weeks before the average last frost date.

✔ **Use a cold frame.** A *cold frame* speeds seed germination and shelters plants from frost. The frame is a bottomless box, usually constructed from wood. The structure has a slanting, tight-fitting top made of old windows or other transparent or translucent materials such as plastic or fiberglass. A typical frame is approximately 3 feet wide and 6 feet long with an 18-inch-high back sloping down to 12 inches high in the front.

Place the frame outdoors, over a garden bed or against the south wall of your home. Orient the frame so that it slopes to the south. The sun warms the air and soil inside, creating a cozy environment for plants. Sow seeds for transplants directly in the cold frame. (Or grow crops such as radishes, spinach, beets, and lettuce to maturity in the frame.)

Prop the top open during the day for ventilation and lower it at night to conserve heat. If you can't check the frame regularly, consider buying a thermostatically controlled vent opener as insurance against cooking or freezing your plants.

If you like the idea of a cold frame but want even greater temperature control, consider a hot bed. This device is essentially a cold frame with a heat source (commonly electric heating cable) to warm the soil. The cable usually includes a built-in soil thermostat preset for about 75 degrees Fahrenheit, ideal for germinating most seeds.

When tender plants are ready for the garden, you need to protect them from frost. Here's a rundown of useful frost guards:

✔ **Hot caps:** These devices are individual covers that work like miniature greenhouses. You can make hot caps yourself or buy them in stores. To make your own, cut the bottom out of a plastic gallon milk jug. Anchor it in the ground with a stake and leave the cap off so that your plant doesn't bake inside. Commercially produced hot caps are made of translucent wax paper, plastic, or fiberglass.

✔ **Water-filled cloches:** A couple of different kinds are available, one with thin plastic, flexible walls and one with heavier, stiff walls. In both cases, you fill the walls with water. During the day, the water absorbs solar heat. As the water cools down at night, it releases heat slowly, protecting the plant inside from temperatures as low as 16 degrees Fahrenheit. Use cloches to protect seedlings from late spring frosts.

✔ **Row covers:** Drape lightweight synthetic fabrics, called *floating row covers,* over the plants. The covers let light and water pass through while protecting plants from temperatures as low as 24 degrees Fahrenheit, depending on the fabric you use. The fabrics are available in a variety of widths and lengths.

Row covers of slit plastic are cheaper but usually require more work because they need support from hoops or a frame. You also have to pull the plastic aside to water. Plastic covers create higher daytime temperatures than fabric, which may be advantageous when you're trying to give heat-loving plants like peppers a boost in cool weather.

✔ **Recycled junk from your house.** Every so often, an unexpected late spring frost catches you off guard. Usually, the frost prediction comes about the time green, tender, young plants dot the garden. To save plants, rummage around for anything that may protect them without crushing them. Cardboard boxes, old sheets, empty buckets, or even newspaper spread over the plants lend a few degrees of protection. Just remember to remove the stuff the following day, or the plants may bake.

In addition to providing frost protection, serious cold-climate gardeners often warm the soil in early spring before planting. They spread a soil-warming, plastic-type mulch over the soil surface and cut holes in it for the transplants. After planting, they protect plants with floating row covers.

Clear plastic traditionally has been the mulch of choice for heating the soil, but weeds really thrive under it. Now you can use a new high-tech option called *IRT mulching film*. This green film heats up the soil as well as clear plastic does, but blocks the portion of the light spectrum that supports weed growth. (Clear plastic is still the best to use if you want to *solarize* or heat the soil sufficiently to destroy insects, fungi, and weed seeds. This technique is most effective in hot summer regions that have many consecutive sunny days.)

Gardening beyond autumn

Consider these tips on foiling the first frosts of fall:

- ✔ **Cover up.** You often can face an occasional light frost before the first big killer. On those crisp, clear evenings when a light frost is forecast, throw a few bedsheets or floating row covers over tender crops. With a little effort, you can prolong the harvest of summer crops.

- ✔ **Spray on frost protection.** What if you forget — or are just too tired — to cover up crops on a chilly evening? Well, you have a second chance to save them (after you rest, of course). Turn on your garden sprinkler during the late-night hours (as soon as the temperature drops below 33 degrees Fahrenheit). Leave the water on until the sun warms the air up above freezing. A fine spray of water is more effective than large water droplets.

- ✔ **Plant again.** Cool-season plants tolerate frost. You can plant a second crop of many flowers and vegetables in mid-to-late-summer for a late autumn or winter. These plants grow quickly in the still-warm soil of summer and start maturing about the time tender crops are declining. Kale (both edible and ornamental), beets, chard, pansies, and turnips are among the stars of the post-frost harvest.

Gardening all year

Frost is the culprit that usually dictates the beginning and end of the gardening season. Planting dates revolve around the first and last average frost dates. If you don't know the dates for your area, ask a nursery professional or call your extension office. The extension system phone number is usually listed in the phone book among the state university numbers or under *Extension* in the business section.

In mild-winter regions, where an occasional light frost is as bad as it gets, the best way to stretch the season is to keep on gardening right through winter. Winter gardening has many benefits: Pest and disease problems are fewer; you don't have to water much, if at all; and winter crops are varied, nutritious, and delicious. In addition to the cool-season vegetables, annual flowers such as pansies, calendula, stock, and primrose thrive in winter. Autumn is prime planting time for winter gardening, although you can plant some crops, such as lettuce and beets, in succession through the winter.

If you want to reap every last tomato in autumn but don't want to hassle with protecting individual plants from frost, you have a couple of other options:

✔ Pick your green tomatoes right before the first frost. Arrange them in a single layer on a shelf or table and cover them loosely with newspaper. Check frequently for ripeness and toss any that start to rot.

✔ When frost is predicted, cut or pull your plants and pile them together. Cover the pile with plastic. The tomatoes continue to ripen.

Toughening up transplants

Vegetable seedlings that you grow indoors at home or purchase from a greenhouse in spring need to acclimate gradually to the brighter light and cooler temperatures of the outside world. This process, called *hardening off,* slows plant growth, causing the plants to store more food internally and increase the thickness of their outer leaf layers. Basically, hardening off toughens up transplants for the cold, cruel, outside world.

To harden off your transplants:

✔ A week or two before you intend to set plants out in your garden, stop fertilizing and reduce the amount of water you give the plants. Take your plants outside for a half hour of filtered sunlight — setting them under an arbor or open-branched tree — during the warmest part of the day. If the weather is windy, put the plants somewhere where they're sheltered or construct a windbreak out of pieces of wood.

✔ Gradually increase the amount of time that the plants spend outside and the intensity of the light that they're exposed to so that by day seven, they're out all day. Also, make sure that you bring the plants in every night.

Another option is to move your plants to a cold frame, opening the cold frame more each day and closing it at night. Plants that you raise in a cold frame from the time that they're young seedlings need much less hardening off.

Don't overharden your plants. Certain crops, such as cabbage and broccoli, can *bolt* (flower before they're supposed to) quickly if you repeatedly expose seedlings over three weeks old to temperatures lower than 40 degrees Fahrenheit for a couple of weeks.

Digging into organic gardening

Organic gardening is the latest rage in vegetable gardening, but in many ways, organic gardeners use good, simple gardening practices and common sense. Some of the basic facets of organic gardening include feeding the soil — not just the plants — with organic fertilizers, manure, and organic matter; rotating crops; planting a diverse group of crops; solving pest problems by planting disease-resistant varieties; using barriers (covers that keep bugs away from plants); releasing beneficial insects; and using the least harmful biological and plant-based sprays.

The fertilizers and pesticides that commercial organic gardeners can use vary from state to state. A movement is in process to create national standards to define organic gardening. As a home gardener, how you define organic gardening is a matter of personal preference.

Using wood ashes to provide nutrients

Wood ashes are a source of potash and phosphate, although the exact amounts of these nutrients depend on the type of wood burned (hardwoods generally contain more nutrients than softwoods), the degree of combustion, and where the wood was stored (for example, dry storage prevents nutrient leaching). A general analysis is usually in the range of 0 percent nitrogen, 1 to 2 percent phosphate, and 4 to 10 percent potash. But the major benefit of wood ashes is as a *liming agent* to raise the pH of the soil. Naturally, if you live in an area where soils are alkaline, don't use wood ashes as a soil amendment; they raise the pH even higher.

Apply wood ashes to your soil in moderation (no more than 10 to 20 pounds per 1,000 square feet of garden) because they may contain small amounts of heavy metals, such as cadmium and copper. These metals build up in plants if you add too much wood ash to the soil and can kill the plants or harm you if you eat lots of those plants.

Harvesting and drying herbs

Harvest herbs throughout the growing season because most plants benefit from being cut back. The best time to harvest herb leaves is just as the plants begin to set flower buds — the time when they have their maximum flavor and fragrance.

Cut herbs in the morning when the dew has dried but before the sun is very bright, because many herb oils in the leaves *volatilize* (evaporate) into the air in the heat of the day. After cutting them, wash the herbs, pat them dry, and hang or lay them in a warm, well-ventilated place that's out of direct sunlight until they're dried.

Label and store the herbs in sealed glass or plastic containers out of direct sun.

To freeze herbs, wash and pat them dry. Then chop them by hand or in a food processor. Place the chopped herbs in labeled plastic containers and then freeze them.

A good, quick way to freeze herbs is to add a bit of water to the herbs in the food processor and then pour the herbs into ice-cube trays and freeze them. When you need herbs for stew, soups, or sauces, just pop in an herb cube.

Picking ingredients for your compost pile

Good ingredients for compost include animal manure, coffee grounds, conifer needles, eggshells, grass clippings, hair, hay, leaves, sawdust, seaweed, shredded newsprint, soil, straw, vegetable and fruit scraps, and weeds — almost any plant matter. Remember to aim for a 3:1 ratio, three parts brown and dry matter to one part green and gooey.

Not everything organic belongs in a compost pile. Don't add bones or meat scraps; diseased plants; pet feces; any vegetation that has been sprayed with a pesticide or herbicide; or allelopathic plants, such as eucalyptus. (An *allelopathic* plant is one that contains chemicals that stunt the growth of other plants.)

Everything decomposes much faster if you shred or chop it before you add it to the pile.

Digging properly to avoid backache

To avoid a date with a chiropractor, dig *ergonomically,* a fancy term that refers to a design or method to reduce "operator fatigue and discomfort." If you already have big-league back problems, consider buying ergonomic tools.

Here's how to use just about any digging instrument (fork, shovel, spade) safely and effectively:

1. **Keep the handle of your tool straight up and down.**
2. **Put your foot on the *tread,* or footrest, and use your weight to drive the tines or blade into the soil.**
3. **Bend at the waist and knees to push the handle down and forward.**
4. **Straighten your waist and knees to lift and turn the dirt.**

Watering

You can't make the sun shine, but you can make it rain. If your plants sag during summer's dog days, they're telling you, "A little water, please." Plants, after all, are about 90 percent water, and even moderate wilting can damage them.

Wilting is an obvious red flag; curled or dull-colored leaves are two other signs that your plants are thirsty. Because too much moisture also causes plants to wilt, check the soil before you water. If you find dryness to a depth of 3 inches, you probably need to water. (Keep your eye on plants growing in pots: You may need to water them every day.)

Say when

Going out at noon to splash your plants with a little cool water is a wonderfully mindless activity — one that refreshes you but doesn't do diddly squat for plants. The water may wet the soil surface, but little or no moisture reaches the plants' roots.

If the rain gods aren't kind, the general rule for flowers and vegetables is to provide 1 inch of water per week, plus another ½ inch for every 10 degrees above 60 degrees Fahrenheit. No rain during a week in the 90s? You need to supply about 2½ inches.

Many plants do fine with less water than garden flowers and vegetables require — 1 inch a week is usually plenty.

Water by the numbers

To calculate how many gallons equals 1 inch of water, multiply the area of your garden by 0.083. Then multiply that product by 7.5. For example, if your garden is 10 feet by 10 feet, then its area is 100 square feet.

100 x 0.083 x 7.5 = 62.25 gallons

To know how long you need to water with your hose, first measure how long it takes to fill a 5-gallon bucket. Then divide the number of minutes by 5 to determine the gallon-per-minute rate. For example, if your hose filled the bucket in 1 minute, it runs at 5 gallons per minute, and you have to water for about 12 minutes to apply 1 inch of water (or 4 minutes of watering three times a week).

Soil considerations

Just as you need to water more in hot climates and less in cool ones, you need to water differently depending on the texture of your soil. Whether your soil is primarily sand, loam, or clay not only affects how plants grow, it affects how and how much you need to water. You may add giant amounts of organic matter when you prepare your garden, but even amended soils fall somewhere on the sand-loam-clay continuum.

When you water, keep in mind that

- ✔ **Sandy soil drains quickly, retaining water poorly.** Instead of watering all at one time, water three or four times for shorter periods. Plants growing in sandy soil usually require more water than those in clay soil, so you need to water them more often.

- ✔ **Loam soil retains water better than sand, but less well than clay.** Water moderately, perhaps twice rather than all at once.

- ✔ **Clay soil, which holds moisture well, also takes longer to move the water down to plant roots.** Water slowly for long periods of time. You need to water plants growing in clay soil less often.

Garden flowers, vegetables, and fruits require extra water when they're forming flowers or fruits. In contrast, herbs, most of which have small flowers and are grown primarily for their leaves, need even moisture throughout the garden season.

Install a rain gauge and keep track of rainfall, but don't be a slave to numbers: If you received an inch of rain in the past week but your plants clearly show that they're thirsty, water them. If you haven't received rain but your plants look great, don't do a thing except feel grateful.

Water smart

Keep the following tips in mind:

- ✔ **Water the plant, not the plot.** Rather than spraying a large area with a hose or setting up an overhead sprinkler — both lose water to evaporation and often wet some areas, such as paths, that don't need moisture — make sure the water goes where it's needed: the soil around your plants.

- ✔ **Use drip irrigation.** An inexpensive but efficient way to get water to your plants is to use a *soaker hose* (or drip hose), which has tiny holes from one end to the other. Lay it around your plants or between rows; water oozes out, slowly and gently. In addition to conserving water — through reduced evaporation and runoff — a soaker hose waters without wetting foliage.

  You can make your own soaker hose by capping one end of an old hose (parts are available at hardware and garden stores) and punching small holes in it with an awl. To water a small area, punch a few small holes in the bottom of a 1-gallon milk jug and place the jug next to the plants that need water.

- ✔ **Water during the morning or evening hours.** Water evaporates less during these times.

- ✔ **Water deeply.** Plants take in water through their roots, so the soil needs to be wet to a depth of at least 6 inches. You may need to water some plants with shallow roots more frequently but less deeply.

- ✔ **Add humus.** Organically rich soil retains moisture well. You can always add more humus to your garden.

- ✔ **Keep weeding.** Weeds use water too — keep them out of your garden.

- ✔ **Don't overfertilize.** Plants that grow slowly use less water than those that grow rapidly.

- ✔ **Be aware of wind and sun patterns.** Wind and sun steal moisture from plants. Create a windbreak if your plants are growing where summer breezes are fierce.

✔ **Recycle water.** Use runoff from your roof to water your garden. Some household wastewater — gray water from the laundry, kitchen sink, and bath — is safe to use in the ornamental garden, but is not recommended for edibile foods or herbs. Don't recycle water that contains borax or great amounts of chlorine bleach. Apply gray water to the soil; don't pour it directly on your plants.

✔ **Mulch.** Mulch reduces the soil temperature and conserves moisture.

Chapter 4

Sharing Your Space with Pets

● ●

In This Chapter

▶ Covering your canine bases

▶ Bringing a feline friend into your home

▶ Enjoying beautiful birds

▶ Flipping over fish

● ●

So that little critter in the window melted your heart? If you're a new pet owner — or already have a mini-zoo at home — you gain a special pleasure from life. No matter what type of animal you adopt, the returns are the same: faithful companionship, fulfillment from nurturing, and simple joy. Raising and caring for a pet takes commitment, however, and this chapter gives you great advice on everything from training and grooming to health and nutrition for dogs, cats, birds, and fish.

Leading a Dog's Life

If you spend some time observing even the smallest, most adorable dogs, you will see characteristics of the ancestry of all canines: the wolf. Despite the best human efforts to change canines, dogs are still, at heart, the animals they came from — pack animals with a language and behaviors that make them a good fit in human families.

Holding the keys to dog-training success

The right attitude is every bit as important in dog training as the right equipment — a properly fitted collar and leash. Here are a few basic rules to keep in mind as you begin the business of molding your dog's behavior:

Puzzling parentage with mixed breeds

Mixed breeds, mongrels, or mutts. Call them anything you want, but millions of these dogs are out there, each and every one of them a true original. Still, you can do a few things to improve your odds with mixed-breed dogs.

Work with shelters and rescue groups that test the temperament and check out the health of the animals they put up for adoption. The best shelters and rescue groups take the concept of adoptability a step further, putting dogs with problems through training and working with new owners after placement to smooth over the rough spots.

However, don't ever encourage breeder irresponsibility by taking a mixed-breed puppy from the kids outside the supermarket or from the kind woman selling them for $5 at the flea market.

✔ Be prepared to dedicate time to training on a regular basis.

✔ Be consistent in your approach.

✔ Be on the same team: Work with your dog, not against him.

✔ Be positive about training.

✔ Be fair when correcting your dog.

Knowing when your dog needs immediate veterinary care

The following symptoms are sure signs that you and your dog need to visit a vet — pronto. Remember that when in doubt, day or night, don't wait: Call your veterinarian!

✔ Allergic reactions, such as swelling around the face, or hives, most easily seen on the belly

✔ Any eye injury, no matter how mild

✔ Any respiratory problem, including chronic coughing, trouble breathing, or near drowning

✔ Any signs of pain including panting, labored breathing, increased body temperature, lethargy, restlessness, or loss of appetite

✔ Any suspected poisoning, including ingestion of antifreeze, rodent or snail bait, or human medication

✔ Any wound or laceration that's open and bleeding, or any animal bite

With purebreds, breeding counts

Health and temperament problems are rampant in purebred dogs, and your chances of getting a dog with a problem increase dramatically when you buy from a less than reputable source, such as a casual backyard breeder. This is especially true of popular breeds such as Labrador Retrievers, Golden Retrievers, Bull Terriers, and Rottweilers.

Most purebred dogs in the United States are registered with the American Kennel Club (AKC), but the AKC is not a brand name, like Sony or Chevrolet. The organization, which is actually a federation of breed and kennel clubs, neither breeds dogs nor certifies breeders.

All the time you may spend reading about dog breeds, considering various breeds, and finally choosing a breed is completely and totally wasted if you rush out and buy from someone who isn't raising good examples of the breed.

- ✔ Seizure, fainting, or collapse
- ✔ Snake bite
- ✔ Thermal stress, either too cold or too hot, even if the dog seems to have recovered
- ✔ Trauma, such as being hit by a car, even if the dog seems fine
- ✔ Vomiting or diarrhea, anything more than two or three times within an hour or so

Getting the skinny on dog food preservatives

In the last few years, the use of preservatives — primarily BHT, BHA, and ethoxyquin — to keep the necessary fats in pet foods from going rancid has generated a lot of controversy. Pet experts have blamed these synthetic preservatives for just about every known pet health problem.

But here's something to bear in mind: No good scientific evidence exists to support the decision to avoid synthetic preservatives. If the issue worries you, choose a food that doesn't have these preservatives. But be aware that you may very likely be falling prey to marketing strategies and fear rather than scientific fact in making your decision. In fact, more data exists supporting the *beneficial* effects of these products in foods (reduced cancer rates, fewer birth defects, and so on) than the negative effects.

Raising a vegetarian dog

Unlike cats, who are true carnivores, dogs can thrive on a carefully balanced vegetarian diet. You can even meet a dog's need for protein without meat.

Dogs would probably not choose to live without meat, however. The choice is made for them by owners, usually those who, for ethical reasons, are against the killing of other animals for food. (For some dogs, though, vegetarian diets are a way to fight food allergies.) Vegetarian diets are popular enough that some companies include no-meat dog foods as part of their product line.

Discovering the dangers of chaining your dog

In many parts of the country, fenced yards are uncommon, so many people keep their dogs on chains. Tethering a dog for a short while is okay in a pinch — never with a choke collar, though — but a tethered existence is not a good one. And don't ever leave a chained dog unattended. If you're considering chaining, keep these things in mind:

- ✔ Dogs who spend their lives on chains are more likely to become dangerous, biting anyone who comes onto their turf.

- ✔ In a handful of cases, a dog has tried to jump a fence, didn't have enough chain to clear, and ended up hanging himself from his collar on the other side of the fence. Dogs have also wrapped their chains around trees and died because they were unable to get to water on hot days.

An alternative to chaining is to walk your dog or buy him a kennel run.

Considering cautions about bones

Rawhide, hooves, and bones can cause problems with aggressive chewers. Some large dogs are capable of chewing off and swallowing big chunks of rawhide, and pulverizing bones and hooves. Doing this can cause internal problems — for example, bone bits can create a blockage that may require surgical removal.

Know your dog's chewing style. Pressed rawhide and large knots are best for hearty chewers. Watch to see that your pet isn't swallowing big chunks, and be sure to discard these treats when they become worn enough for your dog to swallow them in one big gulp.

Deciding on collar size

Fashion aside, collars, harnesses, halters, and leashes perform a very vital function: They help you to train your dog and allow you to keep him out of trouble in public. Collars also protect your dog by carrying identification. Remember the following when choosing a collar:

- ✔ **Buckled or quick-snap collars:** Measure a couple of inches down the neck from your dog's head, and then add two inches. For tiny dogs, add an inch. When trying on collars, you need to be able to fit two fingers snugly between collar and neck; one finger on a small dog.

- ✔ **Slip collar:** Commonly called a *choke collar*, this collar needs to fit a little more loosely because you fit it over a dog's head instead of wrapping it around his neck. After you measure your dog's neck, add an inch-and-a-half for small dogs and up to three inches for large ones — you should just be able to slip the collar over your pet's head and no more.

Delivering the word "No"

Almost without fail, people use the word "no" too much and incorrectly when raising a puppy. Used constantly and especially if used in a whiny, pleading manner, "no" loses its value as a training tool.

Deliver the command "no" firmly and sharply, as guttural as a low, barky growl — comparable, in other words, to how a puppy's mother expresses her displeasure.

You can use both "no" and a guttural "argh" sounds as correction words, but don't use "no" as a warning word. Consider using something like "I wouldn't" when a dog is contemplating something like a second assault on something you told him to leave alone.

Building your puppy's vocabulary

Expanding your dog's vocabulary is a good idea for two reasons:

- ✔ **A rich vocabulary offers an alternative to the "no, no, no" pattern so many pet owners fall into.** Instead of constantly correcting your puppy for jumping (for example), correct him with one "no!" and then say "off!" as you put him on the floor.

- ✔ **Living with a dog with a bigger vocabulary is more pleasant.** So use your imagination and teach your pup as much as you can. Remember, though, to be consistent in your wording — don't say "off" one time and "down" the next.

Losing canine baby teeth

You may be delighted when you see adult teeth replacing those sharp little puppy teeth at or around the age of four months. Your dog goes from 28 deciduous teeth to 42 permanent ones. However, problems can occur.

Sometimes dogs retain their baby teeth after the adult ones come in, a situation that can cause many difficulties, including the misalignment of permanent teeth, incorrect development of the jaw, and infections. Check your puppy's mouth weekly while adult teeth are erupting to ensure that she's not retaining any baby teeth. A double row of teeth, especially in the front, tells you that your pup may need some veterinary dental assistance.

Have your veterinarian check out any suspicious developments. Retained baby teeth need to be surgically removed.

Dealing with doggy breath

Controlling mouth odors is both a grooming and a veterinary issue. Although some groomers and dog owners scale plaque themselves, these techniques don't address the problem at the root line, so regular cleanings under anesthesia by a veterinarian are essential to ensure dental health. In between, attention two or three times a week with a toothbrush and a toothpaste designed for dogs slows the reformation of plaque and extends the time between dental scalings.

Knowing when to spay or neuter

While puppies are traditionally spayed and neutered between the ages of four and six months, your vet can safely perform either procedure at as early as eight weeks. So at what age should *your* puppy be spayed or neutered? The traditional six months is still fine. Earlier is fine, too; in fact, veterinary organizations have given their full approval to the early procedure. Some veterinarians are not comfortable operating on the youngest puppies, however, and if this is the case, follow your vet's recommendation.

House-training without a crate

Of course, house-training without a crate is possible — the process is just more difficult, more time-consuming, and messier. Use this positive approach:

- ✔ **Keep your puppy where you can keep an eye on him — and keep him in a small, safe area when you cannot.** Baby gates are ideal both for keeping a puppy near you and creating an area for him to stay in while you're gone.

- ✔ **Use the same schedule for going out.** Take your pooch out first thing in the morning, after play and eating, at lunch and dinner, and last thing at night to make his life regular and predictable.

- ✔ **Watch for a puppy's "gotta go" motions.** Whenever you see your dog sniffing and circling, whisk him outside. Sometimes you just aren't fast enough. If you catch him in the act, say "no" sternly, and then take him outside to finish the job. Clean up the area thoroughly and without comment. See Chapter 1 for clean-up tips.

Debunking doggie myths

Here are some of the most common misconceptions about dogs — and the facts.

- ✔ **One dog year is equal to seven human years.**

   According to the American Animal Hospital Association, the first eight months of a dog's life equals 13 years in human terms — birth to puberty, in other words. At a year, a dog is a teenager, equivalent to a 16-year-old human, with a little filling out still to do. After the age of two, when a dog's about 21, every dog year equals approximately five human ones.

   These are ballpark estimates, because the fact is dogs age at very different rates. Small dogs may hit puberty at five months, while some large ones may be more than a year and a half old before a female comes into heat for the first time.

Submissive urination

Submissive urination can drive loving pet owners to the brink of sanity because your pet may seem to be flaunting her bad behavior. She comes up to you and piddles right in front of you! Don't lose your temper: Your dog is acting out of fear and trying to placate you with a classic canine show of submission.

A puppy or dog who has this problem is very sensitive and lacks confidence. Recognize that submissive urination is not a house-training problem: It's a relationship problem. Don't punish your pet for submissive urination. As you work to develop a loving and trusting relationship with your puppy, her confidence grows, and her fear decreases along with submissive urination.

✔ **A hot, dry nose means a fever.** A dog has a fever when a thermometer properly inserted into his fanny exceeds 102.5 degrees. His nose has nothing to do with it.

✔ **A dog needs to go through one season before being spayed.** Wrong, wrong, wrong. In fact, the opposite is true: Spaying before your puppy comes into season reaps health benefits. Spaying before the first season reduces to almost nothing the chances of your pet getting mammary tumors — canine breast cancer — later in her life. And of course, without the uterus and ovaries, your pet is also safe from cancer in those parts of the body, as well as life-threatening infections.

✔ **Spaying and neutering makes dogs fat.** The basic truth for pets is the same as for people: Too much food and too little exercise make dogs fat. You may need to adjust the levels of both after your dog recovers from surgery to make sure that he or she stays in shape. The activity level of male dogs, in particular, may decrease after neutering because they're not so anxious to get out and roam after the alluring scents of females in season.

✔ **A dog's mouth is cleaner than a human's.** Whoever thought this one up apparently never observed the things a dog takes into her mouth, some of which are quite disgusting, as any dog lover knows. Should you avoid your dog's kisses? Unless she's just eaten something disgusting, let her lick. A slurpy dog kiss isn't going to hurt you.

✔ **Dogs eat grass when their stomachs are upset.** The common wisdom on this one is that grass makes dogs throw up, so they seek it out when they have tummy aches. But many dogs eat grass constantly, with no after effects.

✔ **Adding oil to a dog's diet solves skin problems.** A lot of what people add to a dog's meal falls into the "can't hurt, might help" category — no proven benefits, but doing so makes the human feel better. The truth is that oils (including some oil supplements veterinary dermatologists prescribe) can help some skin and coat problems. But this fact doesn't mean you should just start chucking things into the mix whenever your dog's coat or skin doesn't look right to you.

Making sure that skin problems are correctly diagnosed is important before treating with a blanket cure-all like oil, which, after all, adds fat to the diet of a pet who may not need more.

✔ **Brewer's yeast and garlic control fleas.** No solid evidence exists that garlic cloves or brewer's yeast deters fleas when taken internally.

> ✔ **A barking dog won't bite.** A really, really, dangerous myth, and probably the one most in need of correcting. Either barking or growling can telegraph the intention to attack, which is why watching a dog's body language for signs of aggression is important.

Ingesting common poisons

Dogs can mistakenly pierce a tightly closed container or knock low-placed plants to the ground. Prevent emergencies by keeping all toxic substances away from them. In case of an emergency, ask your vet how to induce vomiting.

Dealing with a thunder-struck pup

Here's a list of do's and don'ts for when you want to handle a puppy's fear of thunder. The don'ts first: Don't coddle your puppy. Don't permit him to hide between the sheets or climb onto the couch. Don't isolate him. All these things make the fear worse. Depending on how bad your situation is, do try one or all these approaches:

> ✔ Turn on some classical music and play it loud.

> ✔ Set the example. Lead your puppy on his leash while you act completely calm.

> ✔ Find (or make) a thunderstorm tape recording. Play it on low volume while you play your puppy's favorite game with him. Slowly increase the volume.

> ✔ Ask your veterinarian for tranquilizers to soothe your puppy before a storm.

Digging in the dirt

Although some breeds, such as the small terriers, have a true propensity for digging, all dogs dig to some extent at one time or another. Here are some of the more common reasons for digging:

> ✔ *Allelomimetic behavior,* or mimicking. (This may spell trouble for your gardening efforts. You plant, your dog digs up. Try gardening in secret and out of sight of your dog.)

> ✔ To bury a bone and to dig up a bone.

> ✔ To see what's there, because it's fun, or to find a cool spot.

> ✔ Boredom, isolation, or frustration.

Getting gunk out of pet fur

Many things your pets get into — or that get onto them — often have to be clipped out. But before hauling out the scissors, try some of these techniques:

🖊 **Burrs:** Spray a little cooking spray on the area, and then gently use your fingers to work the burr free. (If your cat freaks at the hissing of a spray can, go straight for the scissors.)

A pet that's covered in burrs, mats, or dried paint or tar is best sent to a groomer to be clipped short. Not only is this solution easier on you both, it's considerably more attractive than having dozens of short-clipped areas. Don't worry: The hair grows back faster than you may think.

🖊 **Mats and tangles:** Sprinkle the area with cornstarch and carefully slide sharp scissors through the base of the mat and slice it a couple times through the middle. If you're patient — and gentle — you can often work the fur free with your fingers. To finish the job, comb through the area with a wide-toothed steel comb and then a brush to remove the dirt and dead hair that caused the problem in the first place.

🖊 **Fleas:** A flea comb can catch the pest, but you still need to launch a flea-control program to kill the microscopic flea eggs.

🖊 **Ticks:** Never touch a tick with your hands. Use a tick remover or tweezers, grasp the body firmly, and pull with a steady motion.

🖊 **Paint or tar:** Never use solvents to remove paint or tar: Solvents irritate your pet's skin, are toxic if tasted, and are flammable! Instead, clip the affected area out.

Cats are extremely sensitive to petroleum-based products, so wash your cat in mild dishwashing liquid to remove petroleum-based products. Tar may soften in mineral or vegetable oil but most likely needs to be clipped out.

🖊 **Gum or other sticky substances:** You can try a little peanut butter to lubricate the fur enough to slide the gum out, but it's rough going. Clipping is usually the answer.

🖊 **Skunk:** The best cure for skunk odor is a mixture of one quart hydrogen peroxide, one-fourth cup baking soda, and two tablespoons dish soap. Wet your pet thoroughly with the mixture, let sit a few minutes, and then rinse well. *Caution:* Do not attempt to keep this mixture on hand — it explodes any closed container you put it in, which is why such a surefire cure isn't commercially available.

If your pet comes home sprayed, the first thing to do is check his rabies vaccination status — rabid skunks can behave belligerently. If your pet is current on his shots, go ahead with the bath. If you see any new bite wounds, however, stop and call your veterinarian immediately, for your pet's sake and your own. Rabies is not something to take any chances with!

The cure to digging is rather simple: Don't leave your dog unattended in the yard for lengthy periods. Tire out your dog so he's too tuckered to dig, by playing ball or running with him. Of course, you can always cover your yard with Astroturf or green cement!

Considering Cats as Companions

Although you still hear about people who dislike cats, their voices aren't the dominant ones today. More people love cats and are working to make their cats' lives better than ever before.

And your cat, always the boss, approves of your ongoing efforts to make him happy.

Chatty cats

Siamese are probably best known for being chatty, but other breeds keep up their end of the conversation, too. The Balinese (a long-haired version of the Siamese), the Oriental Shorthair and Colorpoint Shorthair (also versions of the Siamese), and the Tonkinese are all talkers. Other feline conversationalists include the Bombay, the Burmese, the Rexes, and the Ocicat.

The quietest cat breeds are generally those with heavier builds and more mellow dispositions: the Persian, the British Shorthair, and the Maine Coon.

Explaining cats' "extra" senses

Two phenomena documented by cat lovers over the years suggest that cats have a few more things going for them than mere humans can understand:

- **The ability to "predict" seismic events, such as earthquakes.** Cats appear to be sensitive to signs of increasing tension underground, a theory promoted by those who claim that before an earthquake, the number of lost cats increases — presumably because they're attempting to escape from danger.

- **The ability to return "home" from hundreds of miles away.** Although some of these cases are surely mistaken identity on the parts of the people and cats involved, others are well documented, and experiments have shown that cats have a particular sensitivity to the earth's magnetic field and so are masters of direction.

Litter health risks, real and not-so-real

One health risk that seems to have no basis is the purported problem with clumping litter causing intestinal blockage — and death — in kittens. To date, no scientific study exists to confirm such a problem.

To err on the safe side, some veterinarians suggest avoiding clumping litter until the kitten is out of the taste-testing-everything curiosity stage. But even that advice is just a precaution for kittens only, and you don't need to fear any harm if you use clumping litter with adult cats.

Walking the cat?

You can train your indoor cat to enjoy an outing on a leash. For this treat, you need a harness. (Because cat collars are made to enable cats to slip out of them, don't use a collar with a leash.) Choose a harness designed for cats, not for dogs, in a figure-8 design. Harnesses, like collars, come in many colors, with lightweight leashes to match.

Don't expect your cat to heel like a dog, however. Walking a cat consists of encouraging your pet to explore, with you following, offering plenty of praise, and maybe a treat or two.

Teaching your cat to use a cat door

After you install a cat door, just leave it be for a week or so until your cat takes its presence for granted. (Remember always that cats aren't keen on change.)

To teach your cat to use the door:

1. **Tape the flap up securely for a few days so that he comes to appreciate the fact that he can conveniently come and go on his own schedule.** *Securely* is the key word here. If your cat gets clobbered by the flap, he may not use the door for quite a long time.

2. **Put the flap down and put a little butter or margarine on the bottom edge of the flap.** Encourage him with tasty treats and praise from the other side. You can also drag toys on a string through the door.

My cat can have asthma?

Cats frequently get *feline asthma*. In most cases, just like in humans who suffer from asthma, veterinary researchers are stumped as to why.

The signs of asthma in cats are similar to those seen in humans — difficulty breathing, wheezing, and coughing that often sounds like gagging. If she's having trouble breathing, a cat sits with her neck extended and inhales and exhales rapidly with her mouth open.

Feline asthma can come on suddenly and be very serious — frightening to observe. Like an asthmatic person who can't breathe, your cat can panic. Do all you can to minimize stress while your cat is having difficulty breathing.

The first time your cat has a problem breathing, take her immediately to your veterinarian or to an emergency clinic. Call ahead so that the clinic can prepare for your arrival, and prepare yourself for a stressful wait while the staff finds the cause of your cat's breathing difficulties. Just remember that cats having difficulty breathing are quite fragile, and too much handling can worsen their condition to the point where they may even die.

Although no one knows the cause of feline asthma, minimizing exposure to dust (use low-dust litter and leave off the litter box hood), smoke, aerosol sprays, and other irritants is essential.

Catnip and other leafy delights

Catnip — *Nepeta cataria* for you botanists — produces bouts of ecstasy for those cats that like the stuff. A substance called *nepetalactone* that's present in the leaves and stems causes the behavior, which lasts for just a few minutes and can include rolling, rubbing, leaping, purring, and general uninhibited happiness. Kittens under the age of 3 months do not react to catnip, and even in those cats that truly adore the "high," the plant is nonaddictive and harmless.

Valerian is another herb that makes cats happy, and you can easily grow the two herbs as part of a cat garden.

Dealing with hairballs

Veterinarians call them *trichobezoars,* but cat lovers call them "hairballs," or, more commonly, "gross." Whatever you call them, hairballs — hair that's ingested as a cat grooms himself and then vomited back up in clumps — are a normal part of living with a cat and are usually not indicative of a health problem. If coughing up a

hairball is an intermittent event — a couple times a month or up to
once a week or so — and your cat appears otherwise normal, you
probably don't need to be concerned.

Your veterinarian may suggest the use of a mild laxative (mineral
oil) preparation or an increase in fiber in the diet to help the hairballs "pass" in most situations. Canned pumpkin is a great way to
increase the fiber in the diet. One or two teaspoonfuls mixed daily
with canned food or with the water from a can of tuna (for humans)
keeps things moving nicely.

If your cat's pattern of coughing up the occasional hairball changes,
make an appointment with your veterinarian to find out why.

Professional grooming

If you have a longhaired cat, you may find that the mats get out
of hand from time to time. If this happens, your cat is probably
better off being clipped down. You can try this yourself, but your
relationship with your cat will probably be better off if you have a
professional do the dirty work. Cat skin is loose, and you can easily
nick your feline friend if you don't know what you're doing. Here are
some things to keep in mind:

- Ask your veterinarian or breeder for a recommendation to a
professional groomer and check out the setup before dropping
your cat off.
- Consider mobile groomers.
- Discuss sedation with your vet. In general, only a veterinarian
should sedate a cat.

Helping your cat adjust to a new home

For many cats, one of the most stressful events of their lives is a distracting time for their owners as well — changing addresses. Combine
travel with suddenly being in unfamiliar surroundings — which may
even smell like former animal occupants — and you can understand
why more than a few cats spend a very long time hiding after a move.
Help your cat adjust with the following tips:

- **Plan ahead with updated nametags.** Order an ID tag with your
new address and phone number as soon as you know them, and
add it to your cat's collar along with the old ID. For a quicker

solution, use paper-key tags (available cheaply from your local
hardware store) for temporary ID.

✔ **Establish a safe room.** Designate a *safe room* before and after
any move — a room where your cat isn't going to be disturbed.
A spare bathroom is ideal. Outfit the safe room with food and
water, a litter box, a scratching post, a bed, and toys. Don't feel
bad about confining your pet: She's more comfortable in a
small space, and she isn't subjected to the stress of seeing
people — perhaps strangers — tromping out of the house with
her belongings.

✔ **Use a carrier wisely.** After you arrive at your new home, don't
pull your cat out of her carrier. Instead, put the carrier in her
safe room, open the carrier door, and let her come out into the
room when she wants to — even if she stays in the carrier for
an hour or more.

✔ **Introduce the new home slowly.** After a day or two of being
in the safe room, open the door to the room and let your cat
explore at will, on her terms — but just within the limits of the
house. You need to keep your cat completely inside for a couple
weeks even if she's not an indoor cat. This period of home
detention helps her to form a bond with her new surroundings.

✔ **Be patient.** Although your cat's likely to settle back into her
old, good habits in a couple weeks if you keep her confined and
allow her to relax, talk to a veterinarian about any problems
that continue. Your cat may be ill, or she may need anti-anxiety
medication to help her settle in.

Preparing a homemade diet

You can create a diet for your cat by using fresh meats or other protein sources,
grains, vegetables, and mineral and vitamin supplements, but you can't plan
such a diet casually. Several books offer "natural" or "raw-food" diets, and
information on these feeding plans — as well as lots of discussion — is preva-
lent on the Internet.

No study has shown that homemade diets are any better for your pet than a
high-quality commercial food — and a homemade diet may not provide *all* the
60 or so nutrients your cat needs in the right amounts and ratios.

Many veterinarians with clinical experience have bad feelings about preparing homemade meals for your cat. They recommend waiting for solid evidence
of benefits before endorsing something that may not be best for your cat. In the
end, the decision is yours, of course, but you need to make sure you're making
a fully informed choice before proceeding.

Setting the record straight about cat myths

Experts now know more than ever before about cats, but a surprising amount of false information still hangs about. Get wise to the following fictions:

- **Cats have nine lives.** Cats have but one life, and they need your love and protection to make their lives long, healthy, and happy.

- **Cats need to drink milk.** Cats *do* love milk, as anyone knows who's ever been around a cow barn at milking time. However, milk can prove a very messy proposition, producing an uncomfortable gastric disturbance and even diarrhea. After the age of 12 weeks or so, some cats (like some people) lose the ability to digest the lactose in the milk; for those cats, milk isn't recommended.

- **Cats purr only when they're happy.** Careful observers of the cat know that purring isn't just a sound of contentment. Purring tends to be a sign of friendship, either when the cat is contented with a friend or when she is in need of friendship — as with a cat in trouble.

- **Cats eat plants if they're sick.** Many cat owners assume that cats eat plants to help bring up whatever's upsetting their tummies. Although experts debate how much plant matter is necessary in a cat's diet, one thing is obvious to anyone who's ever tried to maintain both houseplants and a house cat — cats nibble on greens simply because they love to.

- **Cats are dangerous around babies.** You *don't* need to find a new home for your pet if you become pregnant, no matter what well-meaning relatives and friends may say. Cats do not maliciously smother or suck the breath out of babies.

- **You can keep cats from using their claws.** Despite all efforts to keep cats from clawing up the furniture, the best you can do for your cat and your possessions is redirect your pet's scratching effort, because he needs to scratch. Scratching stretches his muscles and allows him to mark his territory. Digging claws into the corner of your sofa is one way your pet makes himself feel at home, leaving his own reassuring scent behind from scent glands in his feet.

- **Only hungry cats hunt.** Pouncing and leaping on any little thing that moves is a sign of your cat's hunting prowess. The cat's tendency to play with its prey is a matter of the animal's not being hungry enough to eat it but still being instinctively driven to hunt. And so the cat pounces again and again.

- ✔ **Cat fur causes allergies.** If people are allergic to animals, their bodies are reacting not to fur but to *dander*. A cat generously applies these particles to her fur by the act of grooming and to every surface she rubs against. Every shake puts the particles airborne, where allergic humans can easily inhale the dander into the sensitive tissues of the lungs or sinuses.

- ✔ **All calicos are female.** Actually, almost all calico cats *are* female, but not quite all. About 1 in 3,000 so-marked cats are male. The gene that governs how the red/orange color in cats displays is on the female chromosome.

Common dangers to cats

Forewarned is forearmed. The following can help you protect your cat from several avoidable dangers.

- ✔ **Strings and similar things:** Your cat may possibly decide to eat his plaything — and that's where the fun stops. Any sort of yarn, ribbon, Christmas tinsel, or string can cause havoc in your cat's intestines, causing a problem that a vet may need to surgically treat.

   Even if your pet's not really the playful type, she may find one kind of string irresistible: Juice-soaked string from a roast or turkey. Dispose of these tempting dangers carefully, putting them in a container your cat can't get into.

- ✔ **A shocking experience:** Chewing on electrical cords is more of a risk for inquisitive kittens, but protecting any cat against electrical cords doesn't hurt. Tuck cords out of the way, and if you notice any you can't hide, coat them in something nasty, such as Bitter Apple (available at pet-supply stores) to convince your cat or kitten to chomp elsewhere.

- ✔ **The warm and deadly dryer:** Cats love warm, dark hiding places, and a dryer full of freshly dried clothes is a favorite spot of many. So what's the worry? Some cats have been killed after their owners have accidentally closed and turned on a dryer with a sleeping cat inside.

   Prevention is simple. Keep the dryer door closed and make sure whoever's doing the laundry knows to always check for your cat — just in case.

   If you find your cat in the dryer, oven, washing machine, or dishwasher, take a deep breath and do something that seems cruel but has your cat's best interest at heart: Scare the fur off him. Close the door with him inside, and then pound on the appliance for a few seconds. Then open the door and let him make his escape.

✔ **Pain medicines that kill:** Never give your cat *any* medication without clearing it with your veterinarian first. In particular, be careful with painkillers. Although you can safely give aspirin to arthritic dogs, the smaller size and different metabolism of cats make aspirin a dangerous proposition for them. Acetaminophen, the active ingredient in Tylenol, can kill your cat, as can some of the newer, longer-lasting painkillers available in nonprescription form for human use.

✔ **Attack of the killer plants:** Indulge your cat with plants he can nibble on but make sure he isn't munching on anything that can make him sick. You can discourage cats from chewing on houseplants, but you can't guarantee they'll leave them alone. Your best bet is to make sure that anything your cat can get into isn't going to hurt him. Although you obviously can't control what your outside cat is eating on his rambles, always be looking for signs of illness.

✔ **Garage dangers:** Most people just don't keep very neat garages. In addition to ignoring the drips and puddles coming from you car — which can include deadly antifreeze — be mindful of the location of stored insecticides, paints, cleaning supplies, and fertilizers, all of which can be toxic.

Another garage danger: The door. A garage door in the open position makes a nifty high hiding place for a cat, but that secure perch can injure your pet if you set the door in motion while he's there.

✔ **Antifreeze:** Be extra careful when changing your car's coolant. Most antifreeze poses a severe risk to animals — and to children, as well. Less than a teaspoon of this deadly substance can kill a cat. Antifreeze has a sweet taste that may appeal to your cat, or your pet may ingest a lethal dose merely by licking her paws clean after walking through a spill.

Less toxic kinds of antifreeze are now available. They're made from propylene glycol instead of the ethylene glycol of conventional coolants. These new products are available at most auto-supplies outlets. Make the change!

✔ **Four-wheeled menaces:** Cats are heat seekers, and many of them discover that engines are warm for a long time after they're turned off. These cats slip into the engine compartment from underneath and settle in for a catnap. A running engine is no place for a kitty to be, however, and the cat that's still inside after the car's started can get badly injured or killed.

Even if your own cat's an indoor one who never has access to the engine compartment of your car, you can save another cat's life by getting into one simple habit: Before you get into your car — especially on a cold morning — pound on the hood for a couple seconds. If a cat is in your engine compartment, she's sure to wake up and take off at the sound.

✔ **Apartment buildings:** New York City vets see lots of cats who've fallen — or maybe jumped — from high-rise apartments. Some cats survive a fall like that. Many others don't. Prevention is the key to avoiding such accidents: Keep screens on your windows, and never let your cat out on your terrace.

✔ **Dog flea dips:** Never use a flea-control product designed for dogs on your cat. Insecticides walk a very fine line: They contain enough toxins to kill the parasites but not enough to endanger the pet. A product engineered to meet these challenges for dogs may not do so for cats. Check the label. Ask your veterinarian. Call the manufacturer *before* using any product. Your cat's life is at stake.

Birds

Although birds have unique needs and desires, many are highly affectionate and social. Successful bird-lovers, for their efforts, get to share their lives with these marvelous, winged companions.

Signs of a healthy bird

Too often, bird-owners fail to notice early clues of illness because their pets are particularly skilled at hiding these signs. At the very least, you need to know what's normal for your bird so that you can spot changes that mean illness — and call your veterinarian. A healthy bird:

✔ Behaves normally, perching without problems, moving with coordination, using the full body without favoring one side or the other.

✔ Bears weight evenly, all four toes present on each foot and in proper position.

✔ Is alert and responsive.

✔ Breathes easily, with no sign of laboring and tail-bobbing.

✔ Has eyes, ears, and nostrils that are free of debris.

✔ Has healthy plumage. Feathers have normal color and structure, with no signs of improper development or excessive wear. No evidence of damage from feather-picking, improper housing, or other trauma.

✔ Consistently produces droppings that are normal in appearance. No pasting of waste on the fanny.

✔ Has a well-muscled body of appropriate weight, not obese. Skin is smooth and translucent without excessive amounts of fat showing underneath or excessive flakiness or crustiness.

Food and drinks your bird should avoid

You know what healthy food is in human terms — fruits and vegetables, beans, rice, pastas, eggs, lower-fat meats such as chicken, and whole-grain breads. These are the foods you can share with your budgie, cockatiel, or any parrots. The foods you know that you really shouldn't be eating — high-fat, high-sugar junk food — are bad choices for you and your bird, so just knock it off.

Some foods that are perfectly fine for you (in moderation, of course) are absolutely off-limits to your pet bird. Top of the list: avocado (and anything with avocado in it) and chocolate. Also, don't share alcoholic or caffeinated beverages with your pet bird.

Talking birds

Not all parrots talk, not even those from the species known best for their mimicry — the double-yellow-headed and yellow-naped Amazons and the African greys. If you're absolutely set on owning a talking bird, buy one who talks already — and make sure you hear the conversation before you plunk down payment.

You can teach your parrot to talk by:

✔ **Repeating words clearly and frequently.** Try using tapes or computer programs that say the same language over and over.

✔ **Using words in their proper context.** Try to set up an association your bird can grasp. For example, every time your bird lowers his head to request a scratch, ask him, "Wanna scratch?" and then scratch him.

✔ **Having a one-bird household.** Two birds may be more interested in talking their own language with each other than figuring out your expressions.

The nitty-gritty on grit

The idea that all pet birds need grit is a myth that seems to be taking a long time to die. Some pet birds, such a finches and canaries, can make use of an occasional small amount of grit (a couple of grains of grit every couple of months) — but most budgies, cockatiels, and other parrots don't need grit at all. Ask your vet if you have any grit questions.

What about the words or sounds you *don't* want your bird to mimic? The best you can do is ignore them, providing neither positive nor negative reinforcement. And be fair: If you think your bird's swearing is fun in private, you have to live with the behavior when the minister's over for dinner, too.

Bird and human diseases

Although birds may become infected with human influenza type viruses, those bugs rarely make a bird ill. Human colds and flues come and go, and so it's easy to imagine people thinking what looks the same in people and bird is, in fact, the same illness, but it's usually not. If your bird is sick with what appears to be cold- or flu-like symptoms, chances are very high that something else is going on, and you need to call your veterinarian.

Potty-training your bird

One of the less-pleasant aspects of sharing your life with a bird is dealing with the droppings. With patience and consistency, you can teach your bird to relieve himself on command, in a place of your choosing.

Start by observing your bird — the times of day he's most likely to relieve himself and the body language he uses just before, such as tail wagging or stepping back. Pick your desired command ("Go potty" or "Hurry up" work fine — just as long as you're consistent.)

When you see your bird getting ready to go or you know it's the usual time he does, ask him onto your hand or finger and hold him over a wastebasket, newspaper, toilet, or other "poop zone." Give your potty command and praise him when he obeys — even though the response is just a coincidence at first, of course.

As with all pets, birds are capable of passing some diseases to humans. These diseases, called *zoonoses*, don't represent much of a concern as long as you're careful to engage in good habits such as hand-washing before and after handling pets, and making sure your bird remains in good health.

Fish

You can easily become a successful fishkeeper. All you need is a little bit of help to get your tank set up — and you're ready to enjoy the fascinating relaxation and enjoyment that these pets can supply.

A happy, healthy aquarium is your goal. Avoid the following goofs, and you can be well on your way to fantastic fish.

- ✔ **Go away on vacation and forget about your fish.** While on vacation, make sure you have a reliable friend who can continue to care for your pets just in case you're gone longer than originally planned. Another option is to purchase tablets or automatic feeders from your local fish dealer, which dispense food to your fish while you're gone.

- ✔ **Playing fish doctor without a license.** Many new hobbyists tend to overmedicate their tanks at the very first sign of disease. But you can take care of a large number of diseases through natural methods such as frequent water changes. Avoid the temptation to pour medicine after medicine into your tank in hopes you can find the right cure.

- ✔ **Letting your cat attack your fish.** For many cats, an uncovered aquarium is a free sushi bar. Make sure that the hood you buy for your new aquarium fits properly and snugly. If you happen to own a particularly strong or fat cat, weight the hood down with some heavy object.

- ✔ **Feeding your fish seven-course meals.** A good combination of flake, frozen, and live food helps to promote good health in your wet pets. However, you need to realize that a fish's stomach is no larger than its eye, and overfeeding rapidly fouls the tank and eventually leads to disease or death.

- ✔ **Mixing fish species.** Mixing apples and oranges may be great for a fruit salad, but it doesn't work in your aquarium. Check with your local dealer if you're unsure about the compatibility of any species.

✔ **Adding too many fish.** You may be tempted to add just one more fish to your home aquarium. All fishkeepers fall prey to this "shoehorn syndrome" at one time or another. Remember, overcrowding can be deadly.

✔ **Not doing your homework.** Skilled fishkeepers do their homework before setting up a new type of system, and they investigate specific habitat requirements prior to purchasing unknown species of fish. The Internet, your local library, and tropical fish magazines can provide you with a lot of good information.

✔ **Being a hypochondriac hobbyist.** It does not take long for a new hobbyist to get emotionally attached to his fish. But the more you bond with them, the more you may overpamper them. Checking in on your fish every 30 minutes, constantly fiddling around with the equipment, and rearranging the decorations in order to achieve the perfect environment just isn't good for the fish.

✔ **Buying used or inexpensive equipment.** Always check out used equipment before purchasing it, if possible. Be wary of old aquarium stuff at the neighbor's garage sale. Sure, you may get lucky and purchase some good aquarium equipment at yard sales, but as the old saying goes, you get what you pay for.

Recognizing dangers of ash in fish food

Manufactured fish food usually contains a certain amount of *ash,* which is inorganic in nature, and contains pieces of fish bone and scales. Aquarium food manufacturers are starting to reduce the total amount of ash in their products because it may be harmful to fish and can contribute to water fouling. (Look for food with less than 12 percent ash content.) Check the can's label for ash levels in food products, or call the manufacturer if the container doesn't list food ingredients.

Chapter 5

Your World on Wheels

The United States' love affair with autos began 80-some years ago and has continued growing year after year. The tips and suggestions in this chapter can help you make sure that you and your car have a long-lasting affair to remember.

Maintaining Your Automobile

A well-maintained vehicle is less prone to those unfortunate surprises that can inconvenience you or leave you stranded. This section offers some things you can do yourself to help minimize future problems.

Spend 15 minutes under the hood and save your sanity

If the idea of committing yourself to a regular under-the-hood checkup seems less than alluring, consider this: *Spending 15 minutes a month going through the following under-the-hood checklist can prevent 70 percent of the problems that lead to highway breakdowns!* Convinced? Once a month or every 1,000 miles, be sure to check your:

- ✔ Air filter
- ✔ Accessory belts
- ✔ Battery
- ✔ Coolant

- ✔ Hoses
- ✔ Oil dipstick
- ✔ Automatic transmission fluid dipstick
- ✔ Brake fluid
- ✔ Power-steering fluid
- ✔ Windshield wipers and windshield washer fluid
- ✔ Wiring
- ✔ Tires

Checking the oil yourself

Oil reduces the friction in your engine and keeps it running smoothly. Check your oil at least once a month to make sure that your car has enough oil and that the oil isn't contaminated.

To find out whether your car needs oil, do the following:

1. **When the engine is cold (or has been off for at least ten minutes), pull out the dipstick and wipe it off on a clean, lint-free rag.**

   The oil dipstick typically has a ring on the end of it and sticks out the side of the engine. See Figure 5-1.

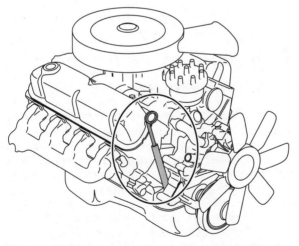

Figure 5-1: The oil dipstick is located on the side of the engine.

2. **Shove the stick back in again.**

   If the dipstick gets stuck on the way in, turn it around. The pipe it fits into is curved, and the metal stick bends naturally in the direction of the curve if you put it back in the way it came out.

3. **Pull the dipstick out again and look at the film of oil on the end of the stick (see Figure 5-2).**

[ADD | | FULL]

Figure 5-2: This is one time when you want to follow directions from a dipstick.

4. **Notice how high the oil film reaches on the dipstick and the condition of the oil.**

   If your oil looks clean enough but only reaches the "Add" level on the dipstick, you need to add oil. You can get some oil the next time you fill up at the gas station, or you can buy a bottle at an auto supply store and add it yourself. You can determine the proper weight oil to purchase by looking in your owner's manual.

   If the oil is dirty and grimy or smells of gasoline, you probably need to have it changed. You can pay a mechanic or an oil-change place to change it for you or change the oil yourself. The task is easy and can save you money.

5. **Put the dipstick back in.**

Knowing how often to tune up your car

Tune-up intervals vary from one vehicle to another. Tune up most older cars every 10,000 to 12,000 miles or every year, whichever comes first. Newer cars with electronic ignition and fuel injection systems are scheduled to go from 25,000 miles to as many as 100,000 miles without needing a major tune-up.

See your owner's manual for recommended tune-up intervals, but be aware that even if it says that the vehicle doesn't require *scheduled* tune-ups very often, checking periodically that your car is working at peak efficiency is in your best interest. If you do a lot of stop-and-go driving or pull heavy loads (like a camper or boat), your ignition system may need to be tuned more often, no matter what type of system you have.

Here are some of the symptoms that tell you that your ignition system probably needs to be tuned or adjusted:

✔ **Your car stalls a lot.** The spark plugs may be fouled or worn, the *gap* may need adjusting, or the idle speed or an electronic sensor may need to be adjusted. Stalling can also be caused by problems with the fuel system. If you're having trouble pinpointing the cause, you can help your automotive technician diagnose the problem if you're aware of whether the engine stalls when the weather is hot or cold, or when the air conditioner is on.

✔ **Your car gets harder to start.** The problem can be in the starting system or can be due to an electronic component, such as the starting sensor or the ignition system's computer. The problem may also lie in the fuel system, so have that checked out, too.

Extending the life of your brakes

Riding your brakes causes them to wear out prematurely. The excess heat can also warp disc brake rotors and brake drums.

Although being cautious is always a good policy, try to anticipate stopping situations well enough in advance to be able to slow down by releasing the pressure on your gas pedal and then using your brake pedal for that final stop. In slippery conditions — or situations that call for slowing down rather than stopping — if you have traditional brakes, pump your brake pedal to reduce speed and avoid sliding rather than jamming on your brakes and screeching to a halt.

If the road is slippery and your vehicle is equipped with an anti-lock braking system (ABS), *don't* pump the brake pedal; simply apply firm, steady pressure and keep steering.

Four things to consider when buying tires

Before you rush out and buy a set of tires, you have a couple of things to consider.

Types of tires

Choose the type of tires that meets your needs:

✔ **Basic all-season tires** are standard equipment on most cars. If "M+S" (mud and snow) is printed on the sidewall, the tire performs well in inclement weather without the need for snow tires.

✔ **Touring tires** are generally more expensive than basic all-season tires. Whether they're worth the money depends on the individual product.

- ✔ **Performance tires** have a wide, squatty profile and are designed for people who drive "aggressively." They perform better in terms of braking and cornering but are usually noisier and wear out more quickly.

- ✔ **Light-truck tires** come in a variety of styles designed for normal conditions, driving on- or off-road, or both. The thicker treads on the off-road variety offer better traction on unpaved surfaces.

- ✔ **Snow tires** may be better than all-season tires for driving in mountainous areas with heavy snowfall, but they're noisy and don't handle as well on dry roads, so use them only when necessary.

- ✔ **"Run-flat" tires** can be driven on without any air pressure inside the tire. The sidewalls have special inserts that prevent the tire from caving in when the tire loses air pressure. You can drive some run-flat tires up to 50 mph for 50 miles or more without further damaging the tire.

  Running on a run-flat at high speeds for a long period can damage them, so car manufacturers incorporate a warning system, complete with a warning light on the instrument panel.

Your driving habits

Before making a decision about a particular type of tire, take a close look at your driving habits:

- ✔ **Are you hard on tires?** If you tend to "burn rubber" when cornering, starting, and stopping, you know where that rubber comes from. A pair of cheaply made tires wears out quickly, so buy the best quality you can afford.

- ✔ **Do you drive a great deal and do most of your driving on high-speed freeways?** A tire with a harder surface takes longer to wear out under these conditions.

- ✔ **Do you drive a lot on unpaved rocky roads, carry heavy loads, or leave your car in the hot sun for long hours?** You need higher-quality tires that have the stamina to endure these challenges.

- ✔ **What's the weather like in your area?** Today, front-wheel drive vehicles with high-tech *all-season* tires get better traction than the old snow tires, which you had to replace when warm weather set in. However, if you drive under extreme conditions, you may want to check out tires designed for them.

- ✔ **Do you drive mostly in local stop-and-go traffic, with many turns?** Softer tires with wider treads may suit you best.

Longevity

How long do you intend to keep your car? Putting a pair of expensive tires on a vehicle that you intend to get rid of in 10,000 or 20,000 miles is foolish. On the other hand, if you intend to keep your vehicle for a few years, you save money in the long run by opting for more expensive, longer-lasting tires.

If you drive only a couple of thousand miles a year, don't expect a pair of 40,000-mile radials to last forever. Rubber treads tend to rot eventually because of the ozone in the air, which causes cracks and hard spots in the sidewalls. If you've used your tires for more than 40,000 miles, even if the treads are in good shape, have the tires checked to make sure that deteriorating rubber hasn't made them prone to blowouts and leaks.

Specifications and technical stuff

In addition to knowing which kind of tire is best for your car, keep the following tips in mind when you shop for tires:

✔ You can find the proper tire size for your car in the owner's manual or on a sticker affixed to the vehicle. If neither exists, ask your dealer.

✔ Although you should never buy tires that are smaller than those specified for your vehicle, you can buy tires a size or two larger (if the car's wheel clearance allows it) for better handling or load-carrying ability. However, you need to buy these larger tires in pairs and place them on the same axle. Ask your mechanic or a reputable tire or auto dealer for advice about the proper size range for your vehicle.

✔ Never use two different-sized tires on the same axle.

✔ If you're replacing just one or two tires, put the new ones on the front for better cornering control and braking.

✔ Remember that you have to "break in" new tires, so don't drive faster than 60 mph for the first 50 miles on a new tire or spare.

✔ Store tires that you aren't using in the dark, away from extreme heat and electric motors that create ozone.

Checking tire inflation and alignment

Underinflated tires wear out faster, create excessive heat, increase fuel consumption, and make your vehicle more difficult to handle. Tires that aren't properly balanced or are out of alignment wear out rapidly, increase wear and tear on the steering and suspension system, and may take you for a bumpy or unsafe ride. You can avoid many of these problems simply by checking the air pressure in your tires and by looking for signs of wear and misalignment at least once a month and before every long trip.

How do you know whether your wheels need aligning? Look at your tires to see whether they show any of the tread-wear patterns in the following section and pay attention to how your car steers and handles. Does it pull to one side? Does the steering feel loose and sloppy? Is your car hard to handle after a turn? If your tires show any unusual wear patterns and/or you answered yes to any of the preceding questions, your car probably needs an alignment.

Checking your tires for wear

To determine whether you need to buy new tires, have your wheels balanced, have your wheels aligned, or change your driving habits, simply read your tire treads for clues. Table 5-1 and Figure 5-3 show you what to look for.

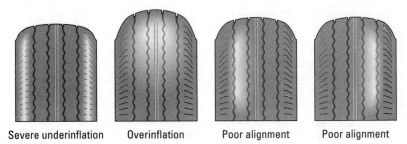

Severe underinflation   Overinflation   Poor alignment   Poor alignment

Figure 5-3: What the signs of poor tread wear mean.

Table 5-1	How to Read Your Treads	
Clue	*Culprit*	*Remedy*
Both edges worn	Underinflation	Add more air; check for leaks
Center treads worn	Overinflation	Let air out to manufacturer's specifications
One-sided wear	Poor alignment	Have wheels aligned
Treads worn unevenly, with bald spots, cups or scallops	Wheel imbalance and/or poor alignment	Have wheels balanced and aligned

(continued)

Table 5-1 *(continued)*

Clue	Culprit	Remedy
Erratically spaced bald spots	Wheel imbalance or worn shocks	Have wheels balanced or replace shocks
Edges of front tires only worn	Taking curves too fast	Slow down!
Saw-toothed wear pattern	Poor alignment	Have wheels aligned
Whining, thumping, and other weird noises	Poor alignment, worn tires or shocks	Have wheels aligned or buy new tires or shocks
Squealing on curves	Poor alignment or under inflation	Check wear on treads and act accordingly

Most tires have tread-wear indicators built into them. These bars of hard rubber are normally invisible but appear across treads that have been worn down to $\frac{1}{16}$ of an inch of the surface of the tire (the legal limit in most states). If these indicators appear in two or three different places, less than 120 degrees apart on the circumference of the tire, replace the tire.

If your tires don't show these indicators and you think that they may be worn below legal tolerances, place a Lincoln penny head-down in the groove between the treads. If you can see the top of Lincoln's head, you probably need to replace your tire.

Wasting time on warm-ups

When you start your car in the morning, do you warm it up before you drive off? If you do, no good! Most manuals caution you not to indulge in lengthy warm-ups. They waste fuel, pollute the air, and increase wear on your vehicle.

If your vehicle isn't starting up immediately, try the following:

- ✔ **If your vehicle has fuel injection,** an automotive technician needs to set things right.
- ✔ **If your car has a carburetor,** check your choke.
- ✔ **If you have trouble starting up on cold mornings,** check your thermostat.

Solving and Repairing Car Problems

Despite the best care and maintenance, sometimes things go wrong. Parts break, wear out, or malfunction, and you need to repair something or take your car to be fixed. Here's how to go about these tasks.

Buying the right parts for your car

To buy the proper spark plugs and other parts for a basic tune-up, you must know your vehicle's specifications (or "specs," as the pros call them).

You can find all the information you need in your owner's manual, and most of it is also printed on metal tags or decals located inside your hood or fenders. Some cars may have decals inside the lid of the glove compartment, on the body in the door frame, or in the spare tire well.

You should know or be able to find all the following:

- ✔ **The make of the vehicle** (for example, Ford or Honda).

- ✔ **The model** (Taurus, Accord, and so on).

- ✔ **The model year** (for example, 1988 or 2002).

- ✔ **The number and type of cylinders in the engine** (4, 6, 8, V-4, V-6, or V-8).

- ✔ **Whether the vehicle has an automatic or a manual (standard) transmission.**

- ✔ **The engine displacement:** How much room there is in each cylinder when the piston is at its lowest point. (For example, a 300-cubic inch 6-cylinder engine has a displacement of 50 cubic inches in each cylinder.) The bigger the displacement, the more fuel and air the cylinders in the engine hold.

  Engines on older cars may be listed in cubic inches, such as 302, 350, 454, and so on. Newer cars may be listed in liters (1.8, 2.3, 5.9) or cubic centimeters (2200, 3400, 3800).

- ✔ **The kind of fuel system:** If your engine has a carburetor, you need to know how many carburetor barrels it has. It may be a 1-barrel, 2-barrel, or 4-barrel carburetor. ("Barrel" may be abbreviated as "bbl" on some specifications.) If your engine is fuel-injected, you may need to know whether your car has *throttle body* injection or *multi-port* injection.

Getting the best possible deal on repairs

A big repair job is like major surgery. Not only do you want the best possible surgeon, but you also want to be sure that the surgery is necessary and that it's done under the best possible terms. Therefore, whenever you bring your vehicle in for maintenance or repair, follow these guidelines:

- ✔ **If you're dealing with a new shop or you're faced with major repairs,** *get at least a second opinion and an estimate of costs* **from another repair shop.** If you notice a big difference in costs, additional estimates and opinions are in order. If one shop is much lower in price than the others, this isn't necessarily the best place to go. Be sure that the work is the same quality before you go for the cheapest job.

- ✔ **Ask for a written estimate.** Many states require one anyway and require the shop to call you if they find that the job costs more than originally estimated. Beware of general statements; try to get as detailed an estimate as possible.

- ✔ **Ask that all the parts that are replaced be returned to you, regardless of whether the laws in your state require it.** That way, you can be sure that you're getting what you pay for.

- ✔ **Ask for credit for the core charge on any rebuildable part that's going to be replaced with a new part.** If you're buying a rebuilt part as a replacement, the core charge should be deducted from the price of the part that you buy in exchange for trading in your old part, which is then rebuilt and sold to someone else.

Checking the invoice carefully

Make sure that the invoice for the job includes a written guarantee on parts and labor, and find out whether any of the parts installed comes with its own warranty. (This is especially important if you're paying for a big job that involves expensive parts.) Knowing just where the responsibility lies in the event of a dispute or a malfunctioning part always pays off.

A standard mechanic's invoice has separate areas, each of which serves a different purpose. Every invoice should have a space for a written estimate and a number where the mechanic can reach you if necessary. Typically, mechanics ask you to sign the estimate.

Be sure to read the small print above the signature line before you sign. The small print should cover only your approval of the estimate and the fact that you're willing to allow the technicians to drive your vehicle in order to test, diagnose, and repair it.

The reverse side of the invoice often contains information about the shop's warranty and the mechanic's lien, which allows service facilities in some states to sell your vehicle if you refuse to pay for services. For this reason, if a dispute occurs, always pay your bill and *then* seek restitution.

Establishing a good relationship with your mechanic

Finding a mechanic who is reliable, honest, intelligent, efficient, and relatively inexpensive isn't enough. Aim for "most favored customer" status. After you discover an outstanding automotive shop, the ball is in your court to establish a good and lasting relationship that can have the shop going out of its way to make you happy. Even though most small businesses are struggling to stay alive these days, a good independent service facility is an exception.

Here are some guidelines for dealing with your mechanic:

- **Call for an appointment.** Don't just show up and expect the shop to drop everything and take care of you.

- **Get your vehicle into the shop early (by 8:30 or 9:00 a.m. at the latest) if you hope to get it out the same day.** If you're on your way to work, allow sufficient time to give the technician or service writer a full account of what you want done or what you've found to be wrong with the car. Sometimes a test drive helps to demonstrate the problem, so make sure that you have the time to accompany the mechanic if possible.

- **Bring along a written list of the things you want serviced or repaired.** Include a phone number where the mechanic can reach you if questions arise or if the work is going to cost more than the mechanic originally estimated.

- **On your list, be as specific as possible about the symptoms you've experienced.** Try organizing the information in the following way:

  - *What* is happening ("The car stalls, pulls to the right, runs roughly, seems to be losing power, or is overheating.")

  - *When* it happens ("The car hesitates when I accelerate, doesn't start when it rains, smokes when I change gears, or pulls to the left when I brake.")

  - *Where* the trouble seems to be located ("I smell the gas more powerfully when I sit in the rear seat, there's a vibration under the front seat, or there's a squeak under the right front fender.")

If you can provide enough information to help the shop diagnose the trouble easily, you may not have to pay for test drives and electronic diagnostic procedures that can cost more than the simple adjustments or repairs that are necessary.

✓ **Provide the clearest information you can regarding all the symptoms, but *do not diagnose the problem yourself!*** If you tell a shop that your vehicle needs a specific job done on it, then that's the work that the shop will do, and you will pay for it, *whether the vehicle needs it or not.* If you want to inquire whether the trouble *might* be caused by a malfunction in a specific part, then do so, but keep your information in the form of a question. The final diagnosis must be up to the repair shop so that it can be responsible if the diagnosis turns out to be wrong.

✓ **Keep a maintenance record on your vehicle and bring a photocopy for the shop's records if it hasn't done the past maintenance.**

✓ **Don't press to get the job done fast unless you're really in a bind.** Making a diagnosis, getting the proper parts, doing the work, and testing the results takes time. Nobody likes to work under pressure.

✓ **Call to make sure that your vehicle is ready before you come to pick it up.** If it isn't, try to be understanding (unless the shop is chronically slow about getting work done). If it's a matter of parts that the shop ordered but weren't delivered on time, realize that the shop can do very little about the situation. If the shop is simply overbooked with work, be polite but firm about your need to get the vehicle back as soon as possible.

✓ **When the vehicle is ready, ask what was wrong and what they did to repair the problem.** Keep a repair log, and add the information to it for future reference.

✓ **Be prepared to spend a little time test-driving to be sure that the job's been done to your satisfaction.** You're better off returning immediately with your complaints than showing up several days later.

✓ **Show your appreciation for a job well done.** A phone call to the manager or a letter that the shop can display, praising a technician's work, means a lot to a service facility.

Tracking down strange sounds

You probably know how your vehicle sounds when it's running properly. If you hear a strange or different sound, pay attention to it and react accordingly.

✔ **If a fan belt or accessory belt "sings" (makes a continuous, high-pitched sound),** readjust or replace it. Belts should have at least half an inch of play and shouldn't be frayed, cracked, or glazed on the underside. Some belts tend to sing more than others. Rubbing a bit of petroleum jelly on the undersides of these belts usually quiets them down.

✔ **If your radiator "sings" (similar sound to belt, different tune),** check the radiator pressure cap. The rubber gasket may be worn, and steam from the hot engine may be escaping past it. Don't remove the radiator cap if the car is hot or has been driven recently — the steam can burn you.

✔ **If your tires squeal on curves — and you aren't speeding —** check the tires' inflation pressure, treads, and alignment.

✔ **If you hear a whining or humming sounds on curves,** your wheel bearings may be wearing.

✔ **If your tires "tramp" (make a weird, rhythmic sound as you drive),** check inflation, tire wear, and wheel balancing.

✔ **If you hear squealing when you step on the brake,** you've probably worn the brake pads down too far. Get them replaced immediately. Some disc brakes are naturally noisy, but if the sound gets louder, take heed.

✔ **If something ticks rhythmically while your engine idles,** shut off the engine, wait ten minutes, and then check the oil level. The hydraulic lifters that operate the valves in your engine can make these noises if you're down as little as a quart of oil. If the level is low, add oil up to the "Full" line on the dipstick and check again in a couple of days. If you have enough oil, have a mechanic check the valve adjustment if your car has adjustable valves (some don't). Faulty valves can seriously affect your car's performance and fuel consumption.

✔ **If you hear a loud knocking sound in your engine,** pull to the side of the road *immediately* and call for road service. The sound may be just a loose rocker arm or carbon buildup inside the engine, but if it's a loose bearing or a faulty piston, letting it go unheeded can destroy the whole engine.

Mild knocking or "pinging" may be the result of using fuel with the wrong octane rating. Check your owner's manual to see whether your vehicle needs low-octane or premium gas.

✔ **If you hear the engine running after you turn off the ignition,** your engine is *dieseling.* This condition is often due to using fuel with too high an octane rating, but a tank of inferior gas or an idle speed that's set too high may also be the culprit.

✔ **If you hear rumbling noises coming from under or toward the rear of the vehicle,** the trouble may be a defective exhaust pipe, muffler, or catalytic converter; or it may be coming from a worn universal joint or some other part of the drive train. Have a service facility put the car up on a hoist and find the problem.

✔ **If you hear clunking under your vehicle, especially when you go over a bump,** check the shock absorbers and suspension system. If the sound is toward the rear, your tailpipe or muffler may be loose.

✔ **If you hear a whistling noise coming from under the hood,** check the hoses for vacuum leaks. If the whistling comes from *inside* the vehicle, the weather-stripping probably has a leak.

✔ **If you hear an unlocatable sound,** get an old stethoscope from a medical supply house or ask your family doctor. Take off the rubber disc and insert a piece of tubing in its place (about 1½ inches works fine). Then put the plugs in your ears, run the engine, and move the tube end of the stethoscope around the hood area. The stethoscope amplifies the sound as you near the part that's causing the sound.

✔ **If your brakes squeal,** the brake linings may be glazed or worn. Some disc brake pads have built-in wear sensors that squeal when you need to replace them. Even though some disc brakes tend to squeal under normal circumstances, you're better off to have the brakes checked or check them yourself.

✔ **If the car idles with an offbeat rhythm,** it isn't becoming creative; it's probably misfiring — one of the spark plugs or the wires that connect them to the distributor cap may be at fault. Try the following:

  • *With the engine off,* check the spark plug cables for breaks or shorts in the wiring.

  • *With the engine off,* remove the spark plugs one at a time and check whether they're clean and properly gapped. Replace any that are fouled or burned.

If that doesn't help, have a technician check the ignition system with an electronic engine analyzer.

✔ **If the idling is rough but even and your vehicle has a carburetor,** the carburetor settings may need to be adjusted. If that doesn't work, you may need to replace the carburetor. Fuel-injected vehicles don't have carburetors, and a technician must check and adjust complex electronic systems.

An easy way to see whether your car is idling evenly is to place a stiff piece of paper against the end of the tailpipe while the car is idling (with the emergency brake on, please). Doing so amplifies the sound and enables you to hear the rhythm. A misfiring cylinder comes through as a pumping or puffing sound.

✔ **If your car sounds like a jet plane or makes some other loud, abnormal sound,** a hole in the muffler is probably the cause. Replace it immediately: Traffic cops hate noisy mufflers, and carbon monoxide hates people!

✔ **If the horn is stuck,** your vehicle is producing what may be the worst noise it can make. *Before* this happens, have someone honk your horn until you can locate it under your hood. Most cars have two horns. Each has a wire leading to it. If your horn gets stuck, pull these wires to stop the noise — sometimes you have to pull only one. When you have the horn fixed, tell the mechanic that you pulled the wires and find out why the horn got stuck. (If you can't get at the horn wires, disconnect one battery terminal or pull the fuse that goes to the horn to stop the noise.)

✔ **If your car sounds like an old taxi, especially when you drive it on a bumpy road,** it may just need lubrication. However, the problem may be worn shock absorbers or struts, suspension ball joints, or broken stabilizer links.

If you hear suspicious rattles, squeaks, or vibrations, you may be able to save yourself some money by checking and tightening the following items before seeking professional help:

✔ **Loose screws and bolts:** Check both inside the vehicle and under the hood.

✔ **Rearview and side mirrors**

✔ **Dashboard knobs and trim**

✔ **Sound-system speaker grills**

✔ **Window and door cranks and locks**

✔ **Ashtray:** Is it empty? Does it fit snugly?

✔ **Glove box:** Is the door shut tight? Is anything in the glove box rattling around?

✔ **Hubcaps:** If your vehicle has them, remove them and check inside for pebbles.

✔ **Outside trim**

✔ **Trunk:** Is something stashed in there moving around?

If none of these is the culprit, or if the noise persists, have a repair facility find the cause. Often, something inside the vehicle vibrates sympathetically because another part of the vehicle is running roughly.

Handling Roadside Emergencies

Sometimes the inevitable happens. You lock yourself out of your car, you get a flat tire, your battery is dead, or you overheat.

Getting back into a locked car

Here's an "emergency" that may not be dangerous, but certainly can be exasperating!

If you tend to be feather-headed and leave the keys in your car fairly often, you may be tempted to hide an extra key somewhere on the vehicle. However, unless you're very clever about where you hide it, you may be inviting someone to steal your car or its contents. Those little magnetic boxes that stick to the metal surface of the car frame are the best bets, but *be sure to place your box in an obscure and hard-to-reach area where it can't jiggle loose and fall out.* Be imaginative. Struggling a little to reach that extra key is better than giving your car away easily. And *don't* hide your house key with it. You don't want to give *everything* away, do you?

If you don't hide an extra set of keys on your car, here's how to get in without a key:

- **If your car has the old-style door locks with little buttons that go up and down:** Obtain a wire coat hanger, straighten it out, and bend the end of it into a little hook. Insert the coat hanger between the rubber molding and the side window or vent window and then, carefully, with the dexterity of a jewel thief, hook it around the door button and pull it up.

- **If your car has new, smoother locks:** Your vehicle has less of a chance of being stolen, but you also have a harder job getting into it without a key. You may be able to use the hanger to hook or push the gizmo near the door handle, but most newer locks straighten out your hanger before they budge. Sorry!

- **If you're in a parking facility or near a service station:** Attendants often have a gadget called a "jimmy" that they can slide between the window and the door and operate the locking mechanism. Asking certainly doesn't hurt. If they have one, ask them to do the job for you and be generous with your thanks. They've just saved you a lot of time and money.

✔ **If you have to call a locksmith:** Remember that you need to be able to prove that you own the vehicle before the locksmith performs and work, and you probably have to pay immediately. (Hopefully, you didn't lock your wallet in your car along with your keys.)

Some good news: Auto manufacturers now code each car key, and if you have the key code number, a locksmith can make you a new key as long as you have identification and can describe the vehicle in terms of its vital statistics. General Motors car keys have little coded tags that you knock out of the key and keep, other U.S. cars come with little metal tags with the number on them, and most foreign carmakers engrave the number right on the keys.

As a valuable favor to yourself, write down the code number where someone at home can read the information to you in an emergency. Also record the number — without identifying what it is — in your pocket address book or in your wallet *before* you lose your keys. If you don't know the code number for your keys and you bought the car, new or used, from a dealer, the dealer may still have the number on file. Failing that, a good locksmith may be able to analyze a key in fairly new condition and come up with the proper code for it.

✔ **If you get totally freaked out and decide to break a window:** Break the little vent window, if you have one. It's cheaper to replace, and sometimes the latch breaks before the glass does.

If you have to break the glass, wrap something around your hand and use a stone or other heavy object. Keep your head away from flying glass, although most auto glass is shatterproof. And *don't* break a window that interferes with visibility while you're driving home to face the jeers of your family and friends.

Changing a tire

Even if you're a member of the AAA or CAA, you may still find your-self stuck with a flat tire on a remote road with no telephone in sight. On these occasions, all traffic generally vanishes, leaving you helpless unless you know how to change a tire yourself. Everyone needs to have a general idea of what's involved:

1. **Secure the vehicle so that it doesn't roll.**

2. **Jack up the vehicle.**

3. **Remove the old tire.**

4. **Put on the new tire.**

5. **Put away the jacking stuff and the old tire.**

6. **Drive happily into the sunset.**

But the job gets sticky in a couple of places. Unless you're properly equipped, you can find yourself out of luck and in for a long wait for help to come along. The following sections explain in detail, and in order, how to change a tire.

If you own a luxury car with an air suspension, you need to turn the system off before jacking up your car. Vehicles with air suspensions have an on/off switch located in the trunk area.

Removing a hubcap

If you have an older car that still has hubcaps (instead of wheel covers), the first task in changing a tire is to remove the hubcap of the injured tire:

1. **Use a screwdriver or the flat end of a lug wrench to pry off the hubcap.**

   Just insert the point of the tool where the edge of the cap meets the wheel and apply a little leverage. The cap should pop off. You may have to do this in a couple of places; it's like prying the lid off a can of paint.

2. **Lay the cap on its back so that you can put the lug nuts into it to keep them from rolling away.**

Loosening the lug nuts

Lug nuts are those big nuts that hold the wheel in place. Most garages retighten them with a power tool, and unless you've done the job yourself by hand, they're pretty hard to loosen.

Before you begin, you have to figure out whether the lug nuts on the wheel you're working on are right-hand threaded or left-hand threaded. This isn't a "left-handed hammer" joke; the threads determine which way you turn the wrench. The lug nuts on the right side of a vehicle are always right-hand threaded, but the nuts on the left side *may* be left-hand threaded. Look at the lug nuts on your car; in the center of the lugs you should see an R, an L, or no letter at all:

 ✔ A lug with an R or with no letter is right-threaded. Turn it *counterclockwise* to loosen it.

 ✔ A lugs with an L is left-threaded. Turn it *clockwise* to loosen it.

For the purposes of sanity, assume that your car has right-threaded nuts. If you have a couple of lefties, just turn the wrench in the opposite direction as you follow these steps to loosen the lug nuts:

1. **Find the end of the cross-shaft wrench that fits the lug nuts on your car and fit it onto the first nut.**

   Always work on lug nuts in rotation. That way, you don't forget to tighten any later.

2. **Apply all your weight to the bar.**

   If the nut has been put on with a power tool and you can't get it started, a piece of hollow pipe, fitted over the cross-shaft wrench, may magically add enough leverage to start the nut easily.

Don't remove the lug nuts completely; just get them loose enough so that you can remove them by hand *after* raising the car.

Jacking up the car

Use jacks only to get a vehicle off the ground. Never use them to hold a vehicle in place. Even if you're simply changing a tire, you need to make sure that you block the other wheels so that the car doesn't roll off the jack. You must use jack stands when you work underneath your car; if you don't, you run the risk of serious injury or even death.

Before you attempt to jack up your vehicle, observe the following safety precautions:

- ✔ **Never change a tire on a freeway or highway.** Not only can you be seriously injured, but you can also fall prey to carjackers. Don't exit the car on the side nearest traffic; use a cellular phone to call road service or the AAA. If you have no cellular phone and a public phone isn't near enough to make a call and get right back into your car, hang a white rag or a white piece of paper out of the driver's side window and wait for the highway patrol to rescue you.

- ✔ **Always park a vehicle on level ground before you jack it up.** If you get a flat tire on a hill and can't coast to the bottom without killing the tire completely, then park close to the curb, turn the wheels toward the curb, and block the downside wheels securely to prevent the car from rolling.

- ✔ **Never jack up a vehicle without blocking the wheels.** Even if the car is on level ground, use bricks, wooden wedges, or metal wheel chocks to block the wheels at the opposite end of the car from the end that is to be raised.

If you find yourself faced with the job of changing a tire and you have nothing with which to block the wheels, park near the curb with the wheels turned in. This may not keep you from getting hurt if the car rolls off the jack, but at least innocent motorists and pedestrians don't have to deal with a runaway driverless car!

✔ **Be sure that your gearshift is in Park (or in First if you have a manual transmission) and that the emergency brake is on** *before* **you jack the car up.**

After you observe the preceding safety precautions, follow these steps:

1. **If you're going to remove a wheel to change a tire, remove the hubcap and loosen the lug nuts** *before* **you jack up the car.**

   After you jack the car up, the wheel turns freely, which makes getting a hubcap off harder and makes starting the nuts almost impossible.

2. **Place the jack under the part of the vehicle that it should contact when raised. If you're using jack stands, place them near the jack.**

   To find out the proper place to position the jack for your particular vehicle, check your owner's manual. If you have no manual, ask the service department at your dealership to show you the proper place, or follow these rules:

   • Never place the jack so that the weight of the vehicle rests on something that can bend, break, or give.

   • Try to place the jack so that it touches either the car frame or the big bar that supports the front wheel suspension.

3. **Lift the vehicle by using the jack.**

   How you accomplish this depends on the type of jack you're using:

   • If you have a *hydraulic* jack, place the handle into the appropriate location and pump up and down. Use nice, even strokes, taking the jack handle from its lowest to its highest point on each stroke to cut down on the labor involved.

   • If you have a *tripod* jack, turn the crank.

   • If you have a *scissor* jack, insert the rod or wrench over the knob and then crank.

4. **If you have jack stands, place them under the car, near the place where the jack is touching the vehicle. Raise the stands until they're high enough to just fit under, and lock them in place. Lower the jack until the car is resting on the jack stands. Then remove the jack.**

Substituting boxes, stones, or bricks for jack stands is very dangerous. They can slip out or break while you're under the car. A jack can do the same thing, so if you're going to work under your car, be sure to buy a pair of jack stands.

5. **Before you begin to work, wiggle the car a little to make sure that it's resting securely on the jack or the jack stands.**

Doing so also tells you whether you have the wheels blocked properly. You're better off if the vehicle falls while all four wheels are in place. (It bounces just a little.)

Changing the tire

After you safely jack the vehicle up and remove the lug nuts, follow these instructions to change the tire:

1. **Remove the spare from the trunk if you haven't already done so.**

2. **Grasp the flat tire with both hands and pull it toward you.**

   The flat tire sits on the exposed bolts that the lug nuts screwed onto. As you pull the flat off, it should slide along the bolts until, suddenly, it clears the end of the bolts and you find your-self supporting its full weight. Tires are heavy, so lower it to the ground (if you haven't already dropped it).

3. **Roll the flat along the ground to the trunk to get it out of the way.**

4. **Lift the spare onto the lug bolts.**

   Because tires are heavy, you may have a little trouble lifting the spare into place.

5. **After you have the spare tire in place, replace the lug nuts and tighten them by hand.**

   Give each lug nut a jolt with the wrench to get it firmly into place, but wait until the car is on the ground before you really try to tighten the lug nuts.

6. **Replace the jack, lift the car off the jack stands (if you used them), and lower the car to the ground.**

7. **After the car is resting on the ground, use the lug wrench to tighten the lugs as much as you can.**

   You don't want to twist them off the bolts or ruin the threads, but you don't want the wheel to fall off, either. Use a hollow pipe if you're worried about tightening them sufficiently, or step on the right-hand arm of the lug wrench after the nut is tight.

8. **If your car has hubcaps, place the hubcap against the wheel and whack it into place with the heel of your hand.**

   Cushion your hand with a soft rag first so that you don't hurt it. And don't hit the hubcap with a wrench or hammer — doing so dents it. Whack it a couple of times, in a couple of places, to be sure that it's on evenly and securely. If replacing the hubcap is too much of a hassle, or if you don't have the time, you can drive and install the hubcap later.

9. **Put the flat in the trunk where the spare was located, and put your tools away.**

   Don't forget to remove the wheel blocks, and *don't forget to have that flat fixed!*

If you get caught in the middle of nowhere with a flat tire and are unable to change it yourself, you can get rolling again without riding on the flat. If you carry an aerosol can of nonflammable inflator/sealant, simply screw the nozzle of the can onto the valve stem of the flat tire, and it fills the tire with air and some sort of goo that temporarily seals the puncture. Because there's still some question about how permanent this fix is and its ultimate effects on your tire, use inflator/sealant *only* in emergencies, get to a service station as soon as possible, and ask the attendant to try to remove the stuff before fixing the tire.

To make the job easier, you may want to go out and check the lug nuts on your car now. If they're on hideously tight, loosen them with a lug wrench and a pipe and retighten them to a reasonable tension so that you don't have to struggle at the side of the road.

Using a travel fire extinguisher

A fire extinguisher isn't really a tool, but it's a *must* for your vehicle. Get the 2¾-pound dry chemical type.

An engine fire won't necessarily ruin your car — if you can extinguish it quickly. A gasoline leak can be ignited by a stray spark from your spark plug wires. The resulting fire looks awful, but it's really burning on the *outside* of your engine. If you put the fire out quickly, your vehicle may suffer little or no damage. If the flames are any-where near the fuel tank, forget the heroics; just run for it and throw yourself to the ground if you think that the tank may explode.

Because your fuel tank is located right under your trunk compart-ment, keep your extinguisher under the *front* seat of your car, in a suitable bracket that prevents it from rolling under the pedals when you stop the car.

Six things to try when your car doesn't start

Your car may not start for a number of reasons. The following list outlines the most common circumstances and tells you what action you can take to try to remedy each situation:

- ✔ **The car is silent when you turn the key in the ignition.** Check the battery terminal cable connections. If they look very cor-roded, force the point of a screwdriver (with an insulated or wooden handle) between the connector and the terminal post and twist it to lodge it firmly. Then try to start the engine. If it starts, you need to clean or replace your cables.

- ✔ **The car makes a clicking noise but doesn't start.** This sound usually means a dead battery. If not, check the wiring to and from the starter for a loose connection.

- ✔ **The car cranks over but doesn't start.** Check the fuel supply to your engine. If that's okay, check whether the electrical spark is getting through.

- ✔ **The engine starts but dies.** If your car has a carburetor, check your carburetor adjustment and your choke to see whether the choke is first closing and then opening. If you have fuel injec-tion, you need to seek professional help.

- ✔ **The car doesn't start on rainy days.** Check inside the distribu-tor cap for dampness. If you find moisture, get some mechanic's solvent from your friendly service station — they use it to clean car parts — or buy an aerosol can of it at an auto supply store. To evaporate any dampness inside the distributor cap, turn the cap upside down and pour or spray some solvent into it. Swish it around and pour it out. Then dry the cap as best you can with a clean, lint-free rag and replace the cap.

  Use only *clean* solvent; even a tiny speck of dirt can foul the points. Gasoline doesn't work as a solvent because a spark can ignite gasoline fumes and cause an explosion or a fire.

✔ **The car doesn't start on cold mornings.** For vehicles with carburetors, check the choke. Is it closed? Does it open? If you have fuel injection, you need to have a professional diagnose the cold-start problems.

Jumping a start

If your battery dies, you may be able to use jumper cables to jump a start from some Good Samaritan's car — with one important exception. If either vehicle has an electronic ignition system, the use of jumper cables may damage it. If your vehicle is one that may be damaged in this way, you may find a warning to that effect in the owner's manual or on a decal under the hood. Even if you don't find a warning, it pays to be sure, so call the service department at your dealership and ask about your vehicle's make, model, and year.

If you can safely use jumper cables on your vehicle, make sure that the battery on the Good Samaritan's vehicle has at least as much voltage as your own. Don't worry about whether your car has negative ground and the GS's car has positive ground, or your car has an alternator and the GS's car has a generator — as long as you hook up the cables properly (and the proper way is the same in every case), you can safely jump your car.

To safely jump a start:

1. **Take out your jumper cables.**

   If you don't have jumper cables, you have to find a Good Samaritan who not only is willing to assist you but has jumper cables as well.

2. **Place both cars in Park or Neutral, with their ignitions shut off and their emergency brakes on.**

3. **Remove the caps from both batteries (unless they're sealed).**

4. **Connect the cables.**

   The positive cable has red clips at either end, and the negative cable has black clips. Attach the cables in the proper order:

   1. First, attach one of the *red* clips to the *positive* terminal of *your* battery (it has "POS" or "+" on it, or it's bigger than the negative terminal).

   2. Attach the other red clip to the positive terminal of the GS's car.

3. Attach one of the *black* clips to the negative terminal on the GS's battery.

4. Attach the last black clip to an unpainted metal surface on your car that *isn't* near the carburetor (if your car has one) or battery.

5. **Try to start your vehicle.**

   If your vehicle doesn't start, make sure that the cables are properly connected and have the GS run his or her engine for five minutes. Then try to start your car again. If it still doesn't start, your battery may be beyond help.

6. **Disconnect the cables, thank the Good Samaritan, and resume your life.**

   Don't shut off your engine; drive around for a while to recharge your battery.

If your alternator light stays on or the gauge on the dashboard continues to point to "Discharge" after your car's been running, make sure that your fan belt is tight enough to run your alternator properly. If your battery keeps going dead, have a professional check both the battery and alternator.

Dealing with an overheated vehicle

Even the happiest, most beautifully tuned vehicle overheats occasionally. If you find yourself in stop-and-go traffic on an extremely hot day, chances are that your car's dashboard temperature indicator may rise or a warning light may come on. Here's how to help your vehicle regain its cool:

✔ **At the first sign of overheating, shut off your air conditioner and open your windows.** Doing so decreases the load on the engine and helps it cool off.

✔ **If you continue to overheat, turn on the heater and blower.** Doing so transfers the heat from the engine to the interior of the car.

✔ **If you're stopped in traffic and the temperature gauge is rising, shift into Neutral and rev the engine a little.** Doing so makes the water pump and the fan speed up, which draws more liquid and air through the radiator. The increased air and liquid circulation helps cool things off.

REMEMBER

✔ **Try not to ride your brakes.** Crawl along slowly, on little more than an idle, rather than moving up and then braking repeatedly. Brake drag increases the load on the engine and makes it heat up.

✔ **If you think that your vehicle is about to boil over, drive to the side of the road, open the hood, and sit there until things cool off.** Don't open the radiator cap under these circumstances, and if your engine boils over, don't add water until the engine is quite cool again. If you *must* add water when the engine is still a *little* warm, add the water while the engine is running in Neutral.

Part II
Staying Healthy and Fit

In this part . . .

Good health is about so much more than just not feeling sick. Good health is about eating right, exercising your body, finding ways to de-stress your hectic life, and dealing effectively with injuries and illnesses should they arise. If good health sounds like a lot of work, then you need the simple suggestions and easy hints in this part to make feeling good an everyday event for you and every member of your family.

Chapter 6

Nutrition Know-How

- -

- -

*E*ating right isn't always easy, and making sense of nutritional information can feel like deciphering code. This chapter takes you beyond the four basic food groups and gives you the important breakdowns on protein, fat, cholesterol, carbohydrates, and all those vitamins and minerals. You discover the foods to avoid, the items to stock up on, and the diet that can help clear your arteries, prevent cancer, and keep your bones from turning brittle.

Because you're a unique individual, consult with a professional healthcare provider for a complete interview and evaluation of your present condition. If you receive advice that is contrary to the information this reference provides, follow the practitioner's advice because your practitioner bases his or her advice on your unique characteristics and condition.

Understanding Vitamins and Minerals

Health is a lifelong journey that works best when you take charge of your own process. Experiment with the supplements this section covers, especially after gaining an understanding of how isolated nutrients can affect the balance of other nutrients and processes in your body.

The top supplements for easing 15 common conditions

Table 6-1 lists common conditions and the nutritional supplements that can help make them better.

Table 6-1	Top Supplements That Help Ease Common Conditions
Condition	*Nutritional Supplements*
Arthritis pain	Multivitamin, vitamin C, vitamin E, selenium, glucosamine, ginger, turmeric
Back pain	Vitamin C, glucosamine, calcium, magnesium, St. John's wort, ginger
Colds	Zinc, vitamin C, vitamin A, echinacea, yarrow, peppermint, elder
Constipation	Vitamin C, psyllium seed, cascara sagrada, flaxseed
Fatigue	Multivitamin and mineral supplement, folic acid, Siberian ginseng, ginseng root, licorice root, vitamin B-12
Hay fever	Vitamin C, quercitin, nettles, eyebright, reishi
Insomnia	Melatonin, magnesium, 5-HT, valerian, kava, California poppy
Obesity	Chromium, magnesium, vitamin C, vitamin E, vitamin B-6
Osteoporosis	Calcium, vitamin D, magnesium, boron, red clover, nettles, horsetail
Parasites	Acidophilus, black walnut, garlic, multivitamin and mineral supplement, grapefruit seed extract, artemesia (mugwort)
Poor memory	Vitamin B-12, lecithin, folic acid, ginkgo
Premenstrual syndrome	Calcium, magnesium, vitex, motherwort, evening primrose oil, dandelion
Sore throat	Zinc, vitamin C, echinacea, sage
Sprains and strains	Vitamin C, glucosamine, magnesium, St. John's wort oil
Stress	B vitamins, vitamin C, vitamin E, calcium, magnesium, Siberian ginseng, California poppy

Ten (plus one) vitamins and minerals that you can get naturally

Table 6-2 tells you what foods to eat to get your vitamins and minerals as nature intended.

Table 6-2	Natural Sources of Top Vitamins and Minerals
Vitamin/Mineral	*Natural Sources*
Calcium	Yogurt, broccoli, leafy greens, sesame seeds
Folic acid	Brown rice, leafy greens, salmon, whole grains
Iron	Leafy greens, nuts, seeds, raisins, liver, beef
Magnesium	Grains, legumes, vegetables, nuts, seeds, seafood
Potassium	Fruits and vegetables, whole grains, nuts and seeds
Selenium	Yeast, wheat germ, rice, and other whole grains
Vitamin A and beta-carotene	Yellow and orange fruits and vegetables, egg yolk
Vitamin B	Whole grains, vegetables, nutritional yeast
Vitamin C	Citrus, bell peppers, tomatoes, strawberries
Vitamin E	Vegetable oils, nuts, seeds, whole grains, dark green leafy vegetables
Zinc	Oysters, meat, eggs, whole grains, pumpkin seeds

Antioxidant vitamins and minerals

Antioxidant vitamins and minerals are some of the most important nutrients in foods. They slow the aging process and can lower your risk of heart disease. Here are the foods in which you can find them naturally.

- **Beta-carotene:** Fruits and vegetables that are orange and dark green

- **Selenium:** Shrimp, lobster, scallops, clams, chicken breast, eggs, Brazil nuts, brown rice, and mushrooms

- **Vitamin C:** Citrus, berries, and sweet peppers

- **Vitamin E:** Cold-pressed, unrefined vegetable oils, whole wheat, kale, lamb, eggs, mackerel, and herring

The healthiest fats

Quality fats are actually an *essential* part of a healthy diet. The following fats and oils belong in your kitchen.

✔ Organic, unsalted butter

✔ Extra-virgin olive oil

✔ Flaxseed oil

✔ Unrefined vegetable oils such as unrefined safflower oil and unrefined sesame oil

The USDA Food Guide Pyramid

The *Food Guide Pyramid* is a research-based food guidance system developed by the USDA (United States Department of Agriculture), supported by the Department of Health and Human Services, and recommended by numerous health researchers. The Food Guide Pyramid (see Figure 6-1) focuses primarily on fats as they pertain to heart and artery disease, as well as good nutrition.

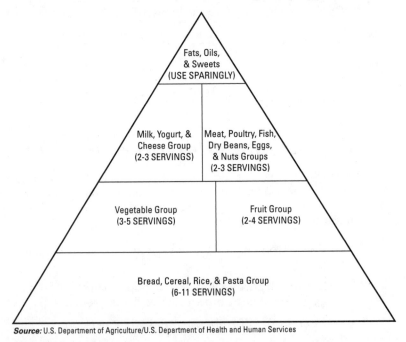

Source: U.S. Department of Agriculture/U.S. Department of Health and Human Services

Figure 6-1: The USDA Food Guide Pyramid

The government suggests you eat a wide variety of foods, with plenty of grains, vegetables, and fruits to provide the fiber, minerals, and vitamins you need in a diet that's both low in fat and saturated fat and cholesterol. The Food Guide Pyramid isn't a rigid prescription, but a visual guide for healthy eating. This is the government's suggestion:

- ✔ **Fats and sweets:** Eat sparingly.

- ✔ **Dairy, milk, yogurt, and cheese:** Eat 2 to 3 servings daily. Children need 2 cups of milk or yogurt or 4 ounces cheese daily.

- ✔ **Fish, poultry, meat, nuts, eggs, and dry beans:** Eat 2 to 3 servings daily. Children need two 2- to 3-ounce servings of cooked lean meat, poultry, or fish daily.

- ✔ **Vegetables:** Eat 3 to 5 servings daily.

- ✔ **Fruits:** Eat 2 to 4 servings daily.

- ✔ **Grains, breads, cereals, rice, and pasta:** Eat 6 to 11 servings daily.

Children ages 2 through 6 need fewer calories and less food generally. Give them 3 to 4 servings of veggies daily, 2 of fruit, and 6 of grains, breads, rice, and pasta daily.

Drink eight or more glasses of water daily.

Dieting to Lose Weight

How much you eat isn't a matter of willpower or lack of it. It's an inborn, powerful biological drive to assure human survival. Every time you undereat or deny your body's need for food, you actually crank into high gear a complex system of chemical reactions that tells you to eat. A vicious cycle? You bet. Here are some ways to get back in touch with your natural hunger cues — not the external or emotional cues that sometimes call you to eat whether or not you're actually hungry.

Getting over over-eating

Arbitrary portion sizes and years of parental instruction to "clean your plate" have conditioned people to ignore their innate ability to tell when they've had enough to eat. Re-learning to recognize and respect your hunger and satisfaction signals takes time. The following techniques can help:

✔ **Eat slowly.** Your brain needs up to 20 minutes to get the message that your body has had enough to eat.

✔ **Don't wait until you're famished to eat.** You're apt to overeat when you're absolutely flat-out starving. Eating three meals and two or three small snacks is one way to make sure that you're never too hungry or too full. Remember, what counts is the total number of calories you consume each day, not how often you eat.

✔ **Pay attention to how you feel, and eat mindfully.** You need to eat slowly to recognize the sometimes-vague signals that you've had enough to eat. The goal is to internalize those feelings. Until you can hear and heed the conversations your brain and stomach are having, wear clothing with waistbands — something snug around your middle can serve as a reminder to stop eating when it feels tight.

✔ **Buy only single servings of foods that you crave, or you may find it difficult to stop eating even when you're full.** Many people use a product more freely when they aren't worried about running out, when price isn't important (larger packages are often cheaper per serving than smaller ones), and when space is tight (larger packages take up lots of room). So if ice cream in the freezer tempts you, don't buy it in gallons. Single-sized servings, purchased one at a time, may be a wiser move.

If you tend to skip meals or eat too infrequently, adjusting and recognizing your hunger signals can take some time. When you recognize a hunger signal, wait 10 to 15 minutes. If you still feel hunger, eat.

Why women eat more premenstrually

If you just can't say no to premenstrual cravings, you have a good reason: Your body doesn't want you to. Research shows that women eat differently during the second half of their cycles — surprisingly, though, only if they have ovulated that month. When an egg is released and is not fertilized, the body secretes progesterone to start the menstrual flow. If no egg is released, the surge in progesterone doesn't occur. Progesterone makes heat, burning energy in the form of calories. Women subconsciously and automatically eat more to make up for the calorie deficit. The average increase was about 260 calories, but some women eat up to 500 extra calories a day. Women on birth control pills don't ovulate, so they don't experience progesterone's fuel burn.

Full but not satisfied? That may be your body's way of telling you that the meal you just ate wasn't well-balanced. Some researchers think that your body has a feedback system that tells your brain when it has enough carbohydrate, fat, and protein. When a meal is heavy in one nutrient and light in the others, you get little satisfaction from your meal.

Avoiding eating disorders

Some people think that if dieting didn't exist, far fewer eating disorders would exist, and people wouldn't get caught in the following cycle:

- ✔ Severe calorie restrictions make them ravenously hungry and may lead to anorexia nervosa.

- ✔ They overeat in response to unbearable hunger, which may promote bulimia nervosa and binge eating disorder.

- ✔ They panic about gaining weight, which brings them back to dieting and all the physical and psychological consequences that accompany food restriction.

 The vast majority of dieters, however, don't turn their diet plans and activities into eating disorders. Contrary to popular belief, eating disorders aren't just about being fat or thin, about food or weight. Experts view eating disorders as a combination of physical, emotional, spiritual, and cultural factors gone awry. Eating disorders are very complex and take a long time to treat and cure. If you think you may be experiencing an eating disorder, talk to a doctor or counselor.

Handily measuring portion sizes

To avoid having to pull out a kitchen scale or measuring cups every time you want to eat, try this trick: Use your hand to estimate portion sizes. (Amounts approximate an average woman's hand.)

- ✔ **Your palm** is the size of a 3-ounce serving of meat, fish, or poultry.

- ✔ **Your cupped hand** can hold about 2 ounces of nuts or small candies, such as M&M's, but only ½ ounce of chips, popcorn, or pretzels.

- ✔ **Your thumb tip** is a teaspoon and good for tracking high-fat and often forgotten calories, such as the swipe you make through the brownie batter or the dip into the peanut butter jar. If your dunk is three times the size of the tip of your thumb, then you're eating a tablespoon.

✔ **Your thumb** is about 1 tablespoon of liquid (or cookie dough) measured from tip to second joint. It also approximates an ounce of cheese — a food that's easy to overeat.

✔ **Your fist** is a cup. A cup of ice cream or frozen yogurt is 2 servings. Ditto for cereal, pasta, or rice. Half a cup of fruit or vegetables counts as 1 serving. (Aim for at least 5 servings a day.)

Shopping for Healthful Groceries

Mother Nature packs some foods with healing nutrients. Be sure to stock up and include these winners regularly in your meals.

✔ Fatty fish: Salmon and sardines

✔ Naturally raised meats and poultry

✔ Orange winter squash: Hubbard and acorn

✔ Reddish-blue fruit: Berries and grapes

✔ Dark leafy greens: Kale and collards

✔ Cruciferous vegetables: Cabbage and broccoli

✔ Whole grains: Whole wheat and brown rice

✔ Legumes: Beans and lentils

✔ Seeds: Pumpkin and sunflower

✔ Raw nuts: Almonds and walnuts

✔ Healing flavorings: Onions, garlic, and chilies

Five tips for diet-friendly grocery-shopping

Here are some tips for making sure that your grocery list is diet-friendly and that your trip to the store is as quick and painless as possible:

✔ Plan your menus when you're hungry (you may find that they're more interesting); shop when you're not (you have more control).

✔ Forget using coupons unless they're for food items that you usually buy. The savings can be tempting, but the purchase can add up to a diet disaster.

✔ Check your cupboards, freezer, and refrigerator in advance to avoid duplicating purchases.

✔ Get familar with your store's layout and write your list according to it. You're less apt to forget items. Or write your list according to categories: frozen foods, produce, meat, and dairy, for example.

✔ Refuse to let free samples tempt you. (If you're not hungry, you're better able to pass them by.)

Be sure to eat before shopping and to feed the children, too. Hunger makes controlled shopping difficult for adults and nearly impossible for children.

Ten words you want to see on food labels

When shopping for whole foods and food not loaded with chemicals, keep an eye out for words you can trust to mean that the food is natural and of high quality. Ironically, the only word you can't trust is *natural*, which food manufacturers use to describe all sorts of foods, good and bad. Look for the following:

✔ Whole

✔ Unrefined

✔ Unprocessed

✔ Minimally processed

✔ Raw

✔ Hormone-free

✔ Free of antibiotics

✔ Residue-free

✔ Free-range

✔ Organic

Ten foods to buy organic — and why

Certain foods are known to be grown with especially high levels of pesticides or, like butter and liver, to be a concentrated source of such chemicals. Treat yourself to the organic versions of the following: strawberries, bell peppers, spinach, peaches, celery, apples, apricots, green beans, butter, and liver.

Choosing foods wisely based on the information that you can glean from Nutrition Facts labels is a key to successful dieting. Here's the skinny on the most important information featured on the Nutrition Facts label:

- ✔ **Calories:** The calorie total is based on the stated serving size — so if you eat more or less than what the label lists as one portion, you need to do the math.

- ✔ **Dietary fiber:** Choose the foods with the most fiber. Research shows that people who eat lots of fiber also eat fewer calories. A food is considered to be high in fiber if it has at least 5 grams of fiber per serving.

- ✔ **Serving size:** Notice how the food manufacturer's serving size compares to the size you usually eat. For example, does your normal serving of ice cream measure more than the standard ½ cup? Servings per container can help you estimate sizes if a measuring cup or spoon is not handy.

- ✔ **Total fat:** For dieting, keep total fat to less than about 20 to 30 percent of calories. If you eat 1,500 calories a day, that's no more than 33 to 50 grams. Remember, the % Daily Value numbers on Nutrition Facts labels are based on 65 grams of fat a day (30 percent of total calories) and calculated on a 2,000-calorie-per-day diet.

All the nutrients that a food contains are important; however, to achieve weight loss, the total fat and calories are the most important to track.

Table 6-3 lists some other terms you see on food labels.

Table 6-3	Label Lingo
What the Food Label Says	*What It Means*
Fat-free	Less than ½ (0.5) gram of fat in a serving
Lowfat	3 grams of fat (or less) per serving
Lean (on meat labels)	Less than 10 grams of fat per serving, with 4.5 grams or less of saturated fat and 95 milligrams of cholesterol per serving
Extra lean (on meat labels)	Less than 5 grams of fat per serving, with less than 2 grams of saturated fat and 95 milligrams of cholesterol
Less (fat, calories, cholesterol, or sodium)	Contains 25 percent less (fat, calories, cholesterol, or sodium) than the food to which it is being compared

What the Food Label Says	What It Means
Reduced	A nutritionally altered product that contains at least 25 percent fewer calories, sodium, or sugar than the regular one
Lite (Light)	Contains ⅓ fewer calories or no more than ½ the fat of the higher-calorie, higher-fat version; or no more than ½ the sodium of higher-sodium version
Cholesterol-free	Less than 2 milligrams of cholesterol and 2 grams (or less) of saturated fat per serving
Low-calorie	Fewer than 40 calories per serving

Smart shopping up and down the aisles

Your menus, shopping list, and filled grocery cart should be in the same proportion as the Food Guide Pyramid: Bread, cereal, rice, and pasta are the foundation on which you build the rest of your purchasing. Fruits and vegetables come next in order of predominance, and then meat and dairy. Last are fats, oils, and sugar. The following are some specific buying recommendations.

Breads, cereals, rice, and pasta: Use these tips to get more nutrition from the breads and baked goods you buy.

- ✔ When you buy breads, make sure that the first grain on the ingredient list is a whole grain, such as whole wheat, oats, or millet. Note that rye and pumpernickel breads aren't whole grain, even though their color may make you think that they are. Their fiber content is similar to that of white bread, but the calorie content is often slightly higher because molasses is added for color.

- ✔ Baked goods should have 3 grams of fat or less per serving. And cereal should have at least 3 grams of fiber per serving.

- ✔ Baked goods from the in-store bakery don't usually have nutrient labeling. Look at the ingredient list to see what kinds of flour are used. Go for the ones that list whole-grain flours first.

- ✔ When you read labels on packaged mixes, be sure to look at the "As prepared" column. Many mixes call for you to add fats or eggs during preparation.

- ✔ Ramen noodle soups are flash-cooked in oil before packaging. They are high in fat.

USRDA versus RDA versus DV: What's the difference?

Ever wonder what happened to the % USRDA (U.S. Recommended *Daily* Allowance) that used to appear with the nutrition information on your cereal box? It has changed to % DV (Daily Value). In addition to certain vitamins and minerals, the % DV includes other nutrients provided by a serving of that particular food — such as fat, sodium, cholesterol, fiber, protein, and carbohydrate. Although many of the % Daily Values for nutrients are based on a 2,000-calorie-per-day diet, the DV for cholesterol, sodium, and vitamin A, vitamin C, calcium, and iron are set at a constant amount for all calorie levels.

Fruits and vegetables: Want to get more nutrition from the fruits and vegetables you choose? Use these tips:

- In general, the darker the color, the higher the nutrient content. Dark salad greens such as spinach, watercress, and arugula contain more nutrients than pale ones such as iceberg lettuce. Deep orange- or red-fleshed fruit — such as mangoes, melon, papaya, and oranges — are richer in vitamins C and A than pears and bananas, but pears and bananas are especially good sources of potassium and fiber.

- Most produce is virtually fat-free, with the exception of avocado and coconut.

- Dried fruits are a healthy, high-fiber snack food, but because most of their water has been removed, the nutrients are concentrated and the calories are higher. Keep an eye on serving size.

- Many dried fruits, especially bananas, cranberries, and dates, have sugar added to them.

Dairy: Lowfat dairy products are among the best-tasting fat-reduced items in the supermarket — and they have all the calcium of the full-fat varieties. Here's what to look for:

- Buy only lowfat (1 percent) or fat-free (skim) milk. Two-percent milk is not lowfat.

- Buy only lowfat or nonfat yogurt and cottage cheese. Creamed cottage cheese (4% milk fat) is made with whole milk.

- Buy lowfat cheeses, labeled "part skim," "reduced fat," or "fat free." However, strongly flavored full-fat cheeses are fine if you use them sparingly.

Better burger beef

A burger made with 4 ounces of regular ground beef or chuck and cooked to well-done has only 12 calories more than a same-size, extra-lean one, and has almost the same number of calories as one made with lean ground beef. The big difference is in price and flavor — ground chuck wins on both counts.

- ✔ Buttermilk contains no butter and is available in lowfat and fat-free varieties. Some dieters find that its thicker texture is more satisfying than that of fat-free milk.

Meat, poultry, fish, dry beans, eggs, and nuts: Without meat, you may have a tough time getting enough zinc and iron — two nutrients that help maintain your energy and performance. Don't short-change yourself nutritionally by making unhelpful sacrifices. Shop smart instead.

- ✔ Some of the leanest cuts of beef are flank, sirloin, and tenderloin. The leanest pork is fresh, canned, cured, and boiled ham; Canadian bacon; pork tenderloin; rib chops; and roast. Lean lamb includes roasts, chops, and legs; white-meat poultry is lower in fat than dark.

- ✔ Meat labeled "select" is leaner than meat graded "choice."

- ✔ Ground turkey and chicken can contain the skin, which makes them high in fat and calories. Look for ground turkey or chicken *meat* for the lowest fat. Ground turkey breast is lower still.

- ✔ You don't have to remove the skin of chicken before cooking, which sacrifices juiciness. The meat does not absorb its fat or calories. But be sure to remove the skin before eating.

- ✔ Self-basting turkeys have fat injected into the meat. Avoid them if you're dieting.

- ✔ ½ cup of beans or 3 ounces of tofu equals a serving of protein. Check the ingredient list for *calcium sulfate.* Tofu processed with it is a good source of calcium.

- ✔ 2 tablespoons of peanut butter counts nutritionally as an ounce of meat, but at 190 calories and 16 grams of fat, it's hardly a dieter's best bet. Even reduced-fat peanut butter has 12 grams of fat — and because it has added sugar, the reduced-fat and regular versions have the same number of calories.

Fats, oils, and sweets: These foods add calories without contributing much in the way of other nutrients to your diet. Use them sparingly. But do remember that when you plan carefully, you can make room for these fun foods, too. One *level* teaspoon of sugar has 16 calories —

surely not enough to ruin your diet, but if you have 3 cups of coffee and a bowl of cereal a day and use 2 teaspoons of sugar in each, that's a quick 128 calories. If you substitute non-calorie sweeteners for this amount of sugar and make no other changes in the way you eat, you can lose 1 pound in a month.

Eating Healthily While Eating Out

As a rule, the less expensive the restaurant, the more apt the kitchen is to use generous amounts of fat and high-fat cooking techniques — inexpensive and easy ways to add flavor to food. Keep this advice in mind when dining out:

- ✔ **If you consider restaurant meals special occasions, you automatically set yourself up for overindulging.** Don't go overboard. At the same time, remember to look at the meal in context of the entire day's eating, or what you plan to eat over several days.

- ✔ **Be a fat detective.** Ask questions about preparation and request substitutions.

- ✔ **Portions may be huge.** You often get twice the amount you really need to eat. Don't be embarrassed to ask for a doggie bag.

- ✔ **Menus are organized with the focus on protein, and the servings of protein are much too large.** So, cast your eye over to the side dishes section and choose from the plainer ones (that is, those without sauces). Another way to create a better balance may be to order your entree from the appetizer section.

- ✔ **Most meals eaten out include alcohol.** Not only is alcohol calorie-heavy and nutrient-poor, but it also lowers your resolve to eat healthfully. If you enjoy a cocktail or wine when eating out, plan to limit your intake of wine, beer, and spirits to one, and drink it with, not before, the meal.

You may think that you must avoid certain types of restaurants or cuisines while you're dieting. Not true! The following sections guide you through various cuisines and food scenarios and tell you what's "safe" and what's not.

Chinese meals

Eat the way the Chinese do. Rice is the centerpiece of the meal, with meat and vegetables selected from the serving dishes almost one bite at a time.

Choose more of these:	Eat less of these:
Bean curd (unless fried)	Anything served in a bird's nest
Fish, shrimp, and scallops	Breaded, fried, or batter-fried foods
Hot and spicy	Sweet and sour dishes
Served on a sizzling platter	Twice-cooked dishes
Vegetables	Crispy noodles on the table
Velvet sauce	Sweet duck sauce

Delis and sandwich shops

Go to lunch with a friend and split a sandwich, or order an extra roll
or bread to make two sandwiches out of the meat in one — taking
one home for later. Most restaurants that serve sandwiches also
have soup. Order a bowlful of a soup made without cream and eat it
with an unbuttered roll for a lower-calorie meal.

Choose more of these:	Eat less of these:
Bagels	Rueben sandwiches (grilled corned beef, sauerkraut, and Swiss cheese with Thousand Island dressing)
Baked or boiled ham	Bologna
Beet salad	Extra cheese
Breads, especially ones made with whole grains	Hot pastrami and corned beef
Carrot and raisin salad	Knockwurst and liverwurst
Extra tomato, lettuce, and veggies for sandwiches	Tongue
Mustard (not mayo)	Meatballs
Pickles	Mortadella
Roast or smoked turkey	Sausage and peppers
Sliced chicken (not chicken salad with lots of mayo)	Eggplant or chicken parmigiana
Tuna	Salami

Fast food

Often, the only option when you're on the go is fast food. Even a small soda is a generous portion, so be sure to order a diet one or a seltzer and drink it all before going back for more food — it can fill you up.

Choose more of these:	Eat less of these:
Baked potato	Onion rings
Grilled chicken	Chicken nuggets (they often include the skin), fried chicken, or fried fish
Fat-free or lowfat milk	Cheese sauce
Fat-free salad dressing	Croissants
Salad with the dressing on the side	Salad dressing (unless it's fat-free)
Single burger (regular or kid-size)	Sauces and high-fat add-ons such as cheese, chili, and tartar sauce
Small fries	Large and jumbo-size fries

French fare

Unless the restaurant specializes in *nouvelle cuisine* (the updated style of cooking that relies more on fresh ingredients and less on classic butter-enhanced sauces), you'll be hard-pressed to find diet-friendly foods. Start with an appetite-taming green salad (easy on the dressing) or a clear soup.

Choose more of these:	Eat less of these:
Au vapour (steamed)	*A la crème* (in cream sauce)
En brochette (skewered and broiled)	*A la mode* (with ice cream)
Grillé (grilled)	*Au gratin* or *gratinée* (baked with cheese and cream)
	Crème fraîche (similar to sour cream)
	Drawn butter
	En croûte (in a pastry crust)
	Hollandaise or Remoulade sauce
	Puff pastry

Indian cuisine

Indian cooking utilizes plenty of fat — usually clarified butter. Roasting *tandoori* style is a good lowfat cooking method, but other dishes are often stewed and fried. Often, the chef gives the breads a shimmer of butter before serving them.

Choose more of these:	Eat less of these:
Chutney	Chickpea batter used to deep-fry
Dahl (lentils)	*Ghee* (clarified butter)
Masala (curry)	*Korma* (cream sauce)
Matta (peas)	*Molee* (coconut)
Paneer (a fresh milk cheese)	*Poori* (a deep-fried bread)
Pullao or *pilau* (rice)	*Samosas* (fried turnover appetizers)
Raita (a yogurt and cucumber condiment)	

Italian dining

Bread on the table served with butter or olive oil can be a diet buster. Ask for tomato sauce for dipping. Order vegetables à la carte as long as they're not cooked with lots of fat or deep-fried. And instead of a creamy dessert, order a lowfat cappuccino with fruit.

Choose more of these:	Eat less of these:
Light red sauce	Alfredo
Marinara sauce	*Alla panna* (with cream)
Pasta (other than those stuffed with cheese)	Prosciutto, salami
Piccata (lemon-wine sauce)	*Carbonara* (butter, eggs, bacon, and sometimes cream sauce); *Frito misto* (fried mixed vegetables or seafood)
White or red clam sauce (but ask the wait staff; some clam sauces are made with cream)	*Parmigiana* (baked in sauce with cheese)
Wine sauce	Fried eggplant or zucchini

Japanese food

If you eat in the balance that the Japanese apply — heavy on the vegetables and light on the fats and meats — Japanese food can be a dieter's dream.

Choose more of these:	Eat less of these:
Clear broth	*Agemono* (deep fried)
Miso (fermented soy) and *Miso* dressing	*Katsu* (fried pork cutlet)
Nabemono (a one-pot dish)	*Sukiyaki* (a one-dish meal made with fatty beef)
Mushimono (steamed), *Nimono* (simmered), *Yaki* (broiled), and *Yakimono* (grilled)	*Tempura* (batter-fried)
Sashimi and sushi	

Mexican meals

Most Mexican food is fried or cooked in lots and lots of fat. Use salsa instead of salad dressing, guacamole, or sour cream on entrees. Ask for cheese toppings to be omitted, or ask whether lowfat sour cream and cheese are available.

Choose more of these:	Eat less of these:
Black bean soup and gazpacho	Chimichangas
Ceviche (fish or scallops marinated in lime juice)	Extra Cheese
Chili	Refried beans
Enchiladas, burritos, or soft tacos (skip the sour cream, guacamole, and most of the cheese)	Tortilla shells
Fajitas	Sour cream

Diet-fine pizza

If you can, start with a small salad to take the edge off your appetite. Order it with the dressing on the side or extra vinegar to thin it.

Also, don't leave your naked pizza crust ends on your plate — that's not where the bulk of the calories are, and the crust is a good source of lowfat, filling carbohydrate.

Choose more of these:	Eat less of these:
Canadian bacon	Bacon
Grilled chicken	Meatballs
Part-skim cheeses, or strongly flavored ones	Extra cheese and olive oil
Shrimp	Pepperoni
Tuna	Sausage
Vegetable toppings, especially broccoli and spinach	Olives

Airline food

You can order a special meal for a flight as long as you give the airline 24 hours' notice. What you get to eat when you order a special meal varies, but rest assured that if you request a low-calorie tray, it will be low-calorie. Vegetarian meals, which flyers order more frequently than any other type, aren't regulated. Although many are low-cal and lowfat, don't bet on it. Make sure to ask.

Choosing Healing Foods

Food affects your body chemistry, including the aspect of that chemistry that influences mood. Depending on their levels, neurotransmitters in the brain, hormones, and blood sugar can raise your spirits or bring them down. In fact, every meal you eat affects your emotions to some degree. The trick is to have this effect of food work in your favor.

Improving your mood with food

You probably already know that food affects your mood and have your own supply of fast-acting "comfort foods" when you need them. Here are some ways in which food can help when you're feeling out-of-sync.

Refreshing yourself with water

Fatigue, both physical and mental, can be a sign that your body is dehydrated. If you're working late at night and feeling tired, try having a glass or two of fresh water instead of reaching for yet another cup of coffee, and you find that you perk up within a few minutes. Water is especially energizing if you drink several glassfuls *quickly*.

Although coffee and caffeinated teas give you a quick energy boost, this high is soon followed by a low, especially if you're overly tired. To combat this effect, make sure that for every cup of coffee you drink, you drink twice that quantity of water.

Calming yourself

Eating carbohydrates such as potatoes, cereals, and sweets can help you feel relaxed and give you a sense of general well-being. When you're all worked up, have a couple of handfuls of popcorn or one or two slices of whole-grain bread with all-fruit preserves. You can feel a difference in 20 to 30 minutes, and the effect lasts two to three hours.

Carbohydrates aren't soothing if you eat them with protein at the same meal. A plain baked potato works fine. A baked potato with butter and sour cream isn't as effective. Having a *small* amount of fat along with a starch can enhance the effect of the carbohydrate, however.

Coffee at the end of a meal can pull you out of the lethargy that follows. But it can also bring on jitters. Some people cure their chronic anxiety simply by going off all caffeine.

Perking up

If you're feeling lackluster and not up to speed, you may need protein foods to produce alertness, faster reaction times, and an increased ability to concentrate. When you compose a protein meal to increase your alertness, limit your intake of fat and carbohydrates for maximum effect. For example, have some tuna or snack on a cup of plain yogurt. The effects of eating protein last about two to three hours.

Staying even-tempered

You can use food to keep you from emotional extremes caused by swings in blood sugar levels and hormone imbalances — those times when emotions overtake you for no apparent reason or when you overreact to a situation.

✔ **Steadying blood sugar levels:** The primary fuel of your brain is blood sugar, or glucose. Low blood sugar can leave you low on energy, and it can also trigger emotions. If glucose levels drop gradually, you may experience some emotional instability, but a sudden drop can trigger anxiety. To manage glucose levels:

- Eat three meals a day and, if necessary, a mid-morning and mid-afternoon snack.

- At each meal, include protein, complex carbohydrates, and fats.

- Avoid all concentrated sweets, including refined white table sugar, honey, maple syrup, and fruit juice. Have whole fruit instead.

✔ **Balancing female hormones:** When estrogen levels peak, a woman is likely to feel irritable and anxious or suffer mood swings. Excessive levels of progesterone, in relation to estrogen, can trigger weepiness and depression. *Phytohormones,* which are hormonelike compounds you find in plant-based foods, can help minimize the swings in hormone levels. Specific foods that are high in phytohormones include soybeans, currants, and buckwheat.

Eating for a healthy heart

Heart disease is the number one cause of death in the United States. To reduce your risk of heart disease, you need to know which heart-healthy foods you can purchase and prepare, as well as which ingredients, such as sugar and certain fats, you need to stay away from.

✔ **Fats and oils:** The American Heart Association's general dietary guideline is to consume no more than 30 percent of your calories as fat. But many health experts believe that a truly heart-healthy diet contains no more than 20 to 25 percent of calories from fat. The percentage of fat in the average American's diet is about 40 percent.

✔ **Transfatty acids:** *Hydrogenated oils* (refined oils that are further processed to make them solid at room temperature) and oils and fats heated to high temperatures contain *transfatty acids* — unnatural, manmade molecules. Studies have linked their consumption to a higher risk of heart disease. You find hydrogenated and partially hydrogenated oils in the ingredient lists of many food products, including cakes, crackers, cookies, and shortening. Margarine also contains transfatty acids (this is the reason many people have switched back to butter). Fried foods are also a source.

Chocolate chemistry

Chocolate contains *phenylethylamine,* a mood enhancer, and *theobromine,* which has a stimulating, caffeine-like effect and triggers the release of endorphins, which produce the euphoric sensation of being in love. Make sure that you're not using chocolate as a crutch for coping with day-to-day stresses. Have chocolate only once in a while, and when you crave chocolate, have the best so that you really feel satisfied.

You do have a choice of healthy fats. You can cook with butter in modest amounts. (Heating it to high temperatures doesn't create transfatty acids.) And unrefined cooking oils, such as extra-virgin olive oil, are never processed at high temperatures or hydrogenated. You can safely use these oils as salad dressings or when cooking at lower temperatures.

Cholesterol

High levels of cholesterol in your blood increase the likelihood that cholesterol deposits on the walls of your arteries, initiating the development of *atherosclerosis*, which can lead to heart disease. Your liver manufactures most of your cholesterol, but about 15 percent comes from cholesterol-containing foods such as meats, poultry, dairy products, and seafood. If you're one of the 25 percent of folks whose livers can't adequately manage cholesterol levels, producing high cholesterol levels, you need to limit your intake of cholesterol and saturated fat.

Antioxidants

A diet high in antioxidants such as beta-carotene, vitamins C and E, and selenium, has been associated with a significantly lower risk of heart disease, as well as a lower incidence of signs of heart disease such as chest pains. Even if you take an antioxidant supplement, you still need to eat a variety of foods that supply antioxidant nutrients. Such foods include orange or dark-green fruits and vegetables; citrus, berries, and sweet peppers; cold-pressed, unrefined vegetable oils, whole wheat, kale, lamb, eggs, mackerel, and herring; shellfish, chicken breast, Brazil nuts, brown rice, and mushrooms

Nutritional factors in hypertension

Hypertension, or high blood pressure, is a risk factor for heart disease. Research indicates that a variety of genetic, environmental, and nutritional factors can lead to this condition, including excess weight, lack of exercise, alcohol, smoking, caffeine, and stress. Exposure to the toxic metals lead and cadmium can also be a factor.

A diet high in sodium does *not* promote hypertension unless you're among the 10 to 20 percent of Americans who are salt-sensitive. (Half of all individuals with hypertension have this sensitivity.) A diet that is low in potassium and high in sodium can bring on hypertension in susceptible persons. If you need to cut back your sodium intake, eat fresh and minimally processed foods and avoid eating high-salt items such as catsup, luncheon meats, canned soups, and frozen dinners. Research shows that deficiencies of magnesium and calcium also can lead to hypertension.

Reducing your cancer risk at every meal

The effect of diet on cancer risk has been a prime focus of scientific research in recent years. The American Institute for Cancer Research, based on the results of thousands of nutrition and cancer studies, suggests the following:

- Eat a varied diet based primarily on foods of plant origin.

- Have five or more servings of a variety of fruits and vegetables daily — and eat this much year-round.

- Consume a variety of minimally processed, starchy staple foods — that is, whole grains, legumes, root vegetables, and tubers. They should provide 45 to 60 percent of total calories. Limit the consumption of refined sugar.

- Limit red meat, if eaten at all, to less than 10 percent of total calories, about one 3-ounce portion a day. Eat fish and poultry instead. And cook meat and fish at relatively low temperatures to avoid charring and burning. Eat cured and smoked meats and meat and fish that are broiled or grilled by direct flame only occasionally, if at all.

- Limit intake of oils and fats, particularly those of animal origin. Total dietary fat should provide from 15 percent to a maximum of 30 percent of total calories.

- Restrict or avoid drinking alcoholic beverages. Men should have no more than two drinks a day and women no more than one drink a day.

Cancer-fighting compounds in fruits and vegetables

Researchers are identifying more and more compounds in produce that help prevent the initiation of cancerous cell growth. Some compounds may even arrest cancer growth after it begins. These substances include common vitamins and minerals, as well as a collection of *phytonutrients* with less familiar names. To get *all* these nutrients, eat a *variety* of fruits and vegetables.

Here's a quick run-through of these nutrients.

✔ **Antioxidants:** Scientists are examining specific antioxidants for their effects on cancer. What scientists do know for sure is that antioxidants work together. Consuming only one type of antioxidant isn't as beneficial as eating a variety of foods that supply all of them. See "Antioxidant vitamins and minerals" earlier in this chapter for a list.

✔ **Folate**: Folate plays a unique role in slowing cancer. It has the ability to repair DNA after it's been damaged — especially important in cancer that is spreading.

Folate is destroyed by heat, so the best source is raw foods. One easy way to increase your intake of folate is to eat more guacamole made with fresh, mashed avocados, a great source of this nutrient. Other foods that contain good amounts of folate and that you can enjoy raw are boysenberries, cantaloupe, alfalfa sprouts, broccoli, and cauliflower.

✔ **Iodine:** One theory regarding the increase in the incidence of cancer is that it's due to exposure to radioactive materials in the environment. Sea vegetables, including seaweeds such as nori and kombu, contain iodine, a mineral that protects against radiation.

The breakfast nutrition solution

Breakfast is a particularly important meal in terms of how much energy you have throughout the day. If you eat only something starchy, like toast or an English muffin, and wash it down with coffee, you may have energy for a couple of hours at most. Instead, give yourself some protein and fat as well to keep your body, and your brain, going strong until lunch. If you're a slow starter in the morning, you particularly need to make the effort to feed yourself. Try the following:

✔ Whole-grain toast with almond butter and all-fruit preserves

✔ Poached eggs and home fries with toast

✔ Sautéed polenta and turkey sausage

✔ A toasted whole-wheat bagel with smoked salmon

✔ Whole-grain pancakes and nitrate-free bacon

Cooking with onions and garlic

Onions and garlic belong to the same family of foods and promote heart health in similar ways. These flavorings play a role in preventing blood clots, lowering cholesterol levels, reducing blood pressure, and normalizing blood lipids. If you have a hamburger or a steak, you can counteract the effects of the saturated fat in the meat by having, on the side, a salad made with raw onion and garlic.

Finding foods that fight common problems

You can use foods to treat a number of ailments. The following sections cover some of the most common conditions and suggest helpful foods. For more lifestyle-based hints about treating common conditions, check out Chapter 8.

Treating colds and flu

Certain foods, herbs, and spices can help prevent these ailments and speed your recovery.

- **Drink plenty of fluids.** When you're down with a cold or flu, drink eight glasses of liquid throughout the day and evening. Mostly drink filtered water. If you crave fruit juice, drink it in a highly diluted form. Better yet, enjoy juicy whole fruit such as melons.

  Hot fluids are even more effective in inhibiting viruses. Enjoy soothing broths made from fresh and substantial ingredients, such as root vegetables, beef bones, and pieces of chicken. Mint and other herbal teas are also good choices.

  Because fever causes sweating, you need to drink plenty of water to replace fluids you lose in perspiration.

- **Eat foods with medicinal properties.** *Garlic* has both antibacterial and antiviral properties and is a potent immune enhancer. If you feel like you're coming down with something, cut one or two cloves of raw garlic into bite-size pieces and swallow like pills.

  Onions, especially raw, fight bacteria and viruses and trigger the release of fluids that dilute mucus. Half an onion a day is an ample dose.

  Watercress helps clear up phlegm and is high in healing minerals.

Sea vegetables or *seaweed* supply abundant minerals, which support the healing process. Add them to a cucumber salad or miso soup.

Echinacea and *goldenseal,* medicinal herbs that you can take as teas, provide powerful immune function support.

✔ **Eat foods high in nutrients that fight infection.** Vitamin A or beta-carotene (sweet potatoes, carrots, winter squash, cantaloupe, and greens), vitamin C (sweet peppers, broccoli, papayas, kiwis, rose hips, and mangoes), and zinc (oysters, pork, beef, pumpkin seeds, chickpeas, cashews, oysters, and mushrooms) support your natural immune response.

Beef liver is also loaded with vitamin A, selenium, and zinc, but only eat organic liver.

✔ **Use warming condiments for congestion:** If you have chest congestion, put a pinch of cayenne in a cup of hot water and sip away. Tightness in the chest seems to melt away.

Add an ounce of powdered ginger to a bathtub filled with very warm water and soak in it. The ginger helps you perspire and eliminate toxins.

If you have a dry cough, munch on some crushed fennel seeds or drink fennel tea.

Fruit can be a cooling and soothing food when you have a cold and congestion. Spike the fruit with pepper for an added benefit.

Easing a sore throat

If you have a sore throat, gargling with warm salt water is an instant, although short-lived, cure.

To keep a sore throat at bay, eat lightly and keep meals vegetarian. Have fresh vegetables, tropical fruit such as mangoes and papayas, whole grains, legumes, and other mineral-rich foods.

Zinc is especially beneficial. Sucking on zinc lozenges is a proven and effective therapy.

A time-honored remedy for a sore throat is to have a cup of tea sweetened with honey, which has antibacterial properties, especially if you use raw honey. This may help you feel better in the short term, but having a lot of honey can actually make your sore throat worse. A better choice is unsweetened tea made with slippery elm bark, and try some licorice tea, which can relieve pain.

Warding off bronchitis and sinusitis

Many of the same foods, drinks, herbs, vitamins, and minerals good for treating colds and flu benefit bronchitis and sinusitis. Eat foods that support the immune system and stimulate drainage of congested areas. A good expectorant is comfrey. Ginger tea also helps the body cough up phlegm.

Coping with hay fever and asthma

Both hay fever and asthma are allergic disorders. To counteract symptoms, increase your intake of garlic and onions (which are anti-inflammatory), horseradish, cloves, cinnamon, ginger, rosemary, and thyme to help clear sinuses. Avoid red meats and mucus-forming foods and increase your intake of vitamin C and omega-3 fatty acids (a fatty acid in fish and sea vegetables), which counteract inflammation.

A folk remedy for hay fever is honey from local hives, which contains pollen from plants that may be triggering your symptoms. Eating honey may act like an allergy shot. Be sure to use honeycomb or unfiltered, cold-pressed regular honey.

Asthma can be brought on by an allergic reaction to food, eating certain food additives — the preservatives *sulphur dioxide* and *benzoate,* and the dye *tartrazine* — and, in some cases, low stomach acid. Common food allergens that cause an immediate asthmatic reaction are (in decreasing order of frequency) eggs, fish, shellfish, nuts, and peanuts. Milk, chocolate, wheat, citrus, and food colorings usually cause a delayed reaction.

Treating asthma with diet may require the elimination of all animal foods, as well as supplementation with vitamins and minerals, in particular, magnesium. Increase magnesium-rich foods, including green vegetables.

A traditional remedy for asthma is licorice, a powerful anti-inflammatory, which you can drink as tea. Black and green tea contain theophylline, which dilates the bronchial passageways that become constricted in an asthmatic attack. Use tea in concentrated form to counteract an attack.

Dealing with indigestion

Individuals, as they age, may produce insufficient stomach acid and need to take hydrochloric acid supplements. Many people also take enzyme supplements to aid in the digestion of carbohydrates, proteins, and fat.

> # Benefits of starchy foods
>
> Potatoes and other starchy foods, such as grains, also play a role in cancer prevention. When you eat starch, some reaches your colon, where bacteria break it down into short-chain fatty acids. These fats may inhibit cancerous growths on the walls of the intestines. Whole-grain complex carbohydrates, which supply fiber, also speed the elimination of waste products, reducing the chance of colon cancer.

Antacids are not the best way to stop indigestion. Here are better ways:

- Chew your food well, but not with your mouth open. Don't talk while you're chewing.

- Slow down. Dine. Don't gulp.

- Eat smaller meals.

- Don't drink a lot of fluids with meals.

- Add foods to your meals that are also digestive aids, such as celery, asparagus, parsley, horseradish, oats, fennel, ginger, and cinnamon.

- Limit your intake of high-protein foods, such as meat and dairy products, which increase the amount of acid the stomach produces. Avoid hard-to-digest fatty foods.

- For dessert, have fresh papaya and pineapple, which contain food-digesting enzymes. (You can also supplement with digestive enzymes, specifically amylase, protease, and lipase.)

- Finish your meal with peppermint tea to relax tense muscles in the stomach and intestines.

Taking antibiotics can kill off the friendly bacteria in your gut and cause intestinal upset. Active bacteria yogurt can remedy this because it replenishes the beneficial bacteria. But don't take the yogurt with the antibiotic. Wait two hours so that the antibiotic and yogurt don't combine in your stomach. Milk products, including yogurt, inactivate most antibiotics.

Try these tips to settle your stomach:

- **Try ginger to calm nausea.** Crystallized chunks of ginger are delicious, or you can drink ginger tea. Peppermint and chamomile teas are also good for settling your stomach.

✔ **If nausea results in vomiting, replenish lost fluids.** Drink herbal teas and sip these slowly to treat your stomach gently. If your body asks for salt, be sure to have some to replace minerals that you loose along with the fluids. A salty broth may taste good. Fluids are especially important for babies and young children, who can quickly become dehydrated.

Fruit juice, especially orange and grapefruit juice, is highly acidic and can irritate the stomach. Coffee and black tea, too, are highly acidic.

✔ **When you feel like eating again, begin with easily digestible foods, such as bananas, rice, and dry toast.**

✔ **When nausea occurs, supplement with vitamin B6.** Treatment with a combination of vitamin K and vitamin C can also be very effective.

If you have nausea and vomiting but you don't know why, immediately seek medical advice to rule out a more serious health condition.

Controlling constipation

Adding fiber to your diet is the primary treatment for constipation, in particular, insoluble fibers such as cellulose. To help with constipation:

✔ **Eat bran, which contains cellulose.** The dosage is 1 to 1½ cups of bran a day. The most effective is corn bran, while the least irritating is oat bran. For best results, be sure to drink plenty of water.

✔ **Use common herbal laxatives, such as senna, aloe vera, cascara sagrada, and psyllium seed husks.** A standard dosage of psyllium is 2 rounded teaspoonful in a full glass of water after meals. Use these herbs as treatments; don't rely upon them habitually.

✔ **Eat figs and prunes, which are excellent laxatives.** Although eating these fruits or drinking prune juice can be therapeutic, don't use them to compensate for a diet low in fiber.

Coping with ulcers

Spicy foods were once thought to bring on ulcers. In fact, however, *capsaicin,* the active ingredient in chili peppers not only reduces pain but stimulates circulation in tissue lining the digestive tract. Other outdated theories suggest that high-fiber foods irritate ulcers and that soft-textured diets are beneficial. Milk and milk products were also a standard part of ulcer diets. Today it's known that the calcium and protein in milk and milk products stimulate production of stomach acids. At first, the milk soothes the tender tissue, but then makes the condition worse.

New research confirms that infection with the bacteria *Heliobacter pylori* is the actual cause of ulcers and can be treated with medication. However, you can still support the health of the tissues in your digestive tract by eating foods that contain vitamin A, vitamin E, and zinc, which help maintain the structure and function of skin tissue. Eating foods such as orange squash, unrefined vegetable oil, and seafood, which contain healing essential fatty acids, can protect against ulcers.

Beer, tobacco, and coffee (whether caffeinated, decaffeinated, or half-caff) can damage tissues lining the stomach.

The following foods can help when you're suffering from an ulcer:

- ✔ **Fresh, filtered water provides effective and quick-acting pain relief by diluting stomach acids.** This remedy also works for pain due to inflammation of the stomach (*gastritis*) and the intestinal tract (*duodonitis*), as well as heartburn.

- ✔ **Raw, fresh-made cabbage juice is an ulcer remedy long in use.** Experts recommend drinking one quart a day. Spring and summer cabbage is the most effective. Mixing the cabbage juice with some celery juice makes it more palatable.

- ✔ **Licorice helps tissues heal and stimulates the secretion of mucus.** The average licorice candy is flavored with anise, not licorice. Look for authentic licorice in health-food stores.

- ✔ **New Zealand manuka honey is more effective in studies than antibiotics in doing away with the suspect *Heliobacter pylori* bacteria.**

- ✔ **Herbs such as chamomile, goldenseal, sage, aloe vera, and slippery elm soothe and heal ulcerous tissue.**

- ✔ **Bananas and plantains, especially green plantains, are a traditional cure for ulcers in many countries.** These foods help build tissue that is more resistant to acids by stimulating the production of protective mucus and the growth of cells to thicken the stomach wall. Cooked with garlic, they taste out of this world!

Ironically, taking antacids that contain calcium can *promote* ulcers. The calcium stimulates acid secretion.

Foods that increase congestion

Various common foods promote the accumulation of phlegm. To reduce mucus, cut back on your intake or eliminate sugar, eggs, potatoes, and turnips. Grains also increase mucus, especially those high in gluten, such as wheat, barley, oats, and rye. Also cut out milk and diary products. Many people report that after they stop eating dairy foods, their sinus conditions greatly improve.

Managing urinary tract infection

Urinary tract infection (UTI) is very common in women. Drinking cranberry juice can cut your rate of infection by nearly half and also greatly reduce your risk of reinfection. Blueberries work in the same way.

Buy 100 percent cranberry juice concentrate at a natural-food store and dilute it yourself with filtered water.

In addition, garlic fights types of bacteria that are associated with UTI, while parsley, celery root, and other foods that function as diuretics help flush infection from the urinary tract.

Preventing osteoporosis

Some 25 million Americans have *osteoporosis,* or porous bones, a degenerative disease that affects bone mass and bone strength. Eating acid-forming foods triggers your body to remove calcium along with other alkaline minerals from the bones to buffer the acids. (Also, if you're sedentary, your body may simply be unable to build bone.)

Foods that contain calcium include cornmeal, whole wheat, brown rice, kidney beans, broccoli, dark leafy greens, okra, kale, acorn squash, butternut squash, figs, papayas, hazelnuts, Brazil nuts, almonds, canned fish with their bones, blackstrap molasses, goat cheese, and yogurt. Another good source is chicken soup, made with the bones and a little vinegar, which helps pull the calcium from the bones into the broth.

Using calcium-containing antacids to increase calcium intake can be counterproductive because antacids decrease stomach acidity, contributing to decreased absorption of calcium.

Besides calcium, many other minerals are essential for bone strength. Leading the list is magnesium. The balance between magnesium and calcium is very important in lowering your risk of osteoporosis. If milk is your main calcium source, be aware that milk contains only a trace amount of magnesium and is high in protein that promotes the excretion of calcium. Boost your magnesium by eating whole grains, beans, broccoli, potatoes with their skin, figs, plantains, avocados, cashews, Brazil nuts, pumpkin seeds, and shrimp.

Colas are exceptionally high in phosphorus, which the body must keep in balance with calcium. Remember as you down your next cola that your body quickly responds by drawing calcium from bones.

Bone-building also requires a host of other nutrients — boron, copper, manganese, silicon, strontium, and zinc, as well as vitamin B6, folic acid, vitamin C, vitamin D, and vitamin K. Be sure to eat a considerable variety of fruits, vegetables, nuts, and seeds. That way, you're more likely to consume this wide assortment of nutrients.

Chapter 7

Starting a Fitness and Exercise Program

*E*xercise can't prevent ingrown toenails, freeway congestion, or the high number of bad TV sitcoms, but the simple act of moving your body can work wonders. This chapter provides the information you need to start or expand your fitness program — no matter your current fitness level.

Because you're a unique individual, consult with a professional healthcare provider for a complete interview and evaluation of your overall health prior to beginning any fitness program. If you receive advice that is contrary to the information this reference provides, follow your practitioner's advice, because it is based on your unique characteristics and condition.

Weight Training

Many different reasons for lifting weights exist, but most of them have to do with looking better. Sculpted arms and toned "abs" have become somewhat of a fashion statement. However, even more compelling is the fact that lifting weights helps:

✔ Keep your bones healthy

✔ Control your weight

✔ Increase your strength

✔ Boost your energy

✔ Improve your heart health

✔ Improve your quality of life

Lifting weights safely

Weight training is safe, but this doesn't mean that you don't feel occasional muscle soreness after lifting — especially if you're new to the game or haven't worked out in a while. The following guidelines can help you keep soreness to a minimum.

✔ **Warm up before you lift.** Before you pick up even a 2-pound dumbbell, you need to warm up your muscles with at least five minutes of easy aerobic exercise. Your warm-up increases the temperature of your muscles, making them more pliable and less susceptible to injury. Walking, jogging, stairclimbing, and stationary biking are excellent warm-up activities for the muscles south of your waistline. But to prepare your upper body muscles, you need to add extra arm movements to these activities. So, swing your arms fairly vigorously as you walk, jog, or use the stairclimber.

✔ **Start with an easy set.** If you're planning to do more than one set of an exercise, start by performing 8 to 10 repetitions with a very light weight. A warm-up set is like a dress rehearsal for the real thing.

✔ **Lighten up.** If you go too heavy, you may lose control of the weight and drop it on yourself or on someone else. Or you may strain so hard to lift the weight that you tear a muscle. Or you may end up so sore that you can barely lift your feet up high enough to climb stairs.

✔ **Observe the speed limit.** Lifting weights too quickly is a good way to injure yourself. When you're pressing, pushing, lifting, or extending at the speed of a greyhound, you can't stop mid-rep if weight plates come loose, you're positioned incorrectly, or something just doesn't feel right. So take at least two seconds to lift a weight and two seconds to lower it. If you're causing any banging and clanging, slow down your pace.

✔ **Don't hold your breath.** You don't need to inhale and exhale with the gusto of a Lamaze student, but don't hold your breath. Lifting weights temporarily causes your blood pressure to shoot up, which normally isn't a problem. But when you hold your breath, your blood pressure rises even higher — and then suddenly comes crashing down. This drastic drop may cause you to pass out and, if you have a heart condition, can put you in serious jeopardy.

✔ **Use proper form.** Subtle form mistakes, such as overarching your back or cocking your wrist the wrong way, can lead to injury.

✔ **Always cool down.** If you do a fairly fast-paced weight workout, complete the workout with five minutes of slow aerobic exercise. The aerobic cool-down gives your pulse, blood pressure, and breathing a chance to slow down before you hit the showers. If you lift weights at more of a plodding pace, with plenty of rest between sets, a few minutes of stretching can suffice as a cool-down.

✔ **Rest a muscle at least 48 hours.** You're welcome to lift weights on consecutive days — just don't exercise the same muscle two days in a row. When you lift weights, you tear apart your muscle cells. They need a rest day to repair themselves so that they come back even stronger. If you ignore this rule, weight lifting may make you weaker rather than stronger. At the very least, your muscles feel too tired to perform at peak operating levels.

Six signs of over-exercising

Many individuals starting an exercise program don't realize how easily they can *over-exercise*. Watch out for these warning signals:

✔ **Difficulty finishing:** If you can't complete your exercise program with energy to spare, decrease your pace, distance, or intensity.

✔ **Inability to carry on a normal conversation during exercising:** If this happens, you're working too hard. Slow down!

✔ **Faintness or nausea after exercising:** If your exercising is too intense or if you stop exercising too abruptly, you can feel faint. This happens because increased blood flow may cause blood to pool temporarily in your extremities and make it difficult for your heart to maintain an adequate output. Decrease your pace and increase the time of your cool down.

✔ **Chronic fatigue:** If during the remainder of the day or evening after exercise you feel tired rather than stimulated, you're exercising too hard. If you feel very fatigued or have chest pain after exercise, decrease the pace of your workout.

✔ **Sleeplessness:** A proper exercise program makes a good night's sleep easier, not more difficult, to achieve. If you're having more difficulty sleeping normally, decrease the amount of exercise until your symptoms subside.

✔ **Increased aches and pains in your joints:** Some muscle discomfort is inevitable when you start exercising after being very inactive. However, your joints should not hurt or continue to feel stiff. Make sure that you're doing your warm up correctly. Muscle cramping and back discomfort may also indicate poor warm-up technique. If symptoms persist, consult your physician.

Choosing Your Guru

If you're a fitness rookie, you can progress more quickly if you have a seasoned professional to follow — someone (in real life or in the form of a video) who can teach you the ropes and keep you motivated. This section explains what qualities to look for in a fitness guru and what you can expect to gain from a trainer, a class, or a video.

Personal trainers

Personal trainers have become famous firming up fleshy actors and actresses for movie roles. Even if you're not going for an Oscar, a good trainer can still help you perfect your technique, design or update your program, and keep you motivated. This section covers what you need to know to choose the right trainer for you.

Who's a qualified trainer?

In terms of skills and education, the title *fitness trainer* doesn't mean a darn thing. In some gyms, the trainers on staff aren't even certified by a single professional organization. Here are some tips to help you find a trainer you can trust.

- ✔ **Look for certification.** Although no laws exist requiring trainers to have any particular training or certification, more and more trainers are becoming certified by professional organizations and university programs. Many health clubs now require their trainers to have at least one certification, and as the personal training profession becomes increasingly competitive, many private trainers are earning certifications in order to stay ahead of the competition. This surge in certifications is good news for you. Certification doesn't necessarily mean that a trainer is the most knowledgeable and skilled in the field, but it does show that your trainer considers fitness a serious career choice, not just a way to pay the rent.

- ✔ **Hire an experienced trainer.** Don't be shy: Ask for references and call a few of the trainer's other clients. Do as good a job screening potential trainers as you'd do checking out potential employees. You can even ask for a resume.

- ✔ **Make sure your personalities mesh.** Trainers are human beings, which means that they come in all different personality types. Some are enthusiastic. Some are downright perky. On the other end of the spectrum are trainers who missed their calling as maximum security prison guards. Interview a few trainers and choose one who makes you feel comfortable.

✔ **Expect good teaching skills.** Good trainers speak to you in your native tongue, not in jargon. If you don't understand something, a trainer needs to be able to find another way to explain the point. Also, good trainers prepare you to venture out into the world alone.

On the other hand, beware of trainers who talk too much. Some trainers give so many pointers you may feel overwhelmed.

✔ **Count on personal attention.** Look for a trainer who showers you with questions about your goals and thoroughly evaluates your health, strength, cardiovascular fitness, and flexibility. Some trainers give a 65-year-old woman the same basic program that they give a professional hockey player. Look for evidence that you're getting a custom-designed routine. If you find that you're performing exercises that are either far too difficult or way too easy (and the trainer doesn't seem to notice or care), you're getting the trainer's same old song and dance.

Many trainers specialize in certain types of clients, such as seniors, children, pregnant women, multiple-sclerosis patients, or ultra-endurance athletes. If you have a specific goal in mind or have special circumstances, seek out a trainer who has the training and experience to meet your needs.

✔ **Make sure that your trainer carries liability insurance:** If you get hurt, you may be looking at thousands of dollars in medical bills, even if you have medical insurance. A trainer's liability coverage may foot the bill if you can prove your injury is a direct result of the trainer's negligence. Many insurers award coverage only to trainers who are certified, so liability insurance is often an indication that your trainer has some credentials.

You can't always assess a trainer in one interview or even in a couple of sessions, so if you start to sour on the first trainer you choose, don't hesitate to find another one.

How to act during a training session

Take an active role in your training sessions, especially if you're going to have just a few of them. To get the most out of your training sessions:

✔ **Show up on time.** Trainers are professional people with busy schedules, so show them some courtesy. Honor your trainer's cancellation policy (and avoid chronic cancellations).

✔ **Have a good attitude.** Your trainer doesn't want to hear you whine about your boss or your latest speeding ticket.

✔ **Speak up.** The more questions you ask, the more information you're likely to remember. For example, when you perform an exercise, don't feel stupid about asking why you pull the bar down to your chest rather than to your belly button. A good trainer has coherent answers on the tip of his tongue.

✔ **Listen to your trainer.** Trust that your trainer has more experience than you do. Of course, always ask questions if you don't understand something, and if your trainer's advice sounds out of line, you don't need to heed it.

Using fitness videos

A video can teach you a lot about weight training that a book or magazine can't. You can witness an exercise being performed from start to finish and pick up new routines. Some videos even feature fancy graphics that indicate which muscles you're working during each exercise.

Perhaps the main reason that exercise videos are so popular is the convenience. You can roll out of bed and look as gruesome as you want to look and still get your workout in.

You can find fitness videos that use dumbbells, barbells, rubber exercise bands, rubber balls, machines — or a combination of these gadgets. Some videos combine strength training with aerobics or step aerobics routines. Many are suited to beginners; others you can grow into. And if you find instructors who you really respond to, chances are you can find additional tapes featuring the instructor.

 Consider renting a video before you buy it. After all, if you buy a tape and the instructor annoys you or the workout is too easy or too confusing, the only way you use that tape is as a coaster at your Super Bowl parties. Large video rental stores and public libraries carry a decent array of workout videos. Try several different tapes until you find a few that you like and *then* invest in tapes of your own.

Designing your basic workout

One excellent strategy for staying out of a rut with your training is *periodization. Periodization* simply means organizing your program into different *periods,* each lasting about four to eight weeks. Each period has a different theme. For example, one month you may use weight machines, and the next month you may switch to dumbbells and barbells. Or you can change the number of sets, repetitions, and exercises you perform from one period to the next.

The following introductory periodization program includes five distinct phases, each lasting about a month. (However, depending on your goals, each phase can be as short as two weeks or as long as eight weeks.) You can repeat this cycle over and over again. Here's a look at each phase:

✔ **Prep phase:** During this period, you prepare your body for the challenges ahead with a basic workout. Use light weights, perform 1 to 4 sets per muscle, do 12 to 15 repetitions per set, and rest 90 seconds between sets.

✔ **Pump phase:** In this phase, you step up your efforts a bit. You lift slightly heavier weight, perform 10 to 12 reps per set, do 3 to 8 sets per muscle group, and rest only 60 seconds between sets.

✔ **Push phase:** In this period, you do 8 to 10 reps per set, resting 30 seconds between sets. You do only two or three different exercises per muscle group, but you do several sets of each so that you can use more advanced training techniques.

✔ **Peak phase:** In this phase, you focus on building maximum strength. Do 6 to 8 reps per set, 15 to 20 sets per muscle group but fewer different exercises. For instance, you may only do 1 or 2 leg exercises, but you do multiple sets of each exercise and 6 to 8 repetitions per set. Rest a full two minutes between sets so that you can lift more weight. This phase is your last big effort before you take a break from heavy training.

✔ **Rest phase:** In this phase, you either drop back to the light workouts you did in the prep phase, or you take a break from weight training altogether. Resting gives your body (and your mind) a chance to recover from all the hard work you're putting in. After your break, you move back into your next periodization cycle with fresh muscles and a renewed enthusiasm for your training.

If you're hell-bent on toning or building up your body, you may be tempted to skip the rest phase. Don't. If you never rest, at some point your body starts to break down. You stop making progress, and you may injure yourself. If you want to get fit, resting is just as important as working out.

Flexibility

Stretching, bending, and twisting exercises increase your range-of-motion and reduce stiffness.

Five rules for safe stretching

Although you probably know that stretching is one of the most important components of any fitness plan, careless, uninformed stretching isn't going to make you more flexible, and it may even injure you. Here are the basic rules for a useful and safe flexibility workout.

✔ **Stretch as often as you can — daily if possible.** Always stretch after any workout, be it cardiovascular, strength training, or whatever. When you stretch on days you don't work out, be sure to warm up with a few minutes of easy movement like shoulder rolls, gentle waist twists, or light cardio activity.

✔ **Move into each stretching position slowly.** Never force yourself into a stretch by jerking or snapping into position.

✔ **Notice how much tension you feel.** An effective stretch can rate anywhere from "mild tension" to "the edge of discomfort" on your pain meter. It should never cause severe or sharp pain anywhere else in your body. Focus on the area you're stretching, and notice the stretch spread through these muscles.

✔ **Hold each stretch for ten slow counts.** After you find the most comfortable stretch position, stay there or gradually deepen the stretch. Bouncing only tightens your muscle — it doesn't loosen it. Forceful bouncing increases the risk of tearing a muscle.

✔ **Take at least two deep breaths, as you hold each position.** Deep breathing promotes relaxation and sends oxygen into your muscles.

Expanding your repertoire with yoga and Pilates

Incorporating yoga and Pilates into your fitness program helps you build and stretch not only your muscles, but your mind.

Some yoga and Pilates practitioners claim that yoga and Pilates are superior to weight training because these disciplines can make you stronger without creating bulky muscles. However, while yoga and Pilates *can* build strength without bulk, so can strength training with light free weights or machines. So, choosing yoga or Pilates simply because you're trying to develop strength without bulk is buying into a fitness myth.

What's the difference between yoga and Pilates?

Yoga, developed in India more than 5,000 years ago, consists of a series of poses, known as *asanas,* that you hold anywhere from a few seconds to several minutes. The moves, which require a blend of strength, flexibility, and body awareness, are intended to promote the union of the mind, body, and spirit. Most yoga styles include the same basic poses but differ in terms of how quickly you move, how long you hold each pose, how much breathing is emphasized, and how much of a spiritual aspect is involved. Some styles offer more modifications for beginners. Other styles are for people who can already fold themselves in half like a piece of foam rubber.

Pilates (pih-LAH-teez) is an exercise form named after Joseph Pilates, the former carpenter and gymnast who invented the technique for injured dancers at the turn of the twentieth century. Many Pilates moves were inspired by yoga, although some were patterned after the movements of animals, such as swans, seals, and cats. Pilates mat classes involve a series of specialized calisthenics exercises; rather than hold the positions, as in yoga, you're constantly moving. Private lessons can take place on medieval looking machines with names such as *The Cadillac* (which looks like a four-poster bed that's been rigged for torture) and *The Reformer* (which resembles a weight bench souped up with assorted springs, straps, and pads).

However, plenty of other excellent reasons exist for you to take up these alternative modes of exercise. Here's a rundown.

✔ **Yoga and Pilates engage your whole body.** For instance, when performing a thigh exercise, you don't simply straighten and bend your leg, as you do in a traditional weight training exercise. Instead, you must engage your butt muscles in order to sit evenly in the seat, use your abs and lower back to avoid wiggling back and forth, work your upper body muscles to keep your back and neck in alignment, and so on. The benefit of working so many muscle groups simultaneously is that this is the way you're likely to use them in everyday life.

Yoga and Pilates also place particular emphasis on your "core" muscles — your abdominals, lower back, and dozens of small spinal muscles that don't get much action in a weight machine workout. This is a type of strength worth developing: It can help you stand up straighter and move more loosely and comfortably.

Avoid fitness program overload!

First, realize that you can't do everything in life! You can't be a full-time invest-ment banker *and* a professional TV critic *and* a world-class pole vaulter. By the same token, you can't devote yourself to weight training, yoga, *and* Pilates — especially when you're also (hopefully) doing cardiovascular exercise.

For a weekly schedule that's livable, try lifting weights twice a week and doing either yoga or Pilates twice a week. Doing any of these activities just once a week typically isn't enough for a beginner to see results and get the hang of proper technique. For weight training, yoga, and Pilates, repetition is extremely important. And also work in cardiovascular activities three to four times a week.

✔ **Yoga and Pilates increase your flexibility.** You may never be able to fold yourself into a human half sandwich, but if you put time and effort into these pursuits, your body can become sur-prisingly pliable.

✔ **Yoga and Pilates can improve your balance, coordination, and concentration.** When you first try a new move, you may tip over sideways. You may practice for several years just to start to perform some moves with grace and fluidity. These disci-plines require a lot of concentration and body awareness. You can't simply go through the motions and expect to get much out of the technique.

Six easy yoga stretches

The benefits of yoga are many, including relaxation, stress reduc-tion, increased energy, improved flexibility, increased strength, and improved circulation. As an added bonus, many people find that reg-ularly practicing yoga helps relieve depression, increase alertness, and improve overall well-being.

Ease into yoga slowly — you're not in a rush. However, practicing daily is recommended. The following six stretches can get you on your way to flexibility.

Yoga stretch one: The Snake

Use this posture to stretch your chest, stomach, and upper back muscles while strengthening your arms and upper body.

1. On a towel or mat, lie face down on your stomach with your arms bent, hands palm down resting on either side of your neck.

2. Pressing your hands and lower arms into the mat, slowly raise your head and upper chest until they're completely off the floor.

3. Gradually straighten your arms as you push your head, chest, and torso as far up as you can.

   Be sure to keep your pelvis flat on the floor and your legs extended.

4. Hold position for a count of five.

5. Slowly bend your arms as you ease your torso down to the mat.

6. Gradually return to the starting position with your face on the mat (see Figure 7-1).

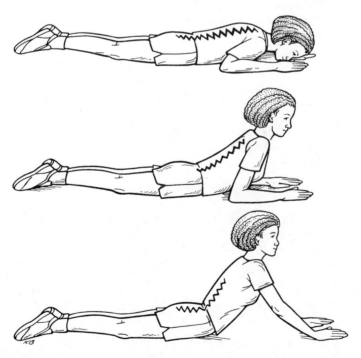

Figure 7-1: The Snake is a great stretch for the upper back, chest, and stomach muscles.

Yoga stretch two: The Cat

This exercise helps increase spinal flexibility.

1. **Assume a hands-and-knees position on your exercise mat with your neck parallel to the floor.**

   Position your knees about 12 inches apart, with your arms straight down and your fingers pointing forward.

2. **Contract your stomach muscles and roll your head forward until your chin touches your chest as you round your back upward toward the ceiling.**

   Allow your entire torso to contract and form a hollow.

3. **Gradually release the contraction and roll your head back to its original position.**

4. **Arch your back slightly, creating a curve going the opposite way.**

   Don't stick your rear-end out, let your stomach muscles relax, or sway your back to accomplish this position; these things can put too much pressure on the disks between your vertebrae.

5. **Repeat, slowly forming the hump, and then ease into a slight arch (see Figure 7-2).**

Figure 7-2: The Cat increases spinal flexibility.

Yoga stretch three: The Pretzel

Use this exercise to stretch your inner thigh and hip.

1. **Lie on your back on your exercise mat, legs bent and arms at your sides.**
2. **Cross your right leg over your left leg, with your right foot just clearing your left knee.**
3. **Grab your left thigh with both hands and pull it toward you while keeping your legs in the crossed position.**
4. **Hold this position for at least 5 seconds.**
5. **Slowly release, and then repeat with the opposite leg (see Figure 7-3).**

Figure 7-3: The Pretzel loosens the hip and increases the flexibility of the inner thigh.

Yoga stretch four: Knee-to-Chest Stretch

This exercise loosens up the hip joint while stretching your lower back and buttock muscles.

1. **Lie on your back on your exercise mat, legs extended and arms at your sides.**
2. **Bend your right leg, grab it with both hands just below the knee, and pull it gently toward your chest as far as it can go.**
3. **Hold your leg at its maximum position for a count of five. Make sure your other leg is straight and on the floor.**
4. **Slowly release and repeat with your left leg (see Figure 7-4).**

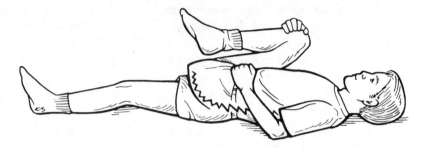

Figure 7-4: The Knee-to-Chest Stretch is great for your lower back, buttocks, and hip joints.

Yoga stretch five: The Spinal Twist

Exercises that twist the spine are good for maintaining the flexibility of the spine and the *oblique* muscles — muscles that run diagonally along your side.

1. **Lie on your back on your exercise mat, legs extended and arms at your sides.**

2. **Bend your right knee and bring it toward your chest, grabbing hold of it with both hands behind the thigh.**

3. **Extend your right arm straight out to the side, keeping it flat on the floor and making a 90-degree angle to your body.**

4. **Using your left hand, pull your right knee across your body, as if to touch it to the floor beside your left hip.**

   Your right foot should stay in contact with your left knee and your right shoulder should stay flat on the floor. Your left leg should stay straight.

5. **Turn your head to the right, as if looking at the right wall.**

6. **Hold this pose for a count of 10, then slowly return to your original position.**

7. **Repeat, bending your left knee this time. One time on each side is sufficient.**

Yoga stretch six: The Child's Pose

This posture stretches your entire back, your buttock muscles, and your upper arms, while putting you into a dreamy state of relaxation.

1. **Sit on your mat with your legs tucked under you, heels directly under the buttocks.**

   Place your knees about 12 inches apart.

2. **Roll your upper body head first toward the floor, until you can place your forehead on the floor in front of your knees. Place your palms on the floor on either side of your head.**

3. **Slowly extend your arms in front of you as far as possible.**

   Make sure that your buttocks stay in contact with your heels and your feet stay on the floor.

4. **Hold this position for a count of 10, then slowly return to the sitting position.**

5. **Repeat 5 times.**

Seven equipment-free Pilates exercises

Pilates, in addition to building long, lean muscles, is a great way to increase your flexibility. The following Pilates mat exercises help you discover how to move better and stronger in daily life by expanding your flexibility.

Actually, you can use the floor or a towel instead of a mat. But some moves require some cushioning for your neck, spine, and pelvic bones. So consider having a mat around for when you do need it.

Getting into the starting position

The three starting positions are the foundation of other Pilates moves, and you need to practice them first.

- ✔ **Starting position #1:** Lie flat on your back, with your knees bent and your feet flat on the floor (see Figure 7-5). Elongate your arms and rest them at your sides. Properly align your pelvis, find a neutral spine, and tighten your abdominal.

- ✔ **Starting position #2:** Lie flat on your back with your legs extended (see Figure 7-6). Keep your arms elongated and resting at your sides. Check your pelvis. Is it still aligned?

- ✔ **Starting position #3:** Sit up on your buttocks with your weight just behind your pelvic bones (see Figure 7-7). Extend your legs, straighten your back, and open your shoulders.

  You can do any exercise that starts with #3 by sitting on a folded-up blanket or towel if you have tight hamstrings and have trouble straightening your legs or sitting up tall.

Figure 7-5: Pilates Starting position #1.

Figure 7-6: Pilates Starting position #2.

Figure 7-7: Pilates Starting position #3.

Pilates exercise one: Spine Stretch

Tight backs and legs can lead to hurt backs and legs. Figure 7-8 shows you the Spine Stretch.

 1. **Use Starting position #3 (refer to Figure 7-7) but move your legs apart so the space is just wider than your shoulders.**

2. **Flex your feet so that your toes face the ceiling. Rest your hands palms-down on the mat between your legs.**

   If your hamstrings are too tight to sit comfortably, sitting on a small pillow or pad, as Figure 7-8 shows, can relieve some of the tension.

3. **Inhale, then exhale and, starting from your head, roll one vertebra at a time downward.**

   Walk your fingers outward between your legs away from you. Only go as far down as you can while keeping your pelvis upright and your abs tight. That may mean you don't go very far, but you can still feel the stretch.

4. **Inhale while down. Or if you want to stay there a few counts, inhale and exhale, then inhale again before coming back up. Exhale and roll the spine back up starting with the vertebrae in your lower back.**

5. **Repeat 6–8 times.**

Figure 7-8: Spine Stretch.

While doing this stretch, try to avoid jamming your chin to your chest or bending at your hips (and sinking into your low back).

Pilates exercise two: Saw

Imagine that in this exercise you're trying to "saw" off your toe with your hand as you reach it downward (see Figure 7-9).

1. **Use Starting position #2 (refer to Figure 7-6), but add some space between your legs so that your knees are as wide as your shoulders. Reach out your arms to your sides at shoulder height.**

2. **Inhale and rotate the spine (not just the arms!) to the right, keeping your hips square to the front.**

3. **Reach your left arm forward and down in the direction of the** *outside* **of the right foot you're turning toward.**

   Keep your pelvis tall and not tucked or collapsed. The reach forward comes from back and hamstring flexibility.

4. **Roll upward, feeling as if you're stacking each of your vertebrae one on top of the other, and use your abs to initiate the roll up.**

5. **Rotate back toward center, and repeat on the left side.**

6. **Repeat 5–6 times on each side.**

Figure 7-9: Saw.

 While doing this stretch, try to avoid lifting one hip bone off the ground as you reach toward the opposite leg, tensing your neck and shoulders, or letting your toes relax forward.

Pilates exercise three: Breaststroke

The following is a simplified version of a popular but fairly complex Pilates exercise (see Figure 7-10).

1. **Start lying stomach-down with your thighs together. Place your hands, palm-down, on the floor underneath your shoulders.**

2. **Inhale, then exhale and reach (lengthen) your arms forward as if you're trying to stroke through the water, continuing to pull the top of your head away from your tailbone and turn the palms in to face each other.**

3. **Inhale while you circle your arms back toward your hips keeping them parallel to the floor (like you're swimming along again).**

   Your palms rotate outward as your arms circle back, then return to a palms-down position. Lengthen and lift your upper back slightly, pulling the top of your head forward.

4. **Finish by bringing your hands back down below your shoulders as you lengthen down onto the floor.**

5. **Repeat 8–10 times.**

   If this exercise is too complicated or difficult, leave your hands on the floor and just practice lifting and lengthening your spine while breathing.

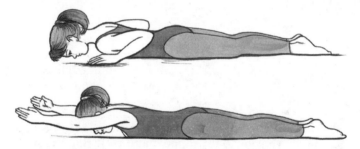

Figure 7-10: Breaststroke.

While doing this stretch, try to avoid tensing and lifting your shoulders and tightening your neck muscles.

Pilates exercise four: Spine Twist

This is a great movement for improving your back's mobility. See Figure 7-11.

1. **Use Starting position #3 (refer to Figure 7-7) with your arms reaching out to your sides at shoulder height.**

2. **Inhale and rotate your torso to one side while keeping the hips square to the front and unmoving (that's the hard part, so focus).**

   Be sure to carry your arms along with the shoulders. Your eyes follow your hands in the direction you're rotating.

3. **Exhale and return to the center and aligned position. Repeat to the other side.**

4. **Repeat 4–5 times each side.**

Figure 7-11: Spine Twist.

While doing this stretch, try to avoid moving your feet forward and back to compensate for not moving your hips, tensing your back and shoulders, or losing the tightness in your abdominals.

Pilates exercise five: Side Kick

This Side Kick is a different animal than those leg lifts everybody did in the 1980s. Instead of flailing your leg around, this exercise (see Figure 7-12) makes you focus and use your mind to become aware of your muscles.

1. **Lie on the mat on your left side with your left arm tucked under your head for support and your right hand flat on the mat in front of your chest for balance.**

    Your body "hinges" forward slightly at your hips for additional balance. But avoid curving your body; the position is more like a very wide V, with the point of the V being your hips. Keep your right hip stacked right on top of your left; not leaning forward or backward.

    Don't let your middle just hang there. Keep your pelvis aligned, spine straight (no sagging), torso lengthened, and abdominals tight.

2. **Raise your right leg so that it's level with your hip, then inhale and flex your foot (bend your foot at the ankle) while you bring the leg forward in front of your body slightly and *pulse* twice to the front.**

    This pulse is like a little tiny, nearly stationary, kick to the front.

3. **Exhale and bring your leg back behind your body a little with your toes pointed and pulse once.**

4. **Repeat 6–10 times, then switch sides and do the same with your left leg.**

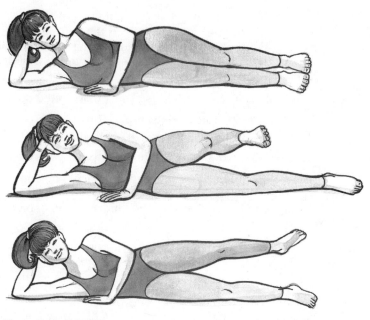

Figure 7-12: Side Kick.

While doing this stretch, try to avoid throwing your torso forward and backward when you move your leg or releasing your tight abdominals.

Pilates exercise six: Side Bend

This exercise gives a wonderful tone to your arms and upper body, as well as a stretch through the torso (see Figure 7-13). Figuring out the position takes a little time though, so be patient. Other names for this movement may include Twist or Mermaid.

Tightening your abdominals in this exercise is extremely important because of the balance you need to maintain to keep from, well, teetering over and falling flat on your face.

1. **Find the starting position by kneeling on both knees, then allow your lower legs to pull out to the left so your right hip is on the ground as your right arm reaches to the floor to support your side-leaning position. Now extend your knees farther out to the side until they're bent at about a right angle.**

2. **Stay seated on your right hip, but lift your top, left knee upward, opening the leg, and place that foot on the ground just in front of your right ankle. Rest your left arm lightly on your right knee.**

3. **Inhale and lift your left hip toward the ceiling, at the same time straightening your knees and lifting your left arm up and all the way over your head so that you end up in a big C-shaped position.**

   Make sure that your weight is evenly distributed on both feet.

4. **Exhale and lower your right hip to the ground, returning to a seated position with your left arm resting on your left knee.**

5. **Repeat 3–5 times on each side, or fewer if you need to.**

   As a modification, you can leave your right knee on the ground when you lift your hips up and just move your left foot out so the leg is straight. That gives you more points of balance.

Figure 7-13: Side Bend.

While doing this stretch, try to avoid rolling your top hip forward or backward, tensing your neck and lifting your shoulders toward your ears, and sinking into the lower shoulder.

Pilates exercise seven: Pushup

This exercise challenges your upper body. Its name may sound familiar, and its directions may ring familiar, but with these pushups you put so much focus into each miniscule part that you can't just crank 'em out (see Figure 7-14). You can really feel the few you do!

1. **Start by standing in a good, balanced posture: Abdominals tight, your pelvis aligned as it is when you're on your back, your arms relaxed by your sides, and your feet together with toes pointing straight ahead.**

2. **Inhale and roll forward, leading with the top of your head, unstacking one vertebrae at a time. Allow your hands to slide down your legs until your upper body is as low as you can go.**

   If this hurts your back or is in any way uncomfortable, bend your knees as your roll down. You can also stop the roll with your hands resting on your thighs. If you have a back injury, please consult your physician about doing this or any other exercises.

3. **If your hamstrings are flexible and your hands or fingers can reach the ground, walk your hands straight out into a pushup position.**

   If your hamstrings are tight, after you roll down as low as you can go, bend your knees and place your hands on the floor in front of your feet. Then walk yourself forward into the pushup position.

4. **Do one exacting and lengthening pushup, lowering your chest to the ground, then lifting your body back up to the pushup position, until your elbows are straight.**

   You can do up to 4 if you're stronger. You can also lower your knees to the ground to do a modified pushup if you'd like.

   If just maintaining this pushup position with good spinal alignment is hard for you, you may want to leave out the pushup itself and just hold the position for a second, then jump to Step 5.

5. **Walk your hands back to the standing position (bending your knees when you need to, as above), then roll back up one vertebrae at a time, making sure to stack the head absolutely last.**

6. **Repeat 3–5 times.**

While doing this stretch, try to avoid tensing your neck, not letting your head hang down in a relaxed position, losing your tight abdominals, or sagging your head downward when you're in the pushup position.

Figure 7-14: Pushup.

Cardiovascular Exercise

If your goal is to feel better and live longer, a little aerobic exercise goes a remarkably long way.

Research shows that the people who gain the most from aerobic exercise are those who go from being completely slothful to only marginally slothful — not the ones who go from being fit to super fit.

The people in the bottom 20 percent of the population, fitness-wise, are 65 percent more likely to die from heart attack, stroke, diabetes, or cancer than the highly fit people in the top 20 percent. However, when couch potatoes move up just one notch on the fitness scale, by simply adding a daily 30-minute walk, they're only 10 percent more likely to die from these causes than super-fit people.

Walking

One of the best things about walking for fitness is that you need so little equipment. This section tells you what you need to know about choosing the shoes, socks, and, er, support items that keep the spring in your step.

Shopping for shoes

Give yourself at least an hour the first time you shop for walking shoes to make the perfect selection. Follow these suggestions and you can't go wrong.

- ✔ **Shop at a specialty store, rather than a department store, if possible.** This may cost you some extra bucks, but having a knowledgeable salesperson to guide you can mean the difference between a great purchase and getting stuck with unwearable clodhoppers.

- ✔ **If you have an old pair of walking shoes, bring them with you so you can show the salesperson your wear pattern.** Take along the socks you usually wear, too, so that you can size your new shoes the way you actually wear them.

- ✔ **Examine each pair of shoes before you try them on.** Turn them over. Does the shoe have a good strong heel cup? Slip out the insert to discover the shoe's construction. Bend the shoes back and forth a few times. Are they flexible in the forefoot?

- ✔ **Put on *both* shoes and lace them up completely.** Walk around the store for a few minutes to get the feel of the shoe. Whenever possible, try them on a hard-surfaced floor. If the shoes aren't comfy from the second you put them on your feet, put them back in the box and try another pair. Do not buy a shoe with the plan of "breaking them in."

- ✔ **Be prepared to test several different shoe models.** Even if you like the first shoe you lace up, try at least two other models for comparison purposes.

- ✔ **Always shop later in the day, because your feet can swell up to half a size larger during the course of the day.** A shoe that fits well has about a thumbnail's space between your longest toe and the end of the toe box. Always accommodate your longest toe and your largest foot.

✔ **When you find a shoe you like, buy it and try it out for a few days.** If you absolutely love it after three workouts, go back and buy a couple pairs of the same shoe. Shoe companies have a habit of phasing out and "upgrading" shoe models on a regular basis.

Searching for a good sock

Don't go sockless when you walk. Socks absorb sweat and prevent friction between your feet and the inside of your shoe. Sockless walkers frequently complain of blisters, chafing, and athlete's foot. Their feet and shoes often smell bad, too. You don't have to buy socks specifically designed for walking but do look for a few basic traits.

✔ **Socks that are thick, but not too thick, are your best bet.** Dress socks, nylons, and very thin socks don't prevent enough friction to be worn alone, although when worn under your main socks they can help keep your foot from rubbing against the inside of your shoe.

✔ **Cheapo tube socks are a no-no.** These tend to bunch around your toes and lose shape quickly. They also hold sweat and heat up your feet, which can be uncomfortable, especially when you walk in hot weather.

✔ **Stick to synthetic fibers like acrylic and Dupont's CoolMax.** Although natural fibers like cotton and wool feel great at first, they lose their shape quickly and don't do a very good job of "wicking away" moisture.

✔ **Whatever sock you decide on, make sure that it doesn't bunch around the toes or gather at the heels.** This can cause blisters and hot spots.

✔ **Don't buy socks that are too small.** That's like wearing a shoe that's too small; Small socks place too much pressure on the ends of your toes.

✔ **When your socks wear out, lose shape, or have holes in them, chuck them and buy new ones.**

Dressing well for walking

For fitness walkers, clothes need to be comfortable and nonrestrictive. Dress appropriately for the weather and situation, which, of course, changes with the temperature.

For women only: Choosing a sports bra

Proper breast support is vital for physical, psychological, and emotional comfort. Bouncing can cause the small ligaments of the breasts to stretch. Over time, this stretching can lead to sagging. Additionally, bouncing can be distracting and make you feel self-conscious.

Fortunately, finding a good bra is easier than it used to be. You have a couple different options to choose from:

✔ **Compression bras:** This original type of sports bra presses the breasts up against the chest as a single mass. These come in a "crop top" design with one large piece of material to hold your breasts in place. Larger-breasted women may experience discomfort with this type of bra because the breasts can still bounce as a single unit.

✔ **Encapsulation bras:** Larger-breasted women may find this newer type of sports bra helpful. Encapsulation bras hold each breast in a separate cup so they stay in place and don't press against each other. Many are sized like traditional bras up to size DD.

If all else fails and you can't find a bra that stops the bounce, here's a tip that works for many large-breasted women: Wear two sports bras at once. Try a compression bra over an encapsulation bra. The combination creates overlapping support and keep things pretty still, though you may feel a bit overdressed in hot weather.

In warm weather, a light-colored, loose top is best. In direct sunlight, provide your body with as much shade as possible — a light-colored cap with a rim, sunglasses, and of course, a liberal application of sunscreen. Wear shorts or short tights — this is strictly a matter of preference. Synthetic fibers designed to let moisture escape and evaporate quickly are the most comfortable. Clothes made from natural fibers, like cotton, feel cool and comfy when you first put them on, but after you start sweating, the fabric feels wet and clammy. If you like the feel of cotton against your skin, experiment with cotton synthetic blends. To complete your outfit, grab a water bottle or some sort of hydration system.

In cold weather, remember that three thin layers work better on the upper part of your body than one or two thick ones to keep you warm. Each layer traps air, which acts as an insulator to retain body heat. The three layers you need are:

✔ **A lightweight, synthetic layer** to wick moisture away.

✔ **An insulating middle layer** made of wool, Gore-Tex, Polar Guard or other insulating material.

✔ **An outer protective layer** to serve as a shield from wind and water. Make sure the material is *waterproof,* not just water-resistant.

On the bottom half of your body, you can get away with one or two layers, depending on how cold it is and what type of precipitation is falling. Accessorize with mittens and a hat. In general, mittens are preferable to gloves because they keep your hands warmer.

Here's a good rule to follow for your winter workout wardrobe. Dress as if the weather is 10 degrees warmer that it really is. When you first start out, you may be chilly, but after you get moving, you feel just right. You can always stop and peel off a layer if you get too hot.

The four levels of walking

Each of the four levels of walking has its benefits, but if you have a specific goal in mind, you want to make sure you're walking at a level that can get you there.

Level 1: Lifestyle walking

Lifestyle walking is the type of casual walking you do when you stroll through the park or the mall. It's a relatively low-intensity activity, but that doesn't mean it isn't good for you. Lifestyle walking is a good entry-level fitness activity and a sensible starting point for your walking program if you haven't exercised in a while. Most lifestyle walkers walk an average of 2.5 to 3.5 miles per hour, meaning that you cover one mile every 17 to 24 minutes.

Because lifestyle walking is the most straightforward of all walking techniques, it's perfect for beginners who want to help build stamina and muscular strength. Focus on this level if your goal is long-term health and an improved quality of life. Lifestyle walking is a good part of every walker's program because a truly successful health and fitness plan must include an increase in overall movement and daily activity.

Level 2: Fitness walking

Walkers exercising on the treadmill at the gym or high-stepping through the neighborhood engage in *fitness walking.* Fitness walking is a perfect low-impact way to get fit and stay fit. It's an excellent weight loss activity with little risk of injury. You can use it as your main fitness activity if your goals are moderate weight loss, improved health, increased energy, and longevity. Fitness walkers typically move along at a brisk pace of 3.5 to 4.3 miles an hour, covering a mile in a respectable 14 to 17 minutes. Fitness walking utilizes the hips, buttocks, lower back, abdominals, and upper body muscles.

Level 3: High-energy walking

This form of walking is a great calorie burner and muscle shaper. It's a takeoff on the sport of race walking. High-energy walkers zip along at a lightning-fast pace of 4.4 to 6.0 miles an hour, covering a mile in a blazing 10 to 13.6 minutes. Try to include at least some high-energy walking in your program if your goals are increased muscle tone and improved athletic performance, and if you're looking for a calorie burn similar to running but without the high risk of injury. Most walkers use high-energy walking as a hard-day aerobic activity rather than their mainstay workout, although some walkers get addicted to it and use it as their primary cardio workout.

Level 4: Walk-run

Walk-run is the perfect hybrid activity for walkers who have the need for speed but don't want to greatly pump up their risk of injury. Walk-run involves alternating running intervals and walking intervals in order to spike up exercise intensity, work more muscles, and burn more calories. Although you never have to run a single step to get in fantastic shape, you may want to try a walk-run workout at least once in a while. If, however, even short jogging stints make your knees ache, stick with pure walking.

Walking in all kinds of weather

Braving the elements can be a joy, so don't let a little natural adversity keep you from your appointed walking rounds. If you prepare, you can exercise safely and comfortably in just about every circumstance.

Cool tips for walking in hot weather

Of all the types of weather you may run into, hot, humid weather has perhaps the greatest capacity for danger. On a really steamy, hot day, you can overheat and dehydrate very quickly, especially if you're just getting back into shape.

- ✔ **Drink tons of water.** If you heed just one piece of advice about walking in hot weather, make it this one. You know that old rule about drinking eight glasses of water a day? When you exercise in the heat, drink closer to ten.

- ✔ **Always carry a water bottle or some other type of water carrier.** Drink as often as you feel thirsty or more often if you can stand it. Continue to drink after your workout, too, even if you aren't thirsty. Doing so helps you stay hydrated. You can fill your water bottle up halfway with ice cubes and the rest of the way with water or a sports drink so that you always have something refreshing and cool to drink.

✔ **Choose walking clothing made of fabrics such as CoolMax and Supplex that pull moisture away from your body.** Most sporting goods stores and large department stores sell walking and running clothing made from these fabrics. Wear lighter colors because they keep you cooler. Synthetic mesh is also a good idea because the holes allow moisture to escape, yet they also catch any breeze that happens to blow by.

✔ **Sunblock is a must.** Many good sunblocks are formulated especially for exercise and sweating. Consider buying the no-name brands you can get at almost any drugstore because they're inexpensive and work just as well as the pricey brands. Combine sunscreen with a hat to protect your scalp, and a good pair of sunglasses to protect your eyes.

Treading carefully on snow and ice

You can't always tell what kind of terrain is underneath snow cover. As a result, if you're not careful to keep your eyes peeled on the road ahead, a pothole or slick patch of ice may surprise you. Icy hills are especially dangerous.

Lateral stability on snow, slush, and ice presents a real opportunity for injury; you can easily twist an ankle or turn your knee in an attempt to stay upright. High snowdrifts and unplowed streets require an extra effort, too, especially from your buttocks and thigh muscles. Take shorter, quicker strides than normal and hold your arms slightly away from your body to improve your balance. Whenever possible, travel along well-worn paths where the snow cover is minimal and you can see what's coming up.

If footing isn't the greatest, forget about going for broke and setting your course record. Instead, try walking for a set time rather than a specific distance. You expend a great deal of extra energy simply trying to keep yourself upright on snow or ice, so you tire more quickly, and your typical distance may be more than you can handle.

Let someone know where you're going and the approximate amount of time you'll be gone. Stick to familiar territory and, whenever possible, follow a route that has several safe havens like a corner deli, gas station, or a friend's house.

Of course, during a total whiteout or when the mercury dips to impossibly low depths, you're best off to concede defeat and stay indoors.

Singin' — and walkin' — in the rain

Your tolerance to rain is first and foremost a matter of personal preference. Some people love it; others abhor it.

A waterproof jacket and pants usually suffice as protection from the rain. Note the difference between the words *waterproof* and *water-resistant*. Only waterproof garments keep you dry if you're out for a while. The best rain suits allow the moisture from your perspiration to escape without allowing outside moisture to seep in.

Although rain in and of itself usually isn't dangerous, thunder and lightning are a different story. Avoid walking during a thunderstorm, especially out on an open road or field where you're essentially a lightning rod. If you sense that a thunderstorm is coming, get indoors as quickly as possible. Head for shelter and away from open spaces. If you're hiking or trail walking, don't stay on high points such as peaks and ridges. Crouch low, touching the ground with only your feet to minimize the number of contact points along which electricity can travel. If possible, crouch down on an insulating material such as rope or cloth; stay away from anything metallic. Remove any backpack or clothing that's part metal.

Walkin' against the wind

You can't do much about the wind except enjoy it when it's at your back. You can wear a windbreaker and pump your arms more vigorously, but those suggestions only help you so much. Perhaps the best idea is to accept wind as a factor like snow and dry sand that slows you down no matter how you slice it. Use sunblock to minimize windburn and wear sunglasses to protect your eyes from debris that strong gusts can kick up.

Other Aerobic Activities

One of the best ways to stick to a fitness plan is to vary your routine. This section introduces you to two great additional cardiovascular exercises to spice up your plan.

Bicycling

Cycling is a great addition to your cardio repertoire and is a low-impact sport — unless you happen to impact the ground, a car, a tree, or another cyclist.

Buying a bike

If you haven't owned a bike since grammar school, prepare yourself for sticker shock. *Mountain bikes,* the fat-tire bikes with upright handlebars, are somewhat less expensive than comparable road bikes, the kind with the curved handlebars. In both categories, you can't find many decent bikes under $500; many cost more than $2,000. Don't take out a second mortgage to buy a fancy bike, but if you have any inkling that you may like this sport, don't skimp, either. You'll just end up buying a more expensive bike later.

What distinguishes a $500 bike from a $2,000 steed? Generally, the more expensive the bike, the stronger and lighter its frame. A heavy bike can slow you down, but unless you plan to enter the Tour de France, don't get hung up on a matter of ounces. Cheaper bikes are made from different grades of steel; as you climb the price ladder, you find materials such as aluminum, carbon fiber, and titanium. The price of a bike also depends on the quality of all the mechanical doodads that enable your bike to move, shift, and brake.

Find a bike dealer you trust, and know that bike prices are negotiable. Ask the salesman to throw in a few free extras, like a bike computer to measure your speed and distance or a seat bag to carry food and tools.

A helmet and other critical biking equipment

Don't even think about pedaling down your driveway without a helmet snug atop your noggin. Cycling gloves make your ride more comfortable and protect your hands when you crash. Glasses are important to protect your eyes from the dust, dirt, and gravel.

Buy a pair of padded cycling shorts and a brightly colored cycling jersey so that you can easily be seen. Unlike cotton t-shirts, jerseys wick away sweat so that you don't freeze on a downhill after you work up a big sweat climbing up. Plus, jerseys have pockets in the back deep enough to hold loads of snacks. Always carry a water bottle or wear a backpack-like water pouch. Finally, carry gear to change a flat tire, and know how to use it. You can't call the cycling equivalent of the auto club.

Cycling the right way

To protect your knees from injury, position your seat correctly (ask your salesperson for advice) and pedal at an easy cadence. *Cadence* refers to the number of revolutions per minute that you pedal. Inexperienced cyclists tend to use more tension than they can handle, which forces them to turn the pedals in slow motion; their legs tire prematurely, their knees ache, and they cheat themselves out of a good workout.

Road cycling can wreak havoc on your lower back because you're in a crouched position for so long. Relax your upper body and keep your arms loose. Grasp your handlebars with the same tension that you'd hold a child's hand when you cross the street. Pedal in smooth circles rather than simply mashing the pedals downward. Imagine that you have a bed of nails in your shoes, and you have to pedal without stomping on the nails.

Cycling tips for rookies

You can find out a lot about cycling — and get faster in a jif — by riding with a club or friends who have more experience. Here are some pointers to start your cycling career.

- ✔ **Remember that you are a vehicle and are required to follow the rules of the road.** Stop at all signs and lights, and use those hand signals from Driver's Ed. Don't trust a single car, ever. Assume that the driver doesn't see you, even if he happens to be staring you in the face.

- ✔ **When you go off-road, start on wide roads rather than narrow "single-track" trails that require technical skills.** And don't think that you're immune to injury because there are no cars. More crashes happen on mountain trails than on the road because obstacles abound and riders get careless and cocky.

- ✔ **Head into turns at a slow enough pace that you maintain control, and never let your eyes wander from the road.** Never squeeze the brakes — particularly the front brake — with a lot of pressure.

Swimming

Swimming is truly a zero-impact sport. Although you can strain your shoulders if you overdo it, swimming doesn't pound on your joints, and the only thing you're in danger of crashing into is the end of the pool. You can get a great aerobic workout that uses your whole body. Plus, water has a gentle, soothing effect on the body, so swimming is helpful if you're coping with arthritis and other joint diseases.

Swimming is great for people who want to keep exercising when they're injured and for people who are pregnant or overweight. That extra body fat helps you glide along near the surface of the water, so you don't expend energy trying to keep yourself from sinking like a stone.

Lap swimming has the reputation of being drudgery — after all, the scenery doesn't change a whole lot from one end of the pool to the other. The trick is to use an array of gadgets that elevate swim workouts from forced labor to bona fide fun. You can even buy underwater tape players with pretty decent sound.

Essential swimming gear

Having the proper gear can determine if your aquatic fitness program sinks or swims. Check out the following list of essential swimming gear:

- **Body of water:** Preferably one manned by a lifeguard.

- **Swim suit:** Make sure it's a swim suit, not a bathing suit. You don't want a suit that looks good while you're sunbathing but creeps up your butt when you get in the water.

- **Goggles:** A must to prevent eye irritation and to help you see better in the water — especially if you're in a chlorinated pool. Buy goggles from a store that lets you try them on. You should feel some suction around your eyes, but not so much that you feel like your eyeballs are going to pop out.

- **Swim Cap:** A cap so that your hair doesn't get plastered on your face as you swim or turn to straw from the chemicals.

As for the fun swimming gadgets: Many pools let you borrow equipment, but you can buy a whole set for less than $75.

- **Kickboard:** A simple foam board can help you stay afloat and focus your workout on your legs and kicking motion.

- **Fins:** Rubber swimming fins give you a lot more speed and power in the water. If you're a beginning swimmer, you may feel like you're going nowhere without them, and you may have trouble moving fast enough to get your heart rate up.

  You can use fins when you kick with a kickboard, but don't use fins so much that they become a crutch. As you get in better shape, you may want to switch from long swim fins to short fins, which make you work a lot harder. Don't swim with scuba fins; they're too big and too stiff.

- **Paddles:** Swimming with plastic paddles on your hands gives your upper body an extra challenge. Some paddles are flat and rectangular; others are shaped more like your hand, with a comfortable contour in the palm area. Paddles can help you perfect your stroke technique and increase the intensity of your workout, but use them sparingly; overuse can lead to shoulder injuries. (When you swim with paddles, put a *pull-buoy* (a foam gadget) between your thighs. This keeps your legs buoyant so that you can concentrate on paddling rather than kicking.

Swimming the right way

During the bulk of your swimming workouts, you probably do the front crawl, also called *freestyle*. It's generally faster than the other strokes, so you can cover more distance. Don't cut your strokes short; reach out as far as you can and pull all the way through the water so your hand brushes your thigh. Elongate your stroke so that you take fewer than 25 strokes in a 25-yard pool. The fewer strokes, the better. Top swimmers get so much power from each stroke that they take just 11 to 14 strokes per length of a 25-yard pool.

Kick up and down from your hips, not your knees. Don't kick too deeply or allow your feet to break the water's surface. Proper kicking causes the water to "boil" rather than splash.

Breathe through your mouth every two strokes, or every three strokes if you want to alternate the side that you breathe on. You need as much oxygen as you can get. Beginners sometimes make the mistake of taking six or eight strokes before breathing, which wears them out quickly. To breathe, roll your entire body to the side until your mouth and nose come out of the water. Imagine that your entire body is on a skewer and must rotate together.

Swimming tips for rookies

Even if you're the queen of your aerobics class or a champion at cycling uphill, you may still tire quickly in the pool at first. More than almost any other aerobic activity, swimming relies on technique:

- ✔ **Take a few lessons if you haven't swum in a while.** Beginners waste a lot of energy flailing and splashing around rather than moving forward.

- ✔ **Break your workout into intervals.** Don't just get into the pool, swim 20 laps, and get out. Instead, do 4 easy laps for a warm-up. Then do 8 sets of 2 laps at a faster pace, resting 20 seconds between sets. Then cool down with 2 easy laps, and maybe a few extra laps with a kickboard. Mix up your strokes, too. The four basic strokes — front crawl, backstroke, breaststroke, and butterfly — use your muscles in different ways.

- ✔ **If swimming is your bag, join a Masters swim club.** These clubs, located at university and community pools nationwide, are geared toward adult swimmers of all levels. A coach gives you a different workout every time you swim and monitors your progress. Best of all, you have buddies to work out with.

Don't worry about being slow; the coach groups you in a lane with other people your speed. If you have a competitive spirit, you can compete in Masters meets, where you swim against others who are roughly your speed.

✔ **If you find swimming a big yawn but enjoy being in the water, try water running or water aerobics.** Water running is a pretty tough workout because the water provides resistance from all directions as you move your legs. It's an excellent workout for injured runners because even though it's non-impact and easy on your joints, it helps maintain aerobic conditioning. And don't assume that water aerobics is for little old ladies. With the right instructor and exercise program, you can get a challenging water aerobics workout.

Chapter 8

Healing Thyself

· ·

· ·

*T*he old saying goes that, once in a while, pain comes into everyone's life, but that doesn't mean that you can't do something about it! This chapter offers easy and powerful solutions to some of the most common medical conditions that people cope with. Better health is possible — just start reading, and you're sure to start feeling better.

Because you're a unique individual, consult with a professional healthcare provider for a complete interview and evaluation of your present condition and constitutional make up. If you receive advice that is contrary to the information this reference provides, follow the practitioner's advice, because your practitioner bases his or her advice on your unique characteristics and condition.

Arthritis

Ouch! There it goes again! That grinding pain in your hip; those aching knees that make walking from the kitchen to the bedroom a chore; the stiff and swollen fingers that don't allow you to twist the lid off a sticky jar or even sew on a button. The good news is that you can manage your arthritis, if not cure it, with a combination of medical care, simple lifestyle changes, and good old common sense.

Types of arthritis

Some organizations define arthritis as a group of more than 100 related diseases, ranging from bursitis to osteoarthritis. The following broad classifications conform to those widely accepted by the medical community:

- ✔ **True arthritis:** Conditions in which arthritis is the major part of the syndrome and the primary disease process. Common types include ankylosing spondylitis, gout, osteoarthritis, and rheumatoid arthritis.

- ✔ **Arthritis as a major player:** Arthritis is present and is usually a major part of the syndrome, but is not the primary disease process. Common types include Lyme disease, Reiter's syndrome, scleroderma, and systemic lupus erythematosus.

- ✔ **Arthritis as a minor player:** Arthritis may appear, but it is a minor part of the syndrome. Common types include bursitis, tendonitis, Paget's disease, polymyalgia rheumatica, Raynaud's disease, and Sjogren's syndrome.

- ✔ **Arthritis as a companion condition:** Arthritis may be present, but it constitutes another separate disease process. Common types include carpal tunnel syndrome, fibromyalgia, and myositis.

Always consult your medical practitioner to determine whether you're dealing with arthritis or another disease or disorder.

Helpful and harmful foods in the arthritis battle

The idea that foods, vitamins, minerals, and other substances can aid in the battle against arthritis is not new. What is new is that researchers are finding out *why* certain foods can be helpful — and why others can make a bad situation worse.

The good guys

Which fruits, vegetables, meat, or fish should you eat? You aren't going to find any absolute rules, but the results of studies and case histories suggest that the following foods may be helpful:

- ✔ **Anchovies and other fish:** Three-and-a-half ounces of anchovies contain almost a gram and a half of omega-3 fatty acids. The omega-3 fatty acids help regulate the *prostaglandins,* which play a role in inflammation and, hence, pain. However, anchovies are extremely high in sodium, so if sodium-sensitivity or water retention is a problem for you, choose a different kind of fish.

✔ **Apples:** Not only can an apple a day keep the doctor away, but it may also help to hold your arthritis at bay. Apples contain *boron,* a mineral that appears to reduce the risk of developing osteoarthritis and relieve pain for people who already have the disease.

✔ **Cantaloupe:** This sweet fruit contains large amounts of vitamin C and beta-carotene, the plant form of vitamin A. These two powerful vitamins help to control the oxidative and free-radical damage that may contribute to arthritis.

✔ **Chili peppers:** Chilies contain *capsaicin,* which gives them their heat. Capsician also helps to block pain by encouraging certain nerve cells to run through their supply of substance P, which they normally use to help transmit pain signals.

✔ **Curry:** A combination of spices that often includes turmeric, garlic, cumin, cinnamon, and so on, curry contains powerful antioxidants that may help relieve inflammation and reduce pain.

✔ **Garlic:** Although never tested in large-scale studies, garlic has been found helpful in many case studies. Garlic contains sulfur, which experts believe helps relieve certain arthritis symptoms.

✔ **Grapes:** These bunches of bite-sized fruit are good sources of the mineral boron, which is important for strong bones.

✔ **Mango:** A sweet treat, mangoes are packed with three powerful antioxidants: vitamin C, beta-carotene, and vitamin E.

✔ **Nuts:** Almonds, peanuts, and hazelnuts are good sources of boron, a mineral that helps keep bones strong.

✔ **Papaya:** A single papaya contains three times the RDA for the antioxidant vitamin C, plus more than half the daily allotment of beta-carotene.

✔ **Water:** Drinking eight glasses of water per day can help battle gout by flushing uric acid from the body.

The bad guys

No foods actually cause arthritis. At worst, they may exacerbate a pre-existing condition. However, *some* foods do give *some* people trouble, so you may want to consider cutting back or avoiding the following:

✔ **Nightshades:** Peppers, potatoes, eggplant, and tomatoes are some of the members of the *nightshade* family of vegetables. Some people feel that eating nightshades aggravates their rheumatoid arthritis and other forms of the disease. Although no study proves this, if you feel that eating nightshades worsens your symptoms, avoid them.

- **Organ meats:** Liver, kidney, sweet bread, and other organ meats contain the *purines* that can trigger gout. If you have gout, avoid other foods high in purines, including sardines, anchovies, and meat gravies.

- **Processed meat:** Cold cuts, hot dogs, bacon, and other processed meats contain various chemicals that may trigger allergic reactions, bringing about arthritis-like symptoms. Or, they may cause flare-ups of existing arthritis conditions. Scientists are unclear whether these substances actually trigger arthritis or allergies, or whether they tend to replace the vegetables, fruits, and whole grains that provide nutrients you need to hold arthritis at bay.

- **Foods containing linoleic/arachidonic acid:** The omega-3 fatty acids help reduce inflammation, but *linoleic acid,* an omega-6 fatty acid, does the opposite. You find linoleic acid in salad or cooking oils, such as corn, safflower, and sunflower. You can find linoleic acid in many kinds of fast food, and large amounts of it are fed to the cattle that eventually end up in your grocery store. To avoid linoleic acid, switch to olive, flaxseed, or canola oil for cooking, eat less meat and poultry, and avoid fast foods. At the same time, increase your consumption of fish and other foods that contain helpful omega-3 fatty acids.

Hot paraffin wax treatments

Hot paraffin wax treatments are a nice, comfortable way to warm up painful joints in your hands and feet. These treatments sustain their warmth because they use wax as insulation. A physical therapist usually applies hot paraffin wax treatments, but you can do it yourself at home.

How do hot paraffin wax treatments work? Your painful hand or foot is repeatedly dipped into a blend of melted wax and mineral oil and allowed to cool in between immersions so that the wax can harden. When the build-up is thick enough, your hand/foot is wrapped in plastic and covered with towels to preserve the heat. The locked-in warmth can soothe your stiff, painful fingers, or toes. After 20 minutes or so, the wrapping comes off, and the wax is peeled away. As an added bonus, hot paraffin leaves your skin wonderfully soft!

Don't use this treatment if your hand or foot shows any sign of skin damage.

General practitioner versus rheumatologist

Whether you need a specialist depends upon the kind of arthritis you have. If you have osteoarthritis, you may do well under the care of a general practitioner or internist. But if you have a more complicated kind of arthritis (such as rheumatoid arthritis), you probably need to see a rheumatologist.

Rheumatologists specialize in diseases of the joints, muscles, and bones and treat arthritis, musculoskeletal pain disorders, osteoporosis, and various autoimmune diseases. An important part of the rheumatologist's job is proper diagnosis of the disease because symptoms can point to many different conditions. After the rheumatologist pinpoints the disease, proper treatment can begin, so early and accurate diagnosis is crucial. If you don't have a clear-cut case of osteoarthritis, or if your symptoms seem to baffle your family physician or internist, consult a rheumatologist.

Dealing with chronic pain

The goal in chronic pain management is to block pain messages before they reach the brain. You can try several natural ways, including:

- ✓ Exercise that's appropriate to your condition
- ✓ Hot or cold treatments
- ✓ Magnets
- ✓ Massage
- ✓ Relaxation
- ✓ TENS (transcutaneous electrical stimulation)
- ✓ Topical pain relievers
- ✓ Water therapy

On the other hand, several "natural" things can make your pain even worse:

- ✓ Anxiety
- ✓ Depression
- ✓ Fatigue
- ✓ Focusing on your pain

✔ Physical overexertion

✔ Progression of the disease

✔ Stress

Choosing the right doctor to treat your arthritis

Some doctors are more aggressive than others when treating arthritis; some like the idea of alternative approaches. The best way to discover a doctor's philosophy on diagnosis and treatment is simply to ask. You may find the following questions helpful:

✔ Do you consider yourself aggressive or conservative in treating arthritis?

✔ Do you think medication is always, or almost always, the best treatment for arthritis?

✔ How valuable are diet, exercise, and stress reduction in treating arthritis?

✔ Do you favor the use of vitamins, herbs, and other supplements as additional treatments? If so, which ones?

✔ How do you feel about using alternative therapies (chiropractic, massage, homeopathy, magnets, acupuncture, and so on) in conjunction with standard treatment? Which therapies do you feel are best?

No right answers to these questions exist. Ideally, you can find a doctor with attitudes toward treatment that dovetail nicely with your own.

Allergies

The word *allergy* is the ancient Greek term for an abnormal response or overreaction. Contrary to popular belief, weak or deficient immune systems don't cause allergy ailments. Rather, your body's defenses work overtime, making your immune system too sensitive to substances that pose no real threat to your well-being.

Preventing hay fever complications

Frequently referred to as "hay fever," *allergic rhinitis* is the most common allergic disease in the United States. As many as 45 million

Americans suffer from some form of this allergy. Trademark symptoms include runny nose with watery discharge, stuffy nose, sneezing, postnasal drip, and scratchy nose, ears, palate, and throat.

If you have hay fever, consider taking the following preventive measures to keep your sinuses clear in the event that you come down with an upper respiratory infection (such as the common cold) or experience an allergy attack:

- ✔ Take appropriate medications, which your doctor can prescribe.

- ✔ Drink plenty of water to keep your mucus thin and fluid so your sinuses can drain more easily.

- ✔ Be nice to your nose — blow it gently, preferably one nostril at a time.

- ✔ Avoid flying. If you have to travel by air while you have a cold or an allergy attack, use a topical nasal decongestant spray prior to takeoff. The spray prevents the sudden pressure changes from blocking your sinuses and ears.

- ✔ Avoid swimming. You probably don't feel like going to the beach or the pool if you have a cold or allergy attack, and your sinuses don't do well with the pressure changes that swimming and diving involve.

Nasal rebound

No, nasal rebound is not a new basketball technique. This condition results from prolonged overuse of over-the-counter decongestant nasal sprays and drops. Overuse can irritate and inflame the mucous membranes in your nose more than before you used the spray, leading to more serious nasal congestion.

Unfortunately, some people increase their use of topical products as their congestion worsens, leading to a vicious cycle in which more product produces more congestion. When this happens, higher doses do not clear the congestion — they only make it worse.

To break this vicious cycle, you must stop using your topical OTC decongestant. Your doctor may also need to prescribe a short course of oral and/or topical nasal corticosteroids to clear your nasal congestion and allow you to tolerate the discontinuation of the topical OTC decongestant.

Remember, the warning on the label that directs you not to use the nasal decongestant spray or drops longer than three to five days really means three to five days and no more. If your stuffy nose persists beyond this point, consider using an oral decongestant.

Allergy-proofing your home

Although you should avoid or limit exposure to allergens and irritants outside — as well as at work, school, or other indoor locations — avoidance therapy can actually have the most beneficial impact in your home.

You spend about one-third of your life in your bedroom — much of that time in bed. Because you spend so much time there, your bedroom is the most important single area in your home. After you allergy-proof your bedroom, try to use it as much as possible to insure that you give your allergies a rest.

Additionally, controlling irritants at home is vital to successful avoidance therapy. Although irritants don't trigger an allergic response by your body's immune system — as is the case with allergens — they often worsen existing allergy or asthma conditions. The most significant irritants include tobacco, aerosols, paints, smoke from wood-burning stoves, glue, household cleaners, perfumes, and scented soaps.

Preventing and managing reactions to insects

Effectively managing your sensitivity to insect stings can mean the difference between enjoying the great outdoors relatively worry-free or risking recurrences of serious allergic reactions.

If you have an insect sting hypersensitivity, consult your doctor about taking preventive measures, such as the following:

- ✔ **Avoid bugging insects, and they usually won't bug you.** This is a no-brainer. If stinging insects are in your vicinity, don't provoke them. Move as quickly and calmly out of the area as possible. If you run, flap your arms, or otherwise get agitated, the insect may sting in self-defense.

- ✔ **Make sure that your children don't poke, prod, hit, or otherwise play with insect hives, nests, or mounds.**

- ✔ **Hire a trained extermination professional to check your home and its surroundings for insect nests.**

- ✔ **Stay away from strongly scented lotions, perfumes, colognes, and hair products.** Likewise, don't wear brightly colored or flower-print clothing. Try khaki and other light-colored apparel. Also, avoid loose clothing that may trap insects.

✔ **Don't use electric hedge clippers and power mowers.** For some reason, electricity excites some species of stinging insects. In general, don't do yard work yourself if you have a stinging insect hypersensitivity.

✔ **If you work outdoors, cover up from head to toe with long pants, a long-sleeved shirt, socks, closed shoes, a hat, and work gloves.** Wear closed shoes (not sandals) or sneakers when you're outdoors.

✔ **Practice caution near flowery plants, blooming orchards (they're in bloom because something's busy pollinating them), bushes, clover fields, eaves, attics, garbage containers, and picnic areas.**

✔ **Have insecticides at hand to zap stinging insects before they zap you.** Insect repellents don't work on stinging insects. Bear in mind that if these products kill insects, then they're also not too good for you either. Therefore, make sure that you use insecticides properly as the manufacturer instructs.

✔ **Be careful when eating or drinking outdoors or when you're near areas where food and beverages are served.** Also, cover the opening to your beverage in between sips and never drink from an open container that's been left outdoors.

✔ **Check to see whether the insect left a stinger, which usually looks like a black thorn or splinter, in your skin.** Carefully remove the stinger, using a tweezer to pry or a credit card to flick or scrape the stinger from your skin. Never squeeze the stinger with your fingers in an effort to remove it. Doing so only pumps more venom into your body, making your reaction worse.

✔ **After a sting, walk slowly, don't run.** Running may increase your body's absorption of the venom.

Asthma

Although asthma is chronicled in ancient history (the Roman emperor Caesar Augustus was one of many historical figures who suffered from asthma), the disease is still very much a part of the modern world. More than 17 million people in the U.S. have some form of asthma. That figure equals three times the number of asthma cases diagnosed in 1960, despite major medical breakthroughs in diagnosing and treating airway obstruction — the basis of this disease.

Examining asthma triggers

Effectively managing your asthma requires you to identify the triggers and precipitating factors that may affect your condition, including:

- ✔ **Inhalant allergens,** including animal danders, dust mite and cockroach allergens, some mold spores, and certain airborne pollens of grasses, weeds, and trees.

- ✔ **Occupational irritants and allergens,** found primarily in the workplace, including dust and various chemicals.

- ✔ **Other irritants that you inhale,** such as tobacco smoke, household products, and indoor and outdoor air pollution.

- ✔ **Nonallergic triggers,** including exercise and physical stimuli such as variations in air temperature and humidity levels.

- ✔ **Other medical conditions,** including rhinitis, sinusitis, gastroesophageal reflux, and viral infections; sensitivities to some drugs and food additives — particularly sulfites.

- ✔ **Emotional activities,** such as crying, laughing, or even yelling. Although emotions themselves aren't the direct triggers of asthma symptoms, activities associated with emotions can induce coughing or wheezing.

Controlling asthma

Controlling asthma means treating the underlying airway inflammation. Think of your asthma as a smoldering campfire in your lungs. If you only pay attention to the embers after they flare up, containing the flames becomes a serious problem. The goal of your asthma management plan should instead be to get your asthma under control to the extent that you only rarely use bronchodilators on an as-needed basis — usually to reduce the risk of symptoms when exposed to unavoidable asthma triggers or precipitating factors, especially exercise.

Also, beware of relying on inhaled short-acting bronchodilators, because the quick relief these products provide can also give you the false impression that your asthma is just a set of symptoms, rather than a serious, underlying medical problem. If zapping your wheezing with a bronchodilator is the only way you deal with your persistent asthma, you may feel fine for a short while. However, if you use your peak flow meter to check your peak expiratory flow rate (PEFR), you quickly realize that your airflow is significantly decreased and your lung functions are below normal.

Knowing enough about your medicines

An informed patient is a healthier person. *Remember:* Making sure that you understand all aspects of your treatment is your responsibility as a patient. Don't hesitate to inquire about medications your doctor prescribes for any ailment. Make sure that you know the following information about your prescription before you leave your doctor's office and begin using a medication:

- The name of the medication, the prescribed dose, how often you should take it, and over what period of time you must use it. Your doctor may provide an instruction card with this information. This card can greatly assist you in communicating with other doctors about the medications you're taking, and it may prove vital in an emergency situation. Likewise, ensuring that the product's name is clearly written is important, because the drug and brand names of many medications sound alike.

- The way the drug works, any potential adverse side effects that may result, and what you should do if any of these side effects occur.

- What you should do if you accidentally miss a dose or take an extra dose of the medication.

- Any cautions about potential interactions between your prescription and other medications you already take or may take, including over-the-counter (OTC) antihistamines, decongestants, pain relievers, vitamins, or nutritional supplements.

- Any effects your prescription may have on various aspects of your life, such as your job, school, exercise or sports, other activities, sleeping patterns, and diet.

- If the medication is for a child, make sure that you know how a child's dosage may differ from an adult's.

- If you're pregnant or nursing a child, make sure that you inform your doctor about these situations.

- Be sure your doctor knows about any adverse reactions you've had to any drugs in the past, including both prescription and OTC preparations.

Use only those products that are clearly identified to treat the symptoms you experience. Also, always be careful to read the product instructions and only take the medication as those instructions say or according to your doctor's directions.

Occasionally, doctors need to prescribe medications "off label" (beyond the manufacturer's official recommendations) in order to achieve maximal improvement in a particular patient's condition.

In addition to the printed information that doctors may provide concerning the drugs they prescribe, you can also request materials from the National Council on Patient Information and Education, 666 11th St. NW, Suite 810, Washington, DC, 20001-4542; phone 202-347-6711.

Heart Disease

Heart disease is surprisingly common in our society and more than a little scary. You depend on your heart to keep you going at full speed — so take a moment to take care of its needs.

Six risk factors that you can control

Although risk factors often are classified as *major* factors or *other* factors, dividing risks into those that you can modify and those that you cannot control is probably even more helpful.

Hypertension

Since landmark studies conducted in the 1960s, there has been no serious doubt that elevated blood pressure represents a very substantial risk factor for both coronary heart disease and stroke. Hypertension is extremely common in the U.S., probably because of the population's nutritional habits, propensity to gain weight, and sedentary lifestyle. More than one-fourth of the adult population in the U.S. suffers from hypertension.

Daily habits and practices, such as appropriate weight control, sound nutrition, and regular physical activity can profoundly diminish the likelihood of ever developing hypertension in the first place and can significantly contribute to the effective treatment of elevated blood pressure.

Elevated cholesterol

By now, almost everyone knows that having a high cholesterol level in your blood is bad. When it comes to risk of heart disease, however, elevated blood cholesterol is one of a number of *lipid problems* (problems with fats in the blood) that can significantly elevate your risk of heart disease. The abnormalities that are particularly dangerous include elevated total cholesterol, elevated LDL cholesterol, low HDL cholesterol, elevated triglycerides, or any combination of the four.

The good news is that by following appropriate lifestyle measures and, in some instances, utilizing medicines that are now available, you can effectively manage this risk factor for coronary heart disease.

Tobacco use

With all the information available about health, heart disease, and cigarette smoking, smokers who fail to understand that smoking poses a very serious threat to their health must have been hiding incommunicado in the wilderness for the last 20 years. Reams of data present a very stark, negative picture: Cigarette smoking (and the use of other tobacco products) is the leading cause of premature death in the U.S. each year, claiming more than 400,000 lives. Although cigarette smoking has declined, about 25 percent of the adult population still smokes cigarettes.

In an otherwise bleak picture, outstanding good news includes:

✔ Stopping smoking lowers the risk of coronary heart disease.

✔ Individuals who quit smoking can anticipate adding two to three years to their life expectancy.

✔ Smoking cessation also improves blood lipids. In one study, LDL cholesterol decreased more than 5 percent and HDL cholesterol increased more than 3 percent in individuals who stopped cigarette smoking.

Physical inactivity

In 1994, faced with overwhelming evidence, the American Heart Association added the first new "major" risk factor in 25 years — a physically inactive lifestyle. Physical inactivity also contributes significantly to a number of the other major risk factors, such as high blood pressure, perhaps elevated blood cholesterol, and often obesity. But if you get off your duff and get active, you can turn this sad picture around.

For great tips about getting in a low-stress, high-benefit fitness routine, check out Chapter 7.

Obesity

In 1998, obesity joined the list of major independent risk factors for heart disease. Obesity also contributes to many other risk factors, such as hypertension and elevated cholesterol and other abnormal lipids.

Unfortunately, in the last ten years, the prevalence of obesity has grown a shocking 34 percent. More than one out of every three adults is now obese — at least 20 percent over desirable body weight. That's not as fat as most people think, either. For example, if your optimal weight is 150 pounds and you weigh 180 — just 30 pounds overweight — you're technically obese even if you think you still look pretty good.

A sensible diet and exercise plan can counteract the negative effects of obesity. Check out Chapter 6 for hints on how to make your diet more healthy.

Diabetes mellitus

Approximately 14 million people in the U.S., or 6 percent of the adult population, suffer from diabetes mellitus. More than 95 percent of these individuals have Type 2 or "adult onset" diabetes. Diabetes represents a significant risk factor for coronary heart disease. In fact, coronary heart disease is by far the leading cause of death in individuals with diabetes.

By working with your physician if you have diabetes, however, you can lower many of the complications of diabetes and also control your blood lipids. Daily steps that you can take to help control diabetes include weight loss if you're overweight, regular physical activity, and proper nutritional habits.

Assessing your risk

Many tests are available to help you assess your risk of developing coronary heart disease in general and first heart attacks in particular. The following test, based on data from the Framingham Heart Study, helps you assess your risk of having a first heart attack. It also gives you a good idea of how you can work to modify your risk factors.

First Heart Attack Risk Test

Fill in your points for each risk factor. Then total them to find out your risk.

_____ **Age (in years): Men**

0 pts. less than 35; 1 pt. 35-39; 2 pts. 40-48; 3 pts. 49-53; 4 pts. 54+

_____ **Age (in years): Women**

0 pts. less than 42; 1 pt. 42-44; 2 pts. 45-54; 3 pts. 55-73; 4 pts. 74+

_____ **Family History**

2 pts. A family history of heart disease or heart attacks before age 60.

_____ **Inactive lifestyle**

1 pt. I rarely exercise or do anything physically demanding.

_____ **Weight**

1 pt. I'm more than 20 lbs. over my ideal weight.

_____ **Smoking**

1 pt. I'm a smoker

_____ **Diabetic**

1 pt. Male diabetic; 2 pts. Female Diabetic

_____ **Total Cholesterol Level**

0 pts. Less than 240 mg/dl; 1 pt. 240-315 mg/dl; 2 pts. More than 315 mg/dl

_____ **Blood Pressure**

I don't take blood pressure medication; my blood pressure is:

(use your top or higher blood pressure number)

0 pts. Less than 140 mmHg; 1 pt. 140-170 mmHg; 2 pts. Greater than 170 mmHg

(or)

1 pt. I am currently taking blood pressure medication.

_____ **Total Points**

If you score 4 points or more, you may be at above the average risk of a first heart attack compared to the general adult population. The more points you score, the higher your risk. (Based on data from The Framingham Study, as adapted by Bristol Meyer Squib.)

Stress reduction and cardiac health

Stress may be dangerous to the heart, but the good news is that some simple strategies may significantly lower stress and thereby improve cardiac health. Here are four ways to lower stress in your life and contribute to cardiac health.

> ✔ **Modify or eliminate circumstances that contribute to stress and cardiac symptoms.** Often people don't realize that aspects of their daily lives can compound problems with stress. Cutting back on caffeine-containing beverages, for example, may make a substantial difference to stress levels and manifestations such as cardiac palpitations. Fatigue and insomnia may also contribute to stress. Be sure to get plenty of rest and a good night's

sleep if you're experiencing symptoms of stress. Avoid the temptation to use alcohol as a way to relax; it may seem to offer temporary stress release but usually leads to greater problems.

✔ **Live in the present.** It may sound simple, but many people spend an inordinate amount of time either regretting the past or fearing the future. Strategies such as biofeedback, visualization, and medication can help you live in the present and substantially lower stress. Check out Chapter 9 for more information on these and other techniques.

✔ **Get out of your own way.** Many people compound the inevitable stresses of daily life by layering on negative feelings concerning their stresses. No one can live a life that is completely free of stress, and allowing feelings of negativity or low self-worth only compounds problems.

✔ **Develop a personal plan for stress.** Developing a personal plan to alleviate stress is one of the more effective ways to handle it on an ongoing basis, rather than allowing it to become free-floating anxiety. Many people find that daily exercise, meditation, "time out" either alone or with family, and other such strategies provide effective ways to control the stresses of daily life.

Ten cardiac symptoms: Which are worrisome, which aren't

Although medical signs and symptoms can overlap, you can distinguish the two on the basis of who is experiencing them. For example, you may regard a nagging, worrisome cough as a *symptom*. Your doctor, however, may regard that cough as a *sign* of congestion of the lungs. In broad terms, then, *symptoms* are feelings or conditions that you experience and then try to describe to your physician. *Signs* are findings that your physician derives from a physical examination that point toward the proper cardiac diagnosis.

The following are ten key symptoms and signs of serious cardiac disease.

Chest pain

Chest pain is probably the most common symptom that causes people to see a cardiologist. Although heart problems are common causes of chest pain, chest pain can also come from a wide variety of structures in the chest, neck, and back that have no relation (other than proximity) to the heart. Pain caused by angina or heart attack is usually located beneath the breastbone, but the front of the chest or either arm, neck, cheeks, teeth, or high in the middle of the back are also possible locations. Exercise, strong emotion, or stress often provokes the pain. Very short bouts of pain lasting five to ten seconds are typically heart-related but are more likely to be musculoskeletal pain. If you have concern about *any* chest discomfort, you must go to a medical facility for further evaluation.

Shortness of breath

Determining whether shortness of breath comes from problems with the heart, the lungs, or some other organ system can be difficult. Exertion can cause temporary shortness of breath in otherwise healthy individuals who are working or exercising strenuously or in sedentary individuals who are working even moderately. But an abnormally uncomfortable awareness of breathing or difficulty breathing can be a symptom of a medical problem. Shortness of breath that occurs when you're at rest, for example, is considered a strong cardiac symptom. If shortness of breath lasts longer than five minutes after activity or occurs at rest, see your doctor.

Loss of consciousness

Loss of consciousness usually results from a reduced supply of blood to the brain. Perhaps the most common loss of consciousness is what people commonly call a "fainting" episode. Being in a warm or constricted environment or in a highly emotional state may bring on this temporary condition. Dizziness and/or a sense of "fading to black" often precedes such episodes. When the heart is the cause, loss of consciousness typically occurs rapidly and doesn't have preceding events. Cardiac conditions ranging from rhythm disturbance to mechanical problems can potentially cause fainting or a blackout. Because such cardiac problems can be serious, never dismiss loss of consciousness in an otherwise healthy individual as a "faint" until you have a complete medical examination.

Cardiovascular collapse

You can't experience a more dramatic symptom or greater emergency than cardiovascular collapse, also called *sudden cardiac death*. Cardiovascular collapse results in a sudden loss of consciousness, but the victim typically has no pulse and stops breathing (whereas the victim of a seizure or fainting spell does have a pulse and continues breathing). Cardiovascular collapse can occur as a complication in an individual who has known heart disease, but sometimes may be the first manifestation of an acute heart attack or rhythm problem. When cardiovascular collapse occurs, resuscitation must occur within minutes, or death follows.

Palpitations

Palpitations, which medical professionals define as an unpleasant awareness of a rapid or forceful beating of the heart, may indicate anything from serious cardiac rhythm problems to nothing worrisome at all. Typically, an individual who is experiencing palpitations describes a sensation of a "skipped" beat; however, people can also describe a rapid heartbeat or a sensation of lightheadedness. Whenever the palpitation is accompanied by lightheadedness or loss of consciousness, you must undertake further examination to determine whether serious, underlying heart rhythm problems are present. Often, you can improve the underlying causes of palpitations by getting more sleep, drinking fewer caffeinated beverages, decreasing alcohol consumption, or trying to reduce the amount of stress in your life. But take the problem to your doctor for evaluation first.

Edema

Edema is an abnormal accumulation of fluid in the body, a type of swelling, and has many causes. The location and distribution of the swelling is helpful in determining what causes it. If edema occurs in the legs, it's usually characteristic of heart failure or of problems with the veins of the legs. Edema with a cardiac origin typically is *symmetric;* that is, it involves both legs. If the edema is an abnormal gathering of fluid in the lungs, called *pulmonary edema,* the typical symptom is shortness of breath. This symptom, too, can be typical in a patient with heart failure. Abnormal gathering of fluid, either in the legs or the lungs, always indicates the need for a complete cardiac exam to determine whether one or both of the main pumping chambers of the heart are not working adequately.

Cyanosis

Cyanosis, a bluish discoloration of the skin, occurs when unoxygenated blood that is normally pumped through the right side of the heart somehow passes into the left ventricle and is pumped out to the body. This commonly occurs in congenital abnormalities that create abnormal openings between the right and left side of the heart. Cyanosis can also be caused by constriction of blood vessels, which may come either from a low output from the heart or from exposure to cold air or water. Any form of cyanosis is a symptom that requires prompt discussion with your physician.

Cough

As anyone who has had a head cold knows, a cough can accompany a viral illness. It can also represent a variety of underlying causes such as cancers, allergies, abnormalities of the lungs, or abnormalities of the breathing tube. The cardiovascular disorders that result in cough are those that cause abnormal accumulations of fluid in the lungs, such as significant heart failure. Take any prolonged or unexplained cough to your doctor. Certainly anytime blood is present in what you cough up, you need to have the possible causes checked out. The same goes for any evidence of bacterial infection, typically yellowish, greenish, or blood-tinged sputum.

Hemoptysis

Coughing up blood of any kind — from small streaks in sputum to large quantities — is *hemoptysis*. This condition can result from a variety of serious diseases of the lungs or even some forms of cancer. Whatever the cause, coughing up blood-tinged secretions is never normal and may represent a medical emergency. If you ever cough up blood in any form — no matter how minor it seems — immediately contact your doctor.

Fatigue

Fatigue may come from a bewilderingly large number of underlying causes ranging from depression, to side effects of drugs, to physical illnesses, including cardiac problems. The ordinary fatigue you feel after working hard is normal, even when you have to crash into bed early. But a significant level of *enduring* fatigue necessitates a call to your doctor, who may want to do additional medical work to determine possible underlying causes.

How to survive a heart attack

The following six-point survival plan, adapted from recommendations from the American Medical Association, can save your life. Take these steps if you or a loved one is experiencing the symptoms of a possible heart attack:

1. **Stop what you're doing and sit or lie down.**

2. **If symptoms persist for more than two minutes, call your local emergency number or 911 and say that you may be having a heart attack.**

   Leave the phone off the hook so that medical personnel can locate your address in the event that you become unconscious.

3. **Take nitroglycerin, if possible.**

   If you have nitroglycerin tablets, take up to three pills under your tongue, one at a time, every five minutes, if your chest pain persists. If you don't have nitroglycerin, take two aspirin.

4. **Do not drive yourself (or a loved one) to the hospital.**

   Ambulances have equipment and personnel who are trained to deal with individuals who are having a heart attack. Driving yourself or a loved one to the hospital is an invitation for a disaster.

5. **If the person's pulse or breathing stops, any individual trained in cardiopulmonary resuscitation (CPR) should immediately begin to administer it.**

   Call 911 immediately, but do not delay instituting CPR.

6. **When you arrive at the emergency room at the hospital, announce clearly that you (or your loved one) may be having a heart attack and that they need to see you immediately. Do not be shy about this.**

Diabetes

The standard definition of *diabetes mellitus* is excessive glucose in a blood sample. The standard level for a normal glucose was lowered in 1997 because too many people were experiencing complications of diabetes even though they didn't have the disease by the then-current standard.

A hormone called *insulin* finely controls the level of blood glucose. In addition to providing the key to entry of glucose into the cell, insulin is the "builder hormone." It enables fat and muscle to form; it promotes storage of glucose in a form called *glycogen* for use when fuel isn't coming in. It blocks breakdown of protein. Without insulin, you can't survive for long.

The following contains the most common early symptoms of diabetes and how they occur. One or more of the following symptoms may be present when diabetes is diagnosed:

- **Frequent urination and thirst:** The glucose in the urine draws more water out of the blood, so more urine forms. More urine in your bladder makes you feel the need to urinate more frequently during the day and to get up at night to empty your bladder, which keeps filling up. As the amount of water in your blood declines, you feel thirsty and drink much more frequently.

- **Fatigue:** Because glucose can't enter cells that depend on insulin as a key for glucose, your body can't use glucose as a fuel to move muscles or to facilitate the many other chemical reactions that have to take place to produce energy. A person with diabetes often complains of fatigue and feels much stronger after treatment allows glucose to enter cells again.

- **Weight loss:** When insulin is lacking for any reason, the body begins to break down. You lose muscle tissue. Some of the muscle converts into glucose even though it cannot get into cells. It passes out of your body in the urine. Fat tissue breaks down into small fat particles that can provide an alternate source of energy. As your body breaks down and you lose glucose in the urine, you often experience weight loss.

✔ **Persistent vaginal infection among women:** As blood glucose rises, all the fluids in your body contain higher levels of glucose, including the sweat and body secretions such as semen in men and vaginal secretions in women. Bacteria and fungi thrive in this high glucose environment. Women begin to complain of itching or burning, abnormal discharge from the vagina, and sometimes an odor.

Type 1 diabetes

Healthcare professionals once called *type 1 diabetes* "juvenile diabetes" because it occurs most frequently in children. However, so many cases occur in adults that doctors don't use the term "juvenile" any more. Some children are diagnosed early in life, and other children have a more severe onset of the disease as they get a little older.

You may get type 1 diabetes if you have certain factors on your *chromosomes,* the DNA in each cell in your body that determines your physical characteristics. If you have several of these factors, your chance of getting type 1 diabetes is much greater than that of a person who has none of the factors.

But just having the risk factors isn't enough. You have to come in contact with something in your environment that triggers the destruction of the cells that make insulin. Doctors think that this environmental trigger is probably a virus, and they've identified several viruses that may be to blame. Persons with type 1 diabetes probably get the virus just like any cold virus, but because they also have the genetic tendency, they get type 1 diabetes.

A small number (about 10 percent) of patients with type 1 diabetes don't seem to need an environmental factor to trigger the diabetes. In them, the disease is entirely an autoimmune destruction of beta cells. If you fall into this category, you may have other autoimmune diseases, such as autoimmune thyroid disease.

Type 2 diabetes

Type 2 diabetes is a disease of gradual onset rather than the severe emergency that can herald type 1 diabetes. *Type 2 diabetes* begins around age 40 and increases in frequency with age. Because the symptoms are so mild at first, you may ignore symptoms for years before they become bothersome enough to consult your doctor. A fairly large percentage of the U.S. population has type 2 diabetes.

Genetic inheritance causes type 2 diabetes, but environmental factors such as obesity and lack of exercise trigger the disease. People with type 2 diabetes are insulin-resistant before they become obese or sedentary. Later, aging, poor eating habits, obesity, and failure to exercise combine to bring out the disease. Inheritance seems to be a much stronger factor in type 2 diabetes than in type 1 diabetes. The chance that a parent with type 2 diabetes has a child with type 2 diabetes (assuming that the other parent doesn't have the disease) is about 10 percent. An identical twin of a person with type 2 diabetes eventually gets the disease much more often than 50 percent of the time. If you're a non-identical brother or sister of someone with type 2 disease, you have a 40 percent chance of getting the disease. All these figures are much higher than for type 1 diabetes.

Symptoms of hypoglycemia

Your body doesn't function well when you have too little glucose in your blood. Your brain needs glucose to run the rest of your body, as well as for intellectual purposes. Your muscles need the energy that glucose provides in much the same way that your car needs gasoline. So, when your body detects that it has low blood glucose, it sends out a group of hormones that rapidly raise your glucose. But those hormones have to fight the strength of the diabetes medication that has been pushing down your glucose levels.

The following symptoms may tip you off that you're hypoglycemic:

- ✓ Anxiety
- ✓ Dizziness
- ✓ Palpitations, or the feeling that your heart is beating too fast
- ✓ Rapid heartbeat
- ✓ Sensation of hunger
- ✓ Sweating
- ✓ Whiteness, or pallor, of your skin

Intelligent people often lose the ability to think clearly when they become hypoglycemic. They make simple mistakes, and other people often assume that they're drunk.

Exercising when you have diabetes

If you're diabetic, you need to check with your doctor before beginning any exercise program, especially if you're over the age of 35 or if you've had diabetes for ten years or longer. Additionally, check with a doctor if you have any of the following risk factors:

✔ The presence of any diabetic complications like retinopathy, nephropathy, or neuropathy

✔ Obesity

✔ A physical limitation

✔ A history of coronary artery disease or elevated blood pressure

✔ Use of medications

After you begin exercising, you can do a lot to make your workouts safe and healthful.

✔ Wear an ID bracelet

✔ Test your blood glucose very often

✔ Drink plenty of water

✔ Carry treatment for hypoglycemia

✔ Exercise with a friend

Eating for hypoglycemia

Whether you have hypoglycemia or simply suffer from a tendency to have low blood sugar, these eating guidelines can help you keep your blood sugar on an even keel.

✔ Avoid sugar and concentrated sweets. These include jam, jelly, colas, all sweet desserts, dried fruit, fruit juice, and such concoctions as the sugar sauce on sweet and sour spare ribs.

✔ Substitute whole grains and whole-grain flour for refined grain and flour.

✔ Eat small meals and eat more frequently, every two to three hours.

✔ In each meal and snack, include a source of complex carbohydrates, protein, and fat. For example, if you eat an apple, have a little cheese along with it.

✔ Eat foods high in vitamin C, because hypoglycemia interferes with the vitamin's metabolism.

Both chromium and manganese play an important role in the metabolism of glucose. People with hypoglycemia are also often deficient in zinc. These minerals are present in many common foods:

✔ **Chromium:** Mushrooms, beets, asparagus, seaweed, potatoes, broccoli, prunes, grapes, whole wheat, brown rice, whole oats, bulgur wheat, clams, beef, turkey, and maple syrup

✔ **Manganese:** Lima beans, chickpeas, soybeans, navy beans, collards, okra, peas, pineapple, bananas, whole wheat, brown rice, buckwheat, Brazil nuts, hazelnuts, sunflower and pumpkin seeds, bass, and trout

✔ **Zinc:** Oysters and other seafood, egg yolks, lamb chops, liver, lima beans, mushrooms, and sunflower seeds

An unusual food that helps lower elevated blood sugar is *nopales,* a form of cactus (the taste is similar to string beans). In studies, nopales lowers elevated blood glucose associated with diabetes. Nopales is sold fresh in markets in the Southwest and is widely available canned.

Be aware that sugar comes in many forms and goes by many names. Many food products contain several kinds of sugar, which add up to a considerable amount! Look for the following sugar pseudonyms on food labels: corn syrup, corn sweetener, high fructose, dextrose, dextrin, fructose, fruit juice concentrate, malt, invert sugar, and evaporated cane juice.

Chapter 9

Understanding Alternative Medicine

A t least one in three people in the United States has tried alternative medicine, most of them without ever mentioning that fact to their conventional physician. That ratio translates into approximately 85 million people. Throughout history, alternative medicine has been popular whenever people were frustrated because conventional treatments didn't work or were expensive, dangerous, and painful.

Some of the pluses of alternative medicine can also be minuses. In particular, the idea of empowered patients responsible for their own health care is great — but it can also be a burden. Separating the wheat (that is, safe and effective alternatives) from the chaff (that is, everything else) can be difficult. This chapter shares insight into how you can find a safe and comfortable fit with an alternative approach to your good health.

Nine Power-Packed Herbs

From ancient pharaohs to today's film stars, humans have long depended on the power of healing herbs. Check out these top ten power herbs and consider putting nature's bounty to work for you — keeping colds at bay, sharpening your memory, and increasing your energy!

You can find herbal products for sale at herb shops, natural food stores, mail-order catalogs and online sites, drug stores, and, with increasing interest in alternative medicine, at supermarkets and discount stores.

✔ **Echinacea — Immune support:** Echinacea can stimulate the immune system, helping to quickly eliminate infections of all kinds. Scientific studies show that volunteers using echinacea overcome the unpleasant symptoms of colds and flu faster than people in a placebo group. Echinacea is a top-selling herb in the U.S. and Europe and has been featured on numerous mainstream news stories. The taste is tingly and exotic; the benefits are hard to beat — you may find that echinacea becomes your constant winter companion. Echinacea liquid products also come in flavors, and some are sweetened.

✔ **Garlic — The heart protector:** In the past, garlic protected people from vampires and werewolves. Today, however, garlic is known as a protector of another sort — against heart attack and stroke. Modern science has thoroughly explored the chemistry and pharmacology of garlic and declares it a valuable aid to keep the heart and blood vessels healthy into old age. It can help keep the blood pressure in the normal range and can lower cholesterol.

Because heart disease and stroke are still the leading causes of death in developed countries, the daily use of garlic seems like a must. But not everybody likes the pungent flavor in their sauces and stir-fry, so products are available that have great benefits and a lot less smell.

✔ **Ginger — The root of good digestion:** When you have a queasy feeling, ginger can help. Several clinical studies favorably compare ginger extract with Dramamine and other over-the-counter products for easing nausea and stomach ailments. If traveling by boat, car, or plane makes your stomach jumpy, ginger can soothe your stomach and help ease digestive upset.

✔ **Ginkgo — Super brain food:** If you feel a major brain strain from work, an extract of the leaves of the ancient ginkgo tree can help. Known for its healing powers for more than 3,000 years, recent research has catapulted this herb to superstar status worldwide. Ginkgo increases circulation to your brain, improves memory and alertness, and protects your heart.

✔ **Ginseng — The energy herb:** For increasing energy and protecting human health, ginseng has taken on a healing and protective aura of magical proportions — it has been in use for over 5,000 years!

American ginseng products can help protect and soothe jangled nerves and regulate your hormones. This ginseng is for cooling out and promoting good sleep and rejuvenation. American ginseng is fine for any age, unlike the red ginsengs that should only be used by people over 40 or so.

Eleuthero, or *Siberian ginseng,* is from a different plant group in the ginseng botanical family than American, Korean, or Chinese ginseng. Eleuthero is used to help you adapt to stress of any kind and to help you maintain balance in all your activities. This herb helps you go the distance, whether you run, play tennis, or engage in any sports activities. It's also great if you travel, reducing the unpleasant side effects of jet lag.

✔ **Kava — The king and queen of relaxation:** Kava has a memorable name *and* a memorable taste — though not completely pleasant, unless you're from Fiji, Vanuatu, or Hawaii, in which case you probably grew up with the herb all around you. Now that the wonderful muscle-relaxing and mellowing-out qualities of the herb are known, it is quickly becoming one of the more popular herbs.

✔ **St. John's Wort — Mood food:** Unless you've been living in a cave, you've probably heard of St. John's wort. Medical doctors throughout Europe commonly prescribe the herb as a safe, natural way to ease depression.

German medical research shows the herb to be just as effective as commonly prescribed pharmaceutical antidepressants, with few, if any, side effects. Over 20 modern clinical trials support the use of extracts of the herb for easing mild, moderate, and even some cases of severe depression. Some forms of insomnia and anxiety also benefit from St. John's wort.

St. John's wort is also widely recommended for use on the skin for healing and easing the pain of burns, cuts, scrapes, and bites. Internally, it's also effective as an antiviral to slow replication of the AIDS virus, help to heal stomach ulcers, and soothe nerve pains.

✔ **Saw Palmetto — A good fate for the prostate:** This not-so-secret herbal marvel is an extract from the fruit of a scrubby palm that grows in northern Florida. Many herbalists feel that the regular use of saw palmetto can improve the health of the prostate gland. For women, regular use can help prevent urinary tract infections and improve the health of the entire genito-urinary tract.

✔ **Valerian — To sleep, to sleep, perchance to dream:** Valerian is known as the sleep-promoting and relaxing herb — studies show that it works on the brain and spinal cord, activating some of the same receptor sites as common pharmaceutical drugs like Xanax and Valium for anxiety, nervousness, and insomnia. Unfortunately, benzodiazepines can also lead to addiction, memory loss, and even worse mental and emotional symptoms than they are designed to treat.

Valerian has none of these side effects and, when you couple it with a natural program of relaxation and good diet, can be as (or more) effective than prescription drugs. Liquid extracts or tinctures made from the fresh roots and rhizomes (underground parts) are calming and relaxing, and you can take them daily as needed. Actual clinical trials show that valerian can help you fall asleep faster and have a deeper, more refreshing night's sleep.

Seven Ways to Add Aromatherapy to Your Life

Nature fills the air with fragrances — all awaiting your discovery through aromatherapy. Be adventuresome and open your nose and mind to explore some common and not-so-ordinary scents that you can welcome into your world.

- **Plant your own fragrant herb garden.** Growing your own herbs for use in aromatherapy not only gives you a good supply of aromatic material, but also makes your home and its surroundings more beautiful and fragrant. You can find plants at local nurseries and herb farms that are open to the public, through mail-order companies, and often at farmers' markets.

- **Get an aromatherapy facial.** Take the time to give yourself a real treat. Men, as well as women, enjoy a facial and benefit from how it conditions your skin. Check your local Yellow Pages for someone who offers aromatherapy facials. You can ask beauty salons and spas for recommendations.

- **Get a massage with an aromatherapy massage oil.** Most massage practitioners use an oil or lotion when they give a massage, and it's usually one that is scented. For the ultimate experience, seek out a practitioner who is trained not only in using different essential oils for their aromatherapy effects, but also in different aromatherapy techniques; you'll be in for a treat. Also consider getting an *Ayurvedic massage,* which uses several types of aromatic oils and is an aromatic experience that you won't forget.

- **Take an aromatherapy class.** As the popularity of aromatherapy has grown, so has the number of educational possibilities. Some courses offer certificates to show that you completed the course, although at this time, no recognized certificates of aromatherapy actually provide you with a license to practice. Still, finding out more about aromatherapy in a classroom setting really brings the topic to life because you can sniff the oils as you discuss them.

✔ **Visit a fragrance garden.** Most major cities have a botanical garden, and these gardens usually include a fragrance garden. The fragrance gardens at the Los Angeles County Arboretum in Arcadia and Strybing Arboretum in Golden Gate Park in San Francisco both have fragrance gardens that are purposely set into a raised bed on a hillside, placing the fragrant plants at your fingertips and at nose level. Both of these gardens are designed with vision-impaired visitors in mind.

If you're not sure where you can find a botanical garden near you, look in the phone book under public gardens. You often can find a small public botanical garden associated with a university. Even if you don't, the botany or biology department usually can point you in the right direction. Local plant nurseries know the whereabouts of various gardens, and you also can track down the local chapter of the Herb Society of America to help out.

✔ **Take an aromatherapy tour.** Look for special tours organized by travel groups or clubs to visit aromatherapy hot spots, such as the lavender fields and essential oil distilleries of Grasse, France. Also, aromatherapy conferences and workshops often have tours of local aromatherapy highlights related to the subject of the conferences.

✔ **Take an aromatic bath.** A bath is a great way to relax and takes about 40 minutes — but please, take as long as you like! Follow these steps for a wonderful, relaxing bath experience:

1. Arrange your bathing supplies: thick scented towel, warm robe, slippers.

2. Put on soothing music.

3. Light incense or place a few drops of your favorite essential oil in a potpourri cooker.

4. Draw a hot bath.

5. Add half a cup of scented bath salts to the water.

6. Make a soothing cup of chamomile tea and drink it while the tub fills.

7. Light a candle and turn off the lights.

   Optional: Add 1 drop of exotic essential oil like rose or jasmine to your bath water.

8. Step into your bath and relax for 30 minutes with no thoughts of the outside world.

9. Emerge and dry off.

10. Dust with a fragrant powder or apply a scented moisturizing cream to your entire body.

11. Wrap up in your warm robe and carry the candle to the bedroom.

12. Place a fragrant sachet under your bed pillow, slip into scented sheets, and enjoy fragrant dreams and a restful sleep.

Taking Mind-Body Fitness Moments throughout Your Day

Take a close look at your day to see where you can best apply some *mind-body techniques.* You may want to pencil a few ideas into various time slots in your calendar or daily planner about specific things you can do or think about.

Mind-body exercise just means looking at and reacting to things a little differently and paying attention to, well, your mind and your body.

✔ **At sunrise:** In the morning, go out onto a deck, a patio, or into a quiet room near a window — someplace where you can watch the sun rise. Let the light wash over you. Just sit and experience the sunrise. Even if you don't have a lot of time to commune with the opening of a new day, just take five minutes to meditate a bit, to go inside yourself and feel a little, and to just experience the quiet. This time may be your only chance before the alarm clocks go off, the kids race through the hall, or your spouse starts asking you about evening plans.

✔ **During midmorning:** No matter where you are, you can find a secluded bench, an empty corner office, a spot behind a building that no one frequents, or even an empty stairwell. Instead of running for a cup of coffee, do some meditation walking or some stretching movements to re-energize you for an upcoming meeting or the rest of the morning's flurry.

✔ **At noontime:** Sometimes when noon rolls around, you hurry off to lunch and eat on the run, or grab a bite in the car or at your desk. Slow down. Take time for yourself away from your daily routine. Even a short break can re-energize and refresh you.

And noon may be the perfect time to actually do some mind-body exercises. You can go to a class or pop in a video or cassette tape, depending on where you are and how much time you're willing to invest.

✔ **In the midafternoon:** Most people enter a slump period around midafternoon, between about 1 and 4 p.m. Forget about getting a large mocha. Go for 5 to 10 minutes of mindful moving about instead. This time of day may be great for a simple brisk walk, but be sure to use it to open your mind and clear your head. You may just need 5 minutes of a standing meditation.

Even if you're stuck at a desk and can't get away, you can probably sit back in your chair for a couple of minutes and breathe consciously and fully. You also can take the long way to the bathroom or lunchroom, making an excuse for some meditation walking.

✔ **At sunset or in the early evening:** In contrast to sunrise, when you energize yourself for the day, at sunset or in the early evening, you want to find peace with your day and slow down your pace. Sunset or early evening can be a grand time to take time before dinner or after work to go through a mind-body routine. If you have a family, ask them to have a snack because dinner won't be happening for another half-hour. If you're hungry, have a light snack (such as some fruit or granola) an hour before your practice so that you don't end up listening to your grumbling tummy while you meditate.

✔ **Before bedtime:** You may find that you can sleep better and more peacefully if you have some time to practice your mind-body movements during the day. If you can't get in a little exercise earlier, then take 10 to 30 minutes at bedtime. The only caveat is this: Right before bedtime, you don't want to do anything that's high-intensity and gets you so hyped up that you can't fall asleep.

Four Fast Ways to Fit Meditation into Your Busy Life

The whole point of meditation is to help you live a happier, fuller, more stress-free life. The following are a few tips on how to practice *mindfulness* so that you can stay open, present, and attentive from moment to moment, even in the midst of challenging circumstances like driving a car in heavy traffic, running errands, doing chores, taking care of the kids, or dealing with stressful situations at work.

Coming back to your breath

Gently paying mindful attention to your breath gradually calms your mind by shifting awareness away from your thoughts and slowing your mind down to the pace and rhythms of your body. With your mind and body in sync, you start to feel a natural ease and an inner harmony and tranquility that external circumstances can't easily disturb.

You can begin calming yourself by stopping whatever you're doing for a moment or two and tuning in to the coming and going of your breath. You may pay attention to the rise and fall of your abdomen as you breathe, or to the feeling of your breath as it enters and leaves your nostrils. Be mindful of these sensations for four or five breathing cycles, enjoying the simplicity and directness of the experience. When you breathe with awareness, you're consciously awake and alive in the present moment. Then resume your normal activities while continuing to be mindful of your breath.

Listening to the bell of mindfulness

Set the beeper on an alarm watch to sound every hour, and when it does, stop, enjoy your breathing for a minute or two, and then resume your normal activities (with greater awareness, of course). Or hear the mindfulness bell in the ring of your telephone or the sound of your computer booting up or the buzzer that goes off in your car before you fasten your seatbelt. Just remember to stop, enjoy your breathing, and keep going with greater awareness and aliveness.

Even nonsounds make great reminders. Whenever you encounter a red light in traffic, for example, instead of indulging your frustration or anxiety, you can remember to tune in, breathe consciously, and let go of your tension and speed. Or you can allow moments of beauty to help you wake up — a beautiful flower, the smile on a child's face, sunlight through your window, a warm cup of tea. Then again, you can always buy a traditional meditation bell and strike it every now and then as a special reminder.

Noticing how situations affect you

Instead of losing touch with yourself as you watch TV or drive your car or work at your computer, you can maintain *dual awareness* — that is, simultaneous awareness of what's going on around you and of how the situation or activity affects you.

Gradually you may start to notice that driving too fast makes you tense, or watching certain TV shows leaves you nervous or agitated, or talking for hours on the phone just saps your energy rather than enlivening you. You don't need to make any judgments or formulate any improvements based on what you discover. Just gently take note. You may find yourself naturally moving away from situations (like habits, leisure pursuits, people, and work environments) that stress you out and gravitating to situations that support you in feeling calm, relaxed, harmonious, and connected with yourself and others.

Applying meditation to familiar activities

Anything you do or experience can provide you with an opportunity to practice mindfulness. But you may want to begin with some of your usual activities — the ones you may be doing now on automatic pilot while you daydream, space out, or obsess. The truth is, even the most routine tasks can prove enjoyable and enlivening when you do them with wholehearted care and attention. The following are some common activities with a few suggestions for infusing them with mindfulness:

- ✔ **Washing the dishes:** If you set aside your judgments, which may insist that you should be doing something more meaning-ful or constructive with your time, and instead simply wash the dishes — or sweep the floor or scrub the tub — you may find that you actually enjoy the activity. Feel the contours of the plates and bowls as you clean them. Notice the smell and the slipperiness of the soap, the sounds of the utensils, the satisfy-ing feeling of removing the old food and leaving the dishes clean and ready for use.

- ✔ **Working at your computer:** As you become engrossed in the information flashing across your screen, you may find yourself losing touch with your body and your surroundings. Pause every now and then to follow your breathing and notice how you're sitting. If you're starting to tense up and to crane your head forward, gently straighten your spine and relax your body. During recurring gaps in the flow of your work, come back to your body, breathe, and relax.

- ✔ **Driving your car:** As an antidote to stress, you can practice mindfulness as you drive. Take a few deep breaths before you start and return to your breathing again and again as you con-sciously let go of tension and stress. Feel the steering wheel in your hands, the pressure of your feet against the pedals, the weight of your body against the seat. Notice any tendency to criticize other drivers, to space out, to become angry or impatient. Pay attention to how the music or talk shows you listen to affect your mood as you drive. When you pay attention, you may be surprised to realize that you and the people around you are actually piloting these 2,000-pound chunks of plastic and steel with precious, vulnerable beings inside. And you may feel more inclined to drive mindfully and safely as a result.

✔ **Talking on the phone:** As you engage in conversation, stay connected with your breathing and notice how you're affected. Do certain topics bring up anger or fear or sadness? Do others bring up pleasure or joy? Do you become reactive or defensive? Notice also what moves or motivates you to speak. Are you attempting to influence or convince this person in some way? Do you have a hidden agenda of jealousy or resentment — or possibly a desire to be loved or appreciated? Or are you simply open and responsive to what's being said in the moment, without the overlay of past or future?

✔ **Watching TV:** Just as when you work at a computer, you can easily forget you have a body when you tune in to the tube. Take a break during commercials to turn down the sound, follow your breathing, and ground your awareness in the present moment. Walk around, look out the window, connect with your family members. (Like many people, you may use food to ground you in your body while you're watching TV, but food doesn't really work unless you're mindful of what and how you're eating.)

✔ **Working out:** Physical exercise offers you a wonderful opportunity to shift your awareness from your mind to the simple, repetitive movements of your body. The next time you hit the exercise equipment or engage in aerobic activity, make a point of following your breathing as much as you can. Or simply be mindful of your body as you move — the flexing of your muscles, the contact with the equipment or floor, the feelings of warmth, pleasure, or strain. Notice also what takes you away. Do you worry about your body image or obsess about your weight? Do you fantasize about your new physique and so forget to be present for what's happening right now? Just notice, and then return to your experience. You may start enjoying your body so much that you stop caring how others see it.

Three Easy Massage Techniques Guaranteed to Relieve Stress

Under certain circumstances, giving or receiving hour-long full body massages — complete with music, candles, and scented oils — isn't practical or even possible. Luckily, you can develop your own massage skills that you can use every day in just about any location to help relieve stress (your own or your partner's).

Headache point

Shiatsu massage practitioners have long noted the "headache point" as helpful in relieving headaches. You can locate this "point" in the webbing of your hand between the thumb and the index finger. But the problem is that most people don't press exactly the right spot when trying to stimulate this point on themselves.

The spot is not directly in the center of the meaty part of the webbing, but rather is against the bone of the hand. To press the point effectively, grasp the webbing between your thumb and index finger with your opposite hand, squeeze it, and then move your thumb in against the side of the hand.

Ear reflexology

According to the zone theory, various points on your ears reflect areas in other parts of your body. The Chinese even have an extensive system of treating many disorders by applying pressure on the ears.

You can give your whole body a boost by simply rubbing your ears with a vigorous little kneading movement between your thumb and first two fingers. Start at the lobe and walk your fingers up around the outside to the top of the ear, giving little tugs outward as you go. Even if this motion does nothing for the rest of your body, it makes your ears feel great.

Hooking the skull

Standing behind your partner, place your thumbs at the base of his skull, on the muscles at the top of his neck. Then use a cat-pawing motion to dig your thumbs further into the muscles there, as if you're trying to hook your thumbs up under his skull. This really loosens up your entire neck.

Make sure not to press directly into the spine with this move, as it may be uncomfortable. Stay about an inch to either side.

Eleven questions to ask before taking alternative medicine treatment

Before you agree to let any alternative practitioner examine or treat you, do a little examination yourself to make sure that this is the right person to provide the type of care you want. Ideally, try to set up a brief consultation (either office or phone) with the practitioner so that you can ask the following questions:

✔ What does the treatment involve? How may it affect my life — incapacitate me, alter my schedule, keep me home from work, and so on?

✔ How do results compare with results from conventional approaches — or just watchful waiting? What are the advantages and disadvantages of this therapy as opposed to other alternatives?

✔ Can I use this method together with conventional therapy?

✔ Does any scientific evidence show that this approach works — and is safe? Was the evidence published — and where?

✔ Have you (personally) used this therapy for other people with a health history or ailment similar to mine? If yes, what happened? Can I talk to some of these people?

✔ How often do I have to visit to your office or clinic for treatment?

✔ How much does each session cost — and does anybody pay for it besides me? How much of this cost is for supplies and how much is for your time?

✔ How many sessions can I expect before seeing results? How long before we can decide whether the treatment is working?

✔ What are the potential side effects? (If the answer is "none," ask again. And then consider going elsewhere — because any effective treatment poses at least a slight risk to some people.)

✔ Are there any activities that I shouldn't engage in, or other drugs — prescription or over-the-counter, conventional or alternative — that I shouldn't take while using this therapy?

✔ Are you willing to talk to my regular doctor about the diagnosis and treatment plan? Do you place any limitations on what you're willing to talk about — and how often you're willing to talk?

Chapter 10

First-Aid Basics

*U*nfortunately, most folks are first-aid illiterate! Although your first instinct may be to panic, panicking has never helped an injured person. In fact, panic usually means two people are in trouble — the injured person and the panicky helper.

Successful first aid starts with the person administering it — even if that's you — staying calm. And the best way to stay calm is by being first-aid savvy. If you know what to do and you have the skills to do it, you can often resolve even the most serious problems.

Of course, some injuries require the help of a medical or EMT (Emergency Medical Technician) professional. When in doubt, always contact professional medical assistance. But, even in situations that require professional help, a knowledge of first-aid can make a major difference.

Some First-Aid Do's and Don'ts

The following are some general tips for you to keep in mind when you're putting your first-aid skills to good use:

> ✔ **DO be polite.** A friend or family member is likely to be comfortable with you helping them in a time of need. However, a stranger may be wary — or even afraid — of your help. Treat an ill or injured person with respect and kindness, not just as a victim who needs saving.

The polite thing to do when you approach a victim you don't know is to introduce yourself — just as you do with any stranger. Find out the person's name and use it as you work. Just a bit of familiarity can calm a victim and make the situation less scary. Also, be sure to mention that you have first-aid training.

If you need to take action that may be embarrassing to a victim (for example, removing a woman's shirt), be as sensitive as possible. Ask bystanders to move away or cover the victim with a sheet or blanket.

✔ **DO remain calm — and calming.** Keep your wits about you and get to work. As you provide care, constantly tell the person what you're going to do and why you're doing it. But be careful not to make any unrealistic promises — that can just make things worse.

✔ **DO obtain consent.** After you introduce yourself — but before you start administering first aid — you must ask and get permission to help from the victim. If a person is under age 18, you must get permission to help from his or her parents or guardians.

Consent can be refused. Although it may go against your best judgment, don't help a person who doesn't want your help. That doesn't mean you can just walk away, though. Call for help, and then stay with the victim until backup arrives.

If a person is unconscious, you can assume that he wants your help. *Implied consent* also comes into play with children under 18 whose parents aren't available to give consent. In that circumstance, you're free to assume that the parents want you to help their child. You may also assume consent when dealing with people with mental or emotional illness who may not understand what's going on.

Sometimes you may have difficulty judging whether to proceed. To determine whether someone is alert and oriented, ask the person her name, date of birth, the date, and who the president is. If the person can answer these questions, she probably knows what's going on. If you're still not sure whether a person who denies help is fully aware of the circumstances, you may want to let emergency medical service professionals decide — they're best equipped to evaluate the situation.

✔ **DO take precautions against infection.** HIV/AIDS is a concern to health care workers today, as are a number of other infectious diseases such as herpes and hepatitis. Remember that infection is a concern of first-aid providers, so be sure you understand the risks.

The greatest risk of infection is associated with blood. For the most part, skin protects against infection by contaminated blood, but any small cut or sore can allow viruses an entry way into the body. ***Bottom line:*** Avoid direct contact with blood. If you must have contact with blood:

- Use a clean cloth, a bandage, or latex gloves as a barrier.

- Wash your hands with soap and water as soon as possible after providing first aid, whether or not you wore gloves.

- Use rubber gloves and disinfectant (¼ cup bleach to 1 gallon of water) when cleaning up blood from surfaces.

According to the Centers for Disease Control and Prevention, HIV is not transmitted through saliva. However, some people who perform mouth-to-mouth routinely as part of their job do use resuscitation masks, which prevent transmission of infections. Studies also show little risk from contact with other body fluids such as urine, vomit, sweat, tears, feces, or mucus, unless they're mixed with blood.

✔ **DO stay alert.** Circumstances can change pretty quickly when you're dealing with an emergency. Whether you're near a raging fire or just in your backyard, keep an eye out for changes.

✔ **DON'T expect too much.** True, you may have first-aid training, but that doesn't make you a superhero. You may find yourself with a victim whom you can't help. A victim may even die while you're providing aid.

That possibility shouldn't stop you from doing your best. Remember that if you find that you don't have the skills to handle a particular situation, you can still call for help, comfort the victim, and reassure the family and bystanders. If no one is able to save the victim, take comfort in the fact that you did what you could.

Evaluating Emergencies

Because every first-aid situation is different, you handle each one differently. But as you approach the scene of an accident or injury, you can follow a few basic steps that are common to most situations. Granted, not every first-aid situation calls for the following steps, but many do:

1. **Call for help.**

   Your first action in any emergency is to call (or to send someone else) for emergency medical personnel. In most communities, you can do this by calling 911.

2. **Check the situation for safety.**

   Many rescuers are injured or die each year trying to help others. You don't want to barge into the scene of an accident if danger is still present. After all, you can't help someone if you become a victim yourself.

3. **Approach the victim.**

   No matter what the injury may be, check whether the person is conscious or unconscious. To do this, touch the person gently and ask, "Are you all right?" Or introduce yourself and ask the person's name to help you determine whether the victim is confused or clear-headed.

4. **Gather more information.**

   If the person is conscious, he may be able to tell you what happened. If the person is unconscious, the circumstances may be more difficult to discern. In either case, check for a medic alert bracelet or necklace as a clue to what's wrong. Bystanders may also be able to tell you what happened.

What if the person is unconscious?

If a person in need of first aid is unconscious, immediately check to see whether she is breathing and her pulse is strong. You can assume that consent has been given in instances where the person is not conscious.

Do not move a victim if you suspect an injured neck or back, as this can cause further damage. If you see any sign of a neck or back injury, leave the person in the position you found them and try to evaluate vital signs from there. The only exception to the "never move" rule is when the victim is in immediate danger — for example, lying in a building that's about to collapse. In this case, the risk of moving the victim is worthwhile.

If you don't find evidence of spinal injury, roll the person onto their back, trying to move the body as a unit. After the person is lying on their back, tilt the head back and raise the chin. Place your face close to the victim's mouth to listen and feel for breathing, and keep an eye on the person's chest to see whether it's rising and falling.

If a person is breathing, check for a pulse. If you detect a pulse, turn your attention to any severe bleeding and then any other injury that calls for first aid.

If a person is not breathing, you need to start mouth-to-mouth resuscitation. If you cannot force air into the lungs, the airway may be blocked, meaning that first aid for choking may be necessary.

If the person has no pulse, begin CPR.

5. Check vital signs.

Check that the person is breathing and has a pulse. If breath or pulse is absent, you need to begin lifesaving measures (namely CPR) immediately.

Creating a First-Aid Kit

Putting together a first-aid kit is a simple task. First, grab your "toolbox," which can be anything from a cardboard box to a tote bag to a watertight case (the latter is best). The easier the box is to carry, the better.

If you don't feel like going through the trouble of collecting the contents of a kit on your own, simply buy one — already complete — at your local drugstore, supermarket, or sporting goods store.

Basic items for any household first-aid kit include

- First-aid book
- Pencil and paper
- Change (for a phone call)
- Matches and a candle
- Blanket (a foil, "space" blanket works well and doesn't take up much room)
- Tissues
- Soap
- Paper cups
- Flashlight
- Medical records
- Emergency phone numbers

Equipment is also necessary. Stash these items in your first-aid kit:

- Latex gloves
- Scissors
- Tweezers
- Syringe (to squirt water and rinse out wounds)
- Thermometer
- Cotton balls

- ✔ Antiseptic wipes
- ✔ Instant cold pack
- ✔ Eye cup (to flush the eye)

Of course, you need bandages and dressings, too:

- ✔ Adhesive bandages (assorted shapes and sizes)
- ✔ Butterfly bandages
- ✔ First-aid tape
- ✔ Elastic roller bandage (in various widths)
- ✔ Flexible gauze roller bandage (in various widths)
- ✔ Gauze pads
- ✔ Eye pads
- ✔ Nonstick pads (3" by 3" or 4" by 4")
- ✔ Triangular bandage (55" across the base and 36" to 40" along each side)

Medications come in handy. Add these to your first-aid kit:

- ✔ Antibiotic ointment (such as Neosporin)
- ✔ Antibiotic spray
- ✔ Aloe vera gel
- ✔ Ibuprofen, acetaminophen, and aspirin (*Note:* Children under the age of 19 should not take aspirin because of the risk of Reye's syndrome, a rare viral disease.)
- ✔ Topical antihistamine (such as Benadryl) or calamine lotion
- ✔ Antacid
- ✔ Motion-sickness medication (such as Bonine)
- ✔ Activated charcoal (use only under the direction of a poison control center)
- ✔ Syrup of ipecac (use only under the direction of a poison control center)
- ✔ Sterile eye wash

If someone in your life has a particular condition, you may want to supplement your first-aid kit with some special supplies. For example, if you know someone with diabetes, include supplies for diabetic emergencies, including glucose tablets, disposable syringes, lancets for blood sampling, test strips for blood sugar, and a urine testing kit.

Be sure to ask your doctor or pharmacist whether your first-aid kit is complete, based on the knowledge of you or your family members' specific medical conditions.

Wound Care

They say that time heals all wounds, and a little first aid helps speed up that process quite a bit. This section provides a quick introduction to the various wounds you may face and how you can take care of them.

For most wounds, getting the bleeding under control and dressing the wound are the most important points.

Closed wounds

Closed wounds are those that don't break the skin. They're often smaller, minor wounds that you can treat by applying an ice pack to the injured area. The cold temperature constricts surrounding blood vessels and keeps swelling and discoloration to a minimum. Overall, risk of infection is slim.

However, closed wounds can also affect internal organs and body systems and may not be visible. How can you tell whether a closed wound is the problem? Look for these signs:

- A rapid, weak pulse
- Clammy skin over all the body
- Pain and tenderness in the affected area, especially if pain seems more severe than the apparent injury calls for
- Thirst
- Restlessness
- Blood in vomit, feces, or urine
- Coughed-up blood
- Swelling
- Discoloration
- A deformed limb (caused by a broken bone inside)

If you suspect someone has sustained a serious closed wound, call for medical help. Don't move the affected part of the body unless absolutely necessary. *Another caveat:* Don't give someone with a suspected internal injury any food or water — even if she complains of being thirsty. You want to keep the victim's throat and airways clear, and food or water may cause choking.

Puncture wounds

Puncture wounds are usually deep but are very small in terms of surface area. Although they don't usually bleed very much, they're still serious. A puncture can damage internal organs and also becomes infected very easily.

To care for a puncture wound, wash it out with running water and wipe the surface with an antiseptic wipe. Bandage the wound with a piece of gauze or a pad. Do not, however, try to plug the hole with a bandage, and do not put antiseptic ointment into the wound. If you seal off the wound, you're increasing the risk of an infection, such as tetanus.

Embedded objects

Bits of broken glass and splinters are just two examples of objects that can become embedded in a wound. Other possibilities include a nail, a fishhook, or even the blade of a knife.

If the object is just under the surface of the skin, try using sterilized tweezers to pull out the object or use a sterilized needle to slip in under the object and lift it out. Always pull the object out at the same angle it went in.

If the object penetrates below the level of the skin, leave it where it is — even if the object is small. Removing it can cause further damage and trigger bleeding. Instead, have a medical professional remove the object.

If you must leave an embedded object in place, be sure to keep it from being moved or bumped when you transport the victim. Or you can use a paper cup to protect the object. Place the cup upside down over the object, tearing a hole in the bottom of the cup if it's too large to cover the object. Then use first-aid tape to hold the cup in place.

Injuries

Here are the basics you need to know when treating the most common types of injuries.

Head injuries

A head injury may mean a problem with the scalp, the skull, the brain, and the blood vessels and fluid around the brain. Even if the head isn't cut or bleeding, the brain inside may be bruised or bleeding.

If a person's head has suffered an injury, the spinal cord may be affected, too. If you suspect any chance at all of a spinal injury, don't move the victim.

Wounds to the scalp

Because of the number of blood vessels in the scalp and head, even a small cut to the head can bleed heavily. To treat these wounds, follow the instructions in the preceding section on wounds. Keep in mind that hair can disguise wounds and make determining how serious a wound is difficult. Also remember that deep wounds may also involve a skull fracture or spinal injury, so don't move the victim or apply a bandage or dressing too tightly.

If you suspect a skull fracture and you need to stop the bleeding, don't apply pressure directly to the wound. Instead, use a ring bandage to apply pressure around the edges of the wound instead of at the center. Another tip to stop bleeding: Raise the victim's head and shoulders slightly to get gravity on your side — but only if you're absolutely sure that no spinal injury has occurred.

If you suspect even a chance of skull fracture or brain injury, don't clean out the wound. Contact may cause contamination and lead to infection. Only clean minor surface wounds to the scalp.

Skull fracture

The human skull is tough, but a severe blow can crack or shatter the bones. Often, skull fractures are hard to diagnose without x-rays because the crack is often small.

Symptoms

Some indications of a skull fracture include

- Pain in the area of the injury.
- A dent or deformity in the skull.
- Fluid or blood coming from the ears or nose.
- Discoloration around the eyes (appears several hours after injury).

✔ Discoloration behind the ear (appears several hours after injury).

✔ Visible skull or brain tissue.

✔ A penetrating wound (such as a gunshot wound).

Treatment

If you suspect a skull fracture, call EMS. Don't move the person, because she also may have a spinal injury. Instead, immobilize the head (in whatever position it's currently in) with cushions or folded blankets placed gently around the head and shoulders. Make sure the blankets don't interfere with breathing.

If you detect any bleeding, don't apply direct pressure to the wound. Instead, use a ring bandage to apply pressure only around the edges of the wound. Don't try to stop any fluid or bleeding coming from the ears or nose, however. This leakage is actually relieving some of the pressure within the skull, and blocking it off will increase that pressure.

Also, don't try to clean a skull fracture because doing so may contaminate the wound and cause infection.

Brain injuries

When the head is struck hard, the brain can be jarred and bruised inside the skull. The injured brain then swells, but because it's trapped within the skull, the tissue has no space to expand. The result is increased pressure in the skull and a reduction in blood flow to the brain.

Three common brain injuries include

✔ **Concussion:** The brain stops functioning temporarily without any permanent damage. No bleeding occurs within the skull.

✔ **Contusion:** This is essentially a bruise to the brain.

✔ **Hematoma:** Broken blood vessels in the brain cause blood to collect and harden in a pocket in the skull. The swollen pocket results in increased pressure within the skull, which may damage brain tissues.

Symptoms

You may be dealing with a brain injury if you notice these symptoms:

✔ An obvious injury to the head, such as a dent or bleeding. You may be able to see pieces of shattered skull or brain tissue in the wound.

✔ Fluid draining from the ears, nose, or mouth.

✔ Loss of consciousness.

✔ Seizures.

✔ Confusion, disturbance of speech, or change in personality.

✔ Paralysis in facial muscles.

✔ Headache that can't be relieved with pain relievers.

✔ Vomiting.

✔ Pupils of uneven size.

✔ Weakness or drowsiness.

Treatment

First, call EMS. Also, take for granted that you're dealing with a spinal injury and don't move the victim. Instead, stabilize the head with soft cushions or folded blankets by placing them gently around the head and shoulders, being careful not to disturb the position of the person. Make sure the padding doesn't interfere with breathing.

While waiting for EMS, keep an eye on the victim's breathing and heart rates and give CPR if necessary (and if you're trained). If seizures occur, use cushions or blankets to protect the head and give first aid for seizures. Don't try to clean a head wound if the person has a skull fracture or brain injury because infection may result.

If fluid or blood is draining from the ears or nose, don't try to stop the flow. This leakage is actually reducing the pressure within the skull — if you block it off, the pressure increases, causing more damage.

If the victim is vomiting, roll him onto one side. Doing so helps the vomit drain from the mouth and keeps vomit from clogging the airways and obstructing breathing.

Finally, do what you can for any other injuries the victim may have, such as bleeding. Keep the person calm until help arrives.

Back injuries

The complexity of the spine, spinal cord, and back increases the risk of injury. It also means you have to be very careful in providing first aid for injuries in order to keep from causing further damage.

The key to handling back injuries is this single rule: Do not move a person with a suspected back or spinal-cord injury. The only exception to this rule is when the person is in immediate danger — for example, lying inside a burning building.

Symptoms

Some indications of spinal or back injury include

- ✔ Pain in the head, neck, or back.
- ✔ Numbness and tingling.
- ✔ Weakness or loss of feeling in the arms or legs.
- ✔ Loss of bladder or bowel control.
- ✔ Inability to move.
- ✔ Evidence the person was thrown some distance or had fallen.
- ✔ Obvious injuries to the face, head, or back.

If a person is unconscious and you're not sure whether she has a spinal injury, assume that she does.

Treatment

First, call EMS. Don't move the person unless she's in immediate danger. If CPR or artificial respiration becomes necessary, perform the techniques without changing the person's position. Treat other apparent injuries also without moving the person.

If the person is vomiting or choking on blood, you may roll her onto one side. Doing so helps blood and vomit to drain and keeps them from blocking the airway.

While waiting for EMS, keep the person warm and calm.

Eye injuries

Sight is precious, and eye injuries can endanger vision. Be sure to get medical attention for any eye injury, even a minor one.

Here's how to deal with some of the most common eye injuries:

- ✔ **Blow to the eye.** Usually, a blow to the eye results in a bruise, known as a black eye. In serious cases, the eye itself may be torn or damaged. A blow may also cause bleeding and open the door to infection. While you probably do not need to contact EMS, a person with a blow to the eye does need to see an eye professional (an optometrist or ophthalmologist) as soon as possible because of the risk to vision.
- ✔ **Penetrating eye injury.** First, call EMS immediately. Then take steps to protect the injured eye. Do not remove the object penetrating the eye. Only a medical professional should take on

that task. Instead, carefully place a paper cup or piece of folded cardboard over the object and bandage it into place. This keeps the object from being bumped or forced deeper into the eye.

When you're bandaging the injured eye, also bandage the good eye. This keeps the injured eye from moving with the good eye.

✔ **Cut to eye or eyelid.** If only the eyelid is cut, you can stop the bleeding by applying pressure to the wound. Then carefully clean the wound and apply a clean dressing. You can treat any swelling around the eye by applying an ice pack wrapped in a towel. Seek professional medical care as soon as possible.

If the eye itself is cut, loosely bandage both eyes to keep them from following together. Don't try to wash out the wound, and don't apply pressure to the eye.

Sometimes, with a cut to the eye, blood can collect within the eye, usually behind the iris. Get medical help immediately if you see this symptom.

✔ **Foreign body in the eye.** A bit of dust, a piece of hair, or some dirt blown by the wind can cause discomfort if it lands in the eye. But irritation is the least of the problems — a foreign object can become embedded in the eye or scratch the eye's surface. The victim may have redness, pain, or burning in the eye, along with a headache and excessive tearing.

If a person gets something in the eye, discourage her from rubbing it. To remove a foreign body from the eye, first wash your hands. Then pull down the lower lid of the eye to see whether you can spot the offending object. If you can see it, touch it gently with the corner of a clean tissue or a handkerchief. The object will stick to the tissue, and you can then pull it free. Don't use a cotton swab or loose cotton wadding on the eye.

If you can't see the object beneath the lower lid, ask the person to look down. Gently grasp the lashes of the upper lid, then pull the lid out and down over the lower lid. Doing so causes tears that may wash the object away.

Here's another trick to try: Hold onto the lashes of the upper lid and pull the lid away from the eye. Then place the stem of a cotton swab or matchstick against the outside of the eyelid and gently pull the eyelid against it. If you can see the object stuck in the lid, remove it with the edge of a tissue, then flush the eye with water.

If your attempts to remove the object are unsuccessful, consult an eye professional immediately. And even if the object is removed immediately, a visit to an eye doctor may be a good idea.

✔ **Chemicals in the eye.** If a chemical gets into a person's eye, rinse the affected eye and face immediately for at least five minutes. Rinse the eye from the inside corner outward, holding the eye open. This ensures that the chemical doesn't rinse into the other eye. After rinsing, cover the eye with a dry, clean dressing and get medical help as soon as possible.

Be sure to get help immediately if drain cleaner, detergent, or another alkaline solution gets into a person's eye. While the injury may not seem so bad initially, swelling and more severe damage may develop through the following hours and threaten sight.

✔ **Light damage to the eye.** Eye burns can occur when someone looks for too long at the sun, doesn't use protective eye gear when welding, or looks too long at the glare on snow or at a tanning lamp. The injury may not be apparent immediately. In fact, pain may not set in for as long as six hours. To treat such injuries, cover both eyes with cold, wet towels and visit an eye professional as soon as possible. Do not allow the victim to rub the eyes, and keep any light from reaching the eyes. Give a pain reliever if necessary.

Blisters

A *blister* is the collection of blood and fluid under the skin that occurs when the topmost layer of the skin becomes separated from its lower layer. A blister is caused by friction or rubbing of the skin, often when you wear shoes that don't fit right or use tools that chafe your hands.

Allow blisters to heal on their own. However, you can

✔ Pierce the blister with a sterile needle and drain the fluid, then cover it with an adhesive bandage until it heals.

✔ Apply a doughnut-shaped pad over the blister and cover that with a bandage.

Whichever method you use, watch for signs of infection (such as redness, pain, swelling, and discharge) as the blister heals. If an infection appears to be setting in, seek medical attention.

Sudden Illness

Sudden problems may arise from an existing medical condition — but some just come out of the blue. The following section helps you prepare for the unexpected.

Heart attack

A heart attack is a scary thing because it can happen so quickly. Some people may know that they have coronary heart disease and that they're at risk, but others don't expect a thing until a heart attack strikes. For more information on dealing with heart disease, see Chapter 8.

Symptoms

The symptoms of a heart attack can be confused with indigestion and other minor chest pains. Here are some clues that you're dealing with a heart attack:

- ✔ A feeling of pressure, fullness, squeezing, or pain in the chest. The pain lasts more than a few minutes or goes away and then comes back.

- ✔ Pain in the shoulders, neck, or jaw that runs down the arms or back.

- ✔ Dizziness.

- ✔ Fainting.

- ✔ Nausea.

- ✔ Weakness with minimal exercise (such as climbing stairs).

- ✔ Clammy skin and sweating.

- ✔ Blue skin or lips.

- ✔ Chest pain during exertion or stress that subsides during a period of rest.

- ✔ Indigestion that antacids cannot relieve.

- ✔ Irregular heartbeat.

- ✔ Difficulty breathing.

- ✔ Shock.

- ✔ Unconsciousness.

To complicate diagnosis, not all of these warning signs accompany every heart attack. A good guide is this: If you suspect a heart attack, call EMS immediately. Even people who seem unlikely candidates for heart attack can suffer them without warning, so you're better safe than sorry.

Treatment

With a heart attack, every second counts, so call EMS immediately if one occurs. The better the care the person receives in the first two hours after the attack sets in, the greater the chance for survival and recovery.

While you're waiting for EMS to arrive, remain calm and reassuring and try to make the victim comfortable. Loosen any tight clothing and cover the person with a blanket. The person can lie down or sit up — in fact, he may breathe easier while sitting up.

Next, help the person take any medication he may have for the condition. If the person has been diagnosed with heart disease, he may have been prescribed *nitroglycerin* to take in the event of chest pain. If the attack is a case of temporary chest pain (called *angina*), nitroglycerin works within three minutes. If chest pain continues, get medical help right away. Don't give any food or drink to the victim.

Of course, you must keep an eye on vital signs — heart rate and breathing rate. If the person stops breathing or the heart stops, begin CPR immediately (if you've been trained to do so).

Cardiopulmonary resuscitation: Knowing CPR for life

Cardiopulmonary resuscitation is a combination of artificial respiration (sometimes called *mouth-to-mouth resuscitation*) and chest compressions, which puts pressure on the heart and forces blood through the circulatory system. CPR is for more than just heart attack victims. In fact, you use it in any emergency when a person's heart stops.

CPR is best performed by someone who has taken a course and is trained in first aid. If you haven't been trained or are not sure what you're doing, call EMS right away. Even when you know how to give artificial respiration, have someone call EMS while you begin the technique.

Here are the steps to take for adults:

1. **See whether the person is conscious. Ask loudly, "Are you OK?" to see whether you get a response.**

2. **Call for help. Ask a bystander to call EMS.**

3. **Lay the person on his back using a rolling motion to minimize injury.**

4. **Check whether the person is breathing.**

   Tilt the head back and lift up the person's chin. (See Step 1 in Figure 10-1.) Then lean close to the mouth and listen and feel for a breath. (See Step 2 in Figure 10-1).

5. **If the person isn't breathing, give artificial respiration.**

   Pinch the nose shut and place your mouth around the victim's. Give two full breaths into the mouth. (See Step 3 in Figure 10-1.) Each breath should last about 1 second. You can tell the breath is going into the lungs if the chest rises and falls with each breath. Let the chest fall before you give the next breath.

6. **After you give the breaths, check the person's pulse.**

   To take a pulse, place the middle and index fingers against the carotid artery in the neck between the voice box at the front of the throat and the muscle at the side of the neck, under the ear. (See Step 4 in Figure 10-1.) A carotid artery is on either side of the neck.

7. **If you can't find a pulse, get ready to begin chest compressions.**

   With one hand, feel for a notch at the lower end of the breastbone and measure two finger widths above that notch. (See Step 5 in Figure 10-1.) Place the heel of the other hand at that spot on the breastbone. Cover that hand with the other and interlock the fingers. Don't put your fingers against the chest — just the heel of the hands.

8. **After your hands are in place, lock your elbows and position your body directly over your hands. (See Step 6 in Figure 10-1.)**

   - **For adults:** Give 15 chest compressions in 10 seconds, depressing the breastbone 1½ to 2 inches with each thrust.

   - **For children age 1 to 8:** Give 5 chest compressions in 4 seconds, depressing the breastbone 1 to 1½ inches with each thrust.

9. **After 15 compressions, give the person two full breaths with artificial respiration.**

10. **Check the pulse again. If you still don't detect a pulse, repeat the 15 compressions. Continue with this cycle of 2 breaths and 15 compressions until the person is revived or EMS arrives.**

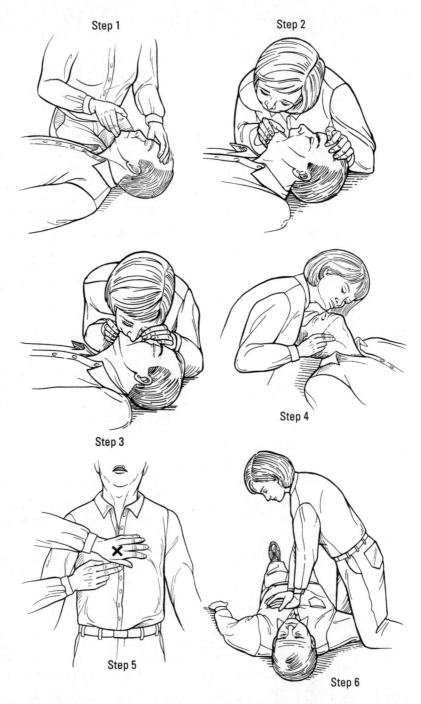

Step 1

Step 2

Step 3

Step 4

Step 5

Step 6

Figure 10-1: These six illustrations demonstrate how to perform CPR on an adult.

Stroke

A *stroke* is caused by a lack of blood flow to the brain. With stroke, an artery providing blood to the brain becomes blocked or bursts, and the tissues of the brain can't receive the oxygen and nutrients. Because brain tissue is damaged with each passing moment when it's deprived of oxygen, fast action is necessary with stroke first aid.

Symptoms

Some signs of stroke include

- Dizziness and falling
- Slurred speech or loss of speech
- Sudden, severe headache
- Weakness or numbness in a part of the body, particularly the face, arm, or leg of one side of the body
- Blurred vision or loss of vision, particularly in one eye
- Unconsciousness

Treatment

If you find yourself with a person who's having a stroke, check breathing and heart rate. If either stop, begin CPR, if you're trained to do so. Have a bystander call EMS as soon as possible. The faster a person gets to the hospital, the sooner he can receive "clot-busting" medications or surgery to help restore blood flow, reducing the risk of permanent brain damage.

If the person is stable, have him rest until EMS arrives. Don't try to give any food, water, or medications, and keep a close eye on vital signs. Make the person comfortable, loosening any tight clothing.

Sometimes a person having a stroke becomes unconscious. If this happens, get the person into the *recovery position* — on one side with the upper arm and leg bent to support the body. Stay with the person until medical help arrives.

Seizures

Your brain is a hotbed of electrical activity — tiny sparks of energy are stimulating millions of brain cells each time you think or move a muscle. *Seizures,* brief periods of involuntary muscle movement, occur when the electricity in the brain becomes uncontrolled. A single seizure usually lasts 30 to 45 seconds.

Conditions associated with seizures include high blood pressure, brain injuries (such as stroke), brain illnesses (such as cancer), fever in children, electric shock, poisoning, choking, and drug and alcohol overdose or withdrawal.

Symptoms

A seizure may have the following characteristics:

- ✔ Short period of confusion or unconsciousness
- ✔ Tingling or twitching in a part of the body
- ✔ Rigid muscles or jerking muscle movements
- ✔ Grunting or snorting
- ✔ Drooling or frothing at the mouth
- ✔ Loss of bowel or bladder control
- ✔ Blue discoloration of the lips

People who've had seizures before can sometimes feel when one is coming on. Signs include a funny taste in the mouth, hallucinations, abdominal pain, or just a feeling that something is going to happen.

Treatment

After a seizure begins, you cannot stop it. But you can keep the person from injury and call for medical help if necessary.

Call EMS if the person has more than one seizure an hour or seizures that last longer than two minutes. Also, call if the person doesn't wake up between seizures. Emergency care is also necessary for people who've never had a seizure before, people with high blood pressure, and pregnant women. People who have a seizure in water or who are otherwise ill or injured should also get EMS attention.

If an infant experiences seizures for the first time, assume the reason is poisoning. Call the poison control center immediately.

If the person feels a seizure coming on, help the person lie on the ground to prevent a fall. Loosen his clothing and clear the area of any hard objects he may run into. If pillows are available, place them around to cushion the victim. Don't move the victim unless you are near a danger that you can't move (such as a flight of stairs the victim may topple down).

While a seizure is occurring, don't try to hold the person down and don't put anything in the mouth or between the person's teeth. The person can't stop the seizure, so just wait until it runs its course and do your best to protect the victim from injury.

If the person stops breathing and becomes blue in the face, *don't* try to give artificial respiration. When the seizure ends, the person will begin breathing again before brain damage occurs.

After the seizure ends, move the person into the *recovery position* — on one side with the upper arm and leg bent for support. This position helps any fluids drain from the mouth and nose. Don't try to give the person any food or fluids until he's fully recovered. As a person recovers from a seizure, keep an eye on vital signs. Stay with the person until he recovers or medical help arrives.

Fractures

A *fracture* is the medical term for a broken or cracked bone. Fractures come in various types:

- In an **open fracture,** the broken bone is exposed through a wound in the skin. This is also called a *compound fracture*.

- In a **closed fracture,** the bone doesn't pierce the skin. This is also called a *simple fracture*.

- A **greenstick fracture** occurs mostly in the immature long bones (arms and leg bones) of children. In this type of fracture, one side of the bone is fractured, but the other side is unbroken.

- In a **comminuted fracture,** part of the damaged bone is broken into fragments or shattered.

Symptoms

Signs of a fracture include pain, swelling, bruising, and an unusual or misshapen appearance (the bone may look deformed). In addition, the victim may have heard the bone snap or may be able to move an injured limb in a strange way. The person may also feel the broken bones grinding against each other. X-rays, however, are the most reliable way to diagnose a fracture, especially a closed fracture.

Treatment

For serious breaks, call (or have someone else call) the EMS. For more minor injuries, give first aid before seeking medical attention. In both cases, keep an eye on the person's vital signs — heart and breathing rates — and be prepared to give CPR if heart and breathing rates fail (and if you're trained).

Don't move the person while you wait for emergency personnel. If you plan to seek medical attention on your own, make sure the injury is stabilized before carefully moving the person.

Slings and splints from head to toe

The key to first aid for fractures is to protect the area against further injury and immobilize the injury to keep more damage from occurring. One of the best ways to do this is with a *splint,* a combination of a bandage and rigid materials (suggestions include sticks, boards, broom handles, cardboard, and even folded-up newspapers and magazines) that holds the injury in place. A *sling,* a hammock of fabric that supports the area and keeps the pressure off, is another technique.

Different injuries require different splints and slings, and the following lists them in head-to-toe order.

- **Collarbone:** Start with a triangular bandage, which measures about 3 feet by 3 feet by 4.5 feet. Spread the bandage over the torso of the victim, with the longest side along the injured person's good side. Place the injured arm on top of the bandage, with the opposite point of the triangle under the elbow of the injured arm. Take the bottom point and fold it upward over the arm and tie it around the back of the neck to the other, topmost point. Adjust the sling so that the hand is elevated a few inches above the elbow. Pin the point at the elbow to the side of the sling to keep the arm in place. Make sure the fingers are exposed to avoid cutting off circulation.

  After the sling is in place, use another bandage to tie the whole thing against the body to prevent movement. Gently wrap a length of narrow bandage around the torso and injured arm and — not too tightly — knot it in place.

- **Arm:** If the upper arm is injured, apply a sling as described for a collarbone fracture and then apply another bandage to tie the whole thing against the chest. See Figure 10-2 for an illustration.

- **Elbow:** If the elbow is in a bent position, splint it in that position. If the elbow is straight, apply the splint to the outside of the arm. First, find a rigid support that keeps the injury in place. If the item is rough, wrap it in a towel or blanket to cushion it. Make sure the support is long enough to extend a few inches beyond the injury for maximum stability.

  Using first-aid tape, bandages, or makeshift ties (strips of towels, sheets, or even clothing), secure to the injured part of the body. Don't tie any knots near or on top of the injury itself — make your ties above and below that area.

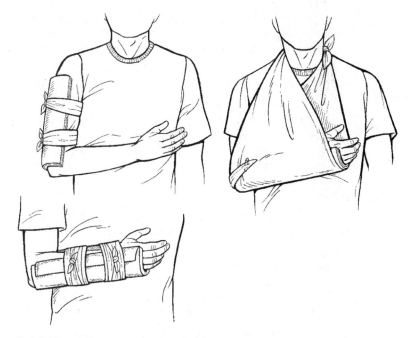

Figure 10-2: Apply a splint to the injured area, and then fold a bandage around the arm and neck to keep the arm from moving.

Don't tie the splint too tightly — you may cut off circulation to the injured area, which causes more harm than good. If the limb begins to tingle or become numb, loosen the ties on the splint.

✔ **Wrist and Hand:** Immobilize the wrist or hand by wrapping it with padding. You may use a blanket, a piece of clothing, or even a magazine or newspaper. Fashion a sling around the arm for additional protection.

✔ **Finger:** Finger injuries don't call for splints or slings. Instead, apply an ice pack wrapped in a towel to reduce pain and swelling and keep the hand elevated. Seek medical attention.

✔ **Pelvis:** An injured pelvis is a serious matter. Don't move a person when you suspect such an injury has occured — rely on EMS to do that job.

✔ **Hip:** Don't move a person with an injured hip unless absolutely necessary. However, if you do need to move the person, you need to apply a big splint.

Wrap two boards in towels. Place one on the outside of the injured hip, stretching from the armpit to the foot. Place the other board along the inside of the leg, from the crotch to the foot. Tie the boards in place around the leg in three places (near the ankle, the knee, and the groin) and then continue to secure the outer board to the torso at chest and waist level.

✔ **Leg:** If the upper part of the leg has been injured, don't move the person unless absolutely necessary. If you must transport a person, apply a splint as you do for a hip injury.

If the lower leg is injured, apply a splint. Find two boards and wrap them in towels to cushion them somewhat. Place one board against the outside of the leg (from hip to foot) and the other against the inside (from crotch to foot). Tie the boards in place around the leg in three places (near the ankle, the knee, and the groin).

✔ **Knee:** If the injured knee is already straight, use the same splint that you do for an injured leg.

For an injured knee that's bent, *don't* straighten it out. Get the person to bend the good knee to the same angle, and then use that knee as a splint to provide some support. If you have a blanket, roll it up lengthwise and place it between the legs before you tie the legs together to provide more support.

✔ **Ankle and Foot:** Immobilize an ankle or foot using a pillow or a folded-up towel or blanket. Apply this soft splint by laying the pillow lengthwise underneath the ankle and foot and folding it up and around the joint. Secure it in two places on the lower leg and in another place against the foot. Keep the ankle or foot elevated to reduce swelling.

✔ **Toe:** An injured toe calls for the application of an ice pack wrapped in a towel to help reduce pain and swelling. Keep the foot elevated, too. You may also want to put some cotton between the toe and its neighbor and tape the two together to immobilize them. If the toe looks deformed, seek medical attention right away.

Chapter 11

Keeping Your Family Healthy

- -

- -

*T*echnically speaking, family health is about much more than preventing illness. *Health* is something that starts long before trips to the doctor and means much more than getting prescriptions filled. In this chapter, you find out what optimal health for every member of your family really means.

Because you're a unique individual, consult with a professional healthcare provider for a complete interview and evaluation of any condition. If you receive advice that is contrary to the information this reference provides, follow the practitioner's advice, because your practitioner bases his or her advice on your unique characteristics and situation.

Finding the Perfect Practitioner

Don't wait until you have a medical problem or, worse yet, a medical emergency to find a practitioner. Not always the best choices, spur-of-the-moment decisions can be costly, too, in terms of money *and* health.

The more thought and effort you put into finding a qualified doctor, the better off you'll be. To boost your chances of success, ask yourself the following questions to pinpoint your needs and attitudes:

    ✔ Do you want a doctor who serves as a constant resource, or one who primarily provides care only during illness?

    ✔ Do you want a doctor who explains the pros and cons and asks for your decisions, or one who makes the medical choices?

✔ What sort of physician or practitioner do you want? Allopath? Osteopath? Specialist?

✔ If you changed doctors in the past, why? What should this new doctor do differently?

✔ Is cost a factor? Does insurance cover care from this practitioner?

✔ Do you have any preferences for male or female, young or old, solo or group practitioners?

Gathering referrals

Begin your search by getting a few good referrals from family members, friends, and neighbors. Word of mouth is still one of the best methods of finding out which doctors are taking new patients and what others think of these doctors.

As you start to look for your ideal doctor, don't forget to check the phone book, physician referral services, newspaper advertisements, and your employer's human resources office.

Getting acquainted

While you're doctor-shopping, be sure to include an all-important "get-acquainted visit" with your prospective physician. If a doctor refuses to meet with you for 10 to 15 minutes, go to the next one on your list. (Fifteen minutes is probably all you can get, but if you prepare, you may be surprised just how much you can find out about a doctor and her staff.)

When you meet the doctor, concentrate on credentials — medical degree, board certification, and other specialized education — and hospital affiliations. If the doctor isn't on the staff of any hospital, he may not be able to serve you when you need him most. Also find out about basics such as office hours and whom to call when you have an emergency and the office is closed. Find out whether the doctor takes calls for questions and whether such consultations carry a fee.

Ask about the doctor's fee schedule and payment plans. A doctor who willingly discusses fees is more likely to be open about other aspects of your medical care. Find out about insurance coverage as well. For more information on providing health insurance for your family, check out Chapter 20.

Children's Health

From the moment of birth (and even before), parents worry about their children's well-being.

Everyone says that kids are tougher than you think. That's true enough, but don't make the mistake of trying to treat children without a doctor's advice and diagnosis. And don't rely on this book as a substitute for medical care.

Handling childhood conditions

Every child gets sick now and then. The following sections describe the most common childhood illnesses, along with symptoms, treatments, and what you can do to help your child recover at home. With the proper treatment, you can greatly reduce the risk of complications, and your child can return to a normal, active life in no time.

Preventing the spread of *all* germs is impossible, but you can help reduce the risks by taking simple precautions. The best and easiest is to wash your hands often and encourage your child to do the same, particularly before meals and at bedtime.

Chicken pox

Also called *varicella,* chicken pox is a mild but contagious childhood disease best known by the itchy rash that it causes.

Recognizing the signs: The symptoms include a low-grade fever, runny nose, slight cough, decrease in appetite, and fatigue and weakness. Anywhere between 24 and 48 hours later, a rash develops on the body, starting on the chest, back, or face. The rash may also appear in the mouth as white ulcers, or as ulcers in the ears and eyes.

Children are contagious from two days before the rash develops until all the lesions crust over, usually five to ten days after the rash breaks out.

Making it better: With viral infections, time is the greatest healer. At times, your doctor may prescribe antihistamines to help relieve itching. To make your child more comfortable and to avoid minor complications:

- Have your child drink plenty of fluids.

- Apply calamine lotion to itchy areas.

- Trim your child's nails or have the child wear mittens to discourage scratching open the rash, which can cause a skin infection.

- Soothe the rash with a bath. Add ½ cup of uncooked oatmeal or ½ cup of baking soda to a warm bath, and let your child soak for 15 minutes. Do not rinse the skin, but do pat dry gently. (To avoid plugging the drain, put oatmeal in a nylon stocking or use a powdered infant oatmeal cereal.)

✔ Use acetaminophen to treat a fever. Never give aspirin or salicylates to a child under the age of 19.

Contact a doctor immediately if your child is vomiting, experiences a painful and stiff neck, is very sleepy, has trouble walking, has a temperature higher than 102 degrees Fahrenheit, has a fever after the fourth day of illness, or is on steroids.

Colds and flu

Young children commonly experience 5 to 12 colds per year. A common misconception is that exposure to cold and wet weather causes colds. Although these conditions can depress the body's immune system, making you more vulnerable to illness, *germs* cause colds, plain and simple.

Recognizing the signs: Healthy children suffer from colds for 7 to 14 days. The contagious phase is the first two to four days after symptoms appear. These symptoms can be so minor, such as a tickle in the throat, that the cold can go undetected during the contagious phase, giving it a chance to spread easily to others. As the cold progresses, the symptoms become more pronounced and uncomfortable. The most common symptoms are sneezing, stuffy or runny nose, watery eyes, cough, earache, sore throat, and fever.

Making it better: With any viral infection, time is the best healer. To reduce the effects of a cold and make your child more comfortable:

✔ Make sure that your child gets plenty of bed rest.

✔ Encourage your child to drink plenty of fluids.

✔ Increase the humidity in the air by using a cool-mist humidifier.

✔ For infants and very young children who cannot blow their noses, use a nasal syringe to remove mucus. Bear in mind, though, that overuse can increase nasal secretions.

✔ Treat a fever with acetaminophen. Never give aspirin to children under the age of 19.

✔ Apply petroleum jelly on the skin under the nose to soothe rawness.

✔ Give older children sugarless hard candy or cough drops to suck on to relieve sore throats.

✔ Check with your doctor before giving your child any cold remedy. Over-the-counter medications can dry out the nasal passages and cause side effects.

Contact a doctor immediately if your child

- ✔ Is under 6 months of age (a time during which a small infant can quickly develop a more serious condition such as pneumonia)
- ✔ Widens the nostrils with each breath or has difficulty breathing
- ✔ Has symptoms that interfere with sleeping, eating, and drinking
- ✔ Does not urinate for more than 8 to 12 hours (a sign of dehydration)
- ✔ Has blue lips or nails
- ✔ Complains of increased throat pain or difficulty swallowing
- ✔ Has thick, green mucus instead of clear mucus
- ✔ Has a cough that lasts longer than two weeks, or a cough so strong that it causes choking or vomiting
- ✔ Complains of chest pain or shortness of breath
- ✔ Has pain in the ear
- ✔ Shivers and has chills
- ✔ Has a temperature higher than 102 degrees Fahrenheit, or has a temperature higher than 101 degrees Fahrenheit that lasts several days, or develops another fever after the initial fever subsides (a sign of a secondary bacterial infection)

Ear infections

Ear infection, or *otitis media,* is the inflammation of the middle ear, the area located behind the eardrum.

Recognizing the signs and knowing for sure: The symptoms of an ear infection in an older child are pain in the ear, a sensation of fullness in the ear, hearing loss, and fever. In a younger child, symptoms are irritability and fussiness, difficulty in sleeping, pulling at the ear, difficulty in or painful sucking, and fever.

An unresolved ear infection can lead to complications. Your child needs to see a physician, especially if symptoms include a fever and previous upper respiratory infection. Only a doctor can determine the exact cause of an earache and provide the best treatment.

Making it better: As many as 85 percent of otitis media cases are caused by bacteria, which antibiotics can eradicate. Some children do not feel relief until 48 hours after starting antibiotics, but if your child experiences no relief at all, discuss with your doctor the possibility of a viral infection (which antibiotics cannot treat) or allergies. Finding the culprit of recurrent ear infections is important because ear infections can affect a child's hearing and speech development.

Anytime your child is sick, ask your child's doctor to check for fluid in the middle ear. Even if your child isn't in pain, the fluid can affect hearing, something that young children in particular cannot communicate to others.

At home, make your child more comfortable. Position the child with the infected ear up. A warm compress on the ear and acetaminophen can help reduce pain and pressure. As long as the infection is not contagious, a child with an ear infection can go outside and play with others. Swimming is not recommended.

Measles

Although measles is usually associated with a severe skin rash, it's actually a respiratory infection. Initial symptoms usually appear anywhere from 9 to 11 days after exposure to the measles virus, and illness lasts 10 to 14 days.

Recognizing the signs and knowing for sure: The first symptoms of measles are irritability, runny nose, eyes that are red and sensitive to light (*conjunctivitis,* or *pinkeye* as it's commonly called), hacking cough, and a fever as high as 105 degrees Fahrenheit.

Within eight days after early symptoms develop, a rash appears. After the rash begins to develop, the initial symptoms subside, except for the cough, which can continue throughout the course of the illness. The rash usually begins on the forehead and works its way down the face, neck, and body. It looks like large, flat blotches that are somewhere between red and brown in color. They often overlap each other to completely cover the skin. It lasts about six days and then starts to disappear. As the blotches shed in a finely textured peel, the skin may look brown. This is only temporary.

One unmistakable sign of measles is *Koplik's spots,* small, red, irregularly shaped spots with blue-white centers found inside the mouth. They usually appear one to two days before the skin rash sets in, and a doctor may notice them upon examining a child.

Making it better: As with any viral infection, antibiotics aren't effective. Treatment usually involves making the child comfortable and watching for complications such as pneumonia.

Someone with measles is contagious from five days after exposure to the virus until five days after the rash disappears. Keep your child home and away from other children during this time. Your child needs to get plenty of bed rest and avoid busy play and activity. To make your child more comfortable during recovery:

✔ Encourage your child to drink plenty of fluids to prevent dehydration.

✔ Use a cool-mist humidifier to relieve your child's cough and soothe the breathing passages.

✔ Give acetaminophen to control a fever of 103 degrees Fahrenheit or higher. Never give aspirin to a child younger than 19.

✔ Darken your child's room. The pinkeye that sometimes accompanies the illness can make bright sunlight painful.

✔ Take your child's temperature at least once each morning and night to monitor progress and spot complications.

Contact a doctor immediately if your child

✔ Develops a sore throat

✔ Complains of an earache or heaviness in the ear

✔ Develops a cough that produces a colored mucus and/or lasts longer than four days

✔ Has difficulty breathing or breathes very fast

✔ Has lips or nails that turn bluish or gray

✔ Has a temperature above 103 degrees Fahrenheit

Asthma

Asthma is a lung disease that causes breathing problems for nearly 10 million people in the U.S. By recognizing and responding to early warning signs, you and your child can manage attacks.

Contact your doctor if your child has chest, throat, or neck pain or severe trouble breathing that seems to be getting worse, especially if the child is breathing rapidly. Pulling at the chest during inhalation and forceful grunting during exhalation are also signs of asthma. Also watch for other, less obvious signs — particularly eyes or fingertips that appear blue or skin that seems darkened. A child with asthma may act agitated, extremely lethargic, or confused.

A complete evaluation of your child's condition helps pinpoint medication that eases the symptoms. Regular checkups, education about early warning signs, and routine monitoring of lung air capacity with a peak flow meter can help decrease your child's chance of experiencing a frightening and severe attack.

Pneumonia

Although pneumonia was once considered extremely dangerous, today most children recover completely with proper medical treatment.

The symptoms of pneumonia include fever, sweating, chills, flushed skin, general discomfort, loss of appetite and energy, cough, fast and labored breathing, wheezing, and a bluish tint to the lips or nails. Contact your child's doctor if you notice any of these signs.

Your doctor may prescribe an antibiotic because determining whether the illness is caused by a virus or bacteria can be difficult. If your child does have bacterial pneumonia, the illness disappears in a few days, but you still need to give your child *all* the antibiotic for as long as prescribed to ensure that you eradicate all the bacteria. At home, don't give your child cough suppressants; coughing is necessary to clear the excessive secretions that the infection causes.

Be sure to check back with your doctor if your child has a fever that lasts more than two or three days after you start the antibiotics, has difficulty breathing, or experiences red, swollen joints, bone pain, stiffness in the neck, or vomiting. These are all signs of a possible infection.

Strep throat

The strep throat bacteria are contained in the droplets of sneezes and coughs, and it can also be spread through close contact with someone who is already infected. The incubation time for strep throat is two to seven days after exposure to the bacteria. Consider your child contagious until after treatment by antibiotics for 24 hours.

Recognizing the signs and knowing for sure: In older children, symptoms of strep throat include painful throat; difficulty swallowing and eating; fever above 101 degrees Fahrenheit; chills; body aches; nausea, vomiting, and abdominal pain; red, swollen tonsils that are dotted with whitish or yellowing specks of pus; and swollen glands in the neck. In infants, the symptoms may not be focused on the throat. They may include runny nose, crusting and sores around the nostrils, a low-grade fever, and poor feedings.

If your child shows any signs of strep throat, see a doctor for diagnosis and treatment. If left untreated or treated incompletely with antibiotics, the bacteria can lead to other, more serious complications, including kidney problems, rheumatic fever, sinusitis, ear infections, pneumonia, and skin infections. At times, a rash accompanies the strep infection. The illness is then called *scarlet fever* or *scarlatina,* but it is no more serious than strep throat alone.

Making it better: Your doctor typically treats the illness with an antibiotic for ten days. You can expect the fever to stop within three to five days, and the sore throat to subside soon after.

To make your child more comfortable during recovery:

- ✔ Add soft foods and more liquids to the diet. Try ice cream, Popsicles, soothing teas, warm soups, and milkshakes.

- ✔ Encourage your child to drink plenty of fluids to prevent dehydration.

- ✔ Let the child rest in bed and play quietly.

- ✔ Help your child gargle. Try a double-strength tea or warm, salty water. Make sure that your child spits out the salty water after gargling because it can upset the stomach.

- ✔ Use a cool-mist humidifier to add moisture to the air.

- ✔ Place a moist, warm towel around your child's neck to help soothe swollen glands.

- ✔ To prevent complications, be sure that your child takes *all* the antibiotics for as long as your doctor prescribes them.

Contact the doctor immediately if your child

- ✔ Develops a second fever after several days of normal temperature

- ✔ Develops a skin rash

- ✔ Complains of an earache or, in a younger child, pulls at the ears

- ✔ Has a nasal discharge with discolored or bloody mucus

- ✔ Develops a cough, especially one that produces mucus

- ✔ Experiences chest pain, shortness of breath, or extreme tiredness

- ✔ Has convulsions

- ✔ Has painful, red, and swollen joints

- ✔ Is nauseated or vomiting

Tonsillitis

Tonsillitis, an infection and inflammation of the tonsils, can be caused by viruses or bacteria. In either case, the tonsils become enlarged and red and are often coated with a yellow, gray, or white membrane.

Recognizing the signs and knowing for sure: In an older child, the symptoms of tonsillitis are a sudden sore throat, pain upon swallowing, stiff neck, loss of appetite, general ill feeling, chills, a fever higher than 101 degrees Fahrenheit, and swollen and tender glands under the neck. In infants, the symptoms of tonsillitis may not be as focused on the throat. The most noticeable symptoms may be poor feedings, runny nose, and a slight fever.

A doctor diagnoses tonsillitis by examining the tonsils. Your doctor may also take a culture to determine whether a virus or bacteria is causing the infection.

Making it better: In 30 percent of tonsillitis cases, the bacteria called *Group A streptococci* is responsible for the illness, and a course of antibiotics treats the infection. In the other 70 percent of cases, the infection is viral, in which case antibiotics don't help — the illness must run its course. When bacteria causes tonsillitis, the fever and sore throat usually last three to five days. When a virus causes tonsillitis, its duration depends on the virus involved. Most people recover almost completely within a week.

To make your child more comfortable during recovery:

- Include more liquids and soft foods, such as soothing teas, warm soups, cooling soft drinks, milkshakes, and Popsicles, in your child's diet.
- Make sure that your child drinks plenty of fluids.
- Check your child's temperature at least once in the morning and once at night. Report any increase in temperature to your doctor.
- Give acetaminophen to relieve pain and reduce fever. Never give aspirin to a child younger than 19.
- Encourage older children to gargle with double-strength tea or warm, salty water. Be sure that your child doesn't swallow the salty water because it can upset the stomach.
- Because dry air can aggravate a sore throat, use a cool-mist humidifier to add moisture to the air, especially during the night.
- If your child is taking antibiotics, be sure that he takes the medication as directed for as long as prescribed.

Contact a doctor immediately if your child

- Develops a second fever a few days after the initial fever disappears (possibly indicating a second infection)
- Develops a skin rash
- Complains of an earache

✔ Has convulsions

✔ Has a nasal discharge that's discolored or streaked with blood

✔ Develops a cough, especially if it produces mucus

✔ Complains of chest pain, shortness of breath, or extreme tiredness

✔ Has painful, red, or swollen joints

✔ Is nauseated or vomiting

Challenges of puberty and adolescent health

Growing up is just plain difficult — even in terms of health. Teenagers need to understand what's going on with their body, how to handle those changes, and how to start taking responsibility for their health.

Reacting to acne

In regards to their skin, teens can pretty safely blame hormones for just about everything that goes wrong.

To help fight acne, wash your face regularly and keep your hair (which is covered with oils of its own) off your face and forehead. Use only oil-free products and cosmetics on your face. Most important: Don't pick at pimples. Doing so can only make matters worse and may lead to permanent scarring.

If acne is particularly bothersome and doesn't subside, talk with a dermatologist or your medical practitioner about what you can do. A number of prescription drugs are available for treating acne.

Fighting back against eating disorders

For some adolescents, weight and appearance can become an obsession that leads to extreme dieting and exercising. Eating disorders may result.

✔ **Anorexia nervosa** is characterized by an obsession with thinness, mostly affecting adolescent girls. The extreme weight loss of anorexia causes serious side effects, including loss of muscle, bone minerals, and menstrual periods. A weakened heart, anemia, and liver and kidney damage may occur as well. In some cases, anorexia leads to death. Adolescents who have anorexia need immediate medical care and psychological counseling.

✔ **Bulimia nervosa** involves eating large amounts of food in a short period and then purging the food from the body by inducing vomiting, using laxatives, or fasting. The physical results of bulimia aren't as noticeable as with anorexia because those with bulimia tend to maintain normal weights. Some negative side effects may include upsetting the body's fluid and mineral balance, damage to the bowels, internal bleeding and infection, and tooth damage and lesions in the esophagus due to exposure to stomach acid during repeated vomiting. In some cases, bulimia may lead to death.

✔ **Binge eating disorder** is more common in males. Those who binge consume food frequently and repeatedly, often in secret. This disorder usually has its roots in stress, anxiety, or depression. Genetics, socioeconomic status, and culture also may play a role.

The first step in treatment is a physical examination to determine the extent of the disease. Mild cases are often treated with counseling that involves talking and working to restructure eating habits and behavior. In more serious cases, immediate hospitalization may be necessary to restore the health of the person with the disorder before therapy can begin.

For more information about eating disorders, contact the American Anorexia/Bulimia Association, 165 West 46th Street, Suite 1108, New York, NY 10036; phone 212-575-6200; or visit their Web site at www.aabainc.org.

Boosting emotional health

Adolescence is a type of roller coaster. Part of the ride can be attributed to hormones, which do affect mood and sex drive. The other part comes from the conflicts that come with growing up: changing relationships with parents and friends, pressure from peers, and the awkwardness of body changes.

Unfortunately, the combination of adolescent stress and/or family problems sometimes sets the stage for serious emotional problems. These stresses may even precipitate mental illness. Professional help is the only alternative.

Everyone experiences short "down" periods now and then. However, when depression becomes prolonged, you need to seek help. Just as with a physical ailment, recovery is quicker if you address the emotional illness as soon as possible. And depression is treatable. Some signs of depression include

> ✔ Chronic sadness
>
> ✔ Feelings of hopelessness
>
> ✔ Avoidance of family and friends
>
> ✔ Diminishing interest in food, school, or recreational activities
>
> ✔ Inability to focus and concentrate
>
> ✔ Physical symptoms such as fatigue, headache, or stomachache
>
> ✔ Insomnia or sleeping too much

For free information about depression, contact the National Institute of Mental Health at NIMH Public Inquiries, 6001 Executive Boulevard, Rm. 8184, MSC 9663, Bethesda, MD 20892-9663; phone 301-443-4513; or visit online at www.nimh.nih.gov/.

Men's Health

Yeah, yeah, you've heard it said hundreds of times: Men simply don't care about their health. Actually, deep down, most men *do* care about staying healthy. (Remember, it was men who started the jogging craze and went to gyms at lunchtime.) The following covers the most common questions men have about their health.

Handling hair loss

Men are simply more likely to lose their hair than women are. According to a study by the American Hair Loss Council, 19.5 million women lose hair in some form, but that number jumps to 33 million for men.

Many factors can cause hair loss, including stress, heredity, chemotherapy, medical conditions, hormonal changes, and old age. Male-pattern baldness, the most common type of hair loss, can begin in men in their late teens or early 20s. By the age of 35 to 40, about 66 percent of Caucasian men show some signs of hair loss. Men who begin to lose hair at a younger age are more likely to suffer severe baldness than men who begin to lose hair at an older age. If your mother's father or her male relatives went bald, you're more likely to eventually have a hair-free scalp. Hereditary male-pattern baldness usually passes through the mother's genes.

Sorry, guys. You can't stop inevitable hair loss that comes with age and genetics. However, if the process is too quick or problematic for your liking, consult your doctor or dermatologist, who may be able to prescribe medical treatment or other alternatives.

Pharmacological treatment

Studies show that drugs can be effective in treating male pattern baldness. As with any medicine, however, successful results vary from person to person.

- ✔ **Minoxidil.** The first word in drug treatment for hair loss today is topical *minoxidil* (Rogaine). Minoxidil doesn't create new hair follicles, but it does stop the shrinking process of existing ones and encourages regrowth of hair that tends to be very fine.

  One disadvantage of using minoxidil is that you commit yourself to it for life. If you stop treatment, any hair that you previously saved or were able to regrow due to the treatment falls out. Possible side effects associated with minoxidil include irritation, rash, itching, and dry or flaking skin. Minoxidil works best at the top of the head and in mild cases of hair loss.

- ✔ **Propecia.** If you don't like the idea of applying medication to your scalp daily, you can try a pill instead. Propecia blocks the enzyme responsible for hair loss. Possible side effects include a decrease in semen, difficulty in achieving erection, and diminished desire for sex. Men with liver problems should avoid using this medication.

  Because of the risk of birth defects to the fetus, pregnant women and women of childbearing age should avoid contact with Propecia. During intercourse, wear a condom to avoid passing the drug to your mate via sperm.

Surgical treatment

Hair replacement surgery is an alternative for men who find that other measures don't help in their fight against hair loss. Discuss your expectations with your surgeon and then decide whether surgery is for you.

- ✔ **Hair transplants (grafting):** This surgical process removes small portions of hair-bearing scalp grafts from the the sides or back of the head and relocates them, about ⅛ inch apart from each other, to the bald or thinning areas. (Don't worry: The grafts taken from the donor sites don't leave you bald in those areas.) The surgeon may either use a special tubelike instrument to punch a small, round graft or a scalpel to remove tiny sections of hair-bearing scalp.

  Expect several surgical sessions (about three hours each) to achieve best results, and you need to take a few months off between sessions for healing. How much coverage you need depends on the texture and color of your hair. Don't forget to bring your wallet: One session can cost between $3,500 and $8,500.

✔ **Flap surgery:** This procedure has the advantage of covering large areas of baldness rather quickly. It involves cutting out a section of bald scalp and lifting off a flap of hair-bearing skin still attached at one end. The hair-bearing flap is moved into its new position and sewn into place, while staying connected to its original supply of blood. The scar resulting from the surgery is covered up by the relocated flap of hair. Flap surgery is more expensive than other procedures: Expect to pay between $3,500 and $10,000.

✔ **Scalp reduction:** This procedure offers dramatic change and is best for covering bald areas at the back and crown. In this process, a piece of skin from the scalp is cut out. The surrounding edges are pulled together and stitched, and the process can be painful due to the extensive tugging and pulling of the scalp. Several sessions may be necessary, and the average cost is $1,600 per procedure.

Alternatives to surgery

Hair additions consist of human or synthetic hair, or a combination of both, and give you the appearance of fuller hair. Check your local hair salon and wig store to find hair additions or ask your doctor for a reference.

✔ **Hair weaves:** Weaves are made by weaving or braiding human or synthetic hair into your existing hair. Hair weaves aren't without problems because they make it difficult to keep the hair and scalp clean. Also, because technicians weave the new hair into your existing hair, the weave can stress the existing hair, which may possibly cause more hair loss. Another downside is that as your natural hair grows, technicians must reposition the extensions every four to six weeks. Expect to pay up to $2,500.

✔ **Toupees:** These items are made from either human or synthetic hair and are kept in place with adhesives or clips. Toupees vary in quality, and the bad ones are easy to spot. Human hair toupees look very natural but tend to break down sooner and can cost around $1,000. If you're active, synthetic toupees are better because they're easier to keep clean and last longer.

✔ **Wigs:** Like toupees, wigs are made from either human or synthetic hair and cover the head more fully than other options. Prices are comparable to that of toupees.

Self-care

Your goal is to protect your hair follicles from damaging chemicals, styling techniques, and other products. Hair products that change the color (dyes and bleaches) or texture (perms and straighteners) of your hair can damage your hair follicles. What you do to your hair can also damage the follicles — drying your hair with a hair dryer or braiding and cornrowing your hair, for example. If your scalp is sensitive, stick to gentle shampoos and conditioners, such as those made for infants.

✔ Avoid stress, and you can keep more of your hair. Deal with stress through exercise, rest, and other mechanisms that help both your sanity and your hair.

✔ Try a new hairstyle if you have partial hair loss. Cut your hair short or blunt because either style makes hair look thicker and less patchy.

✔ Stay away from gels, as they tend to clump hair together, emphasizing thinning hair.

✔ For something more simple, try a completely bald look. Bald is trendy!

Understanding prostate disease

The prostate gland can be much more troublesome to men than its small size suggests. In fact, it causes a range of difficulties that more or less fall into three major categories. Two are common but benign. The third occurs less frequently but can be life-threatening.

✔ **Benign prostatic hyperplasia:** Otherwise known as *benign enlarged prostate,* BPH is the most common disease of the prostate gland, affecting 6 out of every 10 men between the ages of 40 and 59.

✔ **Prostatitis:** Prostatitis refers to inflammation or infection of the prostate. This condition affects young to middle-aged men primarily.

✔ **Prostate cancer:** Prostate cancer is a very serious disease affecting 1 in 8 American men over a lifetime. This cancer usually grows slowly and, with early detection, has an exceptionally good prognosis.

Recognizing the signs: Symptoms of prostate problems may include the following:

✔ Frequent urination, especially at night

✔ Difficulty beginning and stopping the flow of urine

✔ Dribbling, hesitant, and thin stream of urine

✔ Sensation of urgent need to urinate

Measure your symptoms

The following questions, based on the American Urological Association questionnaire, can help you and your practitioner measure the severity of your prostate problems. Give yourself a 0 for never; 1 for less than one time in five; 2 for less than half the time; 3 for half the time, 4 for more than half the time; and 5 for almost always. The time frame is over the past month.

✔ How often do you have a sensation of not emptying your bladder completely after you finish urinating?

✔ How often do you have to urinate again less than two hours after you finish urinating?

✔ How often do you find that you stop and start several times when urinating?

✔ How often do you have a weak stream of urine?

✔ How often do you find postponing urination difficult?

✔ How often do you have to strain to begin urination?

✔ How often do you need to get up to urinate during the night?

A score of 7 or less may indicate a mild problem; 8 to 19 may indicate a moderate problem; and 20 to 35 may indicate a severe problem. Talk with your doctor about your symptoms and your score.

✔ Sensation that the bladder hasn't emptied completely

✔ Blood in the urine

✔ Inability to urinate

✔ Involuntary loss of urine (incontinence)

Other symptoms of prostate cancer include painful ejaculation and pain or stiffness in the lower back, hips, and upper thighs. Because of its initially slow progression, prostate cancer often goes undetected for a long time before it's found and diagnosed, usually discovered accidentally while screening for another condition.

Knowing for sure: Your doctor can diagnose a prostate problem through a series of tests, medical history, a physical examination, and a review of urinary habits. Expect a urinalysis and a urine culture. Your doctor may also do a few "hands-on" types of examinations, such as palpitating your bladder to tell whether it's distended and a *digital rectal exam* — a manual exam in which the doctor inserts a gloved, lubricated finger into the rectum and, through the wall of the rectum, checks the prostate for hard or lumpy areas. Your doctor may also do a series of tests known as a *urodynamic* *evaluation* to measure urine flow and *residual urine,* or urine that is left in the bladder after urination. Other tests include blood tests to rule out kidney disease and prostate cancer.

Treatment: You, your doctor, and perhaps a urologist work together to determine which treatment is right for you. Many physicians believe that men whose symptoms are mild (and don't interfere with their quality of life) and who are at low risk of urine retention may benefit from a period of "watchful waiting." As many as one-third of all mild cases of BPH clear up without any treatment at all.

If symptoms become more progressive — and often they don't — medication may be appropriate. Men with severe symptoms may need to consider surgery or another medical procedure.

With prostate cancer, removal of the prostate gland and seminal vesicles is done when the cancer is confined to the prostate gland. Radiation therapy may follow surgery or be used as a treatment tool by itself to treat small tumors or cancer that has spread beyond the gland. For men with advanced cancer who can't have surgery or radiation, hormone therapy, cryosurgery (in which cancer cells are frozen and removed), or biological therapy (in which the body's immune system is triggered to attack cancer cells) may all be options.

Consider both the benefits and possible side effects of each treatment option, especially the effects on sexual activity, urination, and other concerns that can affect your quality of life. Many older men whose prostate cancer is slow growing and is found at an early stage may not need treatment. Instead, your doctor may suggest following you closely and treating you later for symptoms that may arise.

Try the following when dealing with prostate disease:

- ✔ **Consume a low-fat, low-cholesterol diet.**

- ✔ **Reduce your intake of fluids in the evening.**

- ✔ **Limit your intake of coffee and other caffeinated drinks.**

- ✔ **Urinate frequently.** If you overtax your bladder, you only aggravate the symptoms.

- ✔ **Take your time while urinating.** Allow several minutes to empty your bladder as completely as possible.

- ✔ **Avoid spicy foods, citrus juice, and other acidic drinks to make your urine less acidic and less irritating.**

- ✔ **Exercise regularly to increase the flow of blood and oxygen to the prostate area.** Walking and swimming are especially good exercises for men with BPH. See Chapter 7 for tips on exercising.

✔ **Take a warm bath to soften the prostate and relax the pelvic muscles.**

✔ **Avoid constipation, which worsens the symptoms of BPH.**

✔ **Watch your blood sugar level if you're diabetic.** Poorly controlled diabetes weakens the bladder, which then cannot push the urine past the enlarging prostate.

✔ **Watch out for certain over-the-counter and prescription drugs that may trigger the bladder neck to suddenly tighten, blocking urine flow.** Medications that can be troublesome include oral bronchodilators, diuretics, tranquilizers, cold and allergy preparations that contain decongestants, and antidepressants.

Testicular cancer

Testicular cancer can affect men at any age, but it's more common among men between the ages of 15 and 34. Testicular cancer is fast growing, and you can feel it before it spreads beyond the testicle. Fortunately, testicular cancer is almost always curable if it's diagnosed and treated early. The key to early detection is regular testicular self-examination.

Recognizing the signs: Symptoms of testicular cancer include a lump in either testicle, enlargement of a testicle, a feeling of heaviness in the scrotum, a dull ache in the lower abdomen or groin, a sudden collection of fluid in the scrotum, pain or discomfort in a testicle or scrotum, and enlargement or tenderness of the breasts. These symptoms aren't sure signs of cancer, so you need to see your doctor if any of these symptoms lasts as long as two weeks.

Knowing for sure: Your doctor reviews your history and does a physical examination, including careful inspection of the scrotum. Tests include an X-ray, ultrasound, as well as blood and urine tests. If no sign of an infection is present, the doctor may suspect cancer.

A biopsy is the only sure way to know whether cancer is present. To obtain the tissue, a surgeon removes the affected testicle through the groin. The surgeon doesn't cut through the scrotum and doesn't remove just a part of the testicle because if it is cancerous, cutting through the outer layer of the testicle may cause the cancer to spread to the surrounding tissue and lymph nodes. Although this treatment may seem drastic, removing the affected testicle can halt further growth if cancer is present. Removing one testicle doesn't interfere with fertility or the ability to have an erection. Also, you can have an artificial testicle implanted into the scrotum for cosmetic purposes.

Testicular cancer: Are you at risk?

Factors that increase your risk for testicular cancer include the following:

✔ **Undescended testicles as an infant:** The risk for testicular cancer is 3 to 17 times higher than average for boys born with undescended testicles. The risk increases if the condition isn't surgically corrected in early childhood.

✔ **Klinefelter's syndrome:** This rare, chromosomal disorder is characterized by small testicles, enlarged breasts, and a lack of secondary sex characteristics such as beard growth and voice change.

✔ **Gonadal aplasia:** With this condition, the testicles don't develop.

✔ **Hermaphroditism:** This condition is the development of both male and female sex characteristics.

Treatment: Treatment of testicular cancer depends on the stage and type of disease. Treatments for testicular cancer include surgery, radiation therapy, and chemotherapy. Regular follow-up examinations are necessary to ensure that the cancer is completely gone. Testicular cancer seldom recurs after a patient has been cancer-free for three years. Men treated for cancer in one testicle have about a 1 percent chance of developing cancer in the other testicle.

Male infertility

Infertility is a frustrating and complex problem, affecting 6.1 million Americans, or about 10 percent of people of reproductive age. In 27 percent of infertility cases, the problem lies with the man and woman. Twenty percent of the cases stem from the man alone.

At the heart of most male infertility is trouble with the number and *motility* (sperm's ability to swim into a woman's fallopian tubes and fertilize an egg) of sperm. Several factors can affect the number and motility of sperm, including infections, sexually transmitted diseases, environmental toxins, alcohol and drug use, smoking, congenital problems, and hormone insufficiency.

Knowing for sure: Because infertility is a complex condition, your practitioner may refer you to a *urologist*. After the doctor performs a physical examination and asks you about your medical history to rule out any secondary causes of infertility (such as STDs), the doctor tests your sperm for number count and motility.

Treatment: Doctor-prescribed infertility treatment depends on the results of your tests.

- ✔ If damage to the vas deferens or a blockage is the problem, microsurgery can repair the damage (however, it doesn't guarantee fertility).

- ✔ If low sperm counts cause infertility, injections of a hormone that stimulates the testes can sometimes enhance sperm production. Hormone insufficiency can be treated with regular injections of hormones such as testosterone and other hormones that regulate sperm production.

Increase your chances of becoming a daddy

No matter what the tests show, you can boost your sperm production by trying the following tips. Keep in mind that you may try all these things and still have no success. That's when you and your partner need to seek testing. If the woman is over age 30 or has had previous miscarriages, talk to your doctor sooner rather than later.

- ✔ **Avoid stress.** Stress is linked to lower sperm counts, although experts aren't sure what the connection is.

- ✔ **Don't smoke or use alcohol or illicit drugs.** These no-no's can lower sperm counts and possibly contribute to birth defects.

- ✔ **Check your medicine cabinet.** Some drugs can interfere with erections and decrease testosterone levels. Examples include beta blockers, MAO inhibitors, anabolic steroids, and antidepressants. Talk with your doctor.

- ✔ **Stock up on antioxidants.** *Antioxidants* — vitamins C and E, the mineral selenium, and beta-carotene — neutralize free radicals, which can adversely affect sperm production. Eat plenty of fruits and vegetables, brewer's yeast, and whole grains daily to get an adequate supply of antioxidants.

- ✔ **Get enough zinc.** Zinc is linked to good prostate health as well as to healthy sperm. Beef, crab meat, pumpkin seeds, and oysters are good sources of zinc. Just be sure not to exceed the recommended dietary allowance of 15 mg daily without a health practitioner's advice.

- ✔ **Avoid environmental toxins.** Some metals (such as lead), pesticides, and glue and paint chemicals can lower sperm counts. Use safety precautions if you work in an environment that exposes you to dangerous substances.

- ✔ **Have more intercourse.** You increase the chance of fertilization if you and your partner have intercourse at least every other day during your partner's ovulation.

In the end, you may have to consider fertility treatment by assisted reproductive technology (ART). About 10 percent of infertile couples try to get pregnant via artificial insemination, in vitro fertilization (IVF), or a new procedure called *intracytoplasmic sperm injection.* Unfortunately, the odds of pregnancy aren't exceptional. Only half of the couples who seek ART conceive.

Impotence and other male sexual problems

Impotence is a man's inability to have an erection. This condition is also called *erectile dysfunction,* or ED. The causes of impotence can be either psychological or physical, while the degree of impotence can vary from a simple loss of rigidity to a total inability to have an erection. Although impotence can strike at any age, it becomes much more common as men grow older. Among men in their late 70s and beyond, some symptoms of impotence are almost universal.

Impotence doesn't necessarily mean the end of a man's sex life. Depending on the cause of the problem, several possible solutions are usually available, so take heart.

- ✔ **The morning cure:** For many men, the easiest suggestion is to have sex in the morning instead of at night. In the morning, you have more energy, so you can get erections more easily. Also, the male sex hormone, testosterone, is at its peak level in the morning and at its weakest at night. Try waking up, having a light breakfast, and then taking your partner back to bed for a sexual interlude.

- ✔ **The stuff technique.** This technique is just what it sounds like. The man, with the help of his partner, stuffs his nonerect penis into her vagina. Sometimes, after a man begins to thrust, the blood flows into his penis and that elusive erection finally rises to the occasion.

- ✔ **Sex therapy:** In younger men, impotence is more often than not psychological rather than physiological, so curing the problem is usually easy with the help of a sex therapist.

- ✔ **Urologist:** A urologist can make sure that a problem isn't physical. For many men who worry, just hearing from a doctor that they're A-OK is enough to give their penises the psychological lift they need.

- ✔ **Confidence building:** Sometimes masturbation does the trick. Sometimes men need to do confidence-building exercises with their partners. These exercises usually involve prohibiting intercourse for a while, but allowing the couple to engage in other sexual activity. The man can usually get an erection when he doesn't have the pressure of needing an erection to penetrate the woman. After he gets his erection back, transferring that confidence to having erections when he plans to have intercourse is usually easy.

If none of the preceding techniques helps deal with impotence, then you may have to help Mother Nature:

- ✔ **Oral medications:** *Sildenafil* (Viagra) is effective in 75 to 80 percent of men who suffer from ED. You must take Sildenafil one to four hours before sexual activity and sexually stimulate yourself for the drug to take effect. Patients who take Viagra may have some mild side effects, such as headaches or seeing halos around objects, but they seem not to bother most men who take the drug.

- ✔ **Penile implants:** Penile implants are either hydraulic or non-hydraulic. The *non-hydraulic prostheses* are basically semi-rigid rods that doctors surgically implant within the erectile chambers. Although they're reliable, they have one major drawback — after surgery, the penis is always in a rigid state. You can push your penis down when you're not having sex, but the erection may still be visible, which can be embarrassing.

  The surgery required for penile implants does leave soreness in the area, and you can't have sex for several weeks. But most men report very good results and are quite happy. The only men who seem to complain are those whose hopes were too high, and who expected to have erections as strong as the ones they had in their youth. This cannot happen because the erection is permanent, and it needs to be at least somewhat concealable.

  The *hydraulic prosthesis* has a fluid reservoir and a mechanical pump that a man uses to fill the prosthesis and create an erection when he wants one. Men report liking the system, but it is prone to mechanical failure. Like the implant, it requires a surgical procedure.

- ✔ **Injection therapy:** A man injects his penis with a medication that relaxes the muscles, thus allowing the blood to flow into the penis and cause an erection. Although the thought of injecting yourself in that particular spot may not sound appealing, the penis is an area relatively insensitive to pain, so you can barely feel the injections. Most men who use this system report good results. Possible side effects include scarring and, rarely, sustained erections that don't go away without medical treatment.

✓ **Vacuum constriction:** Basically, a man places a vacuum pump over the penis and, as the air is pumped out, blood flows in, creating an erection. He then places a ring at the base of his penis to hold the blood in place. For some, vacuum pumps work wonders. Sometimes mild bruising occurs as a result of using these devices, and some men have difficulty ejaculating after using these devices.

The fact that a man can have an erection does not necessarily mean that his partner is ready to have sex. If a man without ED approaches his wife for sex and she turns him down, he may be frustrated, but he also knows that he can have plenty of additional erections, perhaps even during the course of that same day. But a man who pops a pill or injects himself may be a lot more demanding because he has gone to some "lengths" to obtain his erection. If he doesn't consult with his better half, then she may not enjoy any resulting sexual interplay. So, the decision to use one of the preceding methods needs to be a decision shared between partners.

Women's Health

In this era of information overload, health information for women seems to be everywhere. Yet, despite this glut of information, most women are still confused and overwhelmed. For useful and credible information, read on.

Routine screenings and exams for women of any age

You can head off many problems before they occur by going to your doctor for regular checkups and health screenings. Here's a decade-by-decade list of recommended screenings. Bear in mind, though, that recommendations vary, depending on the group making the recommendation and your individual health status. Check with your doctor to arrange a screening schedule that's right for you.

Age Range	What You Should Do
In your 20s and 30s	Routine physical every three years (if you're healthy)
	Annual gynecological exam with a Pap test*
	Periodic blood pressure screening
	Cholesterol test at least once every five years

Age Range	What You Should Do
In your 40s	Routine physical every two years (if you're healthy)
	Annual gynecological exam with a Pap test*
	Periodic blood pressure screening
	Periodic cholesterol screening
	Mammogram every one to two years
	Annual rectal exam
	Baseline electrocardiogram (EKG) at age 40
	Annual skin exam
	Periodic comprehensive eye exams
In your 50s	Routine physical every year
	Annual gynecological exam with a Pap test*
	Periodic blood pressure screening
	Periodic cholesterol screening
	Mammogram every year
	Annual rectal exam
	Annual colorectal screening
	Annual skin exam
	Periodic comprehensive eye exams
In your 60s, 70s, and 80s	Routine physical every year
	Annual gynecological exam with a Pap test*
	Periodic blood pressure screening
	Periodic cholesterol screening
	Mammogram every year
	Annual rectal exam
	Annual colorectal screening
	Annual skin exam
	Annual comprehensive eye exam

* If the results of three consecutive Pap tests are normal, the test can be performed less frequently at the discretion of your physician.

Easing endometriosis

Endometriosis — which most commonly affects women between the ages of 25 and 40 — occurs when tissue from the lining of the uterus finds its way into the pelvic cavity. Even outside the uterus, the monthly hormonal cycles that govern menstruation affect the errant tissue. However, in the pelvic cavity, no outlet exists for the tissue to break down and pass out of the body during menstruation, so the tissue remains there, often causing pain, the development of cysts, and the growth of scar tissue that may lead to infertility.

Recognizing the signs and knowing for sure: One-third of women with endometriosis have no symptoms and are unaware that they have endometriosis. Others experience one or more of the following symptoms:

- Painful ovulation and menstruation

- Heavy, lengthy menstrual periods

- Painful intercourse

- Constipation, diarrhea, and painful bowel movements and urination

- Vomiting

- Low-grade fever

- Lower back pain

Your physicians may make the diagnosis by using a thin viewing scope, which she inserts through a 1-inch incision in the abdomen during an outpatient surgical procedure. Also, doctors are increasingly using *magnetic resonance imaging* (MRI), a noninvasive procedure that uses magnetic imaging to see the inside of the body, to diagnose the condition. MRIs can detect 96 percent of cases of endometriosis without making an incision.

Making it better: Endometriosis may disappear during pregnancy or after menopause, when periods come to an end. If you have a mild case, you may not require treatment at all. However, treatment is recommended if endometriosis is painful or if you want to have children in the future.

- Regular workouts reduce the risk of developing the condition and also reduce the weight gain and depression associated with the drugs used to treat it.

- Stay away from saturated fats and hydrogenated oils, which contribute to severe menstrual cramps. You can ease some symptoms by getting enough of the vitamins C, E, and B complex and the minerals selenium, calcium, and magnesium.

- Medications, commonly nonsteroidal, anti-inflammatory drugs (NSAIDs), may be prescribed to ease pain. Naproxen sodium is thought to be helpful, too. Additionally, hormonal drug treatments can interrupt the menstrual cycle and suppress ovulation.

✔ A surgeon can remove growths, most commonly through the performance of dilation and curettage (D&C), cauterization, or laser procedure. As a last resort, removal of the uterus may be performed.

For more information about endometriosis, contact the Endometriosis Association, 8585 N. 76th Pl., Milwaukee, WI 53223; phone 414-355-2200, 800-992-3636; or find them on the Web at www.endometriosisassn.org.

Dealing with premenstrual syndrome

Experts recognize 150 symptoms as part of *premenstrual syndrome* (PMS) and believe that the peak progesterone levels that occur in women just before menstruation cause the syndrome. The most likely sufferers are women over 30 and those who are approaching menopause.

Recognizing the signs and knowing for sure: The most common symptoms of PMS include bloating, breast tenderness, changes in appetite and cravings, and emotional changes such as mood swings, anxiety, and irritability. The best way to tell whether you have PMS is to chart your symptoms for three months. If the chart shows a consistent pattern of problems that develop after you ovulate and go away a week after you finish menstruating, you probably have PMS. Be sure to get a pelvic examination from your practitioner, too, to rule out other problems (such as fibroids).

Making it better: To reduce your PMS symptoms on your own, exercise, limit your intake of alcohol and caffeine, eat less salt, and explore complementary therapies such as herbal treatments, yoga, massage, relaxation techniques, and reflexology.

Medical treatment for PMS includes oral contraceptives, diuretics, vitamins, minerals, hormones, and tranquilizers. The tranquilizer Xanax, along with antidepressants, shows promise in treating PMS symptoms.

Eight ways to make a gynecologic exam more comfortable

No woman looks forward to having a gynecologic exam, but those screening procedures may save your life. That said, the following are some ways to make the exam more comfortable:

✔ **Consider your practitioner's gender**. Although you can find qualified practitioners of both genders, some women are uncomfortable having a man perform their gynecologic exam and may find talking about the intimate aspects of their life easier with a female practitioner. If you're comfortable with either gender, choose the practitioner you're most comfortable with and who has the qualifications to treat any specific condition you may have. *Remember:* You can always request the presence of a female nurse during the exam if that makes you feel more comfortable.

✔ **Prepare for your exam**. If a visit is your first exam with a new practitioner, ask her or her staff in advance what procedures she follows. If you're undergoing a new procedure, read about it or ask about it when you schedule the exam. *Remember:* You can't see much of what is going on during the exam. Knowing what's going to occur and how it feels may ease your mind.

✔ **Consider taking someone with you.** You may feel more comfortable if you have your mother, partner, or a close friend with you to offer moral support during the exam. Be aware, however, that having another person with you may in some way compromise your ability to ask questions or speak freely with your practitioner about your symptoms or experiences.

✔ **Empty your bladder**. A gynecologic exam can put pressure on your bladder, making you feel the need to urinate. To prevent this discomfort, visit the restroom before you visit the examining room. First, however, inquire whether your doctor may want a urine sample to analyze, particularly in case of a bladder infection.

✔ **Ask your practitioner to give you a play-by-play.** Because most of your reproductive system is internal, you can't see what's happening during much of the exam. Ask your practitioner to let you know what she's doing as it's happening.

✔ **Ask your practitioner to take comfort measures.** Your practitioner can do a lot of little things to make you more comfortable during the exam. For example, she can put cloth covers over the metal stirrups to keep your feet warm or warm her instruments before she inserts them into your vagina. And if you have a smaller vagina, she may be able to use a smaller speculum. If you're concerned about the size of the instrument, ask your practitioner to show it to you. Ask her whether she's using the smallest instrument available, and ask her to agree to withdraw it if you experience any pain.

✔ **Try to relax.** If you relax your muscles, you can relieve pressure and make your exam less uncomfortable. Take deep slow breaths and relax your muscles, particularly those in your hips, between your legs and your abdomen. And try to think of something pleasant, such as lying on the beach or sitting on a mountain top.

✔ **Remember that you're in charge.** Let your practitioner know whether anything is too uncomfortable or painful. Ask any questions you have. Remove the drape sheet, if you wish, to see your practitioner's face. And remember that you can stop the examination if you feel doing so is necessary. Also warn your practitioner in advance if you have had any past experiences that may make this exam especially uncomfortable, such as a history of sexual abuse. Most doctors are far more patient with you if you warn them in advance.

Managing menopause

Menopause involves much more than hot flashes. It's a phase of life in which ovulation ends and the ovaries begin to produce less of the hormone estrogen. Menopause can occur in women as young as 35, and it usually lasts 2 to 3 years, although it can last as long as 12.

To HRT or not to HRT?

Every woman bumping up against menopause has some tough decisions to make: Opt for hormone replacement therapy (HRT), which can lessen your risk of heart disease and osteoporosis, seek other, natural ways to replace estrogen, or do nothing?

Whatever you choose, don't let someone else make the decision for you. Some doctors believe HRT is the greatest thing since sliced bread and push it on all their patients, and others shun the regimen, saying that menopause is all-natural, come what may. Certainly, you need to speak with your doctor about your options, but make up your own mind based on your own circumstances.

You may consider HRT if

✔ Heart disease runs in your family.

✔ Osteoporosis runs in your family, or you have weakened bones.

✔ You faced menopause at an early age, perhaps before age 45.

You may think twice about HRT if

✔ Breast or endometrial cancer runs in your family.

✔ You have unexplained vaginal bleeding, migraines, endometriosis, fibroids, diabetes, or gallbladder disease.

Recognizing the signs: Think of menopause as puberty in reverse. Common signs include headache, insomnia, hot flashes, vaginal dryness and thinning, reduction in or loss of sexual desire, and night sweats.

Making it better: Menopause isn't a disease and doesn't call for treatment; it's a natural phase of life. Some lucky women — about 10 to 15 percent — get through menopause and the decade or so leading up to it with no discomfort whatsoever. On the other end of the spectrum, about 10 to 15 percent of women become somewhat physically or emotionally disabled by menopausal changes.

You can take some measures on your own to temper the symptoms of menopause:

- ✔ **Exercise regularly, maintain a healthy diet, and try to drink eight glasses of water daily to prevent hot flashes.** Other tips include keeping rooms cool and avoiding spicy and hot foods.

- ✔ **If a hot flash strikes, try taking a cool shower.** Dress in layers of light, comfortable clothing that you can remove if a flash comes on.

- ✔ **Try complementary medicine.** Homeopathy, Chinese medicine, and biofeedback can ease menopausal symptoms.

- ✔ **Start a tofu habit.** Asian women have few problems with menopause because they eat a diet rich in soy, which contains plant estrogens. Try drinking lowfat soy milk or mixing soy powder in your favorite juice. Eat tofu, tofu burgers, and toasted soy nuts.

- ✔ **To fight vaginal dryness, try an over-the-counter lubricant.** Frequent intercourse also helps keep the vaginal lining flexible and promotes natural lubrication.

- ✔ **Practice Kegel exercises, in which you tighten and relax the muscles used for urination.** Strengthening these muscles helps improve urinary and sexual functions as well.

Coping with breast cancer

Although heart disease is a bigger killer of women, breast cancer is the disease that women fear most.

Recognizing the signs and knowing for sure: You can only detect the earliest signs of breast cancer with a *mammogram,* an X-ray of the breast. Outward signs, which appear in the cancer's later stages, include a lump within the breast, thickening or distortion of the breast or nipple, and swelling of the breast.

The diagnosis of breast cancer cannot be made without a *biopsy,* the removal of breast tissue for study under a microscope. Don't panic if your doctor recommends a biopsy, though. Eighty percent of them reveal no cancer. You may encounter two types of biopsies. In a non-surgical *needle biopsy,* your doctor inserts a needle into the suspicious tissue and draws out a sample. You can have a needle biopsy in your doctor's office, often without anesthetic. *Open biopsies* surgically remove a suspicious breast lump for analysis.

Many women are understandably upset when their doctors suggest a biopsy, and they don't know what to expect. To get as much information as possible — and therefore empower yourself — be sure to ask these questions:

✔ What type of biopsy do you recommend? Why?

✔ Who will perform it?

✔ What are the possible side effects?

✔ When do I know the results?

✔ What happens if the biopsy shows cancer?

✔ Does my insurance cover the biopsy?

✔ How accurate is the biopsy? What are the chances that the results may be wrong?

Making it better: When cancer is present, treatment depends on whether the cancer is confined to the breast or has spread.

The two surgical options are lumpectomy and mastectomy. *Lumpectomy,* for the most part, spares the breast, taking only the cancerous lump and the surrounding tissue. A *mastectomy* is the surgical removal of the entire breast and — in the case of a *radical mastectomy* — lymph nodes and chest muscles, too. A ten-year study by the National Cancer Institute suggests that the combination of a lumpectomy and radiation is as effective as a mastectomy in the treatment of early-stage breast cancer.

In addition to surgery, women may also receive additional therapy such as chemotherapy, radiation, hormone therapy, or immunotherapy. Your doctor may also recommend the anticancer drug *tamoxifen.*

Women of average risk can significantly protect themselves from breast cancer by making certain lifestyle changes:

- ✔ Exercise.
- ✔ Eat a diet rich in fish oils, soy products, green leafy vegetables, broccoli, brussels sprouts, cauliflower, and carrots.
- ✔ Boost your fiber intake.

For more information about breast cancer, contact the American Cancer Society, 1599 Clifton Rd., N.E., Atlanta, GA 30329-4251; phone 404-320-3333, 800-ACS-2345; or find them on the Web at www.cancer.org.

Other cancers in women

Cervical and endometrial cancers affect women exclusively. Both cancers involve the uterus.

Cervical cancer

The number of cases of cervical cancer has dropped dramatically over the past 15 years, thanks to widespread use of the *Pap test,* a screening test that can detect the presence of abnormal cells in the cervix even before they become cancerous. When you catch the cancer in its earliest stages, it's 99 percent curable.

Symptoms of cervical cancer include

- ✔ Redness, inflammation, or sores on the cervix (visible during a pelvic exam)
- ✔ Abnormal bleeding
- ✔ Heavy, lengthy menstrual periods
- ✔ Bleeding after menopause
- ✔ Increased vaginal discharge

Although a Pap test detects abnormal cells, cancer is definitively diagnosed through a *cervical biopsy,* a sampling of the cervical cells for examination.

Your doctor can remove the cancer through freezing the lesions, laser surgery, electrosurgical procedures, conization, and, in advanced cases, hysterectomy. After your doctor removes the cancer, he may use radiation therapy or chemotherapy to eradicate any remaining cells.

Endometrial cancer

Endometrial cancer affects the lining of the uterus (the *endometrium*). Endometrial cancer most commonly affects women over 50 years of age. Symptoms of this cancer include

- ✔ Abnormal bleeding after menopause
- ✔ Irregular periods
- ✔ Bleeding between periods
- ✔ Weight loss and pain (in advanced stages)

Unlike cervical cancer, a Pap test cannot detect endometrial cancer because the abnormal cells are too far within the uterus. Diagnosis is done through biopsy. Your doctor can collect a sample during a pelvic exam or through *endometrial aspiration* (which uses a vacuum apparatus) or dilation and curettage (D&C).

Your doctor can also use an ultrasound, which uses sound waves to create an image of the uterus, to spot cancer. A *hysteroscopy*, a procedure in which a fiber-optic viewing scope is inserted into the uterus, may also be helpful.

Endometrial cancer is usually treated by performing a hysterectomy, followed by radiation therapy or chemotherapy. Your doctor may also recommend hormones that discourage cancer growth.

Do you think you're abused?

The following are signs of abuse. You may be a victim of abuse if your partner has ever

- ✔ Threatened to harm you.
- ✔ Hit, kicked, punched, or otherwise physically harmed you.
- ✔ Deliberately destroyed things you care about.
- ✔ Used a weapon to intimidate you.
- ✔ Prevented you from leaving the house or seeing your friends.
- ✔ Prevented you from getting a job.
- ✔ Forced you to have sex when you didn't want to.
- ✔ Blamed you for his or her abusive behavior.

Women and violence

Domestic violence is a pattern of behavior that one person uses to establish control over another person by using threats and fear. Domestic violence includes not only physical beating, but also threats, intimidation, sexual abuse, and exploitation. The attacks usually begin with verbal threats, and then progress to physical violence, with results ranging from bruises and broken bones to death.

Domestic violence occurs across all social, ethnic, economic, and religious boundaries.

If you're in an abusive relationship, you need to plan ahead — both to increase your safety during an attack and to make your departure easier.

If an attack occurs, try to protect yourself. Call the police as soon as possible or inform a neighbor about the violence and ask her to call the police if she hears suspicious noises coming from your house. Know what exits are available to you and keep your purse and car keys ready so you can leave. Identify a safe place to go in such an emergency. Take pictures of your injuries for use in a possible court case.

If you're planning to leave your partner, gather some money, your car keys, and valuable documents, such as birth certificates and other identification papers, and keep them in a safe, accessible place. Identify a place you can go when you leave, such as an emergency shelter, a social service agency, or the house of a friend. Leave clothes with a friend, if possible. And rehearse your escape plan.

You can also seek a protection order from your local police department. Not all batterers obey protection orders, but some do. You may need to ask the police or the court to enforce the order. Be aware, however, that the police cannot enforce the order until the abuser disobeys it.

For help in dealing with domestic violence, contact the National Family Violence Helpline, operated by the National Council on Child Abuse and Family Violence at 800-222-2000, or the National Coalition Against Domestic Violence at 800-799-SAFE or online at www.ncadv.org.

Sexual assault

Sexual assault is a verbal or physical attack with sexual connotations. Although rape is the most well-known type of sexual assault, the term also encompasses sexual harassment, date rape, and incest.

How to protect yourself from violence

You can help protect yourself from violence if you follow a few rules:

- ✔ **Refuse to tolerate abuse.** If you take a stand against abuse early on, you may be able to deter future incidents.

- ✔ **Don't excuse put-downs.** Criticism, ridicule, and name-calling constitute verbal abuse, which may lead to physical abuse.

- ✔ **Don't excuse a slap, shove, push, or punch.** Abuse rarely occurs only once.

- ✔ **Maintain contact with your friends and family and participate in activities.** An abusive partner may try to cut you off from friends and family and monitor and control your every move. Your friends and family can provide you with an outside support system, and maintaining contact with your outside activities may keep your self-esteem intact.

- ✔ **Tell your abusive partner to seek counseling.** If he or she doesn't, leave the relationship.

Sexual assault is a crime of violence, power, and control. Like domestic violence, it can happen to anyone, regardless of age, gender, race, ethnicity, or social class. Strangers, acquaintances, friends, or relatives can commit this assault. In fact, estimates show that 80 percent of sexual assaults against women are committed by someone the woman knows.

Rape

Rape is not about sex. This violent crime causes both physical and emotional anguish for the victim. Rape is humiliating and traumatizing and can do serious damage to a woman's sense of self and well-being.

You have the right to say no to sexual contact and have your wishes honored. This right applies to sexual contact with dates, partners, spouses, and other acquaintances as well as to contact with strangers. Knowing an attacker does not constitute consent.

Date rape is common on college campuses and is often linked to alcohol. It is also linked with a societal belief that when a woman says no, she really means yes. If a man spends money on a date with a woman, he is *not* automatically entitled to sex at the end of the night. Nor is he entitled to sex based on a past relationship or sexual encounter with the woman. The woman *always* has the right to refuse.

To help prevent date rape, make your wishes and desires clear to your partner. Stay in control and don't give in to the influence of alcohol and drugs. Be aware that some men have been known to slip sedatives into the drinks of unsuspecting women. Don't accept a drink you didn't see mixed or have left unattended.

Low libido and other female sexual problems

Sexuality in women seems to be a more complex proposition than it is in men. Some common female sexual problems include:

- ✔ **The elusive orgasm:** The main female sexual problem, simply stated, is that many women have difficulties achieving an orgasm. The complexity of the situation stems from the broad array of reactions that women have to this problem, ranging from a desperate need to experience orgasms all the way to relief at not having to experience them, with many subcategories of reactions in between.

  Because every woman is different, no hard-and-fast rules for becoming orgasmic exist. Finding out what gives you an orgasm, followed by what gives you a fabulous orgasm, is part of the overall procedure of becoming orgasmic. Masturbation can help a women find what she needs sexually to experience orgasm. She can then teach her partner what to do to please her.

- ✔ **Vaginal tightness:** Some women get so tense from the thought of having intercourse that their vaginal muscles involuntarily tighten up to the point where penetration is painful or even impossible. If you have this problem the first time you have intercourse, you may believe that it has something to do with the size of your vagina, but that is very rarely the case. The cause is almost always that the muscles at the entrance to the vagina have contracted tightly as a result of tension.

  If a woman has a clean bill of health, then the treatment involves getting her to relax. What exactly she must do depends on what the other factors are. If she's also never had an orgasm, then discovering how to give herself an orgasm through masturbation may be step one. If she's already orgasmic, then she needs to get her partner more involved in the orgasm-producing process.

- ✔ **Lack of desire:** Some women start out with low sex drives. Others have problems after they have children. Still others don't begin to have such problems until after menopause. A number of women also have low desire after surgery to remove their ovaries or uterus.

The cure for such a lack of desire depends on the cause:

- **Depression:** If you get help for your depression first, then your libido most likely goes up by itself. You may also suffer depression after a hysterectomy, equating the loss of your uterus with the loss of youth, femininity, and beauty. If you also have your ovaries removed, you're thrown into "early menopause," which brings its own set of problems. If you feel low and have recently had a total hysterectomy, speak with your doctor and consider counseling.

- **Childbirth:** New moms sometimes get so emotionally tied up with their babies, not to mention so tired from lack of sleep, that they lose interest in sex. The dads, who may have stopped having sex with their wives during the last month or two of their pregnancy, and who gave her the time she needed to recover from the effects of giving birth, begin to get testy after several months go by. You may have to make a conscious effort to put the spark back into your sex life. Get a relative to babysit or hire a babysitter and go out for a romantic evening. Chapter 12 offers some great tips for encouraging intimacy.

- **Menopause:** Menopause doesn't mean an end to sex. In fact, many women find they have a stronger desire for sex after menopause because they no longer have to worry about becoming pregnant. Plus, menopause is a time when women and their husbands have more privacy because their kids have grown up and moved out. You may have to make some adjustments, such as using a lubricant, but you can still have a great sex life.

Part III

Relationships: Living with the Ones You Love, Like, and Loathe

The 5th Wave   By Rich Tennant

"I heard it was good to use humor when you're having an argument."

In this part . . .

Someone once said that you can pick your friends but you can't pick your family. Wiser words were probably never spoken!

From your spouse to your children to your mother-in-law to your great-aunt Hilda, the following chapters show you how to connect, communicate, and care for all those truly important (and sometimes truly frustrating!) people in your life. You get great tips on fighting the right way, dealing with teenagers, and rekindling your romance.

Chapter 12

Making Marriage Work

*H*ow can any relationship possibly deliver the complete love, great sex, never-ending fun, and permanent security that marriage is supposed to guarantee? It can't. Whenever the inevitable disappointments occur, you or your partner may feel tempted to give up on the marriage. More often than not, calling a divorce lawyer is a mistake. A far better course is to figure out strategies that can make your marriage more satisfying.

The Four Building Blocks of a Working Marriage

When assessing your chances of making your relationship work, ask this question: "Is the relationship *good enough* to meet both partners' emotional needs?" *Good-enough* marriages may not be "made in heaven," but they have a real chance at succeeding for the following two reasons.

▶ Both partners have an ongoing stake in making the relationship work.

▶ Both partners believe that, in the long run, the positive aspects in their marriage outweigh the negative.

The number-one reason why marriages last is that the partners take the words "for better or for worse" to heart. They have made a commitment to work things out, to make changes — and not to quit when things get tough. When partners who are meeting enough of each other's emotional needs are determined to work together, a shaky marriage can become *good enough* — and a good-enough marriage can sometimes become great!

Nobody should tolerate a physically or emotionally abusive partner. Severe substance abuse and mental illness are also signs that a marriage is in danger of dropping below the *good-enough* level, especially if your spouse refuses to get help.

Following are some building blocks you can use to keep your marriage standing strong.

Treasure your commonality

Don't become so involved in the details of day-to-day living that you stop investing time in doing things that the two of you enjoy together.

1. **When alone, write out a list of all the interests and activities that you and your partner have enjoyed sharing at various times in your marriage.**

   Writing out this kind of inventory helps you identify areas you may be neglecting.

2. **Think about why you stopped doing those things together.**

3. **Talk to one another about recapturing the joy of sharing good times and common interests.**

   Be careful not to blame your spouse for not doing more things together. Assessing blame can only serve to create more distance between the two of you.

4. **Make your shared activity a priority.**

   When the memory of good times reawakens your feelings of excitement, don't allow the memory to be extinguished by the same mundane concerns that caused you and your partner to abandon the activity in the first place. Explore solutions.

5. **Make dates with your partner.**

6. **Emphasize activities that are fun.**

   The amount of fun you have together is one of the most important factors in determining marital happiness.

Make room for separateness

Every person needs a certain amount of personal space — and married partners are no exception. Still, some couples feel uncomfortable about doing things without each other.

Use the following guidelines to find a balance of separateness and togetherness that's right for your relationship:

✔ Accept the fact that both of you need a certain amount of personal space.

✔ Recognize that your need for separateness may not always be in sync with that of your partner.

✔ Express your viewpoint whenever you spot a conflict or imbalance. Ask your spouse to do the same.

✔ Negotiate an arrangement that works for both of you. Don't just give in, or you may wind up resenting it.

Make the most of differences

Many couples' personality differences often fuel the fires of romantic love during the early stages of a relationship. But, in time, the same differences can cause problems. People with different ways of doing things suddenly find themselves constantly clashing over such practical issues as neatness, childrearing, and finances.

The following tips can help you and your partner (even if you're vastly different in several ways) build a loving and enduring marriage.

✔ **Combine your strengths:** If your husband is all thumbs and you're handy, take the lead in fixing things around the house. If you tend to overspend and he's skillful at balancing family finances, encourage him take the lead in matters of money. By pooling your different strengths, you and your partner can accomplish more as a team than either of you can ever manage alone.

✔ **Use your differences to mirror one another's positive traits:** Everyone has strengths — as well as frailties and blind spots. The trick is to use your partner's strong points as motivators to stimulate growth in areas where you need improvement.

> ✔ **Remember that your differences were once interesting and pleasurable — not sources of conflict.** That spark of excitement you and your partner initially felt toward each other can be recaptured — if you remember that the same differences that now cause problems once played an important part in why you found each other so attractive.

As you develop a better understanding of the benefits of being married to someone with different personality traits, you may be able to avoid unnecessary conflicts and preserve the positive energy and excitement between you.

Accept that not all problems can be solved

As you strive to build a stronger marriage, you have to accept that many of your incompatibilities will be constantly recycled in different variations throughout your marriage. The following techniques can help you keep marital problems in perspective:

> ✔ Identify what's bothering you and communicate those feelings to your partner.

> ✔ Be aware of what situations press your partner's hot buttons.

> ✔ Ask your partner to discuss a particular problem at a time when you're not fighting about it.

> ✔ Don't feel compelled to reveal everything that's on your mind all at one time, especially if those revelations are likely to exacerbate the problem.

> ✔ Focus on what's working well in your relationship. Build on those strengths and use them as a foundation to overcome (or at least de-emphasize) problems.

> ✔ Recognize that you can work out some problems in the long run, even if you don't see an immediate solution.

> ✔ Always encourage positive changes — however small. When you're unhappy about something in your marriage, you can easily fail to see small improvements that can eventually lead to bigger improvements.

> ✔ Recognize that problem-free marriages don't exist. Research shows that at least a third of most couples' long-term marital disputes never get resolved to each partner's complete satisfaction. These problems have to be continually negotiated throughout the marriage.

As you accept the fact that not all problems can be solved, you'll be better able to take marital tensions in stride and not allow them to destroy what's good in your relationship.

Communicating with Sensitivity and Respect

To become an effective communicator, you have to pay close attention to what your partner is telling you through moods, attitudes, gestures, movements, and actions. The flip side of this skill is recognizing the non-verbal messages you yourself are transmitting. Sharpen your non-verbal communication skills by using the following tips:

✔ **Watch for changes in mood and attitude.** These changes can be signs that things are going on in your partner's life (or psyche) that he doesn't wish to discuss — at least not now. If your partner doesn't address these changes with you, make a written or mental note of these shifts in behavior. Try to remain watchful of how they play out in the days and weeks to come.

✔ **Tune into body language.** Observe the way your partner's body reacts when you ask him a question. Is his body position relaxed and open, or tense and withdrawn? In general, a person who maintains a relaxed, open bearing when you ask a direct question tends to be forthright and truthful. On the other hand, a person whose body suddenly becomes rigid may be concealing something.

✔ **Look for signs of nervousness or tension.** If you notice that your spouse is anxious in the course of conversation, note that this as a possible clue that some thought or feeling isn't being verbally expressed. Uncharacteristic silence or talkativeness may be another sign.

On the other hand, the nonverbal communications of some scrupulously honest people may give the mistaken impression that they're trying to deceive you. That's why you're wise not to draw any firm conclusion from any single clue. Instead, incorporate each nonverbal clue into the total picture of what your partner is communicating.

Saying what you feel with win-win diplomacy

Win-win negotiation is a well-accepted method in the business world for working out differences in a constructive and mutually beneficial manner. This process is effective in any situation in which both parties have an ongoing relationship and, therefore, need to come up with solutions to disagreements that satisfy both parties.

Marriage is supposed to be the relationship in which people have the greatest emotional investment, so it's especially important that every negotiation be win-win for both partners and that neither one walks away completely empty-handed. If one partner feels bullied or taken advantage of, the long-term health of the marriage will certainly suffer.

Negotiate your differences by taking the following steps:

- **Separate personalities from issues.** Married partners sometimes fall into the trap of attacking each other instead of using collaborative negotiation to work out their differences.

  Negative tactics almost always backfire in marriage because they stop you from having a constructive dialogue. When you talk about issues instead of personalities, you can more easily work together as partners trying to achieve a common goal.

- **Communicate with "I" statements rather than "you" statements.** Saying "I feel" means that you're talking from your own feelings and expectations. Statements like "you always do this" or "your problem is" are bound to be received as accusations. Such pronouncements serve to make your partner defensive and block further communication.

- **Don't mind-read or analyze your partner.** People don't like to be told what they're thinking or feeling — much less the reasons why. Instead of acting like a dime-store psychologist, give your partner ample opportunity to express his own thoughts and feelings. Work at being a better listener, even if you think you already understand where your spouse is coming from.

- **Concentrate on finding mutually acceptable solutions.** A mutually acceptable solution always takes both spouses' needs and sensitivities into consideration. This kind of solution lets you both walk away feeling that you've reached an agreement that's in the best interest of your marriage.

  There are usually several answers to a problem — keep trying different solutions until you come up with one that works.

- **Let go of the need to win or prove that you're right.** The ultimate success of any negotiation hinges on working together to achieve a resolution that satisfies the needs of both spouses. You'll find that impossible to achieve if you insist on attacking one another.

Don't talk — or think — about differences in terms of who's right or who's wrong. This feat can be difficult to accomplish because people tend to be attached to their own perspectives. Still, avoid going for the moral high ground if you want to achieve an outcome that's satisfactory to both partners.

Becoming a great listener

How effective one marriage partner is at expressing her feelings ultimately doesn't matter if the other partner doesn't hear her. But when husbands and wives truly begin listening to each other, they see an immediate improvement in the quality of their relationship.

Active listening is a technique that you and your partner can use to make sure you're being heard. After you express a need or a feeling to your mate, ask her to play back what you just said — until you're satisfied that you've been heard. Your partner doesn't have to repeat your *exact* words — as long as she understands the substance of what you said.

If you want to be a good listener, you have to

✔ Train yourself to stay with the talker, word for word, until he or she finishes. Simple, but really difficult.

✔ Suspend judgment and open your heart and head, as well as your ears. Listen to what the person is actually saying — not to what you want to hear.

If you're a talkative person, start out by simply talking less. This one change gives others an opportunity to talk more — while giving you an opportunity to do more listening.

Don't be discouraged if you don't see a radical change overnight. You *will* become a better listener if you make a consistent effort to do so.

Unfortunately, active listening doesn't always work and may actually have the opposite effect. Some people are so self-centered that they'll mistake your willingness to hear them as an invitation to talk endlessly about themselves.

Conquering Conflict

Every marriage has trends or patterns that are often obvious to everyone but the married couples themselves. Patterns are neither bad nor good, in and of themselves. However, after patterns are locked into place, they can be tough to break. That's okay, as long as the interactions aren't hurting you, your partner, or your marriage. Breaking a particular negative pattern and establishing a more positive one is often the key to having a stronger and happier relationship with your spouse.

After you identify a specific problem, you can start making improvements by taking the following steps:

- **Put yourself in your partner's shoes.** Close your eyes and imagine how you might feel in your partner's position. Use everything you know about your spouse to visualize the way he or she is reacting.

- **Go out of your way to show empathy.** Even if you're uncertain about what's bothering your partner, you can help by making it clear that you care. Instead of complaining, greet your spouse with something that expresses your understanding. Prepare a favorite meal or buy a thoughtful gift. Such displays of empathy and affection often generate a positive response.

- **Take the initiative.** One effective way of dealing with your partner's negativity is to ask what's wrong and to share your observations. Another good approach is to communicate that you care by doing or saying something positive. Don't expect your spouse to respond immediately. If you're patient, you may begin to see positive changes. However, if your strategy doesn't seem to be working, try something different. Don't give up!

Some marital problems are symptoms of deeply entrenched personal issues or more serious marital problems than you may realize. If your spouse doesn't respond to any of your efforts, you will almost certainly need some outside professional help.

Positive mirroring

Destructive patterns in a marriage are often caused by *negative mirroring*. When your spouse confronts you in an adversarial fashion, you may feel that you have no other choice but to react in kind — or *mirror* her behavior. Before you know it, the two of you can find yourself caught in the middle of a destructive chain reaction.

The following suggestions can help you and your partner identify and change these patterns.

- **Don't respond to negativity with negativity.** Do your best to respond with understanding and compassion. Let your partner know that you can see she's distressed. Ask what you can do to

make the situation better. If your partner continues to act nega-
tively, say something like: "I want you to know that I'm here for
you. But when I feel attacked by your statements, it's hard for
me to know how to help." If your partner still doesn't open up,
offer a concrete suggestion to change the mood.

✔ **Visualize your marriage as a TV sitcom.** Take a few minutes to
write down the disagreements you have on a regular basis as if
you were scripting dialogue for a TV show. What you're trying
to uncover are the patterns underneath those disagreements,
not what you're actually fighting about. Concentrate on how
the two of you play out the disagreement:

- Do you yell at him? If so, how does he respond to your
yelling? Does he shout back — or does he brood?

- What do you do in response to your spouse's reactive
behavior?

- Are your strategies effective? Do they cause any change in
his behavior?

- If your strategies don't work, do you continue doing more
of the same?

✔ **Do something different to change the script.** Couples in conflict often become competitive with each other in a negative
way. One spouse acts nasty, so the other responds by acting
even nastier. Next time you're tempted to engage in this kind of
destructive communication, do something different to change
the script.

If, for example, you're worried about family finances, don't
express your concern in your usual way of telling your husband
that his spending is out of control. Predictably, he'll counterat-
tack with something about one of your weaknesses, and the
argument escalates. Instead, say something like, "I'll feel a lot
better if we can set aside a certain amount of money each week
for our vacation next summer. Let's work out a budget so we
can do that." This kind of strategic planning diffuses negative
patterns before you and your partner have a chance to play
them out.

Troubleshooting marital problems

You may be attributing marital difficulties to the wrong cause.
Middle-aged men, for example, commonly mistake their fears of
aging for problems in their marriage. People often mistake career
downturns, health crises, and temporary hormonal changes for
defects in their partner or in their relationships.

Any of these personal changes is bound to have an impact on your marriage. However, if you're able to pinpoint the main causes of distress, you're far more likely to take the proper corrective steps.

✔ If you seem to be experiencing some kind of personal crisis, don't automatically blame your spouse or the marriage. Instead, open an honest dialogue in which both of you feel free to express your concerns and your frustrations.

✔ If your spouse seems to be going through a difficult period, consider putting her concerns first — at least for the time being. Instead of assessing blame, work at being a good listener and an active partner in helping her navigate the rough spots.

✔ If the problem is rooted in your patterns as a couple, work together to replace entrenched and destructive interactions with more flexible, positive behaviors.

If nothing that you try works, you may not have identified the "right" cause or hit on an effective solution. In either case, you may want to consider counseling or therapy. You may have correctly identified the issue but are unable to fix it without outside help.

Fighting fairly

For a fight to be fair, one participant must never violate the rights of the other. The following sections detail how to fight fair.

Defer to the partner who feels most strongly

In any argument, one person often feels more strongly about the issues in dispute than the other. In general, figure out whose feelings are more intense and try to let that person have his or her way.

Assume good will

In a marriage where both partners assume good will, the partner who yields on a particular issue has reason to believe that her spouse then will defer her on other major issues when her needs are more intense than his.

Maintain a balance but don't keep score

Partners who are good (and fair) referees can usually tell if things are getting too one-sided. Maintaining a balance is a lot different than keeping score — an undertaking that's both useless and non-productive. After all, how can anybody tell how many points to assign for each victory or loss? Still, that doesn't mean you may not have to remind your partner (however gently) that it's his turn to give in.

Be clear about what you (and your partner) want

Everyone is subject to feelings of anger and frustration at times, but these feelings may not have anything to do with your partner — or your marriage. Before you engage in an argument, be aware of what you want the outcome to be. If your partner appears to be fighting just for the sake of venting emotions, ask your spouse what's really on his or her mind so that the two of you can work together to address the problem.

Go to bed angry, if necessary

There's an old saying that going to bed angry is bad for arguing couples. Often, the opposite is true. In many cases, going to bed with an argument unresolved is better than staying up all night trying to work things out. At bedtime, the two of you may be tense and exhausted from the trials of the day. In that atmosphere, fights can continue to escalate.

Look for exceptions

Partners who are battling tend to forget what's good in their relationship. They frequently make comments like: "You're always insensitive" or "You never take the time to show that you care." When in fact you think about it, you can usually find one or more exceptions.

See the glass as half full, not as half empty

Each person possesses a great deal of power in shaping positive outcomes in their relationships. Part of that power rests in making an effort to focus on what you have, not on what's missing. The key lies in making the following principles a part of your mindset:

- ✓ Be aware that pessimistic thoughts lead to pessimistic behaviors.

- ✓ Work on emphasizing what's good in your relationship; don't dwell on what's bad.

- ✓ Accept the fact that most negative situations (including marital problems) can be altered for the better — if you're willing to be proactive in making that happen.

- ✓ Be the one to start the ball rolling. You can wait around for your partner to change, but why do that when it's within your own power to start turning things around? Making small changes in the way you interact with your partner empowers you to effect bigger improvements in your relationship.

Remember to be kind

It's always a good idea to include kindness and thoughtfulness in your dealings — especially with your spouse. Even when you're embroiled in an argument, a kind word, compliment, or gentle touch can go a long way in showing that you care — and that you're optimistic things will get better.

Apologize when you need to

Some arguments are more contentious than others and require time for healing. If, for example, one partner has verbally abused the other, even his most sincere apology may not gain instant acceptance. He may have to do more or wait longer for those wounds to heal.

Don't look for total victory or unconditional surrender

When you sense that you have the upper hand in an argument, the best thing to do is take a step back and help your partner understand that you're committed to the principle that neither of you can win if one of you walks away feeling like a loser. The two of you are partners and collaborators. Therefore, your ultimate fight isn't for a victory — but for a stronger and happier marriage.

Don't intentionally prolong the argument

Many arguments can't be concluded in one session — and some will never get totally resolved. If your partner appears to have had enough, you're usually best off to drop the issue, at least for the present. If your battle is over some long-standing dispute (which is the case with many marital arguments!), you don't have to worry. Chances are you'll get back to it soon enough.

Don't nag or withdraw

When people feel they're getting nowhere in the same old argument, they sometimes resort to nagging and more nagging. This strategy is doomed to failure because the partner being nagged inevitably tunes out and withdraws from the situation. Expressing frustration by tuning out or emotionally withdrawing from the argument doesn't work either, because the issues at hand haven't been addressed. What you're left with is an impasse that's unsatisfying to both spouses.

Negotiating Family Loyalties

When you get married, your family's patterns often become pitted against those of your spouse's family. Suddenly, you find yourselves dealing with three families: your family of origin, your spouse's family of origin, and the new family that you and your mate are trying to build.

Use the following steps as you negotiate family loyalties:

- ✔ **Sit down and openly discuss the various feelings and expectations that have surfaced — especially those that were never broached before you were married.** The first step in resolving loyalty conflicts is to identify the emotions that are fueling your disagreements, without accusing each other of disloyalty or lack of consideration.

- ✔ **Recognize that sorting out family loyalties takes patience and practice.** When people get married, they almost always have to redefine relationships with their own families. Then, of course, there's a parallel set of issues with your in-laws. In most lasting marriages, spouses eventually figure out a comfortable way to become daughters-in-law or sons-in-law. They often grow to love their brothers-in-law and sisters-in-law. However, it's part of a life-long process of give and take for you, your spouse, and your families.

Each member of your respective families needs time to find a comfortable way to interact with your spouse — and with you as a couple.

The limits that you establish with your parents and in-laws are issues that will have to be continually negotiated and renegotiated throughout your marriage. However, establishing limits is particularly important during the early stages — while a couple is beginning to define itself as a unit.

Keeping in-laws out of your marriage

Use the following steps to begin creating boundaries with your families:

- ✔ **Be clear — but sensitive — in setting the tone with your families.** You can't measure an exact amount of closeness that married couples need to maintain with their families. However, you don't ever have to be insensitive or uncaring in the way you negotiate these dealings. Put yourself in your parents' (or in-laws') shoes. Wouldn't you feel at least a little anxious about being left out of your child's life after he or she gets married?

- ✔ **Come to a mutual decision with your mate about the kind of relationships you want with your families.** It's only natural for you and your spouse to have disagreements about such a highly charged issue. However, your decisions need to be worked out privately — and not aired in front of your families.

✔ **Assess realistically where you are as a couple.** The more experience you have — both as an independent person and as a couple — the easier time you'll have establishing boundaries. At first, your families may feel rejected. They may even accuse you of being cold or unsociable. However, it's up to you to help them understand that your most important concern is nurturing your new family unit while maintaining a connection to your family of origin.

Don't use your spouse as a tool to deal with your parents, particularly in unpleasant matters.

Avoiding housework disputes

The following steps can help you and your spouse hammer out an equitable way to divide family responsibilities:

✔ **Give yourself an attitude adjustment.** If your spouse expects you to assume all household responsibility, remind him or her that marriage is a 50/50 partnership and that you expect your spouse to assume a significant role in this (and all other) aspects of family life.

✔ **Strike an equitable split of family responsibilities.** An equitable split of responsibilities doesn't mean that every duty and chore is split 50/50, or that both spouses are doing half the work at all times. Some couples find it helpful to write down a list of their respective duties for a given week. But ultimately, there's no meaningful way to assign points for what each partner contributes. The key question is: Do both partners have equal influence in how family responsibilities are divided?

✔ **Stay flexible.** Partners who function as a team recognize that they need to do a certain amount of work to keep their family afloat. Both people are ready to do whatever is necessary to accomplish that goal — even if it means giving more than they receive at any given time. This kind of approach requires both partners to be ready and willing to forgo their expectations about who does what for the good of the relationship.

The more flexibility that you and your partner can build into your relationship, the easier you can adapt to unexpected circumstances and renegotiate new arrangements.

Recasting the role of friends

The following tips can help you deal with some friend-related issues that couples encounter:

- ✔ **If your spouse has a general problem with your having friends, you need to help him or her recognize the importance of maintaining separate friendships and separate interests.** When you encourage this kind of freedom, you acknowledge that each of you is an individual with your own needs, and that your growth as individuals ultimately makes your relationship stronger.

- ✔ **If you have a problem with a particular friend or group of friends, ask yourself if there's something problematic in the nature of the friendship.** If you feel troubled about the activities your spouse and his friends are engaged in, criticize the activity, not the friends. Say "I worry when you go out drinking" rather than "I can't stand those guys you go out with on Wednesdays. They're a bunch of drunks."

- ✔ **If you have no specific objection to what your spouse and his friends are doing, remember that you don't need to like his friends — just as he doesn't need to like yours.** Making room for separateness in your togetherness has many benefits. That means giving one another room to do things with people you may not necessarily seek out on your own.

- ✔ **If your spouse's relationship with one or more friends continues to bother you, try to get to the root of the problem.** Ask yourself the following questions:

  - Is the problem based on a real or perceived personality clash? Some people seem to rub each other the wrong way. However, even if you and your partner's close friend never become completely comfortable with each other, you can still accept your spouse's relationship with that person — as long as you conclude that there's nothing in that friendship that's threatening to you, to your mate, or to your marriage.

  - Does the problem stem from feelings of competitiveness? Husbands and wives often feel that they must wage a battle of control to assure themselves that they are their partner's number-one priority. In that case, almost any friend can be perceived as a threat — especially one who appears to be important to the partner.

You may be able to pressure your spouse into abandoning a close friendship. However, this strategy is more likely to weaken your long-term relationship than to strengthen it.

Negotiating opposite-sex friendships

Any friendship that provokes conflicts between you and your partner will cause problems. This situation goes double for friends of the opposite sex.

You can handle conflicts about opposite-sex friendships in one of the following ways:

✔ **Encourage your spouse to participate in the friendship.** This approach works best when you sense that your friend and your partner are likely to get along.

✔ **See your opposite-sex friend without your spouse.** This approach can work only if your partner doesn't feel threatened by the friendship.

✔ **End the relationship.** If you believe that your partner is justified in opposing your friendship with a particular man or woman, such as with a former lover, you may want to think about ending it. However, the decision is yours to make — not your spouse's.

If your partner displays an ongoing pattern of possessiveness or excessive jealousy, no matter how innocent your friendships are, serious problems that pose a threat to the marriage can result.

Developing friendships with other couples

Many marriage theorists view a married couple's ability to develop and maintain friendships with other twosomes as a healthy sign.

If you and your spouse are having difficulty meeting other compatible couples, you may want to try the following suggestions:

✔ Pinpoint the issues that could be interfering with your ability to develop friendships with other couples. Are one or both of you being too critical? Do you expect to have an instant chemistry?

✔ Making a four-way friendship work often takes more time, so expect to have a feeling-out period before all of you are comfortable.

✔ Sit down with your spouse and think about activities you enjoy doing together. Seek out places where you're likely to meet other couples who enjoy the same activities.

✔ If you meet a couple that seems compatible, take the initiative in pursuing the relationship.

Don't put undue pressure on yourself — or your spouse. One reason couples' friendships last is because the interaction is fun for all concerned. If things don't work out, it's not the end of the world, and you will have more opportunities to meet other couples.

Remarrying: A Second Chance

Here are some suggestions for achieving the kind of closeness that may have been lacking in your first marriage:

- **Truly get to know each other.** Perhaps you and your former spouse never fully opened up to one another. Now you have a second chance to know someone on a deeper level — and to allow that person to know you.

- **Don't be afraid to share your most important thoughts and feelings with your partner and to encourage her to do the same.** Listen carefully to what your spouse tells you and allow that person to open up at her own pace.

- **Develop new routines and rituals that don't mirror those of your previous marriage.** Remarriage is an opportunity to be more flexible in how you and your partner negotiate the terms of your relationship; sitting down and rewriting the rules in a way that reflects both of your needs and desires is important.

- **Make a fresh start.** If at all possible, move into a home where neither of you have lived before. Doing so gives each of you the sense that you're truly starting over.

Keeping Love Fresh

Picture your partner and try to think of what you could do to add a touch of romance to his or her day. This time that you spend thinking about romance can reap dividends, maybe not every day, but certainly in the long run. You'll also get in the habit of working to rekindle your romance every day, and you'll find no better way to keep those flames burning brightly than to give them daily attention.

Find time to be together

Too many couples just don't spend sufficient time with each other for romance to grow and flourish. No matter how full your appointment calendar, you must set aside some time to be together.

Don't be afraid to actually make appointments to be together. Spontaneity is great, but waiting for those spontaneous moments may be futile. You're better off to make plans that come to fruition than to hope that you can find a moment or two to be together by chance.

Don't confuse chores with romance. If you use your time together only to plan next week's dinner appointments, how romantic is that? You have to use personal time to be just that: personal. Ask each other how you feel. Stare into each other's eyes. Rub noses.

Getting out of the house altogether may be helpful; a change in scenery may stimulate romance. If you can't get out, then at the very least make sure that you take the phone off the hook and, if you have kids, use that lock on the bedroom door. Romantic moments are very fragile. You must protect them, especially if they're hard to come by.

Concentrate on each other

No matter how tired you are or what crisis is on the horizon, force yourself to concentrate on the here and now and that person sitting next to you. If you find your thoughts drifting off, bring them back to the moment.

Seven great ways to flirt with your mate

Flirting is a delicious, low-budget, irresistible way to make you and your mate feel tingly all over. What could be sexier that that? Here's a quick list of what to do (and not to do) when flirting with your mate:

- ✔ **Use your whole body.** Flirty body language begins with the eyes and works its way all the way down to the tips of your footsies. Lean forward, make eye contact, smile, bend your knees a bit, and untense your hands and arms. Remember to relax a bit; this posturing should be fun, not like defusing a bomb.

- ✔ **Make eye contact.** Looking someone in the eyes is very compelling. And you make a person feel as if they've got your undivided attention, which they should.

- ✔ **Smile, don't smirk.** There's a reason why synonyms for *smirk* include *sneer, leer,* and *grimace:* A smirk is an unattractive and unpleasant expression, so avoid smirking. Smile openly and sincerely — it's irresistible.

- ✔ **Pay attention.** No looking like you're trying to remember if you fed the cat.

- ✔ **Lighten up, don't bulldoze.** Telling your mate that he or she is incredibly hot isn't flirting; it's steering directly into a mountain.

- ✔ **Focus on your partner, not yourself.** Make your mate feel as though every word is a pearl of wisdom.

- ✔ **Don't think you can't do it.** Anyone can flirt . . . even if only a little. Flirting is a sign of confidence and even if you're feeling a teensy bit shaky, give it a try. Practice makes perfect. You don't have to be smooth, just sincere.

Committing to this effort is a matter of prioritizing. Yes, the memo at the office is important, and so is Johnny's runny nose and your mother's trip to Florida. But you have to tell yourself that for this moment in time, your partner is of the utmost priority. Stay focused.

Stroke each other's ego

Both partners must be supportive of each other, exchanging compliments whenever appropriate. Try to keep track of your partner's mood. If he or she seems to be feeling low, make a point of coming to the rescue with some well-chosen ego boosting.

Conversely, sarcasm almost always reduces the level of romance. If one spouse is always worried that a mistake will provoke a barb from the other, that fear will overwhelm any romantic inclinations. Constructive criticism is allowed, but if you're doing the criticizing, wait a few beats before opening your mouth to make certain that what you have to say is really constructive and not just a put-down.

Refeather your empty nest

Even though husbands and wives can experience anxiety about their grown children leaving home, many find this initially painful transition to be a positive force in their marriage. Here's how you can set the stage for a positive empty-nest experience:

- ✔ **Prepare yourself for the inevitable.** Spouses who've spent their entire marriage caring for home and family sometimes fret over what they'll do after their last child leaves. The vast majority of parents readily acknowledge that their children's leaving is an essential part of the life process. Parents usually understand that their children don't need them in the same ways that they used to.

- ✔ **Think of new ways to re-channel your energies — both as individuals and as a couple.** Your children may not have required your physical attention for years. However, after they're out of the house, the sense of freedom may seem more real.

- ✔ **Lay the groundwork with your children for maintaining close ties.** If you don't stay close to your kids after they leave, the pain of missing them continues to linger. Staying close also smoothes the way for positive interactions with your grown child's spouse and his or her family.

- ✔ **Consider downsizing to a smaller home or renovating your present home.** Doing so can give you the feeling that you're launching a new lifestyle.

✔ **Allow time for an adjustment period.** After investing so many years in sharing your home with your children, you're bound to feel some sense of loss when they go. Part of your pain may date back to your own leaving home — and the stresses you may have had with your family of origin during that period. Give yourself time to reflect on those feelings and share your thoughts and anxieties with your partner.

Studies show that couples often experience a kind of second honeymoon after the children are launched. With the kids out of the house, the partners now have an opportunity to re-focus their energies on each other — and on making their marriage more exciting.

During midlife, wives and husbands often find themselves moving in opposite directions and at different paces, forcing both partners to redefine their roles and the balance of power and expectations on which the marriage has rested for decades. This time is an ideal opportunity to redesign your marriage. However, both spouses must be willing to take an active role in the process — or the marriage may not survive.

Nurturing Intimacy and Sex

The sexual union between husband and wife brings more to a marriage than just the easing of sexual tensions. It also brings intimacy, which is an important component to the glue that holds the two of you together.

The ultimate intimacy has nothing to do with sex and is usually done with your clothes on. It's not complicated or difficult, and it can be done over and over, yet it's very, very rare. The ultimate intimacy is to give yourself totally to your partner.

You can find no better feeling in the world than being one with the person you love. During sex, the intensity of that oneness can be terrific, but that feeling is also a source of strength and comfort 24 hours a day. Work toward having the kind of marriage in which you really do feel that you're in this life together.

Keeping romance alive during the hectic workweek

With work, kids, laundry, cooking, and all the other tasks you must attend to every day, romance often gets tucked into the corner and forgotten. What can you do to coax romance back into your life?

- ✔ **Schedule regular appointments with your partner.** Block a few hours during your week for some one-on-one time.

- ✔ **Turn off the TV.** With the boob tube unplugged, you can focus on your partner and get a chance to talk.

- ✔ **Take a night off from cooking.** Prepare double portions of food one night; the next night you can cuddle instead of cook.

- ✔ **Go to bed early.** Get some extra sleep one night in order to stay up late the following evening.

- ✔ **Share household chores.** Play some music while you both do the dishes — these minutes become "together" time.

- ✔ **Wake up a few minutes earlier than usual.** The extra time means you can spend more than a second on your goodbye kiss.

- ✔ **Stay in touch during the day.** Use the phone and e-mail to send funny or tender messages throughout your workday.

- ✔ **Keep a picture of your sweetie in view at the office.** Place a hot-looking picture of your spouse on your desk and look at it frequently.

- ✔ **Don't let your workday spill over into your home life.** No matter what happens at the office, don't let anger or frustration be the first emotion you show your spouse at night. You may feel like you're ready to boil over after a tough day at work; let your partner know that you're going to the park or the mall to decompress for a few minutes before you come home.

- ✔ **Make weekend plans during the workweek.** Give yourselves something to look forward to. By planning ahead, you ensure that some weekend time is carved out for romance.

- ✔ **Follow a nightly family schedule.** Set a firm schedule for your kids; stick to a consistent bedtime every night. Then, set aside at least 15 minutes after your children go to bed to talk with your partner about your day's activities, upcoming vacation plans, or whatever else is on your mind.

Fantastic foreplay ideas

Foreplay isn't just an art to practice on your partner; foreplay can also be a method of visualization for yourself so that when the time comes to make love, you're absolutely ready.

The longer you can extend foreplay, the better the end result will usually be.

Lighting his fire

Following are just a few simple ways you can remind him of why you found him so attractive in the first place:

- ✔ Laugh at his jokes.
- ✔ Serve him his favorite meal in the nude.
- ✔ Cheer with him for his favorite team.
- ✔ Initiate sex.
- ✔ Ask to see his Mr. America impression.
- ✔ Send him an erotic e-mail.

Lighting her fire

Here are some suggestions for ways you can remind her that she still makes you weak in the knees:

- ✔ Send her flowers at the office for no reason.
- ✔ Tell her she's gorgeous.
- ✔ Sign up for dance lessons.
- ✔ Write her a love letter.
- ✔ Wash the windows without being asked.
- ✔ Take her for a walk in the rain.

Caressing by candlelight

Certain sounds, scents, and sights automatically make you think of romance — candlelight is one of them. What you do after the flame is lit is left to your imagination. Or try one of these suggestions:

- ✔ Share a bottle of wine.
- ✔ Play strip poker.
- ✔ Read the *Kama Sutra*.
- ✔ Reminisce about your first date.
- ✔ Watch *Casablanca*.
- ✔ Pretend that you've just met.

Using your lips

You have so many ways to kiss — passionately or lightly, with mouths open or closed, with tongues probing or not — that kissing is truly a gift of the gods. Kissing isn't limited to mouths. You can kiss each other all over your bodies, and both the kisser and kissee should thoroughly enjoy the experience.

Practicing the art of massage

What often happens is that the touching that people do as they remove their clothes leads right into sex. If you're in the mood for stretching things out — and this is not something that has to happen every time — then giving each other a massage is a sensual and relaxing way to begin.

Make the moment as sensuous as you can.

✔ Dim the lights or use candles.

✔ Use some massage oils.

✔ Whatever you do, don't rush the massage; try to really feel each other as much as possible.

✔ Alternate between strong rubs and gentle caresses. Let the sensitive nerve-endings in your fingertips help you get to know your partner in a new way.

Mapping your bodies

With *body mapping,* you aim to discover all the most sensitive parts of one another's bodies: the breasts, the wrists, the thighs. . . .

Body mapping is one of those gifts that keeps on giving because, after you and your partner have explored your bodies and discovered the most sensuous places and what feels best on them, you can use those techniques again and again throughout your love life.

Erogenous zones are the parts of your body that, due to the concentration of nerve endings, are more sensitive to stimulation than the other parts. Erogenous zones can be anywhere on your body, but some of the more popular ones include the buttocks, the perineum (that little line between the anus and the genitals), behind the knees, the nape of the neck, and, of course, the genitals.

What if you or you partner has an erogenous zone on a body part that's not popular? The answer is, go for it. If your partner loves to have her earlobes sucked, then that's what you should spend some time doing. Nothing is "wrong" with favoring one body part or another, and the whole point is to discover places on your partner's body to touch that you may never have imagined could turn them on.

On any given day, a body part that had been an erogenous zone can reverse its magnetic pole and become a ticklish zone. Unless your partner is always ticklish, don't worry if on a particular day you're told not to touch him or her "there." The warning is not personal and probably won't happen the next time.

Five things women wish men knew about sex

Many men say that they *want* to have sex with a woman, but then they don't put any effort into finding out what it actually takes to have good sex with a woman. So all you guys who complain that you don't get enough of "it," read the following tips closely:

- **Chivalry is not dead.** Bringing a woman flowers or chocolate, taking her out to dinner, calling her during the day — all these little details are important, not because of what they cost in terms of money, but because they show that you care, that you're thinking about her, and that she matters to you. Empty gestures aren't chivalrous, and they won't earn a man his rank of knighthood, either. You not only have to show you care, you have to feel it, too.

- **Appearances do count.** Although many men do worry about their hair (mostly because they know that their relationship with it may be rather fleeting), when it comes to the rest of their appearance, many men aren't so careful. Perhaps you're one of those people who doesn't perceive yourself as being sexy, but you are — especially to your partner — so try to look the part.

- **You can't hurry love.** The notion that men get turned on a lot faster than do women is very true; women need time to prepare themselves for sex. If you're like most men, you had no problem giving your partner some of this quality time before you got married or moved in together. You would call ahead, make appointments (called *dates*), go out to dinner, take her for long walks, and look into each other's eyes. As a result, she'd begin to be ready to have sex with you. Patterns of romantic behavior must continue after you say "I do" — not necessarily every time, but often enough to show that you really do care.

- **A clitoris is not just a small penis.** Just because a clitoris grows bigger when the woman gets excited, don't rub it hard. Many women can't bear to have the clitoris touched directly because it hurts. Men need only to caress and rub the area around the clitoris to give just enough stimulation so that the clitoris doesn't actually hurt.

✔ **Women need to bask in the afterglow.** Women take longer to get aroused than men and longer to come down from that aroused state. If you roll over and fall asleep (or get up and go home, or go to the basement to watch the ball game), she will feel abandoned — not a good way to end a lovemaking session.

Five things men wish women knew about sex

Just because a man's apparatus is on view doesn't mean that operating it is all that simple. So pay attention to these tips if you want to get the most from your relationship.

✔ **Lack of sex really can hurt.** *Blue balls* is a term for a man's testicles when they actually ache from the need for sexual release. Now, the pain is not so acute that a man can't stand it; but he's also not putting you on when he says that his testicles hurt.

✔ **Sometimes wasting electricity is okay.** Men get turned on visually. So how about leaving the lights on once in a while? Although you may like to cuddle and be cozy, and being in a dark room with the covers drawn up to your chin helps you feel safe enough to get aroused, as long as the room temperature is warm enough not to cause goose bumps, give your man the visual stimuli he desires.

✔ **Teamwork is important.** The more teamwork you have in your sex life, the more communication you have between the two of you, and the happier you both are. So don't just lie still and expect him to do all the work. The simplest thing you can do is to initiate sex once in a while if you tend to leave that task to him.

✔ **The Playboy Playmate is not a threat.** The man who gets turned on reading — or, if you prefer, ogling — *Playboy* and other such mags isn't going to rush out of the house looking for Miss October. Instead, he's going to come over to your side of the bed and look for you. He loves you for all *your* qualities, one of which may even be that you *don't* look like Miss October (whom he may actually be too scared to go to bed with, fearing he couldn't live up to the moment).

✔ **The day I stop looking is the day I'm dead.** Men will always look at other women; you can't stop them. Your man should use discretion when he's around you, but don't make a big fuss when he looks at another woman (unless he's being obnoxious about it). Remember, if your man stops looking at other women, he's probably also stopped looking at you.

Keeping the fires burning

If you always make love exactly the same way, the routine can become boring. The follow suggestions can help you heat up again.

Make some new moves

Try something a little different and use the memories of those more creative times to add sparkle to all your other sexual episodes. Make love someplace you've never done it, at a different time of the day, or with most of your clothes on — or with only one of you naked and the other one fully clothed. Let your imagination fly and see where it takes you.

Take creativity one step further

A change of scenery can help not only your sex life, but your intellectual and romantic life as well. Tradition dictates that a "sexy" vacation involves going to some warm clime, and sitting on a beach wearing next to nothing while sipping strong rum drinks. However, a vacation that offers intellectual stimulation can also do wonders for your sex life. If you're in a stimulating environment, you and your partner can discover new sides to your personalities, and this type of exploration can be very sexy.

Create an adventure

Be a little daring. Take a risk on a new position. Within reason, the sex act has many variations that don't involve any real harm beyond the risk that one or both of you won't be able to sustain the position or have an orgasm. So you miss one orgasm, no big deal. On the other hand, if you decide that you like a new position, it can bring you many, many orgasms over the course of a lifetime.

Considering Viagra

Although taking a pill such as Viagra to get an erection is certainly a pleasing remedy for a man's sexual problems, you cannot assume that a pill is a cure-all for a couple's romance troubles. In fact, doing so could introduce new problems in your relationship that may be overcome with compromise or professional marriage counseling. A couple's sexual problems stem from the relationship, not from the man's ability to achieve and maintain an erection.

A couple needs to talk about how to integrate such pills into their love life to bring about sexual harmony. When they do, the pills can do wonders.

Get some gadgets

If you need a little more variety in your sex life, consider going to a sex shop. Sex is supposed to be fun, and the gadgets and gizmos featured in these stores are supposed to add to the fun of lovemaking. If you're not comfortable using any of these products, then simply browse. If you don't dare go into a sex store, or if you don't have one near you, the next best thing is to get a catalog or click your way through one of these shops' Web sites.

Watch X-rated videos

Because men get more turned on by visual stimuli, manufacturers aim X-rated videos primarily at the male market, which may not be good for couples as many women find such movies abhorrent. Certainly nobody should force another person to watch anything that they don't like, but you shouldn't take these movies all that seriously either. If you see a couple onscreen engaging in an activity that you want to try, hit the stop button and give it a whirl.

Going for Therapy

Locating a therapist may be more difficult than finding a medical doctor. If you know someone who has undergone therapy, by all means, ask that person for a recommendation. If you don't mind letting other people know that you need help, you can spread the word and see what advice comes your way.

Normally, when you need a medical specialist, you ask your general practitioner for advice. You may begin your search for a therapist the same way. Your doctor may be connected to a larger group of doctors and may be able to recommend a therapist. Even doctors who are not part of a group may know of good local therapists to recommend.

If your friends or family doctor don't prove to be fruitful resources in your search for a therapist, contact the nearest teaching hospital. Or ask for a recommendation from a religious leader from your church or synagogue.

If you want to take a more anonymous route, you can call the American Psychological Association, which has a referral number (1-800-964-2000). You can also search the Internet. The following online sources don't give any kinds of ratings, but at least they're a place to start:

✔ Find-A-Therapist, `www.findingstone.com/find-a-therapist`

✔ American Association for Marriage and Family Therapy,
`www.aamft.org`

✔ Mental Health Infosource Professional Directory,
`www.mhsource.com/referral/docsearch.html`

✔ The Internet Care Directory, `www.caredirectory.com/main.html`

For someone seeking a sex therapist, the American Board of
Sexology (`www.sexologist.org/index.htm`) has a good listing.
And if you don't have access to the Internet, you can write to
AASECT (American Association of Sex Educators, Counselors, and
Therapists), the organization that accredits sex therapists, at P.O.
Box 238, Mount Vernon, IA 52314.

After you select the therapist you like best, discuss with this
professional what you expect to get out of therapy. Your goals
should be realistic. Don't expect that either you or your mate is
going to undergo a complete personality change. You'll usually find
that even some small improvements in the way you interact can
make quite a difference. Your counselor should help you determine
a course of therapy that meets your goals within a time frame that
you both agree on.

Give your therapist a fair chance. You and your therapist (and hopefully your spouse as well) need to develop a relationship in order to
ensure effective treatment. Make sure that you give your therapist
an opportunity to make some progress before you assume that the
treatment isn't working.

Seeking a second opinion

If you go for marital therapy and find that it's not working, give serious consideration to seeing another counselor. Follow this advice
especially if you feel in your heart that you can repair your relationship. Conversely, sometimes a couple goes to a therapist as a last
ditch attempt to save their marriage; deep inside they know that
their relationship is over. If that's the case with you, accept the reading of the first professional you consult.

Not everybody is a good candidate for therapy. Some people try to
use therapists to get what they want. These people agree to go for
therapy, but they have no intention of applying what comes out of it.
Other people try to sabotage therapy. These people hold back,
maybe saying nothing at all in response to the therapist's questions.
Or they tell lies or even try to flirt with the therapist.

A therapist can't do much in these situations. If one partner insists on sabotaging the therapy, the other partner must decide whether to continue the relationship. When a partner doesn't respect the guidelines set down by a therapist, perhaps the relationship is past the point of no return. If that's the case, you must decide — with the help of your therapist — whether or not to stick by this person.

Digging up deeper problems

Another outcome of going for therapy can occur when a therapist discovers some deeper problems at work in one or both partners. For example, if one of the two was sexually abused as a child, that abuse may signify the source of this couple's sexual problem. That person may need to undergo therapy individually in order to deal with the underlying problem before the relationship can be repaired.

If a deeper problem is revealed through your marital therapy, seek a second opinion. Although a therapist may be able to bring out such deeper issues, the therapist may not have the training to treat the specific problem that's revealed. A therapist, psychologist, or psychoanalyst who has successfully treated many people with your same problem is the provider you want. If you doubt whether your therapist can handle some deeper issue that may come up, don't stick with this therapist out of loyalty. Look around to get the best treatment available.

Chapter 13

All in the Family

. . . .

. . . .

Do you ever find yourself saying "Can't we all just get along?!" Well, the tips and hints in this chapter can help you get further down the path to having happy, health relationships with everyone in your immediate and extended families.

Parenting — Ah, the Joys!

Of course, entire books are written about parenting, but the following sections offer some easy suggestions that you can work into your parenting style.

Talking with kids

Contrary to popular belief, kids are not from another planet. To communicate better with children, remember the following things:

✔ **Use simple words for easy understanding.** When your kids know what you're talking about, you'll find getting your point across easier to do. If you think that your kids don't understand something, ask them to say back to you what you said to them. You'll know quickly whether your message is coming across.

✔ **Get to the point.** Pretend that you're on a conversation egg timer. If you don't say what you need to say within a short period of time, you've lost the attention of most children.

✔ **Don't yell.** When you yell at your kids, they don't listen to a thing you're saying. Your point is lost, they're upset, you're upset. *Nothing* is accomplished.

If you reach the point where you're about to yell, stop and leave the room. Just for a second. Take a few deep breaths, get your composure back, and approach the situation again.

✔ **Let children express themselves.** If you let kids open up to you, they'll find that communicating their fears and frustrations is easier to do as they get older.

Teaching good habits

The best way to teach good habits to kids is to make sure *you* are the best example you can be.

Identify the habits that you want your kids to have and build them into your daily routine. If you want your kids to floss on a daily basis, build flossing into their going-to-bed routine. If you expect your kids to pick up their shoes and socks from the living room at night, make a rule that no bedtime stories are read until the living room is shoe-free. After a while — admittedly, probably a long while — you won't even have to say anything to your kids. Tooth flossing and shoe clearing will have become habits.

Cultivating honesty

You can teach honesty by encouraging your kids to tell the truth and to let you know what's on their minds — which shouldn't be a frightening thought.

✔ **Ask your child how he feels and let him know that it's OK to tell you if he's mad at you for a decision that you've made.** Let him know that you won't be angry if he's honest about his emotions.

✔ **Avoid confrontations in ways that make lying easy for your child.** Rather than saying, "Debra, did you color on the wall?" say "Debra, you know you're not supposed to color on the wall." Avoid direct confrontation when you already know the answer. Asking Debra if she colored on the walls, when you saw her do it, sets up your child to lie.

✔ *Be honest yourself.* Don't lie to your children. You're setting an example. If you lie to your children, you're sending them the message that it's OK to lie and they'll do the same.

Disciplining

Here are some tips to constructive disciplining that can help to develop good behavior.

- ✔ **Establish ground rules.** Boundaries include things such as the places where your children are allowed to play, what kind of behavior is permitted, and what your children can play with.

- ✔ **Make your rules realistic.** Don't enforce an unrealistic rule. For example, you may want to create the rule that all toys are to be kept in your children's rooms. But you soon realize that the rule is impossible to enforce because your kids spend all their free time in the family room. So, rethink your rule. Maybe the rule needs to be that all toys are to be picked up before anyone goes to bed.

- ✔ **When you tell your children you're going to do something, do it.** Children need to know that when you say you're going to do something, you do it. Doing so lets them know that they can trust what you say — and that you're a reliable person.

- ✔ **Follow up after discipline to ensure that your children understand why they were disciplined.** Punishment is not effective if your children have no idea why they're being punished.

Working with your partner

Sometimes, you and your mate disagree on how to handle certain situations with your child. You have to treat such situations delicately. You don't want to turn a coloring-on-the-walls incident into a raging debate over how to handle all things, especially if your little one is standing there absorbing everything you say.

Here are some suggestions for handling mutual decision-making.

- ✔ **Don't argue about discipline.** Especially in front of your kids. If you do, they interpret the situation as one parent taking their side and the other one not. Kids store this information and eventually use it against you — not in an evil kind of way, but they do remember what happened and they do bring it up later.

- ✔ **Don't gang up on your child.** If you both see something going on that shouldn't, let one parent deal with it. If you see that your partner's having trouble, offer to help.

- ✔ **Don't jump into an ongoing situation.** If you walk into a room where your partner is already handling a situation, try to keep quiet. Things aren't always as they appear, and you probably don't know what's going on.

Uncovering the Secrets of Successful Stepfamilies

When two people decide to remarry and bring their children from previous marriages into the new marriage, several rules of conduct become crucial. Here are a few tips for newly blended families:

✔ **Sort out your discipline styles.** Issues to discuss include acceptable behavior and the consequences when children misbehave. Predictable rules make your children feel safe and secure.

✔ **Take the primary responsibility for raising and disciplining your own children.** A remarried woman often makes the mistake of assuming that her new husband can automatically assert his authority over her children without any problems. A remarried man often expects his new wife to be an instant second mother to his kids. In reality, a stepparent has to gradually earn a stepchild's respect and, hopefully, his or her love.

✔ **Decide on each child's duties and responsibilities.** Together, work out jobs, expected behavior, and family etiquette. Assign chores so that children feel part of the household, not like guests in a stepparent's home.

✔ **Set precise and specific rules about visitation by former spouses.** Children need stability and predictability.

✔ **Make sure that grandparents and other extended family members, if involved before the divorce, remain just as involved in the newly blended family.** Remember that extended family members may need to mourn the loss of the original nuclear family before they become part of the stepfamily.

✔ **Keep your expectations modest.** Remarried spouses often find that the relationship between their children and new partner is not what they'd hoped it would be. The best strategy is to recognize that you can't control some things, and the best you may be able to do is to foster a cooperative attitude among all concerned.

✔ **Be prepared to deal with unfamiliar situations.** Your chances of forming a cohesive stepfamily improve dramatically if you develop patience in dealing with unfamiliar situations. That means allowing each member of your new family the space and time to adjust to a complex mix of personalities and circumstances.

✔ **Hold regular family conferences.** The goal of a family meeting is to improve communication and make the family environment more nurturing and cooperative.

Surviving the holidays after a divorce

The holiday season can be particularly difficult for divorced families. Expectations of picture-perfect family get-togethers create pressure and stress for everyone involved. In order to get through the holidays with as little stress as possible:

- ✔ **Keep all schedules the same whenever possible.** If you must make changes, tell your children ahead of time or, better yet, allow them to participate in the decision-making. Doing so gives them a feeling of at least partial control over their lives and schedules.

- ✔ **Don't try to squelch fond memories of past holidays.** A divorce doesn't eradicate memories, and in many cases, part of the fun of the holidays is reminiscing about past good times.

- ✔ **When giving gifts, steer clear of any sort of competition with the other parent.** Better yet, coordinate gift choices together. After you give the gifts, don't make restrictive rules about keeping gifts in one parent's home or the other. Children who receive gifts should be allowed to take them wherever they go — no strings attached. Also, help your children make or select gifts for their other parent. By doing so, you teach them to be thoughtful and generous.

Dealing with Your Relatives the Easy Way

The way you interact with various relatives, in-laws, and family friends can have a lasting effect on the future of your relationships. Although every family is unique, the following sections offer some guidelines that work for most families. When you proceed with care, you can reap great results.

Knowing what to call extended family

The names that you use when directly addressing your relatives are very important courtesies.

In all cases, using a pronoun instead of an actual name is an absolute no-no. When a person is within earshot, using words such as *she* and *her* is definitely not courteous; the more you use such words, the more rude they seem.

Caring for aging parents

An infirm parent can add stress to even the healthiest of marriages. The following tips can help married partners who are caring for aging parents:

✔ **Think of the added responsibility as an opportunity for growth.** Spending time with an aging parent can give you an opportunity to become closer with a loved one — and to resolve earlier conflicts that have persisted for years.

✔ **Make certain that your spouse shares the responsibility.** Caring for an older parent needs to be a joint effort — regardless of whether that parent is yours or your partner's. Children who are still at home should be encouraged to participate in the caretaking process.

✔ **Don't let guilt drive your care-taking decisions.** Many conflicting emotions come into play when a parent needs your help. You love that person and want to do your best, but that doesn't mean you should have to jeopardize your marriage because of guilt or a false sense of duty.

✔ **Find out which services your relative requires and the best way to access them.** Some communities provide free or low-cost meals for seniors, shopping assistance, and a variety of other supports. Contact your local social services agency to determine your relative's eligibility. Supplement these services with paid services, as your budget permits. Devote your time to helping with those tasks that *really* require your personal attention.

✔ **Be respectful, but set limits.** Older parents sometimes make unrealistic demands on their adult children. They may claim that allowing strangers to shop or cook for them is unacceptable, which can leave you holding the bag. You must determine which tasks you should do and which you can hire out. More often than not, what your parent or in-law needs most is to be treated with dignity and included in family activities and decisions.

✔ **Be mindful of safety.** Keep an eye open for certain red flags that indicate the need for certain security precautions. Is it still safe for the person to be driving a car? Has he recently become forgetful? Do you see other behaviors that tell you that your relative may be a danger to herself or others?

✔ **Be prepared to make some hard decisions.** However much you love your parent and want to provide personal care, you may have circumstances in which your best alternative is to place that senior in an assisted-living facility. If you get into a serious disagreement about how to proceed, seek out a social worker or counselor with geriatric expertise to help you make a decision.

Here are some easy suggestions for addressing family members:

✔ **In-laws:** If you can bring yourself to call your parents-in-law "Mom and Dad," they'll probably be pleased. However, some people find this practice difficult, at least at first.

✔ **Grandparents:** You can usually address your spouse's grandparents with their last names appended, as in "Grandma Smith." Again, ask directly what the grandparents prefer to be called.

✔ **Aunts, uncles, and cousins:** You're on safer ground with these folks. The rule is "Titles up and given names down." *Up* and *down* refer to age. If somebody prefers a different form of direct address, respect that person's request. Children should always include titles when addressing relatives who are older than they are. When dealing with your spouse's relatives, the general rule is to use the title that your spouse would use.

✔ **Former spouses:** Even with your ex, you should be on your best behavior. Address your spouse by his or her first name. If an introduction is required, use this format: "This is my former husband, Jeffrey Allen. Jeffrey is Sam and Sylvia's father."

✔ **Non-traditional families:** A great many households function like families but have no legally sanctioned family standing. Some men and women live together in very stable (but unmarried) relationships, devoted same-sex couples, and difficult-to-characterize communal arrangements. If you're determined to exhibit perfect manners, accept and introduce members of these interesting families in exactly the manner they desire.

✔ **Stepchildren:** If rules can be written for introducing children from your spouse's previous marriage, you can be sure that they won't work in your particular family situation. Always speak with patience and sensitivity in this area:

- If you're a new stepparent, try introducing the children with "I'd like you to meet Roger's son and daughter, Chad and Elizabeth."

- When you know for sure that things are okay between you and the stepchildren, experiment with, "And these are the children, Chad and Elizabeth." Talk it over with the kids before you refer to them as "our kids."

✔ **Foster children:** Foster children deserve to have that specific title appended and made clear. One of the goals of the foster-child program is the eventual reunification of natural parent and child, and foster children have a tough enough time without title confusion. Introduce a foster child as "my foster daughter, Maria."

✔ **Adopted children:** Forget all about legal details. Adopted children are your real children, and you need make no reference to their adoption. If they want to talk about being adopted in later years, that's their business.

Being careful about keeping score with family

Within every extended family, you'll discover an elaborate system of keeping score. The details may not be written down anywhere, but you can bet that folks have a pretty good idea of where things stand regarding dinner invitations, gifts, and favors.

Reciprocating with meals and gifts

Invitations to meals, especially, should be equalized. It doesn't matter who's inviting whom or whether the invitation is for lunch or dinner, or to your home or a restaurant — meals must be reciprocated.

Gifts, especially to children, should also be reciprocated. Although the value of the gift need not be the same, the thought that goes into the gift should be.

Visiting and vacationing

When traveling far to visit relatives, a little bit of consideration can save you a lot of uncertainty. Keep these suggestions in mind:

- **Discuss the timing of your intended visit before you make definite plans.** Be sure that the dates of your visit coincide with your relatives' agenda.

- **Be definite and specific about arrival and departure dates.** Don't stay longer than three days.

- **Unless you know for sure that your relatives have adequate guest accommodations and expect that you will stay in their house, make reservations at a nearby hotel.** You can always cancel the reservations if Grandma insists that you stay with her.

- **Don't expect to be waited on.** As a houseguest, pick up after yourself, make your own bed, straighten up the bathroom, and so on.

- **Pick up your fair share of the restaurant tabs, admission fees, and entertainment costs.** Don't make your visit a drain on your hosts' finances. And graciously participate in any social activities that your hosts plan.

- **Keep your eyes open to the general décor of the house.** After you return home, send a little thank-you gift to your hosts.

Part IV

Satisfying Careers in Today's Business World

The 5th Wave   By Rich Tennant

"Very good answer! Now, let me ask you another question..."

In this part . . .

*W*ork doesn't have to be a chore — not when you love what you do!

This part is your passport for finding a job that fuels both your pocket book and your passions. Interested in a new career? Want to start your own business? Don't know how to answer those super-tricky interview questions? The answers are yours, straight ahead!

You get the lowdown on how to get the best jobs and get paid what you're really worth, as well as tips for managing your time, cleaning up a cluttered desk, and even coping with the office busybody.

Chapter 14

Cool Careers at Any Age

· ·

· ·

*I*f the perfect career were going to hit you like a lightning bolt, you'd probably have been struck by now. Regardless of how daunting the search for the perfect career may seem, go ahead and start down the career trail, making sure to keep your eye out for cool side paths and ways to customize your journey to suit your strengths. Focusing on a likely route to career happiness is what this chapter is all about.

Choosing a Career That Suits You

Although choosing a career isn't exotic or unusually complicated, you can break down the process into three logical pieces:

- ✔ **Find out about yourself:** Gather insight into the things that really matter to you — your values, interests, and (this is important!) your passions.

- ✔ **Scope the market:** Find out as much as you can about what it takes to get launched and succeed in the careers, jobs, or industries that appeal to you.

- ✔ **Tool up:** Create a reasonably structured plan that's designed to close the gap between the assets you currently possess and the assets you need in order to pursue certain careers.

Ten tips for taking control of your career

In today's rapidly changing workplace, only one person is qualified to make the important decisions — and that's you.

Think of it this way: You're the CEO of your career. Like any CEO, of course, you need to solicit advice from others and, in many instances, rely on the expertise of people who have additional knowledge and experience. Ultimately, though, *you* have to make the big decisions.

To be successful as CEO of your own career, consider the following guidelines:

- ✔ **Know where you're going.** Successful CEOs invariably have a clear vision or direction for their companies. As the CEO of your career, you also need a vision — an overall goal of what you want to achieve with your career.

- ✔ **Develop a plan.** A common pitfall in career management (and in running a company, as well) is getting sidetracked — getting so bogged down with the priorities and pressures of a single day or situation that you lose sight of the big picture — from where you eventually want to go in your career. One way to guard against this pitfall is to create a *strategic career plan,* which is a broad outline of the steps to take to achieve your career goals.

- ✔ **Make every job count.** Every job you take as you progress in your career should be logically keyed to the goals you've established. This way, when you uncover new opportunities, you're able to capitalize on them and run a success-driven job-hunt strategy.

- ✔ **Keep your life well balanced.** Investigate opportunities for alternate work arrangements, such as flextime, part-time employment, job sharing, and telecommuting. These arrangements — when they're compatible with your job duties — give you more control of your time and help to ease the pressures that arise when the responsibilities of your career and your personal life collide.

- ✔ **Find ways to manage yourself.** Only those CEOs who have discovered how to set priorities and manage their time effectively are able to meet their responsibilities. Managing a career is, in many respects, a job unto itself and so it lends itself to many of the principles that apply to time management:

- You set goals.

- You re-evaluate priorities on an ongoing basis.

- You recognize when you're taking on more tasks and responsibilities than you can possibly manage.

Tools such as project-management software or day-planning notebooks can help. More importantly, work on developing a commitment to organization and a sense of discipline.

✔ **Become a better communicator.** Effective communication has always been an important skill in organizational life. But it's a critical skill for anyone who wants to make any sort of mark for him- or herself in today's virtual workplace.

✔ **Expand your network.** For most — if not all — high-level executives, networking has played an important part in their career advancement. True, staying in touch with people takes time and effort — two precious commodities in today's workplace. But if you organize your schedule well, you can usually fit in one or two days per month to mingle with colleagues at an association meeting, trade show, or similar venue. Think of it as an investment.

✔ **Stay on the cutting edge.** No CEO can possibly know every aspect of his or her company. It's unrealistic for you to think that you can keep your finger on the pulse of everything going on that may relate to your career. Even so, take reasonable steps to stay abreast of new developments in your field — especially if you're in an industry that's changing at warp speed, such as high-tech business.

✔ **Conduct yourself with absolute integrity.** Organizational alliances, which are fundamental to business life today, require unqualified trust among all parties. Integrity isn't something practiced now and then, when it's convenient; integrity is a core value that governs everything you do and say.

✔ **Be visible.** Without clamoring for attention, be sure that your supervisor is aware of your hard work and accomplishments. Also, stay open to opportunities outside of your job description — they can serve as springboards to career advancement.

It's up to you — not your boss, coworkers, senior management, or astrologer — to formulate objectives, develop a plan, and follow through with the necessary steps to realize your career goals.

Seven ways to make any job better

Here are some ways to customize your career and make a less-than-perfect job better.

- ✔ **Train your boss.** Yes, in the first week or two, you may need to work longer hours to get up to speed. But as soon as possible, try to get down to a workweek you're willing to sustain. If you want or need to work moderate hours, start conditioning your boss early on to accept the idea.

- ✔ **Get what you want from your boss.** Learn your boss's personality type — whether he's fact-driven or emotion-driven, fast- or slow-paced — and respond accordingly.

- ✔ **Make your workspace feel good.** If an attractive workspace makes you happier, act early. Or, maybe you want a cubicle near the window with a view or far from the elevator. The time to ask is now.

- ✔ **Telecommute.** For many people, telecommuting, for at least part of the week, brings a bit of heaven to their work life. Perhaps best of all, you'll have only a 10-second commute! Of course, many people find working at home too distracting, they miss the collegiality, or they simply don't live in a place conducive to working.

- ✔ **Recruit your very own team of (free!) experts.** Every successful employee has a stable of experts on call. These experts generally fall into four types:

  - **Knowledge gurus:** Experts such as the computer wizard or the person who can recite all your company's product specifications in his sleep.

  - **Wise old souls:** Someone who knows the ropes and can help you figure out how to get your idea implemented or get yourself out of trouble.

  - **Fun people:** The funmeister offers badly needed perspective — some silliness she pulled off the Internet, gossip about who's sleeping with whom, or a recipe for Last-Request Chocolate Cake.

  - **Bosses:** Your dream boss is a mentor, confidante, and rising star — he succeeds, and you may ride on his coattails. How do you get hitched to the boss's star? Start with coffee machine chitchat or by asking for newcomer advice.

Your team of experts requires care and feeding. They're in demand because they're so good. Go out of your way to help them when you can.

✔ **Learn the fast way.** Staying current keeps you competent and confident and increases your employability. But with the information explosion, staying current isn't easy. These tips can help:

- Hire someone who's available to help you learn a new piece of software, or try a savvy co-worker in your office.

- Skim books, read articles, or jump onto your favorite Internet search engine.

- Search online for an electronic discussion group that's related to your career.

✔ **Consider self-employment.** Self-employment is often a fine later step to growing a cool career. Self-employment done right may offer the most secure job: No one can fire you. And, of course, being in control of all the decisions surrounding your work life feels great.

Staying vigilant to the needs of coworkers, customers, and vendors is important. Not only can that help you as an *INtrapreneur* (someone who creates innovations within an organization) but also as an entrepreneur.

Telecommuting: A special situation

Telecommuting is one of the most sought-after alternate work arrangements, but one that can also be the most difficult to establish. Four things are key to keeping yourself and your boss happy.

✔ **Reassure your boss.** Many bosses are control freaks. They're afraid that if you're out of sight, your work will be out of mind. Offer to send progress reports, documentation of how you use your time — whatever stops him from losing sleep over that sybaritic lifestyle he thinks you're living on the company dime.

✔ **Set limits.** Work at home and you have endless temptations: morning tennis, housecleaning, a call to your old girlfriend, and so on. Perhaps the biggest impediment to a successful telecommuting day is kids. If you have young children, childcare may be worth getting so that you can work in peace on days when you're working at home.

✔ **Try to get compensation for telecommuting.** If you're working at home, your employer saves office space, utilities, phone, computer costs, and so on. Why should you have to pay for that?

✔ **Stay in the loop.** Out of sight can mean out of the boss's mind when it comes time for promotions. You also don't get to hear the latest info. Limiting your telecommuting to half-time is often the wise thing to do.

Moving Up, Moving On

Career management is more art than science, and you're undoubtedly going to run into a great many situations in which the choices you face are anything but simple. The two most difficult situations probably involve decision-making in either asking for a raise or quitting your job.

Knowing when to quit your job

Before you do anything, you need to figure out why you're feeling stressed. You may be stressed because you have a new job, your responsibilities are high pressure, your supervisor has set unrealistic goals and expectations for you, or you simply don't enjoy what you're doing.

Adapting to a new job always takes time. Try to organize yourself as much as possible and be sure to devote your attention to the most strategic, high-level tasks and responsibilities. At first, the stress can seem overwhelming. However, as you gain more experience with these assignments, you'll feel more confident in your abilities and know what to do when challenges arise. If you find instead that things aren't improving or that you simply dislike your job, you may want to move on.

Knowing when to ask for a raise

Before you ask for a raise, thoroughly review what you've accomplished, your credentials, and your skills, and revise your resume to reflect your recent accomplishments — pretend that you're reapplying for your job. Consult salary surveys and research compensation trends. Is the labor market so competitive in your specialty or industry that your skills and abilities are more highly valued? If so, discuss your findings with your manager and ask to re-evaluate your compensation level.

For more information on getting paid what you're worth, see Chapter 15.

Chapter 15

Getting a Great Job

● ●

In This Chapter

▶ Getting hired over the competition

▶ Searching for your dream job

▶ Sparkling in an interview

● ●

As a job seeker, you need to have some basic things together: a powerhouse resume, an attention-grabbing cover letter, job searching tools, and star-quality interviewing techniques. This chapter offers an overview of each piece of your passport to landing a great job!

Powerhouse Resumes

Because your resume holds your future in its inky little black lines, make sure that your resume is as powerful as it can be to attract the employer who has the right job for you.

Exposing resume myths

Here's a brief examination of some popular myths about resumes.

- ✔ **The Only-One-Right-Way Myth:** Topics such as the following are open for debate: Which length is best — one page, two pages, or more? Which format is best — reverse chronological or functional format? Which opening is best — objective or summary? *No one way is best.* Remember, the best resume for you is the one that best supports your quest for a job interview.

- ✔ **The 90-Minute-Resume Myth:** Saying that a resume can be written in 90 minutes or overnight is like saying that Michelangelo could have made better time with a roller. Good work takes effort.

✔ **The No-Fun-at-All Myth.** You need not always use a straight pitch nor confine your creative input to a choice between white or ivory stationery. When you feel compelled to come up with clever ways to catch an employer's eye, be dead sure that you know your audience and how the resume will be received.

✔ **The One-Page-or-Bust Myth.** The reality is that your resume should be long as needed to get your concise message across with zip and punch. Try one page for new graduates, one to two pages for most people, and two to three pages for most senior executives.

✔ **The Fibs-Are-Fine Myth.** Don't inflate grades, invent degrees, or concoct job titles on your resume. After you lie, you have no easy way out — people do check.

✔ **The Resume-Does-It-All Myth.** In your job search, your resume is only one marketing tool that can help you get an interview. After you get the interview, the rest depends on you — your skills, your savvy, your personality, your attitude.

✔ **The Resume-Is-to-Blame Myth.** Maybe yes, maybe no. When your resume results in a telephone call from a recruiter who doesn't issue a come-in-and-see-us invitation, suspect that your experience or your education is at fault.

If your resume results in interviews, but no offers appear on the horizon, maybe you've oversold yourself in a resume, or maybe you just don't know how to close the offer. Brush up on your interviewing skills.

✔ **The One-Type-Resume Myth.** You may need more than one type of resume. For example, you'll want a *scannable* resume that's heavy with nouns and graphically without frills for computers, a *plain text* version with no embellishments whatsoever for e-mail, and a *formatted* version loaded with action verbs, underlining, graphics, and other bells and whistles for human eyes.

✔ **The Always-Expect-an-Answer Myth.** The best companies, with plenty of staff and budget, do acknowledge resumes. However, small companies with few staff members to review resumes may take a while to respond — or may never get around to it if you're not the one. If you haven't received a response, call and ask whether your resume was received.

Avoiding resume blunders

Anyone can make the following mistakes, regardless of age or level of experience.

✔ **Excessive vagueness:** Avoid stating an objective too broadly, such as "a position in the paper industry." Excellent resumes focus and target, offering a summary of qualifications rather than defining areas of expertise.

Don't expect an employer to dig through your resume to find out whether your qualifications match the job's requirements.

✔ **Poor organization:** Double-check your work for construction and focus. Open with either a summary of your qualifications or an objective statement. Headings should be vivid and distinct from one another with each entry under its appropriate heading.

✔ **Lack of examples:** Credibility increases with the "storytelling" of solid examples. Rack your brain for concrete examples of each claim: Ask "Who?" "What?" "When?" "Where?" and "How much?"

✔ **Missing achievements:** Without results — measured in some way (numbers, percentages, dollar amounts) — that show how you successfully reached high points in your work efforts, your workplace victories will sound as though you made them up.

✔ **Irrelevant information:** Skip personal information if it doesn't add to the image you're trying to convey. Delete nontransferable skills and duties and bypass references.

✔ **Typos and grammatical oversights:** Proofread for errors in five steps.

- **Spell- and grammar-check on the computer.** Doing this is a good start, but don't stop there. Spelling and grammar checkers don't find words that aren't there — because they're inadvertently left out. Double-check the punctuation and grammar yourself.

- **Slow down.** Use a ruler to read the entire document aloud, line by line.

- **Read backward, from the bottom up.** Start at the lower-right-hand corner, reading backward from the bottom to the top, word by word. This approach is a good way to spot word warts and other blemishes.

- **Get a second opinion.** Beg a hawkeyed word mechanic to proof your resume, one more time. If neither of you can spell a word or find it in a dictionary, change words.

- **Read for content.** Do one more read-through, this time for clarity.

✔ **Not checking small details:** By itself, no single, small flaw is deadly (unless you're applying to be a proofreader). The trouble comes when you add several mistakes together on the same resume, collectively zeroing out your chances.

Cliché-free language can make the difference

Don't burn your resume if it contains some of these too-familiar phrases — freshen it with newer arrivals.

✔ **Hard working:** Highlight examples of your industriousness, your dedication to the job, and your energetic work ethic. Then add vocabulary, such as *motivated, results oriented, driven, goal oriented, achievement oriented, constant follow-through, dedicated, energetic, hard charging, committed,* and *accustomed to a heavy workload.*

✔ **Hands-on achiever:** Give examples of your *direct initiative* and of hands-on-type duties that you've performed. If you consider yourself an achiever, try more eye-catching descriptions, such as a summary of accomplishments with quantified results.

✔ **Bottom-line oriented:** Refresh your vocabulary with words that better describe your work ethic, such as *committed to achieving financial goals, budget driven, focus all efforts on accomplishing financial objectives,* and *pursue budget efficiency.*

✔ **Creative innovator:** This cliché transmits zippo about you. *Creative* by itself is okay, as long as you accompany it with examples. *Innovator,* however, distresses resume readers who wish you'd get to the point. *Creative innovator* is also redundant.

✔ **Seeking a challenging opportunity:** Who isn't? Not long ago, this phrase was kicker lingo. Not anymore. Try: *Seeking a demanding position as _____, a rigorous opportunity as _____,* or *the ambitious responsibility of a_____.*

✔ **One of a kind:** If you try to call yourself a one-of-a-kind anything, no resume reader — after years of breathing hype instead of fresh air — will believe your fatigued claim. Let your achievements speak for themselves.

✔ **Seasoned executive:** Almost every executive is a *seasoned executive.* Rather than sounding dulled by your years of experience, brighten up your image with *steeped in the industry, extensive experience in_____, extensive track record of_____, familiar with all aspects of_____,* and *long history of positive efforts in_____.*

✔ **Team player:** Never label yourself with this frayed-at-the-edges label as no one pays attention to it anymore. Try instead: *collegial, mesh well with co-workers, worked in concert with_____, collaborated with_____, team-task minded,* and *achieve shared goals.*

✔ **Responsible for . . . :** This worn-out workhorse is the crutch in a mechanical listing of duties: responsible for this, responsible for that. Ad infinitum. What you should be spotlighting are skills, achievements, and results.

✔ **Senior-level executive position:** Are there any junior-level executive positions?

✔ **Information overload:** Many resume writers forget that *resume* literally means *summary* — to sum up. Start with a highly selective choice of content and then streamline each item.

✔ **Imitating a flat organization:** Try to portray yourself as having an upwardly mobile track record even if you've held lateral jobs for years. Mention raises (do not specify amounts) and increasing responsibilities, even if your title never changed.

Answering Job Ads

To prove that you're a red-hot candidate whom reviewers had better whoosh into their offices to interview before someone else grabs you, you need a cover letter that targets the desired job, intrigues the reader enough to make room in a busy schedule to meet you, and advertises why you're the best choice over the competition.

All this may sound slightly devilish — like you've got something up your sleeve. And you do: your skills, accomplishments, and experience — which you can use to achieve future great work.

Take these hints to heart as you respond to ads:

✔ **Let your letter reflect the ad's keywords or skill phrases.** If the ad mentions general keywords such as *professional* or *creative*, describe yourself and your record with these exact terms.

✔ **Mine the ad for information about the employer.** Checking the ad itself is revealing. The following tips don't apply to Internet ads but are important for printed ads.

   • **Is the ad large?** This company may be flush with money and pay its people well — or it may be such a poor place to work that high turnover requires constant recruiting.

   • **Is the ad small?** Maybe the firm is new and has a low advertising budget, in which case you can get a jump on the competition by getting in early. Or, if the company is small but undergoing expansion, then respond to the person named in the ad, but at the same time, contact the hiring manager for whom you would work directly.

   • **Is the ad vague?** A blind ad may indicate that a huge response is expected or that a senior-level position is about to open up.

✔ **Refer to the advertisement early on.** Telling the employer how you found out about an opening immediately establishes that you're applying for a position the company intends to fill in the near future.

✔ **Customize your letter for each employer.** Tailor your letter to the requirements that the employer lists.

✔ **Use a linear format when you're a good match.** If you possess a substantial number of the qualifications the ad requests, show those qualifications line by line.

✔ **Use a paragraph format when you're a marginal natch.** Paragraphing allows you to emphasize your strengths at the beginning of paragraphs, sending readers on an archaeological dig to find your weaknesses buried deep inside the text — if they can find them at all.

✔ **Address your letter to a specific individual.** When the advertisement lists no name, call and scout it out. You may need to be resourceful, as companies are often closemouthed.

✔ **Be resourceful in replying to blind ads.** Play detective to find out the employer's name when you respond to a blind recruitment ad with no clue as to the employer's identity.

- Find out the name of the box holder if the ad directs you to send a response to a U.S. post-office box. You can forget about it if the box is at a newspaper or trade journal.

- If you know only the street address, you can use a reverse directory (library copy) or one of the Internet telephone directory resources. If all else fails, drive by. Then call the company and say, "The word's out that you're looking for a _____. Who should I talk to about that?" Get the name and write a cover letter to go with your resume.

- Don't waste time trying to discover an advertiser's identity in a blind ad posted on a commercial Internet site, which often use confidential tools to protect the advertiser's anonymity.

✔ **Focus on experience directly related to the job.** Shine a spotlight on only the benefits you have that the employer wants.

✔ **Mail your letters on Sunday or Monday.** To get a jump on the competition, get something out the same day you see the ad.

Searching for a Job in the 21st Century

Looking for a new job probably isn't on your list of fun things to do. Job hunting is one skill that most people don't care to become really good at. As you conduct your search, however, keep in mind that with every call you make and every letter you send, you're getting closer to the finish line. The more knowledge you gain, the faster you'll get there.

Finding your dream employer

The simplest and perhaps best approach in locating your ideal employer is to find the library with the best business section and tell the librarian that you want a list of employers that meet your specifications. Or, if you're a do-it-yourselfer, the following information can help no matter what interests you.

Finding local dream employers

Here are some ways to find your best bets:

- ✔ Ask friends, colleagues, competitors, suppliers, customers, headhunters, and counselors at local college career centers.

- ✔ Check out the "best" lists: Big-city general newspapers and business newspapers such as *Business Times* (www.amcity.com) and *Crain's* (www.crainsny.com) regularly list the best, fastest-growing, and largest organizations. Search their online sites with terms such as "best companies," "top biotech," and "fastest growing."

- ✔ Ask attendees at a local chapter meeting of your field's professional association.

- ✔ Consult the *Adams Job Bank* series of books, available for more than 20 individual metropolitan areas. These books list thousands of local employers by category and company size.

- ✔ Try the Chamber of Commerce. To avoid the party line, "All our members are good companies," ask a specific question: "I'm looking for a job as an economist. Do you know of any good, fast-growing small companies that might be good places to work?"

- ✔ Ask industry insiders. An easy way to do this is to visit the Web site of an employer in your target field. Often those sites let you send e-mail to some of their employees.

- ✔ Check out features in local magazines and newspapers about fast-growing companies, new product introductions, and profiles of notables.

- ✔ Call your favorite government agencies (see the front of your White Pages) and ask the procurement department for the names of outside contractors that employ people in your target job.

- ✔ Check out your field's category in the Yellow Pages. Sometimes the employer's description in the ad calls out to you.

✔ Check the "associations" listing in your Yellow Pages for a list of local nonprofit organizations.

✔ Don't ignore your current employer. Having your present job tweaked to fit, getting a transfer, or even getting an in-house promotion is usually easier than convincing some stranger to give you the perfect job.

Locating distant dream employers

Here are some easy ways to find on-target employers thousands of miles away:

✔ See *Who's on Top?* at www.hooversonline.com. From among 13,000 companies, the Hoover's business database offers its picks of top companies in categories like "most admired," "fastest growing," and "best companies to work for."

✔ Check out a book called *The Job Vault,* which contains inside information such as strategic direction and corporate culture on more than 500 of America's largest employers.

✔ Use the CD-ROM or online services found at many libraries, plugging in search terms such as "best aerospace companies."

✔ See "The Hundred Best Companies to Work For," published each January in *Fortune* magazine.

✔ Ask on Internet discussion groups. Post this question: "I'm looking for a job as an *(insert desired job).* Can anyone recommend good places to work that may be hiring?"

✔ Read Kathryn Petras's *Jobs* (revised annually) for profiles of top businesses in dozens of industries.

✔ Browse through www.thomasregister.com. This site contains the mammoth Thomas Manufacturing Register, which is product and contact information for 155,000 companies. You can search by company name, brand name, or type of product.

✔ Consult the *U.S. Government Manual* (www.access.gpo.gov/nara/nara001.html) and *The Budget of the United States Government* (www.gpo.gov/usbudget/index.html) for indications of which federal agencies will be growing.

✔ Check Dan Lauber's *Job Finder* series for lists of hundreds of field-specific directories.

Debunking job-hunting myths

The following misconceptions are some of the more common — and most self-defeating — misconceptions about job hunting.

✔ **"Being unemployed puts you at a tremendous disadvantage when you're looking for a job."** This misconception implies that because you're unemployed, the companies you approach assume that you have a major character flaw. Employers today, however, understand that someone may be unemployed for many reasons, such as downsizings, mergers, acquisitions, and so on.

✔ **"Finding a job is harder than any job you'll ever have."** Looking for a job is hard work, but the really hard part is dealing with all the pressures — psychological, familial, and financial — that often arise during the course of a job search. To effectively search for a job, you need to be able to do a lot of the things you already know how to do in a focused, disciplined, and systematic way.

✔ **"When you're unemployed, you can't afford to turn down a job offer."** Unless it's absolutely necessary, don't assume that you have to accept the first job you're offered. Other strategies — temporary work, for example — allow you to keep your job search going until you get an offer that makes sense.

✔ **"The only way to get a good job in many industries is to have the right connections."** Having the right connections is an enormous advantage in any business endeavor — not just job hunting. A major part of conducting a successful job hunt is making the connections you need as your search progresses.

✔ **"Being good at interviews is the most important job hunting skill."** Making a strong, positive impression while interviewing is certainly one of the most valuable skills you can possess as a job hunter. However, don't make the mistake of underestimating the time, effort, and skill it takes to become good at the less obvious — but no less important — aspects of job hunting.

✔ **"The only person you can really depend on in a job search is yourself."** View job hunting as a team activity, asking help from friends, family members, network contacts, and, in some cases, recruiters and professional career counselors.

Firing up your job search eight different ways

Due to the unstructured nature of job hunting — the lack of a boss, set schedule, and clearly defined set of tasks — you need to think about being productive and managing your time efficiently in your job search.

A word about employment agencies

What's the word? Iffy. Yes, employment agencies can give you access to some jobs you may otherwise not know about, but you pay a price. Agencies typically take 30 to 40 percent of what you'd make if you contacted the employer directly. The employer pays, so the agencies are more concerned about satisfying the employer than ensuring that you find a rewarding job. Sure, if you're well-qualified for an in-demand field, including a few employer-paid employment agencies on your list of contacts doesn't hurt. But focus on going directly to employers and jointly deciding what you can do to meet their needs and yours. You'll find a better job and be paid more for it.

Keep yourself on track by using the following tips.

- ✔ **Buy a personal organizer.** If you don't already have one, buy and begin to rely on a personal organizer, such as a notebook-style organizer or an electronic (handheld computer) organizer. Invest in a personal information management (PIM) software package if you're going to be using a computer in your job search.

- ✔ **Plan and prioritize every day.** Be prepared to spend at least half an hour at the beginning of each week and ten minutes at the beginning of each day writing down a to-do list and setting priorities.

- ✔ **Prioritize your tasks.** Rank the items on your to-do list by assigning number values (one to four, for example) based on two general factors: How important is a particular task to your overall goal and how important is it that you complete this particular task that month, week, or day?

- ✔ **Set up a routine.** Plan your weeks and days in as structured a manner as possible — making sure to leave some room for the unexpected. Set aside (within reason) certain days of the week or certain hours of the day for job search activities.

- ✔ **Set goals.** Your goals don't have to involve huge stretches. A daily goal can be simply "Get names of two companies that might have openings." Achieving these goals on a day-to-day basis keeps you in a success mode, nevermind that your ultimate goal — getting hired — is still to be achieved.

- ✔ **Avoid the busywork trap.** For example, spending nearly two weeks filling a database with the names and key data of nearly 300 companies without getting in touch with any of them.

Your job search objective is *not* simply to keep busy — it's to make sure that the things you're doing to keep busy are producing meaningful results.

✔ **Pay attention to your productivity.** Keep a *log* — a daily record of how you actually spend your time in a typical day. Analyzing the log tells you whether what you're actually *doing* throughout the course of a day is strategically keyed to your priorities.

✔ **Meet procrastination head-on.** Everyone tends to put off or postpone to some extent tasks that are difficult, frustrating, or possibly embarrassing. But if you let this tendency get out of hand during your job search, it can cost you dearly in the way of lost opportunities.

If procrastination is simply a bad habit you've gotten yourself into, try some of the following anti-procrastination tips from the experts.

- **The one-a-day strategy:** Establish as one of your daily to-dos the completion of at least one task (neither overwhelmingly difficult or objectionable) that you've been consistently putting off.

- **The paint-yourself-in-a-corner strategy:** Make a commitment — that is, promise someone (other than yourself) that you'll do something at a certain time. Note that, for obvious reasons, this technique works best when the failure to deliver on the commitment can have consequences that you'd rather not deal with.

- **The now-for-the-lollipop approach:** Build in some kind of reward for tackling a task that you've been putting off. The trick here is to make the "reward" something that you wouldn't normally do for yourself.

Starring in Showstopper Interviews

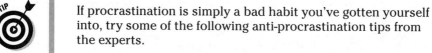

Appearance. Performance skills. Confidence. All are winning — and learnable — traits in job interviews. With a little help, you can acquire these traits and get employers to say "You're the one!"

Unlocking the keys to great interviews

Steal the show with the following concepts that can make you an interview star:

✔ Do your research. Demonstrate your interest in the company by showing what you know about the company — and about the skills needed to get the job done.

✔ Find out what role the company wants you to play. Ask, as soon as possible, about the scope of the job and the ideal person's qualifications for it. Then use specifics to describe your matching skills.

✔ Focus on your skills and other factors that will make you immediately productive. Employers no longer wait for you to practice for six months before being of benefit to them.

✔ Present the appropriate image for the part you seek. Walk it, talk it, and look it — and you have a better chance to "be" it.

✔ Master a 1- or 2-minute commercial in response to "tell me about yourself" requests.

✔ Rehearse answers to likely (and unlikely) questions. Prepare a list of job-related (not self-interest) questions — and ask them.

✔ Concentrate on what you can do for the company, not on what the company can do for you.

✔ Present any potentially damaging information in the most favorable light.

✔ Act in a confident and friendly manner — establish eye contact, smile, and address the interviewer by title and name (Ms. Smith or Dr. Harrison, for example — don't use first names).

✔ Be on time. And don't sit down before you're asked to — or put anything in your mouth (gum, cigarettes, toothpicks, or breath mints).

✔ Behave conservatively. Save your sparkle for the manager to whom you'd report.

✔ Never bring up negatives or bad-mouth previous employers.

✔ Tell true stories that support your claims of relevant skills.

✔ Wait to talk about salary, benefits, and perks until you're offered a job or you're "talking deal."

✔ Prior to leaving, ask when a decision will be made and if you can call back to check how they're progressing on the decision.

Getting paid what you're worth

If you've been offered a job, you may cave in and ask the interviewer to suggest a salary based on what the company would like to spend. But after all your research on your market value and on the company, you'll realize that this cop-out won't bring home top dollars.

You can do better with your salary needs by following these guidelines.

- ✔ **Find a home in the range.** Express your salary requirements in ranges based on the going rate for the job. A range gives you haggling room and shows that you're economically aware.

- ✔ **Plot your salary history carefully.** State your figures slightly above and below the market value so that you're more likely to stay in the game for positions for which you're qualified. For example, "For the past three years, I have earned between ($000 and $000) for my work in this field."

- ✔ **Stonewalled? Try to upgrade the job.** Point out how the job requires more than the standard duties suggested by the job title, and how it fits in a job description that merits a higher pay bracket. Clarify how you plan to minimize company costs through your performance. By using this tactic, you establish your worth to the company and your performance-based reason for asking a higher price.

- ✔ **Use dramatic silences.** Moments of nonverbal communication show your dissatisfaction with the offer, without a word to incriminate you as overly hungry for money. The interviewer may feel compelled by this uncomfortable silence to improve the offer. Or at least open a dialogue in which you can campaign for other kinds of rewards.

- ✔ **No flexibility? Make creative suggestions.** Ask if there's any flexibility in the salary portion of the offer. If the answer is no, get creative and begin talking about alternatives such as a company car, stock options, extra generous mileage reimbursement, parking privileges, additional paid vacations, a shorter work week, or a sign-on bonus.

- ✔ **Determine the fair market value.** Research to find out the *fair market value* of your work before negotiating a price and slip those exact words into the discussion whenever you can. Remember, too, that you can always come down on your price — but coming up is almost impossible after you name a low figure.

Applying interview etiquette

Remember to do the following things:

- ✔ Start with a smile and a firm handshake — obviously!
- ✔ Stand up when your interviewer approaches.

✔ Greet your interviewer by name (using titles unless otherwise indicated), look him in the eye, and thank him for this opportunity.

✔ Leave unnecessary items (totebags, briefcases, day planners, and so on) in your car. When the interviewer shows you to her office, you don't want to spend time packing for the trip.

✔ Give the interview your full attention; appearing organized and professional. Turn off pagers, cell phones, watches, and other beeping gadgets. If you must set your pager on "vibrate" mode, resist the temptation to read messages that come in during your interview.

✔ Watch your language. Swearing is rarely appropriate at the office and never appropriate during an interview. Even if the interviewer swears, you don't have to.

✔ Add other comments and ask questions at the end of the interview. For example, if you feel the questions asked haven't allowed you to explain why you're the right person for the job, now is the time to volunteer that information.

Always be prepared with questions. Even if you feel you know everything already, ask something like, "What's your favorite thing about working here?" or, "What are the greatest challenges your company faces right now?" Avoid questions that you can easily answer through a Web site or annual report — if you ask them, the interviewer may conclude that you didn't take the time to research the company.

Chapter 16

Dealing with the Daily Grind

In This Chapter

▶ Managing people, projects, and yourself

▶ Explaining your ideas

▶ Speaking to groups

Don't let the daily grind get the best of you! This chapter is jam-packed with quick ideas that can help you become a better employee and a better manager of projects and people.

Managing Projects

Even if you don't have the title of "manager," you may frequently manage or lead projects. Rather than feeling overwhelmed, try discovering what you can do *better* (or *differently*) to obtain the results you want.

Running a meeting

If you can master the art of the meeting, you'll be a powerful asset to your organization. Even if you're not planning the meeting, you still need to know what the proper etiquette is for your role as a participant.

Planning a meeting

A meeting can be a good way to disseminate information to several people at the same time because it allows for eye contact, body language, and opportunities to ask questions in order to clarify the information. But you must know the *purpose* of the meeting — what you hope to accomplish — and have an *agenda*. A complete agenda includes a list of topics to be covered, assignments of who should be prepared to cover each topic, time estimates for discussion of each topic, and start and end times. Be sure to leave a little more time than you think you'll need. Your agenda should also include the meeting location and a list of attendees so that they can discuss items before the meeting if necessary.

If you don't set an agenda, participants may arrive at the meeting with their own hidden agendas, possibly ones you don't like. A written agenda puts you in the driver's seat.

Being an effective chair

Your first job is to begin the meeting promptly if you're in charge and to arrive at all meetings on time or a little early, whether you're in charge or not. In some cases, you may need to bend your starting-on-time rule if the boss or some other very important attendee is late. Even so, you probably shouldn't delay for more than about 10 minutes. Most people are late at least once in a while, but frequent lateness is a subtle way of telling others that they're not important — not a good management strategy!

Another important job for the meeting host is to stick to the agenda. Though you've sent the agenda to all participants in advance, you may want to bring along copies to distribute. Keep an eye on your watch so that you can hold up your end of the bargain — participants arrive at your meeting on time, and you do your best to get them out on time.

If you're chairing a meeting, you also are responsible for taking notes. Though other participants may take their own notes, they may not be comprehensive. You want to make sure that everyone who attended the meeting ends up with the same record of what happened. If you're lucky enough to have an assistant, you can ask that person to take the notes and you can simply approve them.

Unless your organization has a specific format for meeting notes, include the date and time of the meeting, list of attendees, agenda, discussion highlights for each agenda item, any decisions made, and any responsibilities assigned.

Participating in conference calls and video conferences

Conference calls and video conferences are wonderful tools when you use them properly; however, these electronic get-togethers require attention to etiquette. When you're on a conference call,

✔ **Put your phone on mute unless you're actually speaking.** What is amazingly hard to remember is to take yourself off mute when you have something to say.

✔ **Listening to the call on speakerphone is fine but pick up the handset when it's your turn to talk.** Never carry on side conversations or type during a conference call.

✔ **Saying your name before you begin talking is a good idea.** If you think everyone recognizes your voice, you're probably wrong. Introduce yourself before the first time you speak and then again if you haven't spoken for a while.

Video conferencing is an entirely different ballgame, and it can be a little disconcerting the first few times you participate. On most systems, there's a slight delay between sound and motion, so wait a few seconds before speaking to make sure you don't talk over anyone on the other end. In addition, you naturally want to look at the monitor while you're speaking, because that's where you see the other people.

Extra-strength procrastination cures

Procrastination is like a credit card: Fun when you use it, painful when the bill comes in. Let's come back to this section later. (Just kidding.)

No matter what your excuse for procrastinating, here's a medicine chest full of cures. These ideas work — if you don't procrastinate about using them.

✔ **Think back to times you've procrastinated.** What were the consequences? Has it hurt your career? Your relationships? Your self-esteem? Sometimes, looking at the price you've paid for procrastinating can motivate you to not let it happen ever again.

✔ **Think back to a time you didn't procrastinate on an unpleasant task.** What kept you from procrastinating then? A rigorous schedule? Someone nagging you? Does that give you a clue as to how to beat your current procrastination? What would you say to get your twin to quit procrastinating?

✔ **Figure out *where* you're least likely to procrastinate.** If at home you play too much with your dog or take too many tea breaks, consider working somewhere else.

✔ **Figure out *when* you're least likely to procrastinate.** Block out that time to get things done and write it in your date book, just as you do an appointment with a friend.

✔ **Just do it!** Do it now, even if you don't feel like doing it. Fight through the discomfort and think how good you'll feel after you've put in a good hour.

✔ **Don't think about how much work you have ahead of you.** That can overwhelm you into procrastination. Instead, think like a mountain climber. Just put one foot in front of the other, and when you get to the top and look down, you'll be amazed at how far you've gotten.

✔ **Use a 10-second task to get you rolling.** Before you start or when you reach a hard part, you may be tempted to grab some coffee, call your friend, or trim your nails. That's when you have to force yourself to get working (on the task, not your nails).

✔ **Create an artificial deadline.** Do you wait until the last minute because you need time pressure to motivate you? Give yourself an insanely short amount of time to get a task done: "I want to have lunch at 12. Let's see if I can write a draft of my report by then."

✔ **Find someone to check in with.** Some folks can go it alone, but many procrastinators find that it helps to have someone to check in with.

Top timesaving organizational tips

Get your act together with these quick and easy hints:

Papers

✔ When you pick up a piece of paper, ask yourself, "What is it? Why do I have this piece of paper? What am I going to do with it?" If you don't have a good answer, throw away the paper or recycle it.

✔ If you need to keep a document, put it in a file folder. Write file labels by hand. Use expandable file pockets to hold your file folders. Avoid hanging files.

✔ When you jot down a Master To-Do List, don't worry about priorities. Just write each task as it comes up on a standard size piece of paper. Review the Master List throughout the day and ask yourself, "What's the most important thing I must do now?"

Telephone

✔ Make a list of the items that you want to discuss with the person you're calling and arrange their sequence so you discuss the most important items first.

✔ Have at your fingertips the files or other papers to which you need to refer.

✔ If you have long-winded callers, limit the length of time that a person can leave a message to 60, 90, or 120 seconds at most.

Participating in the meetings

As a meeting participant, your first rule is to follow the procedures that the host adopts. Also, avoid the temptation to interrupt other speakers, sigh loudly, roll your eyes, or otherwise express your contempt when someone else is speaking. Take notes if you want to. If you're not fond of note-taking and it looks like someone else is, then don't.

You're obliged to stay for the entire meeting unless you have another appointment or another commitment. If so, at the beginning of the meeting let your chair know at what time you have to leave and then leave quietly at that time. If you're unlucky enough to be a participant in a meeting whose chair has not set an adjournment time and the meeting is dragging on and on, pass a note to the chair explaining your other commitment, stand up, excuse yourself quickly, and leave without making a show of it.

E-mail

✔ Try to keep your e-mail messages on one screen.

✔ If you're including a list of items, use a bulleted or numbered list.

✔ If you must send a long message, attach the file as an enclosure or attachment. The e-mail message itself should be a brief-but-thorough explanation about the document you're sending. Don't forget to include the purpose of the document, detailed instructions regarding what the recipient is supposed to do with the document, and the date you need a response.

Managing Others

The heart of management boils down to getting things done through others. This process extends to motivating, coaching, disciplining, and sometimes firing employees.

Eight awesome ways to encourage creativity

To remain vital, organizations need to constantly renew themselves. To stimulate more creative thought:

✔ Encourage others to express their opinions.

✔ Don't dismiss an idea without discussing it.

- Ask and encourage questions.
- Permit employees to attend seminars on innovative practices and concepts, both in and outside your industry.
- Require an idea as admission to a routine meeting.
- Carry a notebook to record your brainstorms.
- Start a book club at work.
- Laugh.

Delegating, in six pain-free steps

Delegation doesn't just happen — you have to work at it. Here are six steps to effective delegation:

1. **Communicate the task.** Describe exactly what you want done, when you want it done, and what end results you expect.

2. **Furnish context for the task.** Explain why the task needs to be done, its importance in the overall scheme of things, and possible complications that may arise during its performance.

3. **Determine standards.** Agree on the standards that you'll use to measure the success of a task's completion. These standards should be realistic and attainable.

4. **Grant authority.** You must grant employees the authority that's necessary to complete the task without constant roadblocks or standoffs with other employees.

5. **Provide support.** Determine the resources necessary for your employees to complete the task and then provide them with the resources. Successfully completing a task may require money, training, advice, and other resources.

6. **Get commitment.** Make sure that your employee has accepted the assignment. Confirm your expectations and your employee's understanding of and commitment to completing the task.

Giving constructive feedback

Constructive feedback is information-specific, issue-focused, and based on observations. It comes in two varieties:

- **Positive feedback** is news or input to an employee about an effort well done.

 ✔ **Negative feedback** is news to an employee about an effort that
 needs improvement. Negative feedback doesn't mean a terrible
 performance, rather a performance in which the outcomes
 delivered should be better.

Both positive and negative constructive feedback come across as
more objective, specific, and nonjudgmental than praise and criticism, which are focused on the person and based on opinions or
feelings. Constructive feedback encourages discussion, so you and
your employee can learn more about the situation and, if needed,
set a positive course of action.

Expressing appreciation and concern

In positive feedback situations, express appreciation. You can express
appreciation in many ways: "Great job," "Thanks for all your help on
this project," or "I really appreciate the good work you did here."
Appreciation alone is praise. Yet when you add it to the *specifics* of
constructive feedback, your message carries an extra oomph of
sincerity.

Be careful not to take the positive for granted. As you look at the
performance of your employees, more than likely you see more
outcomes of positive performance occurring than outcomes that
warrant negative feedback. Yet, often, employees hear about performance only when something goes wrong.

In negative feedback situations, express concern. A tone of concern
communicates a sense of importance and care and provides the
appropriate level of sincerity to the message. Tones such as anger,
frustration, disappointment, and the ever-popular sarcasm tend to
color the language of the message and turn attempts at negative
feedback into criticism. The content of the message gets lost in the
noise and harshness.

Sometimes managers attempt to soften criticism by first saying,
"Now don't take this personally." After that's been said, the employee
will likely become defensive. The purpose of negative feedback is to
create awareness that can lead to correction or improvement in performance. If you can't give negative feedback in a helpful manner, in
the language and tone of concern, you defeat its purpose.

When giving negative feedback, you may want to apply the timeline
of *ASAR* (as soon as reasonable/ready — that is, when *you're* ready).
Sometimes you need time to cool off and get your thoughts in order
before you give negative feedback. Tomorrow is still timely, and
your feedback can come across as far more constructive.

The eight biggest mistakes managers make

Forgetting who pays the bills: Unfortunately, the very nature of management often means that managers spend little or no time with customers. Yet customers need to be at the top of the list of people that managers serve because they pay the bills, and employees are at the top as well because they directly serve the customers.

Getting caught up in the red tape: Some people think being a manager means figuring out innovative ways to slow down or stop creative employee suggestions rather than encouraging and rewarding them. In most organizations — chock full of policies, procedures, and rules — you can always find plenty of paperwork to hide behind. Rather than naming reasons why you can't do something, start thinking in terms of how you can do something.

Not setting clear goals with employees: Goals give people something to strive for — making their jobs more interesting and fulfilling. Managers who fail to set clear goals end up with employees who are confused about their priorities and who probably won't be heading in the direction you think they should.

Talking more than they listen: Smart managers do much more listening than talking. Talented individuals can be found from the very bottom rung of the corporate ladder to the top. Failing to hear all those good ideas because you're busy promoting your personal agenda is a big mistake.

Failing to delegate: Focus on doing the tasks that you're uniquely responsible for (allocating people, money, equipment, and information) and allow employees to do their jobs. Delegate not only the responsibility to get tasks done but also the authority employees need to complete jobs without having to run to you for permission every time a decision needs to be made.

Communicating too little, too late: Information must be available to the people who need it — in real time and as completely as possible. The ability of an organization to identify the latest, most relevant information, process it, and distribute it efficiently to all affected workers is a definite competitive advantage.

Not showing employees that they care: Studies show that the number one motivator for employees isn't cash, vacations, time off, or stock options but a simple verbal thank you from one's boss. Don't get so caught up in your work that you forget to tell your employees "thank you" for a job well done.

Forgetting how to have fun: Because work is serious is precisely why you have to make your workplace fun. Having fun is one of the easiest ways to boost morale in an organization.

Talking face-to-face

Give constructive feedback person-to-person, not through messengers of technology. The nature of constructive feedback is verbal and informal. Talk to the employee face-to-face — or by phone when you physically can't be together. E-mail and voice mail don't work for constructive feedback because they don't allow live, two-way conversation to follow. Nor does the sincerity of the message come across as well, whether it's positive or negative feedback.

State observations, not interpretations

Observations are what you see occur; *interpretations* are your analysis or opinion of what you see occur. Tell what you've noticed, not what you think of it, and report the behavior you notice at a concrete level, rather than as a characterization of the behavior. Observations have a far more factual and nonjudgmental aspect than do interpretations.

Communicating

Communicating is so much more that just talking and listening. Good communication also includes timing, tone, body language, and a host of other factors. The following sections can get you communicating better.

Eight workplace communications goofs

Avoid the following office communication faux pas:

- ✔ **Using e-mail to express concerns.** Instead, go to the source to work out problems in person.

- ✔ **Talking too much in sales situations.** Instead, try to understand the customer's needs and then say something to indicate how you can help meet those needs.

- ✔ **Responding to requests by immediately saying it can't be done.** Instead, emphasize what you *can* do and *when* you can meet the request.

- ✔ **Saying yes when you really don't mean it.** Instead, express your concerns constructively and offer alternatives as to what you think may work better in the situation.

✔ **Sitting by quietly and passively when people discuss issues with you.** Instead, interact with the message you're hearing and provide verbal feedback to check your understanding of the message.

✔ **Dwelling on what's wrong or who's at fault when dealing with problem situations.** Instead, put your focus on working out solutions with others and on how to make the situation better.

✔ **Focusing on yourself — what you like and don't like — as you receive others' messages.** Instead, shift your focus from yourself to concentrating on your speaker's message and work to understand what that message means without passing judgment on it.

✔ **Pushing forward with your idea and disregarding concerns that people have with it.** Instead, listen to and acknowledge the concerns and address them. Sometimes the best way to gain support for an idea about which others have reservations is to show that you hear those concerns.

Six secrets to listening well

In conversations, make it your goal to show understanding of what the speaker truly means. To this end:

✔ Concentrate on what the speaker has to say.

✔ Listen for content and emotion to understand the entire message. Tune into *how* the message is being said, not just what the words are.

✔ Maintain steady eye contact so speakers know your attention is with them.

✔ Give verbal feedback — in one sentence — to confirm your understanding of the message.

✔ Stay patient when people talk to you.

✔ Acknowledge feelings that are important to the message you're hearing. Keep your tone sincere and nonjudgmental when you respond.

Handling the office jerk

Some people don't seem to care whether they hurt someone else or tell a joke at someone else's expense. When you're the target of such behavior, remembering that the perpetrator is almost always acting out of insecurity is difficult to do. Sometimes you can ignore the situation, but more often you need this person's input in some part of your job. Here are some tips to keep in mind so that you can respond appropriately and stay in control:

- **Don't resist the person's remarks.** Instead, validate them. Refusing to strike back eventually bores your attacker.

- **Acknowledge the truth.** Comments that hurt the most often have an element of truth in them. If you know your own flaws, you can accept the kernel of truth without agreeing with the way it was said.

- **Show off the person.** If someone makes a disparaging remark to you in front of a group of people, call attention to that person. With an expansive gesture towards the jerk, say something to the group like, "Well, gee, that didn't sound very nice to everybody did it?" Then pause and let peer pressure take over.

Communicating nonverbally

Assertive speaking is about delivering your message in a positive, direct, and confident manner while maintaining respect for the person or persons to whom you're expressing that message. When your audience feels respected, you'll be effective in your interactions at work, or anywhere for that matter. It's interesting that the tools for assertive speaking are all nonverbal. That's right, they have nothing to do with *what* you say but rather *how* you say it!

Using eye contact to get your message across

Your eyes lend credibility to your spoken messages, give your message much of its meaning, and affect whether the listener believes and trusts your message. To use eye contact assertively:

- **Make steady eye contact.** The idea is to look at people when you're talking to them. Steady eye contact is the key. *Steady* does not, however, mean *constant*. Blinking and occasional glances away are expected and normal.

- **Maintain eye contact.** No set time exists for maintaining eye contact and then momentarily glancing away. In general, eye contact can range comfortably from 6 to 20 seconds in one-on-one interactions, whereas in group situations, the time is less per individual — 3 to 6 seconds — because you want to address everybody in the group.

- **Look in the right places.** Look directly at your listener's face, near the eyes. Looking above and below the face captures less of the listener's attention and can make the listener uncomfortable.

When speaking to others, avoid eye-contact behaviors that make your message less than assertive, such as staring, glaring, looking away, darting glances, blinking excessively, and focusing in on one person.

Using body language to get your message across

Body language refers to everything you do with your body to express your message, including facial expressions, posture, and gestures. You can use body language in ways that positively engage others in your message and that enable you to come across as confident, animated, and relaxed:

- ✔ **Posture:** Sit up and face your receiver as a means of expressing your message assertively. Leaning forward a bit is sometimes helpful as well. Sitting up also helps put strength in your voice.

- ✔ **Facial expressions:** Technically, you can't see your face when you're talking, yet you can sense what your face is doing. The idea in expressing yourself assertively is to show a positive position through your facial expressions.

  You've probably heard the expression about putting a smile in your voice. The muscles in your face change with a smile and help pick up the inflection in your voice.

- ✔ **Gestures:** You may have been told when you were younger not to talk with your hands. What's wrong with using your hands to say something? Not a thing! In fact, you're more dangerous (in terms of boring other people) if you use no gestures at all when you speak.

  Use gestures to come across assertively, to help your message flow properly, and to punctuate or emphasize key points when you're talking. People often do just that in casual and social conversations. Just apply that same effort to your important messages at work.

Avoid body language that can create negative responses, such as:

- ✔ **Slouching:** When you sink into a comfy office chair, you come across as too relaxed. Less energy gets behind your voice as well.

- ✔ **Invading space:** This pitfall occurs more when people are standing and attempting to engage in lively conversation — and they're getting too close for comfort to the other person. Certainly, if the other person is leaning away from you, that's a sure sign you've crossed the comfort zone of physical space.

Be sure to talk to people on a *level plane.* Level plane means being physically at the same level, which can be done only when you're seated together. A conversation of a minute or two when you're standing with someone or when you're walking somewhere is different. When you have important matters to discuss, have a seat with the person with whom you're speaking. When you're both seated, a sense of ease comes into the conversation, and it no longer matters how tall each of you is. You're physically equal and, therefore, more comfortable talking with each other.

✔ **Looking blank:** Showing no emotion conveys a lack of feeling for your own message. If you look disinterested, others may feel that way too.

✔ **Looking stern:** Furrowed eyebrows, frowning, and scowling are uninviting, if not intimidating. Listeners, more often than not, will want to disengage. Also, stern looks have a tendency to increase or exaggerate the sharpness in your tone of voice.

✔ **Displaying threatening gestures:** Finger pointing at someone else or pounding a fist on the table come across aggressively rather than assertively. Such behaviors intimidate, if not disgust, your listener — not exactly positive motivators.

✔ **Folding your arms:** Folding your arms when speaking is different from folding them as you listen. When you're listening — as long as you don't look closed off — folding your arms helps you appear relaxed and receptive to hearing someone else's message. When you're speaking, however, folding your arms makes you come across as stiffer and less interested in your own message — signals that are the opposite of what you want to convey.

✔ **Exhibiting distracting habits:** Picking, scratching, twirling hair, and pulling on jewelry are a few examples of habits that people exhibit when they're talking to someone else. These habits bring attention to you rather than what you have to say; they either turn people off or make them want to laugh for all the wrong reasons.

Public Speaking

Nobody is a "born speaker." Demosthenes — the famous speaker of ancient Greece — was a shy, stammering introvert who taught himself to become a public presenter by rehearsing with rocks in his mouth. If all you have in your mouth is your foot, then you're way ahead of the game.

What makes (and breaks) a presentation

You've probably noticed that some presenters are organized and confident and, as a result, really engage your attention. You've probably seen others who were a chore to listen to and didn't seem to know what they were doing up there on the platform. Table 16-1 gives some pointers on what speakers do right and what you want to avoid.

Table 16-1	Presentation Do's and Don'ts
Pitfalls to avoid	*Positive impressions to pursue*
Looking or sounding nervous: Fidgeting, standing stiffly, and other nonverbal behaviors focus the audience's attention on the speaker's high anxiety level rather than on the talk. This behavior includes sounding monotone, speaking too softly, or making little direct eye contact.	**Displaying confidence and sounding positive:** Sounding authoritative as opposed to authoritarian, and definitive rather than hesitant. Verbal and nonverbal messages match and have an upbeat feel. Even when talking about tough issues, key points are made in a positive way.
Coming across as disorganized: This type of presentation has no flow or direction. The speaker jumps back and forth with various points and sometimes ends up rambling.	**Being well organized:** Presentations should flow in a logical sequence. The points expressed connect in an orderly fashion. Thus the presentation is easy to follow.
Overloading with data, especially using overloaded slides: The speaker is full of details — so much so that what's important in the message gets lost in the minutiae. Slides or overhead transparencies crammed with too much information lose their value, and people stop focusing.	**Giving you a message:** You walk away from the presentation knowing exactly what was important. You grasp the main ideas or themes clearly and don't get lost in detail.
Being vague: When the speaker is vague, all you hear are generalizations and platitudes with no specifics and no substance — a talk about a whole lot of nothing. Likewise, when speakers read nearly every item on the slides or handouts, they insult the audience's intelligence and render their materials nonsupportive.	**Relating well to the audience:** The presenter understands your issues, speaks to them, and does so in language you can understand. You get information that's useful and relevant.

Pitfalls to avoid	Positive impressions to pursue
Sounding like a know-it-all or using too much jargon: Sounding authoritarian replaces sounding authoritative. An arrogant tone and overconfident voice and language come into play.	**Showing sincerity and making your topic understandable:** The presenter's tone and language come across with care and respect. Everyday terms and examples convey a certain genuineness so others want to listen.
Rambling and having no closure: A rambling speaker just won't quit. The speaker's points are lost as he talks on and on. In some presentations, the only way you know it's over is that the speaker stops talking.	**Getting to the point:** The speaker is direct, clear, and, most important, concise. You walk away understanding and remembering the key points because they're stated succinctly.
Trying to be funny too often: Humor in a formal presentation can be a nice touch, but with forced humor or just too much humor, the seriousness of the message gets lost, or worse, wisecracks alienate the audience.	**Having enthusiasm:** In their own style, whether low-key or full of energy, these speakers come across as animated. They sound alive and interested in what they have to say and, as a result, make their topic interesting and worth hearing.
Tinkering with the AV equipment: When speakers become preoccupied with trying to get their audiovisual equipment to work, they tend to occupy the audience's attention with everything but the speech.	**Using visual aids to support the presentation:** Visual aids serve to enhance and work in tandem with the oral message. The speaker uses them as points to talk from or to help make a point.

Overcoming stage fright

Perhaps the biggest challenge you face in giving a formal presentation is yourself. *Stage fright,* a feeling of anxiety or nervousness that arises when you're expected to perform in front of others, is a normal occurrence.

Here are five tips that help you move from high anxiety to relative composure:

✔ **Come prepared.** Be in command of your material and how you want to present it. Winging it (just showing up and trying to talk off the cuff) increases the pressure you feel.

✔ **Recognize that nervousness can be a positive motivator.** You want to have your energy up and not feel flat, so nervousness can provide that spark.

✔ **Use notes to keep you on track and composed.** No need to memorize your presentation — but having a written script of your whole talk may lead you to read the script, losing eye contact with the audience and sounding monotone. Note cards serve as a reference to glance at periodically and to then talk from to your group.

✔ **If you stumble, move ahead.** Musicians make mistakes all the time when they perform. In most cases, they're the only ones who know that they didn't hit a note just right. People in the audience generally don't notice because the musicians just keep on playing. The same principle applies when you're giving a presentation. If you don't say that word just right or make the point as clearly as you wanted, keep going.

✔ **Don't point out that you're nervous.** When you bring attention to anything that has nothing to do with your presentation, you take your audience's attention away from your talk.

How you feel on the inside often has little to do with how you're seen on the outside. People often don't know that you feel nervous unless you tell them. Remember that they came to hear your presentation, not to put you on the spot or make you uncomfortable.

Part V
Getting Personal: Personal Finance

"My portfolio's gonna take a hit for this."

In this part . . .

*L*ike a good map or aerial photograph, this part helps you get a bird's eye view of all your money matters. You find out how to stretch your income, invest like a Wall Street guru, protect your family and possessions with cost-effective insurance, and get a loan in order to purchase that new home, business, education, or boat. This part also points out the biggest potential pitfalls (credit card debt and risky stocks, to name just two) and how you can avoid them.

Chapter 17

Managing Your Money

· ·

· ·

*E*veryone should know the basics when it comes to saving money for the short term and, more importantly, for the long term. Is your spending out of control? How big is your nest egg? What are your financial goals? Take a hard look at your budget and your spending habits and then use the tips in this chapter to help you get what you want.

Budgeting and Saving Money

Debt that you use to invest in your future is *good debt:* Borrowing money for education or your own business results in long-term pay-offs. Consumer debt is *bad debt:* Money you pay for high-interest auto loans and credit card balances are for consumer items that depreciate in value.

Set up a budget

Set up a budget to help you move from knowing how much you spend to successfully reducing your spending:

1. **Analyze your current spending.**

2. **Calculate how much more you'd like to save each month.**

3. **Decide where to make your spending cuts.**

Join a wholesale superstore

Wholesale warehouse clubs like Costco and Sam's Club charge about 30 to 40 percent less than retail grocers.

✔ Buy in bulk at a wholesale club to save money and make fewer shopping trips. You'll have more supplies at home, so there's less need to eat out. You'll reduce visits to the local grocer, who charges higher retail prices.

✔ Perishables run the risk of living up to their name, so don't buy what you can't use. Repackage bulk packs into smaller quantities for the freezer. If you're single, shop with a friend or two and split the bulk package.

✔ Be careful shopping at the warehouse clubs — you may be tempted to buy items you don't really need: electronics, furniture, clothing, toys, and giant canisters of M&Ms. Try not to make impulse purchases, and be especially careful when you have kids in tow.

Eat out more frugally

Eating meals out or getting take-out can save you time but racks up big bills if done too often or too lavishly.

✔ Avoid ordering beverages, especially alcohol. Most restaurants make big profits on beverages. Drink water instead; add zing with lemon or lime slices. (Water is also healthful and reduces the likelihood of your wanting a nap after a big meal.)

✔ Vegetarian dishes, including pasta and rice dishes, generally cost less than meat-based entrees (and are generally healthier for you).

✔ Skip the appetizer and dessert, share it with a dining companion, or enjoy these courses at home.

Save on housing

Housing and all the costs associated with it (utilities, furniture, appliances, and, if you're a homeowner, maintenance and repairs) can gobble a large chunk of your monthly income.

Try the following to reduce your rent:

- ✔ **Move to a lower-cost rental.** The less you spend renting, the more you can save toward buying your own place. Just be sure to factor in all the costs of a new location, including possibly higher commuting costs.

- ✔ **Share a rental.** Your rental costs go way down, and you get more home for your rental dollars. Roommates can be a hassle but can also be a plus — you meet new people and have someone else to blame if the kitchen's a mess.

- ✔ **Negotiate annual rental increases.** If your local rental market is soft or your living quarters are deteriorating, you have some leverage and power. State your case: You've been a responsible tenant, and your research shows comparable rentals going for less. If you can't stave off the rent increase, try to wrangle some improvements to the place.

- ✔ **Buy rather than rent.** Owning your own place should be cheaper than renting, and you have something to show for it in the end. If you buy real estate with a 30-year fixed-rate mortgage, your mortgage payment (your biggest ownership expense) remains constant. Property taxes, maintenance, and insurance costs change with inflation.

Try to minimize your mortgage:

- ✔ **Rent out a room.** Check out the renter thoroughly: Get references, run a credit report, and talk about ground rules and expectations before sharing your space. Don't forget to check with your insurance company to see whether your homeowner's policy needs adjustments to cover potential liability from renting.

- ✔ **Refinance your mortgage.** Keep up-to-date on mortgage rates. If interest rates are lower than when you obtained your current mortgage, you may be able to save money by refinancing.

- ✔ **Reduce utility costs.** New appliances are much more energy-efficient than old ones. If your dishwasher or refrigerator is 10 years old or more, consider buying a new one. Insulate to save on heating and air-conditioning bills. Install water flow regulators in showerheads and toilet bowls. When planting your yard, don't select water-guzzling plants and keep your lawn area reasonable.

Spend less on looking good

Your appearance and good grooming don't have to overwhelm your budget.

Try the following to control clothing costs:

- ✔ **Don't chase the latest fashions.** Buy basic, classic clothing, which doesn't go out of style. If you want the effect of a new wardrobe every year, rotate your wardrobe every second or third year and freshen your look with accessories.

- ✔ **Avoid dry-cleanables.** When you buy clothing, try to stick with cottons and machine-washable synthetics rather than wools or silks that require dry cleaning. Check fabric-care labels before you buy.

Try the following to slash salon expenses:

- ✔ **Rather than scheduling a hair appointment every four or six weeks, see if you can wait an additional week or two between cuts.** Over the course of a year, you can save a bundle!

- ✔ **Periodically, go to a no-frills stylist for maintenance after getting a fabulous cut at a more expensive place.** If you're daring, you can try getting your hair cut at a local training school.

- ✔ **Cut your children's hair.** Buy a simple-to-use home hair-care kit with an electric shaver — no more agonizing trips with little ones to have their hair cut by a "stranger," and the kit pays for itself after just a couple of cuts!

- ✔ **Do your own manicures and pedicures.** Besides saving on regular visits to the salon, you also reduce any chances of getting an infection from tools that haven't been sanitized properly.

Plenty of research shows that makeup from the drugstore is just as good and lots less expensive than designer brands from the department store.

Don't gamble

Getting hooked on the dream of winning (at keno, slots, horses, dogs, day trading, whatever) is easy and tempting, but the odds of winning are always against you. If you go just for the entertainment, take only what you can afford to lose. Gamblers Anonymous (www.gamblersanonymous.org) can help those for whom gambling has become an addiction.

Kick the smoking habit

About 25 percent of all Americans still smoke. Americans spend more than $45 billion annually on tobacco products — that's a staggering $900 per year per tobacco user. The increased medical costs and lost work time costs are even greater, estimated at more than $50 billion every year. Of course, if you continue to smoke, you may eliminate the need to save for retirement.

Check with local hospitals for smoking-cessation programs. The American Lung Association offers Freedom from Smoking clinics around the country and online at www.lungusa.org/ffs/index.html. The National Cancer Institute (800-4CANCER) and the Office on Smoking and Health at the Centers for Disease Control (1600 Clifton Road, Atlanta, GA 30333; phone 770-488-5703) offer free information guides containing effective methods to stop smoking.

Lower your transportation fees

Purchasing the best car you can afford and using it wisely can save you big dollars — so can other transportation alternatives.

- ✔ **Replace high-cost cars.** Nothing says that you're stuck with a car until the bitter end. Dump your expensive car and get something more financially manageable. The sooner you switch, the more money you save. Getting rid of a car on a lease is more of a challenge, but it *can* be done.

- ✔ **Buy regular unleaded gas.** "Super-duper-ultra-premium" gasoline isn't worth the extra expense. Unless your owner's manual indicates otherwise, buy regular unleaded gas. And don't use credit cards to buy your gas if you have to pay a higher price to do so.

- ✔ **Service your car regularly.** Regular car maintenance (oil changes, hose checks) saves you dough in the long run by extending the operating life of the car. Servicing your car also reduces the chances that your car will break down in the middle of nowhere, which requires a humongous towing charge to a service station.

- ✔ **Buy commuter passes.** Purchase train, bus, or subway passes to reduce the cost of commuting. Many toll bridges also have booklets of tickets that you can buy at a discount. Some booths don't advertise that they offer these plans — so ask.

Preparing Financially for Major Life Changes

With a major life change looming, procrastination can be costly. You might overspend and incur high-cost debts, lack proper insurance, or take unnecessary risks. Early preparation can prevent these pitfalls.

Getting married

Even if you largely agree about your financial goals and strategies, managing as two is different than managing as one.

- ✔ **Consider taxes.** You're more likely to be hit with a higher combined tax bill when married if both you and your partner earn above-average incomes. The only way to know what will happen to your tax bill is to get out a tax return and plug in the relevant numbers and see what the IRS will do to you after you're married.

- ✔ **Move the wedding date.** If you're flexible in terms of the timing of your wedding and a late-in-the year wedding will cause you to pay much more in taxes, consider waiting until early the following year.

- ✔ **Discuss and set joint goals.** After you're married, you and your spouse should set aside time once a year or every few years to discuss personal and financial goals for the years ahead. If for no other reason, talking about where you want to go helps ensure that you're rowing your financial boat in the same direction.

Starting a family

The more efficiently you manage your time and money, the better able you'll be to have a sane, happy, and financially successful life as a parent.

- ✔ **Understand your benefits.** Many larger employers offer some maternity leave for women and, in rare-but-increasing cases, for men. At some employers, the leaves are paid and with others, they're not. Understand the options and the financial ramifications before you consider the leave and ideally before you get pregnant.

- ✔ **Rewrite your will.** If you don't have a will, make one now. Name a guardian in the will who will be responsible for raising your children should you and your spouse both pass away. Don't rely on the courts to choose a guardian for you.

✓ **Enroll your newborn in your health insurance plan.** Most insurers give you about a month or so to enroll. New parents tend to forget to do things amidst the whirlwind of time-consuming parenting responsibilities.

✓ **Get Junior a Social Security number.** Without a Social Security number, you can't claim your child as a dependent (and get that tax break).

Caring for aging parents

Many nonprofit organizations offer information and sometimes even counseling to families grappling with caring for elderly parents. Check your state's department of insurance as well as recommendations from local hospitals and doctors.

✓ **Try to be your parents' health advocate.** Speak with your parents' doctors to understand their current medical condition and need for various medications and to help coordinate caregivers. Visit nursing homes and speak with prospective care providers.

✓ **If you're financially supporting your parents, you may be eligible for a number of tax credits and deductions for elder care.** Some employers' flexible benefit plans, for example, allow you to put away money on a pre-tax basis to pay for the care of your parents. Also explore the dependent care tax credit, which you can take on your federal income tax Form 1040.

✓ **Talk with your parents.** Parents don't like talking and thinking about their demise and usually feel awkward discussing it with their children. Discussing wills, living wills, living trusts, and estate-planning strategies, however, can broaden your awareness of their situation and can improve their plans to both their benefit and your own.

Divorcing

Money and disagreements over money are certainly a contributing factor to marital unhappiness. Unfortunately, in many relationships, money is wielded as power by the spouse who earns more of it.

✓ **Detail resources and priorities.** Draw up a list of all the assets and liabilities that you and your spouse have. Be sure that you get all the financial facts, including investment account records and statements. After you know the whole picture, begin to think about what is and is not important to you financially and otherwise.

✔ **Educate yourself about personal finance and legal issues.** Divorce sometimes forces financially unaware spouses to get a crash course in personal finance at a difficult emotional time. Visit a bookstore and pick up one or two good legal guides about divorce.

✔ **If you're covered under your spouse's employer insurance plan, be sure to set the wheels in motion to get those coverages replaced.** If you or your children are still financially dependent on your spouse post-divorce, be sure that the divorce agreement mandates life insurance coverage. Also, don't forget to revise your will.

✔ **With changes to your income, expenses, assets, liabilities, and future needs, your retirement plan surely needs an overhaul post-divorce.**

Receiving a windfall

A flood of money (inheritance, stock options, business success, or lottery winnings) can cause many problems if you're psychologically and organizationally unprepared.

✔ **Decide on your own terms whom to hire and then seek them out.** Brokers and financial advisors may flood you with marketing materials, telephone solicitations, and lunch-date requests. They want to convert your money into their income either by selling you investment and other financial products or by managing your money. Stay away from the sharks, educate yourself, and take charge of your own financial moves.

✔ **Recognize the emotional side of coming into a lot of money.** One of the side effects of accumulating wealth quickly is that you may have feelings of guilt or otherwise be unhappy, especially if you expected money to solve your problems.

✔ **One of the simplest and best investments you can make is to pay off your debts.** You generally borrow money to buy things that you otherwise couldn't buy in one fell swoop. When you have plenty of money, getting rid of debt is a good move.

✔ **To protect your wealth, don't keep it all in one pot.** Mutual funds are an ideally diversified, professionally managed investment vehicle to consider. And if you want your money to continue growing, consider the wealth-building investments — stocks, real estate, and small-business options.

Are you a spending addict?

Officially started in 1976, Debtors Anonymous (DA) is a nonprofit organization that provides support, primarily through group meetings, to people trying to break their debting and spending habits. DA is modeled after the 12-step Alcoholics Anonymous program.

If you answer Yes to at least 8 of the following 15 questions, you may be developing or already have a compulsive debting habit:

1. Are your debts making your home life unhappy?

2. Does the pressure of your debts distract you from your daily work?

3. Are your debts affecting your reputation?

4. Do your debts cause you to think less of yourself?

5. Have you ever given false information in order to obtain credit?

6. Have you ever made unrealistic promises to your creditors?

7. Does the pressure of your debts make you careless of the welfare of your family?

8. Do you ever fear that your employer, family, or friends will learn the extent of your total indebtedness?

9. When faced with a difficult financial situation, does the prospect of borrowing give you an inordinate feeling of relief?

10. Does the pressure of your debts cause you to have difficulty sleeping?

11. Has the pressure of your debts ever caused you to consider getting drunk?

12. Have you ever borrowed money without giving adequate consideration to the rate of interest you're required to pay?

13. Do you usually expect a negative response when you're subject to a credit investigation?

14. Have you ever developed a strict regimen for paying off your debts, only to break it under pressure?

15. Do you justify your debts by telling yourself that you're superior to the "other" people, and when you get your "break," you'll be out of debt?

To find a Debtors Anonymous support group in your area, check your local phone directory (in the "Business" section). Or write to DA for meeting locations in your area and a literature order form at the following address: General Service Office of Debtors Anonymous, P.O. Box 920888, Needham, MA 02492-0009. Or go online at www.debtorsanonymous.org/.

Ending the spend-and-debt cycle

Regardless of how you deal with paying off your debt, you're in real danger of falling back into old habits. Backsliding happens not only to people who file bankruptcy but also to those who use savings or home equity to eliminate their debt.

- ✔ **Limit what you can spend.** Go shopping with a small amount of cash and no plastic or checks. That way you can only spend what little cash you have with you!

- ✔ **Replace your credit card with a charge card.** A charge card (such as the American Express Card) requires you to pay your balance in full each billing period. You have no credit line or interest charges.

Taming Taxes

Countless illegal ways are available to reduce your employment income, but you could very well end up with a heap of penalties, extra interest charges on top of the taxes you owe, or even jail.

Contributing to a retirement plan

A retirement plan is one of the few painless and completely legal ways to reduce your taxable employment income. Besides reducing your taxes, you build up a nest egg so that you don't have to work for the rest of your life.

- ✔ From your taxable income you can deduct money that you tuck away into employer-based retirement plans, such as 401(k) or 403(b) accounts, or into self-employed plans like SEP-IRAs or Keoghs. Take advantage of automatic deductions from your paycheck — you won't even notice!

- ✔ Should your employer not offer the option of saving money through a retirement plan, lobby the benefits and human resources departments. If they resist, you might add this to your list of reasons to consider other employment.

- ✔ If your employer doesn't offer a retirement savings plan, individual retirement account (IRA) contributions may or may not be tax-deductible, based on your circumstances. You should first exhaust contributions to accounts that are tax-deductible.

Organizing your deductions

Setting up a filing system can be a big time-saver when completing your tax return.

The simple approach

If your financial life is uncomplicated, just set up a folder that's labeled with something easy to remember ("2002 Taxes" is a brilliant choice) and put the following in it:

- ✔ Your tax booklet
- ✔ Form W-2 (Tax summary statements on wages paid by your employer)
- ✔ Form 1099 (Investment income)
- ✔ Form 1098 (Home mortgage interest)

The thorough approach

Organize the bills you pay into individual folders during the entire year. This method is essential if you own your own business and need to tabulate your expenditures for office supplies each year. No one is going to send you a form totaling your yearly office expenditures — you're on your own.

The software approach

Software programs can help organize your tax information during the year and can save you time and accounting fees come tax-preparation time. The best programs "interview" you to gather the necessary information and select the appropriate forms based on your responses.

Finding a Good Financial Planner

Locating a good financial planner who is willing to work with the not-yet-rich-and-famous and who doesn't have conflicts of interest can be difficult. Two methods that can serve as good starting points are personal referrals and associations.

One of the best ways to find a good financial planner is to get a personal referral from a satisfied customer who is someone you trust. A referral from an accountant or attorney whose judgment you trust can help as well.

> ✔ **Never take a recommendation from anyone as gospel, no matter who is making the referral — even if it's your best friend or boss.** You must do your homework. The person making the recommendation is (probably) not a financial expert. He may be just as bewildered as you are.

> ✔ **Hire professionals who make referrals to others based on their competence and ethics.** You may get referred to a planner or broker who returns the favor by sending business to the tax, legal, or real estate person who referred you. Good professionals don't do tit for tat.

Associations of financial planners are more than happy to refer you to planners in your area.

> ✔ **The National Association of Personal Financial Advisors** (www.napfa.org) consists of fee-only planners. NAPFA members aren't supposed to earn commissions from products they sell. However, most planners in this association earn their living by providing money-management services and charging a fee that's a percentage of assets under management.

> ✔ **The American Institute of Certified Public Accountants** (www.cpapfs.org) is the professional association of CPAs that can provide names of members who have completed the Institute's Personal Financial Specialist (PFS) program. Many CPAs who complete the PFS program provide financial advice on a fee basis.

Chapter 18

Investing in Your Future

. . . .

. . . .

Knowing the basics of investing helps you select investments wisely and helps you understand the risks and returns. You can't and don't need to earmark *every* dollar, but you should set some major objectives. Doing so is important because the expected use of the money determines how much time you're going to invest it. And that, in turn, helps determine which investment you choose.

Understanding Investment Options

Diversification is one of the most powerful investment concepts. Try to save and place your money in different investments with returns that aren't completely related. By having your money in different places, the odds are that when some of your investments are down in value, others will be up.

Low-risk, high-return investments

Despite what professors teach in top business schools, there *are* low-risk investments that almost certainly lead to high returns:

> ✔ **Pay off consumer debt.** If you're paying 10, 14, or 18 percent interest on an outstanding credit card or other consumer loan, pay it off before investing. If your only source of funds to pay

off debt is a small emergency reserve that's equal in size to a few months' living expenses, paying off debt can involve some risk. Tap into your emergency reserves only if you have a backup source, such as borrowing from a willing family member or against a retirement account balance.

✔ **Invest in your health.** Eat healthy, exercise, and relax.

✔ **Invest in friends and family.** Improve your relationships with loved ones. Invest the time and effort in making them better.

✔ **Invest in personal and career development.** Learn a new hobby, improve your communication skills, or read widely. Take an adult education course or go back to school for a degree. Your investment will surely pay off in higher paychecks and greater happiness.

Keys to stock market success

To maximize your chances of stock market investment success, do the following things:

✔ **Don't try to time the markets.** Anticipating where the stock market and specific stocks are heading is next to impossible. Instead, be a regular buyer of stocks as you accumulate new savings. Buy more stocks when they're on sale and market pessimism is running high.

✔ **Invest in the stocks of different-size companies in varying industries around the world.**

✔ **Pay attention to taxes.** Contribute most of your money to your tax-advantaged retirement accounts. You can invest your money outside of retirement accounts, but keep an eye on taxes. Calculate your annual returns on an *after*-tax basis.

✔ **A good way to invest in stocks is through mutual funds.** Hire an experienced, full-time money manager at a low cost to perform all the investing grunt work for you.

✔ **Stay clear of initial public offerings.** Avoid trendy popular offerings and ones that are issued during times of an overheated stock market.

Mutual funds

Although most mutual fund investors are rewarded for their efforts, you have no guarantees. Follow these simple guidelines to help increase your odds of investment success.

Reading prospectuses and annual reports

Mutual fund companies produce information that can help you make decisions about mutual fund investments. Every fund is required to issue a *prospectus*. This legal document is reviewed and audited by the U.S. Securities and Exchange Commission. Most of what's written isn't worth the time it takes to slog through it.

The most valuable information — the fund's investment objectives, costs, and performance history — is summarized in the first few pages of the prospectus. This part you should read. Skip the rest, comprised mostly of tedious legal details.

Funds also produce annual reports that discuss how the fund has been doing and provide details on the specific investments that a fund holds. If, for example, you want to know which countries an international fund invests in, you can find this information in the fund's annual report.

✔ **Don't expect guarantees.** You can be logical, analytical, and sensible and still end up with some mediocre funds. Fund selection is not a science.

✔ **Consider the source.** You can increase your chances for success by sticking with ethical fund companies that have a history of producing winners with your type of fund.

✔ **Pay attention to fees.** Avoid funds that charge sales commissions (loads) and have high ongoing operating expenses. You have more than enough commission-free (no-load), low-expense funds with great managers and track records as alternatives.

✔ **Beware of buying only past performance.** Historic performance is but one of many factors to consider when selecting funds.

✔ **Remember the power of index funds.** Index mutual funds, which match and track the performance of a broad bond or stock market index, handily beat the vast majority of competing funds.

✔ **Diversify.** At a minimum, invest some of your long-term money in stock funds, both U.S. and international, as well as bond funds. If your assets allow, use at least two funds within each category.

Real estate investments

Real estate isn't a gravy train or a simple way to get wealthy. Like stocks, real estate goes through good and bad performance periods. Some of the best real estate options include

- ✔ **Your own home:** The *equity* (the difference between the market value of the house and the loan owed on it) in your home that builds over the years can become a significant part of your net worth.

- ✔ **Investment property close to home:** Look for strong, local economic growth; a vibrant and diverse job base; and limited supplies of both existing housing and land on which to build.

- ✔ **REITs:** If you don't want to be a landlord, consider real estate investment trusts. REITs are diversified real estate investment companies that purchase and manage rental real estate for investors. A typical REIT invests in different types of property, such as shopping centers, apartments, and other rental buildings.

Bad real-estate investments are characterized by burdensome costs and problematic economic fundamentals:

- ✔ **Limited partnerships (LPs):** Sold through brokers and financial consultants, LPs are so burdened with high sales commissions and ongoing management fees that deplete your investment that you can do better elsewhere.

- ✔ **Time shares:** With a time share, what you buy is a week or two per year of ownership, or usage, of a particular unit, usually a condominium in a resort location. If you pay $8,000 for a week (in addition to ongoing maintenance fees), you're paying the equivalent of more than $400,000 for the whole unit, but a comparable unit nearby may sell for only $150,000.

- ✔ **Second homes and vacation homes:** Most people who own second homes seldom rent out their property. Owning a second home is more of a consumption than an investment decision.

Preparing for Retirement

Most people need about 70 to 80 percent of their pre-retirement income throughout retirement to maintain their standard of living. For example, if your household earns $40,000 per year before retirement, you're likely to need $28,000 – $32,000 per year during retirement to live the way that you're accustomed to living.

Making up for lost time

If the amount that you need to save per month to reach your retirement goals seems daunting, don't despair. Here are ways to make up for lost time:

- ✔ **Question your spending.** You have only two ways to boost your savings: Earn more money or cut your spending (or do both). Most people don't spend their money nearly as thoughtfully as they earn it.

- ✔ **Be more realistic about your retirement age.** If you extend the age at which you plan to retire, you get a double financial benefit. You're earning and saving money for more years and spending your nest egg over fewer years.

- ✔ **Use home equity.** What's the use of owning a house free of mortgage debt when you lack sufficient retirement reserves? You can sell your home and either move to a lower-cost property or rent. Tax laws allow you to realize up to $250,000 in tax-free profit from a house sale ($500,000 if you're married).

- ✔ **Get aggressive with your investments.** The faster the rate at which your money grows and compounds, the less you need to save each year to reach your goals. Earning just a few extra percentage points per year on your investments can dramatically slash the amount you need to save.

- ✔ **Look at jobs that offer retirement plans.** When you're evaluating employers, cash is usually king. But having access to a retirement savings plan is a valuable benefit. Even more beneficial is a pension plan, which pays you a monthly retirement benefit based on your years of service.

Wills, living wills, and living trusts

Estate planning is the process of determining what will happen to your assets after you die. You're insuring that after you die, everything will be taken care of as you wish and that taxes will be minimized.

Wills

You don't need an attorney to make a legal will. What makes a will *valid* is that three people witness it.

- ✔ **If you have children, make a will as soon as possible.** Name a guardian in the will who will be responsible for raising your children should you and your spouse both pass away. Choosing a guardian is daunting but don't let the courts decide on one for you.

✔ **If you don't have children, make a will.** When you die without a will *(intestate)*, your state decides how to distribute your money and other property, according to state law. Without any living relatives, your money may go to the state government!

✔ **Save money with a will.** Without a will, your heirs are legally powerless, and the state may appoint an administrator to supervise the distribution of your assets at a fee of around 5 percent of your estate. A bond typically must also be posted at a cost of several hundred dollars.

Living wills, medical power of attorney

A *living will* tells your doctor what, if any, life-support measures you want or don't want. A *medical power of attorney* grants authority to someone you trust to make decisions with a physician regarding your medical-care options.

Living trusts

A *living trust* effectively transfers assets into a trust. Living trusts keep assets out of probate but have nothing to do with minimizing estate or inheritance taxes.

✔ The advantage of a living trust is that upon your death, assets can pass directly to your beneficiaries without going through probate.

✔ You control the assets in a living trust and can revoke the trust whenever you desire.

✔ Living trusts are likely to be of greatest value to people who are age 60 or older, single, and have assets worth more than $100,000 that must pass through probate (including real estate, nonretirement accounts, and small business)

✔ You do *not* need an attorney to establish a legal and valid living trust. Attorney fees to establish a living trust can range from $700 to $2,000.

Chapter 19

Applying for Loans and Credit

● ●

In This Chapter

▶ Managing your credit cards

▶ Choosing a mortgage

▶ Borrowing for college

▶ Buying a car

▶ Mining overlooked loan sources

● ●

*T*here's a *big* difference between borrowing for something that represents a long-term investment and borrowing for consumption. Debt incurred for consumption can be generally considered *bad debt.* Good debt, such as that used to buy real estate and small businesses, is generally available at lower interest rates than bad debt and is usually tax-deductible. If properly and smartly managed, these investments should also increase in value. Borrowing to pay for educational expenses can also make sense; doing so should increase your earning potential.

Dive into this chapter for answers to all your debt, loan, and credit questions.

Becoming Savvy about Credit Cards

Even with the benefit of today's lower interest rates, carrying a balance month-to-month on your credit card or buying a car on credit means that even more of your future earnings are earmarked for debt repayment. Buying on credit encourages you to spend more than you really can afford.

Getting the most out of your credit cards

Until you get your credit-card debts paid off, make growing your debt more difficult by doing the following things:

✔ **Apply for a lower-rate credit card.** If you're earning a decent income, aren't too burdened with debt, and have a clean credit record, qualifying for lower-rate cards is relatively painless. Some persistence (and clean-up work) may be required if you have nicks in your credit report or have income and debt problems. After you're approved for a new, lower-interest-rate credit card, you can simply transfer your outstanding balance from your higher-rate card.

✔ **Call the bank that issued your current high-interest-rate credit card and say that you want to cancel your card because you found a competitor that offers no annual fee and a lower interest rate.** Your bank may choose to match the terms of the "competitor" rather than lose you as a customer.

✔ **While you're paying down your credit-card debt, stop making new charges on cards with outstanding balances.** Many people don't realize that interest starts to accumulate *immediately* when they carry a balance. *You have no grace period* (the 20-odd days you normally have to pay your balance in full without incurring interest charges) if you carry a credit-card balance month-to-month.

If you hunt around for a low-interest-rate credit card, be sure to check out all the terms and conditions. Start by reviewing the uniform rates and terms disclosure, which details the myriad fees and conditions. Also, be sure that you understand how the future interest rate is determined on cards that charge variable interest rates.

Paying no annual fee

Don't keep a credit card that charges you an annual fee, especially if you pay your balance in full each month. Many no-fee credit cards exist — and some even offer you a benefit for using them.

If you have a credit card that charges an annual fee, try calling the company and saying that you want to cancel the card because you can get a competitor's card without an annual fee. Many banks will agree to waive the fee on the spot. Some require you to call back yearly to cancel the fee — a hassle that can be avoided by getting a true no-fee card.

Some cards that charge an annual fee and offer credits toward a purchase, such as a car or airline ticket, may be worth your while if you pay your credit card bill in full each month and charge $10,000 or more annually. **Note:** Be careful, however, because some people are tempted to charge more on a card that rewards them for more purchases. Spending more than you would otherwise to rack up bonuses defeats the purpose of getting the credits.

If you have a pattern of living beyond your means through buying on credit, get rid of the culprit — the credit card, that is. Cut up *all* your credit cards and call the issuers of the cards to cancel your accounts. And when you buy items such as cars and furniture, don't apply for credit.

If you can trust yourself, keep a separate credit card *only* for new purchases that you know you can absolutely pay in full each month. Don't be tempted to let debt accumulate and roll over for a month or two, or you'll start the whole horrible process of running up your consumer debt again. Rather than keeping one credit card, consider getting a debit card.

Making the Most of Mortgages

Two major types of mortgages exist — those with a *fixed interest rate* and those with a *variable or adjustable rate*.

Usually issued for a 15- or 30-year period, fixed-rate mortgages have interest rates that never, ever change. The interest rate you pay the first month is the same one that you pay the last month and every month in between. Because the interest rate stays the same, your monthly mortgage payment amount doesn't change. You have no uncertainty or interest-rate worries.

Fixed-rate loans are not without risks, however. If interest rates fall significantly after you obtain your mortgage, you face the danger of being stuck with your higher-cost mortgage if you're unable, because of a deterioration in your financial situation or a decline in the value of your property, to *refinance* your mortgage. And, even if you are eligible to refinance, you'll probably have to spend significant time and money to complete the process.

In contrast to a fixed-rate mortgage, an *adjustable-rate mortgage* (ARM) carries an interest rate that varies over time. Like a fidgeting child, the rate rises, falls, and otherwise can't sit still. You can start with one interest rate this year and have different ones for every year, possibly every month, during a 30-year mortgage. Thus, the

Shun balloon loans

Be wary of balloon loans, which look like fixed-rate loans but aren't. With balloon loans, the large remaining loan balance becomes fully due at a predetermined time — typically within three to ten years. Balloon loans are dangerous because you may not be able to refinance into a new loan to pay off the balloon loan when it comes due.

Take such a loan only if the following three conditions are true: You really, really want a certain property; the balloon loan is your only financing option; and you're positive that you'll be able to refinance when the balloon comes due. If you take a balloon loan, get one with as much time as possible before it comes due.

size of your monthly payment fluctuates. Because a mortgage payment makes an unusually large dent in most homeowners' checkbooks, signing up for an ARM without understanding its risks is dangerous.

The attraction of an ARM is its potential interest savings. For the first few years of an adjustable loan, the interest rate is typically lower than on a comparable fixed-rate loan. After that, it depends on the overall trends in interest rates. When interest rates drop, stay level, or rise just a little, you continue to pay less for your adjustable rate. On the other hand, when rates rise more than a percent or two and stay elevated, an adjustable-rate loan should cost you more than a fixed-rate loan.

Another mortgage option is a *hybrid loan,* which combines features of fixed- and adjustable-rate mortgages. For example, the initial rate may hold constant for a number of years — three to five years is common — and then adjust once a year or every six months thereafter. These hybrid loans may make sense for you if you foresee a high probability of keeping your loan seven to ten years or less but want some stability in your monthly payments. The longer the initial rate stays locked in, the higher the rate is.

Choosing between fixed- and adjustable-rate mortgages

Consider the following issues before you decide which kind of mortgage — fixed or adjustable — is right for you.

How willing and able are you to take on financial risk?

Take stock of how much risk you can take with the size of your monthly mortgage payment.

If your job and income are unstable and you need to borrow nearly the maximum that a bank is willing to lend you or have no slack in your monthly budget — that is, you're not regularly saving money — then you can't afford much risk. If you're in this situation, stick with a fixed-rate loan.

Don't take an adjustable simply because the initially lower interest rates allow you to afford the property you want to buy (unless you're absolutely certain that your income will rise to meet future payment increases). Try setting your sights on a property that you can afford — with a fixed-rate mortgage.

If interest rates rise, a mushrooming adjustable mortgage payment may test the lower limits of your checking-account balance. When you don't have emergency savings that you can tap to make the higher payments, how can you afford the monthly payments — much less all the other expenses of home ownership?

If you can't afford the highest allowed payment on an adjustable-rate mortgage, don't take it. Ask your lender to calculate the highest possible maximum monthly payment on your loan. That's the payment you would face if the interest rate on your loan went to the highest level allowed — or the lifetime cap.

On the other hand, you may feel financially secure in choosing an adjustable loan if you have a hefty financial cushion that's accessible in the event that rates go up, if you take out a smaller loan than you're qualified for, or if you're saving more than 10 percent of your income. And remember, even if rates go up, they'll probably come back down over the life of your loan. So, if you can stick with your adjustable for better and for worse, you may still come out ahead in the long term.

How long do you plan to keep the mortgage?

A mortgage lender takes extra risk in committing to a constant interest rate for 15 to 30 years, so they charge you a premium.

Saving on most adjustables is usually guaranteed in the first two or three years because an adjustable-rate mortgage starts at a lower interest rate than a fixed one. If rates rise, you can end up giving back or losing the savings you achieve in the early years of the mortgage. In most cases, if you aren't going to keep your mortgage more than five to seven years, you're probably paying unnecessary interest costs to carry a fixed-rate mortgage.

Avoid loans with negative amortization

As you make mortgage payments over time, the loan balance you still owe is gradually reduced — this process is known as amortizing the loan. The reverse of this process — increasing your loan balance — is called negative amortization.

Taking on negative amortization is like paying only the minimum payment required on a credit-card bill. You keep racking up greater interest charges on the balance as long as you make only the artificially low payment. Doing so defeats the whole purpose of borrowing an amount that fits your overall financial goals. And you may never get the mortgage paid off!

Avoid ARMs with negative amortization. The only way you'll know whether a loan includes it is to ask. Some lenders aren't forthcoming about telling you. You'll find negative amortization more frequently on loans that lenders consider risky. If you're having trouble finding lenders willing to deal with your financial situation, be especially careful.

Buying with less money down

When you buy a home, ideally you should make a down payment of at least 20 percent of the purchase price of the property. Why? Because you'll generally be able to qualify for the most favorable terms on a mortgage with such a down payment.

Here are a number of solutions for coming up with a 20 percent down payment faster or for buying with less money down and solving the down-payment blues:

- ✔ **Go on a spending diet.** One sure way to come up with a down payment is to raise your savings rate by slashing your spending.

- ✔ **Consider lower-priced properties.** Some buyers want their first home to be a palace. Smaller properties and ones that need some work can help to keep down the purchase price and, therefore, the required down payment.

- ✔ **Find partners.** You can usually get more home for your money when you buy a building in partnership with one, two, or a few people. Make sure that you write up a legal contract to specify what will happen if a partner wants out.

- ✔ **Seek reduced-down-payment financing.** Some property owners or developers may be willing to finance your purchase with as little as 5 to 10 percent down. You can't be as picky about properties because not as many are available under these terms — many need work or haven't yet sold for other reasons.

✔ **Get assistance from family.** If your parents, grandparents, or other relatives have money dozing away in a savings or CD account, they may be willing to lend (or even give) you the down payment. You can pay them a higher rate of interest than they've been earning (but still lower than what you would pay to borrow from a bank) and thus be able to buy a home — a win/win situation.

✔ **Obtain private mortgage insurance (PMI).** Some lenders may offer you a mortgage even though you may be able to put down only 5 to 10 percent of the purchase price. Once the property rises enough in value or you pay down the mortgage enough to have 20 percent equity in the property, you can drop the PMI.

✔ **Access retirement accounts.** Some employers allow you to borrow against your retirement savings plan. Just be sure that you understand the repayment rules so that you don't get tripped up and forced to treat the withdrawal as a taxable distribution. You can also make penalty-free withdrawals from Individual Retirement Accounts for a first-time home purchase.

✔ **Look into seller financing.** Some sellers don't need all the cash from the sale of their property when the transaction closes escrow. These sellers may be willing to offer you a second mortgage to help you buy their property. Seller financing is usually due and payable in five to ten years. This gives you time to build up equity or save enough to refinance into a new, larger 80-percent conventional mortgage before the seller's loan comes due.

Be cautious about seller financing. Some sellers who offer property with built-in financing are trying to dump a house that has major defects. Also, the house may be priced far above its fair market value. Be sure that the seller-financing interest rate is as low or lower than you can obtain through a traditional mortgage lender.

✔ **Check out 80-10-10 financing.** This financing is called 80-10-10 because a bank, savings and loan association, or other institutional lender makes a traditional 80-percent first mortgage and you get a 10-percent second mortgage and make a cash down payment equal to 10-percent of the home's purchase price. Where can you get the second mortgage? Either from the institutional lender who provided the 80-percent first mortgage or the previously mentioned seller. From a lender's perspective, 80-10-10 financing is as good as 20 percent down.

Don't get hung up on nomenclature. Just because this financing is known as 80-10-10, that doesn't mean you *must* put down 10-percent cash. The same principle applies if, for example, you can only afford to put 5-percent cash down — 80-15-5 financing is also available. Because a smaller cash down payment increases the lender's risk of default, however, you'll no doubt have to pay higher loan fees and a higher mortgage interest rate for 80-15-5 financing than you'd pay for 80-10-10.

Increasing the chances of getting your mortgage approved

Here's how to increase your chances of having your mortgage approved:

- **Get your finances in shape before you shop.** You're not going to have a good handle on what you can afford to spend on a home until you whip your personal finances in shape. Do so before you begin to make offers on properties.

- **Clear up credit-report problems.** Late payments, missed payments, or debts that you never bothered to pay can come back to haunt you. If you think that your credit report has problems, get a copy before you apply for your mortgage. The major credit bureaus are Equifax (800-685-1111), Experian (888-397-3742), and Trans Union (800-632-1765). Credit bureaus generally charge less than $10 for a copy of your report (you may obtain a free copy if you ask within 60 days of being denied credit, employment, or insurance based on information in your credit report).

  Mistakes crop up on credit reports. The only way to fix the mistakes, unfortunately, is to get on the phone with the credit bureaus and start squawking. When specific creditors have reported erroneous information, call them, too. If the customer service representatives you talk with are no help, dash off a nice letter to the president of each company. For bona fide problems documented on your credit report, try explaining them to your lender. Should the lender be unsympathetic, try calling other lenders. Tell lenders your credit problems up front and see whether you can find one willing to give you a loan. Mortgage brokers can also help you shop for lenders in these cases.

- **Get preapproved or prequalified.** *Prequalified* means that you've spoken with a lender about your financial situation and they've calculated the maximum they'll lend you based on what you've told them. *Preapproval* is more in-depth and includes a

lender's actual review of your financial statements. Although
neither status is binding on a lender to actually make you a
mortgage loan, preapproval means more, especially in qualifying you financially in the eyes of a seller. Just be sure not to
waste your time and money getting preapproved if you're not
really ready to get serious about buying.

✔ **Be up front about problems.** The best defense against loan
rejection is to avoid it in the first place. You can sometimes
head off potential rejection by disclosing to your lender anything that may cause a problem before you apply for the loan.
That way, you have more time to correct problems and find
alternate solutions.

✔ **Work around low/unstable income.** If you're self-employed or
you've been changing jobs, your recent economic history may
be unstable. One way around this problem is to make a larger
down payment. If you put down 30 percent or more, you may
be able to get a no-income verification loan. You may try getting
a cosigner such as a parent, another relative, or even a rich
friend. Be sure that all parties understand the terms of the
agreement, including who's responsible for monthly payments!

✔ **Consider a backup loan.** You certainly should shop among different lenders, and you may even want to apply to more than
one for a mortgage. Although applying for a second loan means
additional fees and work, you can increase your chances of getting a mortgage if you're attempting to buy a difficult-to-finance
property or your financial situation makes some lenders leery.
Also be sure to disclose to each lender what you're doing — the
second lender to pull your credit report will see that another
lender has been there already.

Working Out College Loans

How you'll help pay for your child's college costs depends on your
own unique situation. However, in most cases, even if you have
some available cash that can be directed to pay the college bills as
they come in, you'll probably have to borrow some money.

Demonstrating need: The key to financial aid

Demonstrated need is the difference between what a student's family
is expected to contribute and the total cost for one year of the college or university where a student hopes to enroll. Amazingly enough,

the term for what a family is expected to contribute is called the expected family contribution (EFC). Both the family contribution and the student contribution are included in the EFC.

To treat everyone as fairly as possible, everyone fills out the same instrument of torture, which is something like a tax form. You arrive at your expected family contribution by filling in the blanks of a form called the Free Application for Federal Student Aid (FAFSA).

Borrowing versus saving

If you have nothing stashed away, you'll be eligible for more financial aid than the diligent saver. But much of your financial aid package will likely be in loans. The loans may be low-interest with repayment deferred until after college, but they're loans nonetheless. Eventually, you must come up with the money.

The decision that you need to make, if you're thinking about it several years in advance, is whether you should earn interest now on money you save or pay interest later on money you borrow? That's your choice. And your decision must be dictated by your financial condition.

Keep in mind that the relationship between the amount you save and the amount you must borrow is not precise. You can't say that $10,000 in savings will eliminate $10,000 in loans because too many other factors are involved. As a general rule, however, you can figure that a dollar saved plus interest will eliminate the need to borrow a dollar or two somewhere down the road.

Although more than a few investment firms and financial planners argue that, in the long run, saving for your children's college expenses is far cheaper than borrowing for them, this claim is not necessarily true. If you are able to save in retirement accounts and choose decent investments and then separately borrow the money needed for college costs later, you can come out ahead, thanks to the tax benefits that retirement accounts provide and the increased financial aid you may receive.

Investing for education

What makes for good and bad investments in general applies to investments for educational expenses, too. Stick with basic, proven, lower-cost investments.

✔ **Good investments:** The professional management and efficiency of the best *no-load mutual funds* makes them a tough
investment to beat. The important issue is to gear the investments to the time frame involved until your children need to
use the money. The closer your child gets to attending college
and using the money saved, the more conservatively the
money should be invested.

✔ **Bad investments:** *Life insurance policies* that have cash values,
savings or money market accounts that fail to keep you ahead of
inflation, and *prepaid tuition plans* that allow you to prepay college costs at a specific school (calculated for the age of your
child) are generally unwise as investments for college. You can
earn more with mutual funds, and prepaid tuition plans may
lock your child into a college he or she may not want to attend
while earning you less interest than you can get with other
investments.

Parents are allowed to make penalty-free withdrawals from
Individual Retirement Accounts if the funds are used for college
expenses. Although you aren't charged an early-withdrawal penalty,
the IRS does treat the withdrawal amount as income, and your
income taxes will increase accordingly. On top of that, the financial-
aid office will look at your beefed-up income and assume that you
don't need as much financial aid.

Juggling your money

Saving isn't the only way to have more money available at college
time. You can also juggle your own money in the years before college to make your need — and your financial-aid eligibility — greater
when the time comes. None of the following suggestions is illegal,
unethical, immoral, or frowned upon by picky financial-aid directors.
Just as careful tax planners take advantage of the tax laws to pay the
minimum required by law, careful college planners can take advantage of the financial-aid rules to get the maximum allowed by law.

Put the money in the right place

As you save $4 a day to build up that $44,000 needed for your kid's
college, in whose name do you put the money? If you think you're
being nice to your 8-year-old son by putting his college money in his
name, think again. You're hurting him.

The formula to calculate assets in relation to college costs takes
about 5 percent of parents' assets as part of the Expected Family
Contribution to college costs. But it takes 35 percent of the student's

assets. That's a huge difference! If the $44,000 savings is in Junior's name, a computer will tell him to spend $15,400 of it on his first year at Bigbucks U. If it's in his parents' name, only about $2,200 will go to the Expected Family Contribution. You increase your financial need by about $13,000 simply by changing the name on the savings account.

This asset-shifting tactic, from kids' names to parents' names, is the exact opposite of what you would do to save taxes. Kids' interest income is usually taxed at a lower rate than parents' money because kids usually have less of it. And for kids under 14, the first $600 of interest income is tax-free. You'll have to do some strategic planning to balance your tax needs with your college-cost needs.

Say no thanks to gifts

If Grandma wants to give Stephanie Student a $1,000 savings bond for a college nest egg, don't reject her generosity but ask her to please wait a while. Suggest that Grandma write Stephanie a nice note (grandmothers are good at nice notes) saying that she has a $1,000 bond squirreled away for her college education and that when the time comes, Grandma will write Stephanie a check. Meanwhile, the bond stays in Grandma's name. No formula yet has asked about grandparents' assets.

Tell the family to go to class

If Mom or Dad — or anyone else in the family — has been thinking about going to school for a class or two at night, wait until Steve and Stephanie are ready to be full-time college students.

Everyone enrolled for at least six credits is considered a student by the financial aid formula. Each family member who counts as a student substantially reduces the Expected Family Contribution for all other members.

Sell stocks early

If you plan to sell some investments — stocks, bonds, mutual funds — to raise college money, do so early in the student's high school junior year. Capital gains earned the year before you apply for financial aid (from January of eleventh grade to December of twelfth grade) count as income in determining financial need. Gains realized earlier don't count.

Pay the doctor early

Large medical and dental expenses not covered by insurance are deducted from your income by most of the high-priced colleges using PROFILE as a supplemental financial-aid form. Pay all the medical bills you can by December of the student's senior year.

Pay extra on the mortgage

The more money you can put into your home equity, the fewer dollars you'll show the government's computers that figure your Expected Family Contribution. Home equity is an asset the government's financial-aid formula specifically ignores.

Give carefully to retirement plans

The same government computers that ignore home equity want to know about the money you put into retirement plans, but only in the calendar year before you apply for aid. All the retirement savings you've accumulated in the past are ignored. Fund your retirement plan to the maximum until January of eleventh grade, then slow down.

Considering loans, grants, and scholarships

A host of financial-aid programs, including a number of loan programs, allow you to borrow at fair interest rates. As with some mortgage loans on real estate, federal government educational loans have variable interest rates — which means that the interest rate you're charged varies with the overall level of interest rates. Most programs add 3.1 percent to the current interest rates on three-month to one-year Treasury bills. Thus, current rates on educational loans are in the vicinity of 9 percent. The rates are also capped so that the interest rate on your loan can never exceed a few percent more than the initial rate on the loan.

A number of loan programs, such as *Unsubsidized Stafford Loans* and *Parent Loans for Undergraduate Students (PLUS),* are available even when your family isn't deemed financially needy. Only *Subsidized Stafford Loans,* on which the federal government pays the interest that accumulates while the student is still in school, are limited to students deemed financially needy.

Most loan programs limit the amount that you can borrow per year as well the overall total you can borrow for a student's educational career. If you need more money than your limits allow, PLUS loans can fill the gap: Parents can borrow the full amount needed after other financial aid is factored in. The only obstacle is that you must go through a credit qualification process. Unlike privately funded college loans, a federal loan's main qualification stipulation is that you don't have negative credit (recent bankruptcy, more than three debts over three months' past due, and so on). For more information from the federal government about these student loan programs, call the Federal Student Aid Information Center at 800-433-3243.

In addition to loans, grant programs are available through schools and the government, as well as independent sources. You can apply for federal government grants via the FAFSA. Grants available through state government programs may require a separate application. Specific colleges and other private organizations (including employers, banks, credit unions, and community groups) also offer grants and scholarships.

Many scholarships and grants don't require any extra work on your part — simply apply for financial aid through colleges. Other programs need seeking out — check directories and databases at your local library, your child's school counseling department, and college financial aid offices. Also try local organizations, churches, employers, and so on. You have a better chance of getting scholarship money through these avenues.

College scholarship search services are generally a waste of money; in some cases, they're actually scams. Some of these services charge up to $100 just to tell you about scholarships that either you're already being considered for or that you're not even eligible for.

Getting a government loan

The U.S. government provides about 75 percent of all available financial aid in the U.S., a commitment that far outstrips that of any other major country.

The federal government offers the following grant programs to assist in funding your higher education.

- ✔ **Federal Pell Grant Program:** The 800-pound gorilla in the need-based programs, the Federal Pell Grant Program awards gift money to nearly 4 million students in amounts ranging from $400 to $3,525 yearly. Pell grants are off-limits to graduate students, as well as to students who have already received their bachelor's degrees.

- ✔ **Federal Supplemental Educational Opportunity Grant Program (FSEOG):** The Federal Supplemental Educational Opportunity Grant Program is for students with exceptional need. To qualify, you must be enrolled at least half-time in an undergraduate program at an accredited institution. Grants in the neighborhood of $4,000 are possible on the basis of pure, unadulterated need (poverty). However, most colleges don't receive enough FSEOG funds to pay out maximum eligibility, and $1,000 to $1,500 is considered a good award.

This program is campus-based, which means that although the money comes from the federal government, the colleges hand it out to students who show exceptional need. (Typically, you're eligible for an FSEOG if you're eligible for a Pell grant.) If you think you qualify for the FSEOG, ask your school's financial-aid counselor to put you down for one.

The following federal loans are awarded directly or guaranteed by Uncle Sam and Aunt Feddie:

✔ **Federal Perkins Loan:** The Federal Perkins Loan is the best federal-loan program in the business, offering 5 percent interest! Perkins targets the neediest students — typically those who receive Pell grants. Given to both undergraduate and graduate students, the loans come through a college's financial-aid office. Payments and interest start nine months after college ends if you're at least a half-time student; if your school load drops below half-time, the nine-month countdown to payment begins.

✔ **Federal Direct Student Loan Program** and **Federal Stafford Loan Program:** These two programs are for student borrowers. The difference is where the money comes from. Funds from the Federal Direct Student Loan Program are federal money disbursed through your college. Funds from the Federal Stafford Loan Program come from private sources, such as banks, credit unions, savings-and-loan associations, and educational organizations. Either program — Direct or Stafford — can be subsidized or unsubsidized.

  • If you've demonstrated need, the loan is subsidized, meaning that the government pays the interest while you're in school.

  • If you don't have demonstrated need, you pay interest from the time you get the loan until it's paid in full (although you may elect to defer interest payments until after you graduate). This loan is unsubsidized.

✔ **FPLUS (Federal Parent Loans for Undergraduate Students):** FPLUS loans and Direct FPLUS loans are for parent borrowers. The difference is where the money comes from. Direct FPLUS loans are federal funds disbursed by your college's financial-aid office. FPLUS loans come from private sources, such as banks, credit unions, savings and loan associations, and educational organizations. The maximum that parents can borrow under either of these loan programs depends on the cost of the college and the amount of financial aid that the student receives.

If parents are rejected for an FPLUS loan, the student who wants to enroll in a lower-cost college may actually be getting good news. Students get loans at lower interest rates than parents do, and repayment doesn't begin as quickly — even though the interest is being capitalized.

So even if you anticipate an FPLUS or Direct FPLUS loan rejection, go ahead, Mom and/or Dad, and apply for an FPLUS or Direct FPLUS loan. If your loan is rejected, make a copy of the rejection letter and have the student send it to the college's financial-aid counselor. To make up for the turndown of an FPLUS or Direct FPLUS loan, college students can borrow an additional unsubsidized Federal Stafford or Direct loan as long as the parents' rejection letter is submitted.

The military offers a cornucopia of financial-aid opportunities. Additionally, Uncle Sam and Aunt Feddie offer an assortment of other resources, ranging from medical and nursing scholarships to scholarships from the Bureau of Indian Affairs.

Find out more by ordering *The Student Guide* (annual), published by the U.S. Department of Education, from Federal Student Aid Programs, P.O. Box 84, Washington, D.C. 20044, or call 800-433-3243.

If you're not eligible for subsidized Federal Stafford loans, then start by looking at the Unsubsidized Federal Stafford loans and the Federal PLUS loans, because they're the biggest loan programs. Ordinarily, these two classes of loans are the cheapest, but some private and commercial loans have a lower interest rate than the government's loans.

Asking the right questions about repayment

Choosing the right loan (or combination of loans) makes all the difference. Factor in the following questions as you examine educational loans:

- ✔ Who must repay the bulk of the loan (student or parents)?
- ✔ How little can the family afford to borrow?
- ✔ How much can the family afford to repay (estimate monthly payments)?
- ✔ How much can the graduate expect to earn upon graduation?

Review the rules for repaying your loan with a magnifying glass. For instance, ask these questions:

✔ What happens to the debt if you become permanently disabled or die?

✔ In what circumstances and how should you apply for deferment or forbearance?

✔ If both parents assume a joint loan, who pays how much if they divorce?

✔ Can you begin repaying even before interest accrues?

Loans usually require payment of such charges as loan, origination, and insurance fees, in addition to interest. Students are given options to stretch out payments over 30 years. But remember, the longer you stretch out loan repayment, the more you have to pay in interest. A better idea: Get three jobs if necessary and limit your repayment to ten years.

Taking Out a Car Loan

When you buy a car, not only do you pay the initial sticker price, but you're also on the hook for gas, insurance, registration fees, maintenance, and repairs. Don't compare simple sticker prices; think about total, long-term costs of ownership, as well as the car's individual safety factors.

The *Consumer Reports Buying Guide* summarizes all the latest information on cars and includes a list of the most reliable used cars in various price categories. For you data jocks, *The Complete Car Cost Guide* (published by Intellichoice) is packed with information about all categories of ownership costs, warranties, and dealer costs.

Buy your car with cash

The main reason people end up spending more than they can afford on a car is that they finance it. You should avoid borrowing money for consumption purchases, especially for items that depreciate in value like cars. A car is most definitely *not* an investment. In most situations, leasing is even more expensive than borrowing money to buy a car.

Consider manufacturer's rebates and financing offers

Car manufacturers with their own financing departments may offer lower interest rates on loans and leases than rates that are available from outside credit sources. To insure goodwill, some pay the security deposit and first monthly payment when you lease the next car from them after a previous lease contract with them expires. Others offer perks such as free maintenance, auto club and towing services, emergency hotlines, stolen-vehicle tracking, and other goodies. Generally speaking, the more expensive the vehicle, the greater the perks offered by the manufacturer.

Auto manufacturers run frequent promotions that offer you the choice between a rebate or a low-interest deal. Ask your accountant or a friend who's good with numbers to work out which alternative would be the most profitable arrangement for you.

If you go for the rebate, ask the dealer to base the sales or lease contract on the price of the vehicle *after* the rebate has been deducted, rather than writing the contract for the original price and mailing you the rebate later on. Doing this enables you to avoid paying higher taxes, interest, registration fees, and perhaps insurance, on the pre-rebate price of the vehicle, which may be a couple of thousand dollars more than the vehicle actually costs you.

Borrow if you must . . .

Borrowing the money to pay for a vehicle may not be a bad idea if you intend to keep it for a long period of time and you can't or don't want to lay down cash for it. Of course, borrowing money does have disadvantages:

- ✔ The *total cost* of using a loan to purchase a vehicle is generally lower than leasing it. But your *monthly payments* will usually be higher, and you may fall into the *depreciation* trap — the car depreciates so quickly that you end up owing more on it than you can get out of it if, for some reason, you need to sell the car.

- ✔ Unlike leases, loans are considered debts and may lower your *earnings-to-debts ratio,* which can disqualify you when you try to finance something else, such as a home.

- ✔ The option of financing a vehicle may encourage you to overspend or live beyond your means.

- ✔ Most *lenders* keep the legal title to the vehicle in their name until the loan is paid off. If you can't make payments, the lender may be able to repossess your car and sell it. Banks and credit unions may also be able to withdraw money from other accounts that you have at the same institutions to reimburse themselves if you *default* on the loan.

But I can't buy a new car for cash!

Some people feel that it's unreasonable to expect them to buy a new car using cash. After all, many publications, which not uncoincidentally derive great advertising revenue from auto dealers and lenders, effectively endorse and encourage loaning and leasing to buy a car. But consider the following:

✔ If you lack sufficient cash to buy a new car, DON'T BUY A NEW CAR! Most of the world's population can't even afford a car, let alone a new one! Buy a car that you can afford — which for most people is not a new one.

✔ Don't fall for the new car buying rationalization that says that buying a used car means lots of maintenance, repair expenses, and problems. Do your homework and buy a good, used car and have the best of both worlds. A good used car costs less to buy and should cost you less to operate thanks to lower insurance costs.

✔ A fancy car isn't needed to impress people for business purposes. If clients and others see you driving an expensive new car, they may think that you spend money wastefully or that you're getting rich off of them!

If, in spite of these caveats, you still feel that borrowing money for a car purchase is the best option for you, remember that the best type of loans charge *simple interest* and have a low *APR* with no *prepayment penalties*. (The *APR* is the annual percentage rate, which is the rate of interest you pay each year to finance the vehicle with a loan, expressed as a percentage of the principal. A reduction of as little as 1 percent of the APR can save you thousands of dollars over the life of the loan contract.)

Negotiating the most advantageous terms on a loan

Here are pointers that can help you get the most advantageous terms on a loan:

✔ **Pre-qualify with several different institutions.** Get yourself *pre-qualified* for the best loan available from banks, credit unions, finance companies, and other sources before you negotiate with a dealership. You don't have to accept the loan — unless you signed a contract — but you have the security of knowing that you can negotiate a lower price for a vehicle based on your ability to use the loan to "pay cash on the line."

✔ **Don't tell dealers that you've been pre-approved for a loan from an outside source.** Simply say that you haven't made any decision about whether or not to finance the vehicle and refuse to discuss *any* kind of financing until after you negotiate the lowest possible purchase price for the vehicle. Doing so motivates the dealer to lower the sales price in the hope of compensating for it with profit from financing the transaction.

✔ **Talk financing only after you've agreed on a purchase price.** After you agree on a purchase price for the vehicle, ask to hear the *best* financing terms the dealership has to offer. If their loan isn't substantially cheaper than the one you've pre-qualified for, tell them that you'd rather pay cash or that you've been offered better terms by another source. Refuse to reveal the other lender's identity or the terms of the loan you've been offered. Just tell them the length of the loan and ask them to come up with their lowest simple-interest loan for the same period of time.

If a dealership insists on raising the price you've negotiated for a vehicle if you refuse to accept their financing, you may still have another card to play. If there are no prepayment penalties, you can buy the vehicle for their lowest price by accepting their loan, and then pay it off completely the very first month with money from the better loan for which you pre-qualified. *Major* savings would have to be involved before you should resort to this rather devious strategy, but if you feel that all's fair in love, war, and car sales, you may want to consider doing so if you have sufficient assets to qualify for both loans.

✔ **Challenge documentation charges.** Finance charges are usually imposed on loans, but some lenders also demand documentation charges and other fees. Challenge these, especially if other lenders you've contacted don't require them.

Using the equity in your home

Your home can be a tax-deductible source of cash. As the real estate market rises and falls, homes increase and decrease in value. If your property is now worth more than you paid for it, the difference between its original price and its current value is called *equity*. You can use this equity as collateral on a no-fee home equity loan that enables you to purchase a vehicle for cash. Because the interest on mortgages and home equity loans is usually tax deductible, you'll not only be in a better position to negotiate a lower purchase price, but you'll also get a tax deduction for your interest payments that can be worth more to you than a lower APR for a traditional loan. What's more, with a no-fee loan, you can avoid paying most financing charges, as well.

If you'd like to consider this option, here are a few words of caution:

✔ **If you default on a home equity loan, you can lose your house!** Don't borrow more than you need and be sure that you can handle the monthly payments.

✔ **Borrowing against your home isn't wise when the price of housing is falling.** If the equity used as collateral disappears, you may be forced to repay the loan ahead of time.

✔ **Even if the real-estate market is rising, beware of adding too much to your mortgage debt.** If the market suddenly falls, you may find yourself with a big debt hangover.

✔ **Be sure that your tax deductions and any income from investing the cash you would otherwise have used to buy the vehicle is greater than the interest you pay on the loan.**

✔ **Beware of home equity loans that have higher fees than traditional loans.** Look for *no-fee* home equity loans offered as special promotions by banks and credit companies.

Signing a loan contract

If you decide to finance the purchase of a vehicle with a loan, take the following precautions before you sign anything:

✔ **Ask the financer to supply you with a Credit Disclosure Statement that lists all the charges and fees.** Be sure you understand this statement before you sign anything. Check to be sure the APR is the one you agreed on and that additional charges or fees haven't raised the cost above the rate you were quoted.

✔ **Read the contract slowly and carefully.** If the terms or language are unclear, insist on taking the contract home to read at your leisure or to show to your accountant. If the dealership or potential financer refuses (a common excuse is "the forms are computer generated in numerical order and can't be printed until you're ready to sign"), ask for a photocopy of a similar contract. If you're not allowed to take even a copy of the contract home for review, cancel the deal and leave.

✔ **Make sure the contract has no blank spaces left.** If you find any blank spaces, draw a line through them and write N/A (not applicable) in each space.

✔ **Have the dealership or financer initial any blanks and changes — and initial each one yourself as well.**

✔ **Insist that there be no prepayment penalties.** You definitely want the option to save interest by paying off the loan as swiftly as possible without having to pay to do so.

✔ **Contest documentation fees.** Who pays *you* to do the paperwork associated with your job?

✔ **For that matter, contest *all* fees and additional charges.** What have you got to lose?

✔ **Check the numbers.** Be sure the contract shows the following:

- Proper APR format (a nine-and-a-half percent loan should be stated as "9.5% APR")

- Specific amount that you're borrowing or financing

- Full amount of each monthly payment

- Term of the loan, expressed in months or in the maximum amount of time you have in which to pay it off in full

- Total cost of the deal, including points, fees, down payments, balloon payments, and so on

✔ **Refuse to pay *anything* until the sales contract has been approved by the loan company.** Most sales contracts specify that if the financing involved is not approved, *the customer is responsible for finding other financing.* If you've put enough down to take the vehicle home, you've been driving it, you've added accessories, or — heaven forbid — you've damaged it, you're going to be in for a nasty time if you find out that financing it elsewhere is going to cost more than you'd planned to pay, and you can't return the vehicle!

Often-Overlooked Loan Sources

Before you root through all your closets in search of stray cash to help you pay down that nagging credit card or other costly consumer debt, check out some of these financial-jacket pockets that you may have overlooked:

✔ **Borrow against your cash value life insurance policy, if you have one.**

✔ **Borrow against your employer's retirement account.** Check with your employer's benefits department to see if you can borrow against your retirement account balance. The interest rate is usually reasonable, and as you repay the loan, the interest payments go back into your account. Be careful, though — if you choose to leave your job or are asked to leave, you must repay the loan within only 60 days.

✔ **Sell investments held outside of retirement accounts.** If you have some shares of stock or Treasury bonds gathering dust in your safety deposit box, consider cashing them in to pay down your loan balances. Just be sure to consider the tax consequences of selling, and if possible, sell only those investments that won't generate a big tax bill.

✔ **Borrow from friends and family.** They know you, love you, realize your shortcomings, and — heck — probably won't be as cold-hearted as some bankers. Money borrowed from family members can have strings attached, of course. Treating the obligation seriously is important. It's also best to write up a simple agreement listing the terms and conditions of your loan to avoid misunderstandings. Unless your family members are like the worst bankers, you'll probably get a fair interest rate, and your family will have the satisfaction of helping you out — just don't forget to pay them back.

Refinancing your mortgage

If you have a mortgage that can be paid off early with no penalty, then refinancing is a possibility if interest rates drop. Refinancing your home consists of taking out another loan at a lower rate to pay off the earlier, higher-rate mortgage. (As with any mortgage procedure, you're charged fees, so take this into account when refinancing. Find out whether the costs can be rolled into the mortgage while still offering reduced monthly payments.)

Consolidating loans

When thinking about debt recovery, the first thing most people think of is *consolidating* — hiring a company or getting a loan that consolidates all their bills into one lump with smaller payments than they're making now. Proceed with caution.

Don't consider consolidation until you've lived *successfully* on a budget for six months or more. If you haven't changed your habits, consolidation won't help at all — and could make things worse. Some people actually spend more money the month after they get a consolidation loan because they think that their problems are solved.

Chapter 20

Ensuring a Happy Future with Insurance

. . . .

. . . .

Most people would rather do just about anything except review or spend money on insurance. But because you don't want to deal with money hassles when you're coping with catastrophes — illness, disability, death, fires, floods, earthquakes — you must take care of insurance well before you need it.

This chapter shows you how to get clear answers about insurance polices and also save a buck or two on your premiums.

Gaining Insurance Savvy

Studies by the nonprofit National Insurance Consumer Organization show that more than nine in ten Americans purchase and carry the wrong types and amounts of insurance coverage. Most people are just plain overwhelmed by all the jargon in sales and policy statements. As a result, many people end up purchasing insurance from poor companies, paying more than is necessary for policies, or getting insured through companies with poor reputations for servicing customers with claims on their policies.

Deciding what to do if you're denied insurance

Just as you can be turned down when you apply for a loan, you can also be turned down when applying for medical, life, or disability insurance based on an existing medical problem (a pre-existing condition). When insuring assets such as a home, you may have difficulty getting coverage if your property is deemed to be in a high-risk area.

Here are some strategies to employ if you're denied coverage:

- ✔ **Ask the insurer why you were denied.** Perhaps the company made a mistake or misinterpreted some information that you provided in your application.

Should you be denied coverage because of a medical condition, see what information the company has on you and whether the information is accurate.

- ✔ **Request a copy of your medical information file.** Many people don't know that just as you have a credit report file that details your use (and misuse) of credit, you also have a medical information report. You can request a current copy of your medical information file by writing to the Medical Information Bureau at P.O. Box 105, Essex Station, Boston, MA 02112. You can also visit the bureau online www.mib.com.

If a mistake appears on your report, you have the right to request that it be fixed. However, the burden is on *you* to prove that the information in your file is incorrect. Doing so can be a major hassle — you may even need to contact physicians that you've seen in the past because their medical records may be the source of the incorrect information.

- ✔ **Shop other companies.** Just because one company denies you coverage doesn't mean that all insurance companies will. Some insurers better understand certain medical conditions and are more comfortable accepting applicants with those conditions. Most insurers, however, charge a person with a blemished medical history a higher rate than a person with a perfect health record, but some companies penalize you less than others.

An agent who sells policies from multiple insurers, called an *independent agent,* can be helpful because she can shop among a number of different companies.

Insurance coverage and pregnancy

Before you try to have a baby, be sure that your health insurance plan offers maternity benefits. Also be sure to ask about waiting periods that may exclude coverage for a pregnancy within the first year or so of the insurance. With disability insurance, pregnancy is considered a pre-existing condition, so a woman lacking such coverage should secure it before getting pregnant.

Additionally, most families-to-be should buy life insurance. Buying life insurance after the bundle of joy comes home from the hospital is a risky proposition — if Mom or Dad develops a health problem, she or he can be denied coverage. Also consider buying life insurance for a stay-at-home parent. Even though that parent is not bringing in income, if he or she were to pass away, hiring assistance can cripple the family budget.

✔ **Find out about state high-risk pools.** Check with your state department of insurance (see the "Government" section of your local white pages phone directory) if you're turned down for health or property insurance. A number of states act as the insurer of last resort and provide insurance for those who can't get it from insurance companies. State high-risk pool coverage is usually bare bones, but it beats going without any coverage.

✔ **Check for coverage availability before you buy.** If you're considering buying a home, for example, and you can't get coverage, the insurance companies are trying to tell you something. Rethink any home purchase that that you can't insure.

Deciding whether you need life insurance

You generally only need life insurance when other people depend on your income. That means that a lot of people don't need life insurance to protect their incomes: single people, working couples who could maintain an acceptable lifestyle if one income was gone, independently wealthy people who don't need to work, and retired people who are living off of their retirement nest egg.

If others are either fully or partly dependent on your paycheck, you should buy life insurance — especially if you have major financial commitments such as a mortgage or years of child rearing ahead. Also consider life insurance if an extended family member is currently or likely to be dependent on your future income.

Figuring out how much is enough

When you need life insurance, deciding how much to buy is as much a subjective thing as it is a quantitative decision.

The main purpose of life insurance is to provide a lump sum payment that replaces the deceased person's income. The question you need to ask yourself is how many years of income do you want to replace?

Table 20-1 provides a simple way to calculate how much life insurance you should consider purchasing. To replace a certain number of years of income, simply multiply the appropriate number in the table by the person's annual after-tax income.

Table 20-1   Calculation of Life Insurance Needs

Years of Income to Replace	*Multiply Annual After-Tax Income* By*
5	4.5
10	8.5
20	15
30	20

*You can roughly determine your annual after-tax income in one of two ways. You can get out last year's tax return (and Form W-2) and calculate it by subtracting the federal, state, and Social Security taxes you paid from your gross employment income. Or you can estimate it by multiplying your gross income by 80 percent if you're a low-income earner, 70 percent if you're a moderate-income earner, or 60 percent if you're a high-income earner. (You need to replace only after-tax, not pre-tax, income because life insurance policy payouts are not taxed.)

One way to determine the amount of life insurance to buy is to think about how much you'll need to pay for major debts or expenditures, such as your mortgage, other loans, and college for your children. For example, if you'd like your spouse to have enough of a life insurance death benefit to be able to pay off half of your mortgage and pay for half of your children's college education, then simply add half of your mortgage amount to half of their estimated college costs and buy that amount of life insurance.

Factoring in Social Security survivor benefits

Social Security, if you're covered, can provide *survivors' benefits* to your spouse and children. (However, if your surviving spouse earns more than about $20,000 per year, he or she isn't going to get any coverage.) If either you or your spouse anticipates earning less than $20,000 per year, however, you may want to factor this into how much life insurance to buy. Contact the Social Security Administration at 800-772-1213 (or visit its Web site at www.ssa.gov) and request Form 7004, which gives you an estimate of your Social Security benefits.

The Social Security Administration can tell you how much your survivors will receive per month in the event of your death. You should factor this benefit into the amount of life insurance that you calculate in Table 20-1.

Dispelling common life insurance myths

Insurance salespeople know the buttons to push to get you interested in buying the wrong kind of life insurance. The following are typical arguments that they make for purchasing cash value polices, followed by more reasonable perspectives.

"It's all paid up after X years. You don't want to be paying life insurance premiums for the rest of your life, do you?"

Agents pitching *cash value life insurance* show you all sorts of projections that imply that after the first ten or so years of paying your premiums, you won't need to pay more premiums to keep the life insurance in force. The only reason that you may be able to stop paying premiums is that you've poured so much extra money into the policy in the early years of payment. Cash value life insurance costs about eight times as much as term.

Imagine that you're currently paying $500 a year for auto insurance and an insurance company comes along and offers you a policy for $4,000 per year. The representative tells you that after 10 years, you can stop paying and still keep your same coverage. I'm sure that you wouldn't fall for this sales tactic, but many people do when they buy cash value life insurance.

"You won't be able to afford term insurance when you're older."

As you get older, the cost of term insurance increases because the probability of your dying rises. But life insurance isn't something you need all your life! You typically buy life insurance in your younger years when financial commitments and obligations outweigh financial assets. Twenty or thirty years later, the reverse should be true.

When you retire, you probably won't need life insurance to protect your employment income because you won't have any to protect! You may need life insurance when you're raising a family or have a substantial mortgage, but by the time you retire, the kids should be out on their own (you hope!), and the mortgage should be paid down.

In the meantime, term insurance saves you a tremendous amount of money. For most people, it takes 20 to 30 years for the premium they pay on a term insurance policy to finally to equal the premium they've been paying all along on a comparable amount of cash value life insurance.

"You can borrow against the cash value at a low rate of interest."

Such a deal! That's your money in the policy, remember? If you deposited money in a savings or money market account, how would you like to pay for the privilege of borrowing your own money back?

"Your cash value grows tax-deferred."

Ah, a glimmer of truth at last. The fact that the cash value portion of your policy grows without taxation until you withdraw it is true. But if you want tax-deferral of your investment balances, take advantage of such savings plans as 401(k)s, 403(b)s, SEP-IRAs, and Keoghs. Such accounts give you an immediate tax deduction for your current contributions in addition to growth without taxation until withdrawal.

Life insurance tends to be a mediocre investment. The insurance company quotes you an interest rate for the first year only. After that, the company pays you what it wants. If you don't like the future interest rates, you can be penalized for quitting the policy. Would you ever invest your money in a bank account that quoted an interest rate for the first year only and then penalized you for moving your money within the next seven to ten years?

"It's forced savings."

Many agents argue that a cash value plan is better than nothing — at least it's forcing you to save. This reasoning is silly because so many people drop cash value life insurance policies after just a few years of paying into them.

You can accomplish "forced savings" without using life insurance. Any retirement savings account can be set up for automatic monthly transfers. Employers offering such a plan can deduct contributions from your paycheck — and it doesn't even take a commission! You can also set up monthly electronic transfers from your bank checking account to contribute to mutual funds.

"Life insurance isn't part of your taxable estate."

If the ownership of a life insurance policy is properly structured, it's true that the death benefit is free of estate taxes. This part of the sales pitch is about the only sound reason that exists for buying cash value life insurance.

Insurance salespeople aggressively push cash value policies because of the high commissions. An insurance salesperson can make *eight to ten times more money* (yes, you read that right) selling you a cash value policy than he can selling you term insurance.

Because of the high cost of cash value policies relative to the cost of term, you're more likely to buy less life insurance coverage than you need — that's the sad part of the insurance industry's pushing of this stuff. *The vast majority of life insurance buyers need more protection than they can afford to buy with cash value coverage.*

Cash value life insurance makes sense for a small percentage of people — such as a small-business owner who owns a business worth more than one to two million dollars and who wouldn't want his heirs to be forced to sell the business to pay estate taxes in the event of his death.

Purchase low-cost term insurance and do your investing separately. Life insurance is rarely a permanent need; over time, you can gradually reduce the amount of term insurance that you carry as you accumulate more assets.

Saving Money on Insurance Costs

The point of insurance is to protect against losses that would be financially catastrophic to you, not to smooth out the bumps of everyday life. The following information shows you how to save money on insurance and still have adequate protection in the unfortunate event that you actually *need* it.

Avoiding small-potato policies

A good insurance policy can seem expensive. A policy that doesn't cost much, on the other hand, can fool you into thinking that you're getting something for next to nothing. Policies that cost little also cover little — they're priced low because they aren't covering large potential losses.

The following common "small potato" insurance policies are generally a waste of your hard-earned dollars. These policies aren't worth the cost relative to the small potential benefit.

- ✔ **Extended warranty and repair plans:** Isn't it ironic that right after the salesperson persuades you to buy a television, computer, or car — in part by saying how reliable the goods are — he tries try to convince you to spend more money to insure against the failure of the item? If the stuff is so good, why do you need insurance?

 Product manufacturers' warranties typically cover any problems that occur in the first three months to a year. After that, should you need to pay for a repair out of your own pocket, it won't be a financial catastrophe. Extended warranty and repair plans are expensive and unnecessary insurance policies.

- ✔ **Home warranty plans:** If your real estate agent or the seller of the home wants to pay the cost of a home warranty plan for you, turning down the offer would be ungracious. But don't buy this type of plan for yourself. In addition to requiring some sort of fee (around $30 to $50) if you need a contractor to come out and look at a problem, home warranty plans limit how much they'll pay for problems.

 Your money is much better spent on hiring a competent inspector to uncover problems and fix them *before* you buy the home. Everyone buying a house should expect to spend money on repairs and maintenance.

- ✔ **Dental insurance:** If your employer pays for dental insurance, take advantage of it. But you shouldn't pay for this coverage on your own. Dental insurance generally covers a couple of teeth cleanings each year and limits payment for more expensive work.

- ✔ **Credit life and credit disability policies:** Many direct-mail and credit card firms try to sell policies that pay a small benefit in case you die with an outstanding loan (a credit life policy) or that pay a small monthly income in the event of a disability (a credit disability policy). Some companies sell insurance to pay off your credit card bill in the event of your death or disability.

 Given what little insurance you're buying, these policies are extraordinarily expensive. When you need life or disability insurance, purchase it. But get enough coverage and buy it in a separate, cost-effective policy.

 One exception to the above rule is if you are in poor health and you can buy these insurance policies without a medical evaluation. In that case, these policies may be the only ones you have access to. This is another reason that these policies are expensive. If you're in good health, you're paying for the people with poor health who can enroll without a medical examination and who undoubtedly make more claims.

✔ **Daily hospitalization insurance:** Hospitalization insurance policies that pay a certain amount per day, such as $100, are often sold to older people. These policies prey on people's fears of running up big hospital bills.

What you really need is a comprehensive (major medical) health insurance policy. One day in the hospital can lead to several thousand dollars in charges, so that a $100-per-day policy may pay for less than you expect.

✔ **Insuring packages in the mail:** You buy a $40 gift for a friend, and when you go to the post office to ship it, the clerk asks whether you want to insure it. For a couple of bucks, you think, why not? The U.S. Postal Service may have a bad reputation for many reasons, but it rarely loses or damages things. Spend your money on another gift instead!

✔ **Contact lens insurance:** Yes, this insurance really does exist! The money goes to replace your contacts if you lose or tear them. Lenses are cheap. Don't waste your money.

✔ **Little stuff riders:** Many policies that are worth buying, such as auto and disability insurance, have all sorts of add-on *riders*. These bells and whistles are extras that insurance agents like to sell because of the high profit margin. On auto insurance policies, for example, you can buy a rider for a few bucks per year that pays you $25 each time your car needs to be towed. Having your vehicle towed isn't going to bankrupt you, so it isn't worth insuring against.

Likewise, small insurance policies that are sold as add-ons to bigger insurance policies are usually unnecessary and overpriced. For example, you can buy some disability insurance policies with a small amount of life insurance added on. If you need life insurance, purchasing a sufficient amount in a separate policy is less costly.

Conserving money with higher deductibles

Most insurance policies have *deductibles* — the maximum amount you must pay in the event of a loss before your insurance coverage kicks in. On many policies, such as auto and homeowner/renter coverage, most folks opt for a $100 to $250 deductible.

Here are two benefits to opting for a higher deductible:

- ✔ **You save premium dollars.** Year in and year out, you can enjoy the lower cost of an insurance policy with a high deductible. You may be able to shave 15 to 20 percent off the cost of your policy. Suppose, for example, that you can reduce the cost of your policy by $150 per year by raising your deductible from $250 to $1,000. That $750 worth of coverage is costing you $150 per year. Thus, you would need to have a claim of $1,000 or more every five years — highly unlikely — to come out ahead. If you're that accident-prone — guess what? — the insurance company will crank up your premiums.

- ✔ **You don't have the hassles of filing small claims.** If you have a $300 loss on a policy with a $100 deductible, you need to file a claim to get your $200 (the amount you're covered for after your deductible). Filing an insurance claim can take hours of time and can be an aggravating experience. In some cases, you may even have your claim denied after jumping through all the necessary hoops.

When you have low deductibles, you may file more claims (although this doesn't necessarily mean that you'll get more money). After filing more claims, you may be rewarded with higher premiums — in addition to the headache of preparing those blasted forms! Filing too many claims may even cause cancellation of your coverage!

Saving on your taxes when spending on healthcare

If you expect to have out-of-pocket medical expenses, find out whether your employer offers a *flexible spending* or *healthcare reimbursement* account. These accounts enable you to pay for uncovered medical expenses with pre-tax dollars. If, for example, you're in a combined 35-percent federal and state income tax bracket, these accounts allow you to pay for needed healthcare at a 35-percent discount. In addition to your out-of-pocket healthcare costs, these accounts can be used to pay for vision and dental care.

Be forewarned of some major stumbling blocks to saving through medical reimbursement accounts. First, you need to elect to save money from your paycheck prior to the beginning of each plan year. The only exception is at the time of a "life change" such as a family member's death, marriage, spouse's job change, divorce, or birth of a child. You also need to use the money within the year saved because these accounts contain a "use it or lose it" feature.

Insuring expensive teen drivers

If you have a teenage driver in your household, in addition to worrying a lot more, you're going to spend more on auto insurance. Try to keep your teenager out of your car as long as possible.

If you allow your teenager to drive, you can take a number of steps to avoid spending all your take-home pay on auto insurance bills:

- ✔ **Make sure that your teen does well in school.** Some insurers offer discounts if your child is a high-academic achiever and has successfully completed a nonrequired driver's education class.

- ✔ **Get price quotes from several insurers to see how adding your teen driver to your policy affects the cost.**

- ✔ **Have your teenager share in the costs of using the car.** If you pay all the insurance, gas, oil changing, and maintenance bills, your teenager won't value the privilege of using your "free" car.

Of course, letting teens drive shouldn't be just about keeping your insurance bills to a minimum. Auto accidents are the number one cause of death for teens. So, before you let your teen drive, be sure to educate him or her about the big risks of driving and the importance of not riding in a car driven by someone who is intoxicated. Also be sure that your teens drive in safe cars.

Finding ways to save on home insurance premiums

The following is a list of things you can do to save on home insurance premiums. Even if the following suggestions don't put a dent in your insurance premiums, you can at least reduce risk, your chance of ever having a claim, and the severity of any claim you do file.

- ✔ Install a UL approved smoke detector on each floor. Replace the batteries yearly (doing so on a your birthday is an easy way to remember).

- ✔ Install a UL approved dry-chemical fire extinguisher in the kitchen for grease fires. Check it periodically to make sure it's fully charged.

- ✔ Install a dead-bolt lock on all access doors.

- ✔ Install a motion detector alarm.

✔ Install a central burglar-and-fire alarm. The savings are huge for doing so — often 10 to 20 percent.

✔ Have your fireplace, flues, and chimney cleaned regularly to prevent chimney fires and all the horrible interior smoke damage that results.

✔ If you want a wood stove, buy a UL approved one and have it professionally installed. Don't leave the stove unattended and have it professionally cleaned annually.

✔ Change your locks immediately if your purse or keys are ever stolen.

✔ Install a sump pump system to prevent damage from ground water, which is excluded in virtually every homeowner's policy. Be sure to buy optional sump pump failure coverage.

✔ Keep trees trimmed so that they're safely away from the house.

✔ If you have a swimming pool, have an approved fence installed. Take out the diving board and add a locking pool cover to prevent unauthorized use.

✔ Install a carbon monoxide detector.

Part VI
Fun, Fun, Fun: Hobbies and Entertainment

The 5th Wave   By Rich Tennant

@RICHTENNANT

"The lost art of conversation isn't lost at all. It's been kidnapped and held hostage by your sister-in-law."

In this part . . .

*A*lthough "free time" may sound like a foreign phrase to you, everyone needs some time once in a while to relax and let loose. Perhaps your interests include

- ✔ Packing your bags and journeying to new, exotic destinations
- ✔ Hosting the perfect party with just the right mix of guests, food, music, and atmosphere
- ✔ Knowing exactly what to say in a conversation or to give as a gift
- ✔ Getting in touch with your wild side by enjoying the wonders of nature
- ✔ Collecting objects of beauty — or just losing yourself in a beautiful painting

Wherever your passions lie, the following chapters give beginners — as well as savvy hobbyists — insider tricks-of-the-trade so that you can get more out of your precious free time.

Chapter 21

A Touch of Class: Antiques and Art

• •

In This Chapter

▶ Finding the best deal on antiques

▶ Avoiding bad deals (and dealers)

▶ Enjoying museum visits

• •

A ntiques and art can add so much to your life: esthetic beauty, a sense of history, creative passion, and a lot more. With the easy suggestions in this chapter, your next visit to an antique shop or art gallery can be a fascinating experience. So, dive right in!

Going Antiquing

Each antique has a story to tell, and part of the fun of collecting is gathering those stories.

Collecting antiques is like falling in love: You're constantly discovering new and interesting aspects of the antiques. The more you know, the more you want to know. You never get bored with your explorations, and you want the relationship to last forever. Collecting antiques is also very personal. Each carefully chosen object has its own charm, appeal, and personality, much like the very people who collect.

Whether you're purchasing antiques because of their beauty, or because you simply love older things, or because you're hoping that they'll hold their value, the best rule is to buy what you like.

The following section covers how to get the most out of a visit to an antique store or auction — as well as tips for avoiding getting hoodwinked.

Collectible or antique: What's the difference?

A "legal" antique is something that's 100 years old. This definition was created so that the customs people would know how to tax things. A collectible is just about anything people want to collect that's younger than 100 years. Popular collectibles include Hummel figurines, collector's plates, Depression glass, various toys, and baseball cards.

Collectibles are more volatile than antiques. If you want a collectible that can hold its value and grow up to be a desirable antique, you need to determine the following:

✔ Is the item readily available or quite scarce?

✔ Is the item still being made today?

✔ How easy is the item to reproduce?

✔ How desirable is the item?

Just to keep things from being too cut and dried, some early 20th century items (from the Art Nouveau, Art Deco, and Art Moderne periods) are simply too magnificent to accept the word *collectible.* These "antiques-in-waiting" are truly masterpieces and are often valued more highly than many true antiques.

Formulating your antiquing plan of attack

Before you embark on an antiques shopping spree, you need to figure out your goals. The following questions can help you define and focus your antiquing interests:

✔ **Do you want to own a few antiques of great quality or more antiques of less quality?** The way you approach antique acquisitions will probably be similar to the way you approach other purchases. Buying fewer antiques of greater quality implies a tolerance for delayed gratification and a willingness to research your subject and shop around. If you like quick trips with fast results, you may love getting more items that aren't as costly. (This approach also works if you like long shopping trips with lots of instantaneous gratification.)

Your goals may change as you gain more knowledge of antiques. Many people start out buying inexpensive things and gradually upgrade their collections.

✔ **Do you want to specialize?** Because antiquing is such a wide field, many people develop areas of specialization or expertise. Your specialties can be as broad or as narrow as you want. When you learn about specific areas, you can spot good deals. You know what colors are unusual, what price ranges are normal, and what styles are considered most desirable.

Many collectors choose their specialty by the objects they're drawn to and the types of things they like to study and learn about. Part of developing a specialty is learning about how the object is made, getting hooked up with the collectors' groups, and subscribing to trade journals.

Specialties range from concentrating on

- A certain *period,* such as furniture from the Victorian era
- A *type of object,* such as boxes or teacups
- A certain *category* of collecting, such as glass or porcelain
- Works by *a specific company,* such as Meissen porcelain or Fenton Art Glass
- A certain *pattern of a company,* such as Lincoln Drape pattern attributed to The Boston & Sandwich Glass Company

✔ **Do you want the aesthetic, the functional, or a combo?** You can incorporate functional objects, such as antique desks, chairs, beds, and silverware right into your daily life. Most antiques bring a beauty along with their functionality. By contrast, some people prefer antiques that are simply lovely to look at and display — cut glass, porcelain figurines, or miniatures.

✔ **How do you want to budget your antique purchases?** Whatever your style of purchasing, start out small — and definitely set a monthy or yearly budget for antiquing.

✔ **Where do you plan to put your antiques?** If you have limited space and unlimited appreciation of antiques, ask yourself where you plan to put your antiques. Some antiques are rather grand size-wise and resist being squeezed through contemporary doorways. Before you load an ornately carved four-poster bed into your Volkswagen, make sure that you have enough room to make your bed and lie in it.

If large hungry puppies roam your house, you may not want to see them teething on a Louis XVI chair. Some tables or chairs may not be sturdy enough for thudding children; others can withstand almost anything. Basically, you want your antiques to have a safe place to live where you can see and enjoy them.

Buying the best you can afford

Here's a failsafe purchasing strategy: Always buy the finest piece that you can afford at the time. You will get more long-term enjoyment from an antique that's truly well-made and wonderfully designed.

You're generally better off, investment-wise, to own one top-quality porcelain piece than three lesser-quality pieces or even more than three quality pieces in poor condition. The finest quality work usually maintains its value and resells more easily. Lesser quality antiques are harder to sell and may not hold up as well physically.

"The best you can afford" doesn't necessarily mean the most expensive piece — it means purchasing the best example of the type of antique that you love. If you feel insecure about choosing high-quality antiques, consult with a trusted dealer or an antique-loving friend.

Plunge into antiquing with small purchases while you develop your eye and figure out what areas you want to specialize in. The more you learn about antiques, the better chance you have of getting good value and good quality for your money.

Knowing the five signs of a valuable antique

Before you buy any antique, run it through the RADAR test for value:

- ✔ **Rarity:** A piece may be rare if only a few were made in the first place, if few of the original pieces remain, or if the color, style, subject matter, design, size, or shape is unusual.

- ✔ **Aesthetics:** When all the elements of a piece blend together in perfect harmony and give the item an overall pleasing appearance, then that item really has "it" in the aesthetics department. Some folks believe that an object's aesthetic value is a matter of personal taste. On the other hand, some pieces of art and furniture have almost universal aesthetic appeal. Visiting art galleries and museums is one great way to see antique objects of art that are considered aesthetically pleasing. Books about your areas of interest also show the better pieces.

- ✔ **Desirability:** Desirability is defined by what's in vogue in the current market. A few decades after Tiffany created his now-famous lamps, some people thought of them as gaudy, and so prices were steals by today's standards. Now people covet Tiffany's artistry.

✔ **Authenticity:** Part of the fun of antiques is separating truth from fiction. As technology and the ability to reproduce items become more advanced, identifying the authentic antique becomes more difficult. In the next section, you find clues and tips to help you analyze whether an antique is authentic.

✔ **Really great condition:** The less that was done to the original item to alter it, the more it's worth. That is, the fewer the additions or deletions over the years, the better.

When you find an antique that meets these five criteria, you've probably found an item that's likely to appreciate in value as the years go by.

Separating the real stuff from the fakes

By knowing a little about the periods of furniture manufacture and by looking carefully at the furniture, you'll soon be able to tell the good old guys from the new kids on the block.

You can't rely on just one, or even two, clues. Look at all the following features as you ferret out old furniture.

Dovetail joints

Dovetailing is one clue that the piece may have some age. A *dovetail joint* is the corner joint that brings two perpendicular pieces of wood together. You need to open a drawer to see the dovetailing inside. As a rule, the fewer number of dovetails on each corner, the older the piece. An early 18th century drawer may be joined with one large dovetail. In the later Victorian period, furniture was made with machine-cut dovetailing, often having eight or more small dovetails on a drawer.

Dovetails alone do not assure age. Some high quality new furniture also has dovetails.

Saw marks

Power sawing and sanding has smoothed away all but the faintest traces of saw marks on modern furniture. Look for saw marks on the underside of antique tables, chairs, and drawers, and on the backs of case pieces.

Wear marks

Wear marks are the natural dents, dings, and wearing down furniture gets from daily use. Some specific wear tips:

- ✔ **Chair wear.** Chair legs are a great place to look for wear marks and repairs. The front stretcher (the pieces of wood that stretch between chair legs) should have considerably more wear than the other stretchers. Also, look for shorter back legs from frequent rocking.

- ✔ **Table wear.** The tops of tables sustain most of the wear, although the legs may have endured some kicking. Dents, scratches, and splotches all are signs of natural wear. Sometimes the natural look can go too far. Look at the tabletop and ask yourself how displeasing are the imperfections. If the piece is too beat up, you may need to consider refinishing.

  Try to avoid refinishing a table, as this can diminish its value. Some restoration specialists can touch up even areas that look severe, without refinishing the entire surface.

- ✔ **Case piece wear.** Look for signs of smoothness and wear on the bottoms and sides of drawers. Sometimes, drawers are so worn down that they wiggle around.

  If you want a more functional drawer, you may need to consult a restoration specialist. Choose someone who can preserve as much of the original drawer as possible.

  Look for signs of repair, such as new wood, on the sides of drawers. Because the repair doesn't show — if it's done well — it doesn't greatly diminish the value of the piece.

  Stop and smell your drawers. The insides of old drawers have the kind of musty, old scent you notice when you climb a flight of stairs into the attic of an old house. Reproductions smell of lacquer or fresh wood.

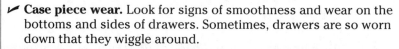

Damaged goods

Damage affects the value of different categories of antiques in different ways. Flaws you can look out for when examining antiques include scratches, breaks, tears, gouges, chips, cracks, signs of repair, missing parts, and discoloration.

Look carefully at each item you're considering buying, inside and out. You want to understand the damage and the changes the piece has undergone so that you can understand if the price pleases you. Also, knowing the flaws of a piece can be a negotiating tool.

The general rule is: How much does the damage bother you? Anytime a piece sustains damage, its value decreases; but a repair job well done that maintains the integrity of the piece can often increase the market appeal of a piece.

Scribe marks

The 18th century craftsmen marked their spot with a knife or cabinetmaker's scribe tool. The *scribe marks* are shallow lines cleanly scratched in the wood. You can usually find scribe marks flying out of the ends of dovetails and almost always near joints.

Wormholes

Wormholes are small uneven holes made by "woodworms," which are, in fact, beetle larvae. Old holes are irregularly shaped and winding (so that a pin can't go straight through them), and they're dark, filled with dirt and wax, and free from fine powder. New holes are dusted with sawdust.

Woodworms usually avoid mahogany, preferring pine, maple, oak, and walnut.

Hardware

Having the original hardware is great. But replacement hardware is common and may not significantly diminish the value. Many old pieces have gone through several changes of hardware, depending on the age of the piece. When you understand the evolution of pegs, nails, screws, and brasses, you can more accurately note the time period of the piece.

The earlier and rarer the piece and the higher the quality, the more important it is to have the original hardware. For a wonderful and more "ordinary" antique, small hardware, such as nails and screws, that's been replaced with skill and a sense of aesthetics doesn't have a big effect on the piece's value. The larger and more prominent the hardware is on a piece, the more significant the loss of value if it's replaced.

Bargaining basics

You've been reading your price guides, you've tiptoed through antique malls, and you've asked questions. Now, you're ready to buy, so you need to be ready to negotiate like an antiquing pro:

- ✔ **Be discrete.** Draw the dealer quietly aside if you want to negotiate.

- ✔ **Handle all merchandise with respect and care.** Dealers are more at ease, and therefore more open to negotiating, when they trust you around their antiques.

- ✔ **Avoid an overly aggressive approach.** Just because the dealer has something for a long time doesn't mean that he wants to sell it for a cheap price. Antique shops don't always have the turnover that's more common in other retail establishments. Because antiques have an intrinsic value (the value generally holds constant or can increase), dealers are willing to wait for the right buyer.

✔ **Avoid overly criticizing a piece.** Dealers can feel very sensitive about having their merchandise criticized. A piece marked "As is" tells you that the dealer knows that things are wrong with the piece. When you need to point out problems with the piece and make comments on its condition, do so in a straightforward and non-accusatory manner.

✔ **Question the price:** If the price marked on the piece of your dreams is higher than the price guides or higher than you want to pay, ask: "How did you come by that price? I'm under the impression the value of a piece like this is (insert the amount)." A reputable dealer should be willing to explain the price of the piece — you may even get an education on the history for a particular piece or an entire category of antique collectable.

✔ **Always make an offer.** Even if you know an asking price is good, try for a better price. Put on a deadpan face and ask, "Would you be willing to do any better on this piece?" After you consider the answer you might gently ask, "Is this your best price?" Or suggest a specific price. Now the dealer knows that you're a serious buyer; he's been offered a deal, and he may be willing to take it.

✔ **Look for (or try to create) package deals.** Trying to negotiate on more than one piece gives the dealer an excuse to give you a discount.

✔ **Find flaws the dealer didn't mention.** Perhaps you find a flaw that the dealer didn't even know about. Subtly remind the dealer that having the piece repaired will cost you. This bargaining tool is often worth 10 percent off or more (depending on the nature of the flaw). No dealer enjoys finding out he has inadvertently purchased damaged goods. It's not worth as much and he has to explain the flaw to future customers.

✔ **Go for the unusual.** Pieces that don't blend into the overall ambience of a shop are often great bargaining opportunities. Erotic pieces, hunting pictures, bronzes that feature dead animals or spiritual elements — often hang around a shop for a long time, looking for a buyer.

✔ **Ask whether the dealer has layaway.** Layaway is usually an interest free payment plan. Many dealers prefer layaway, because it promotes an ongoing relationship. If the dealer is strapped for cash, he may prefer an outright sale. In that case, ask whether paying in full will get you a better price.

✔ **Negotiate for other things.** If you can't get a lower price, try focusing on free delivery, repairs that may need to be made, having the piece cleaned or polished, installations (for such items as lights or large mirrors), or additional research or documentation.

When the dealer has a piece that's totally unusual and unique — or if the dealer has priced the piece appropriately to start with — he may not give a discount at all. If the piece is well-priced and stunning, follow your heart and pay the full price. More antique collectors bemoan the piece that got away than the piece they overpaid for.

Don't push the dealer to his discomfort level. If he says "This is my best" and holds firm, don't press. Remember that you're trying to build a relationship with the dealer. Hopefully, the day will come when the dealer offers you a discount without your even asking.

Appreciating Art

Art doesn't have to be stuffy, boring business. Adding a little art to your life can open your eyes to the beauty of the world around you. Who knows, you may even decide to begin collecting (or creating) art yourself!

Getting the most out of a museum visit

Here's how to visit any museum you've never been to like the pros do.

✔ **Get a postcard.** Go first to the gift shop. (Every museum has one.) Without fail, the pride of the museum's holdings are featured on postcards, enabling you to instantly discover the strengths of the place without getting lost or overwhelmed.

Buy a postcard of what you want to see in the galleries. Postcards are cheaper and are a whole lot easier to lug around than three-pound guidebooks. Proceed to the entrance, flash the card of the painting you want to see, and the guard will motion you to it. If you lose your way, simply flash another postcard at a guard and get further directions.

✔ **Make a "wish list."** As you tour a collection, write down the three items you'd like to steal — that is, the three best works in the entire collection. Share your selections and your reasons for selecting them with your touring partners. Great discussions usually follow.

✔ **Look at what you don't like.** Deliberately go to the galleries containing materials you know you don't like. You usually find something that surprises you. Also, ask the information desk what section of the museum is the least visited and take a look.

✔ **Become a member of the museum.** For freebies, discounts at the gift shops, and for the warm feeling you get when you know you're becoming a lifelong supporter of a place that honors beauty, artistic excellence, and the truth, nothing beats becoming a member of a museum.

✔ **Listen to some music.** Bring along a portable stereo and listen to classical or instrumental music — the combination of art and music can give you surprisingly new insights. Great music choices include Beethoven, Mozart, Saint-Saens, Puccini, Verdi, Telemann, Bach, and many types of chant.

✔ **Dress the part.** Dress as comfortably as you can while still being practical. In general, walking shoes are the best. Abroad, be sure that shorts as well as short sleeves are acceptable.

Buying art

The world of art collecting is full of pitfalls, forgeries, fakes, and just plain bad art. How do you avoid being taken? Forgeries aren't the only problems that you face as an art collector. You also need to know where and how to buy legitimate art. The following information covers some highlights of art collecting.

Never buy art for investment — only for the heart and the soul. Only two percent of all contemporary art ever goes up in value, and old masters can flip up and down wildly.

Knowing where to buy art

You may find a Rembrandt etching in a flea market — it's happened — but the chances are equal to winning the lottery. The best place to buy virtually anything is through an art dealer, especially those dealers who've been in business for several generations and whose operations are run by descendants now.

When you enter an art gallery, be advised that some dealers may try to play the snooty game and sniff when you ask bluntly, "Where's the price list?" The majority, however, are dependent on drop-in business, so feel free to demand service. Be frank, and you'll get the same treatment.

What to collect (and avoid) in the art world

If you want to collect art, you must be aware of which types of art lend themselves to collecting. Not all types are equal for the budding collector:

✔ **Posters:** This somewhat overlooked, affordable field has some chance of modest price appreciation. Yet posters are multiples, and the frightening load of modern replicas that exist is pretty hard to detect.

✔ **Old masters:** Not many of these works are around, and the available ones are often in poor condition. Many auction houses refuse to hand out authenticity warranties on works produced before 1870.

✔ **Drawings:** Even great works are still relatively cheap. But on the downside, drawings are fragile and forgery is rampant. Drawings are super-sensitive to direct sunlight, and most damage can't be repaired. Overrestoration is standard, and many blemished drawings are bleached, giving them an unpleasing, bone-dry white look.

✔ **Prints:** Many great artists made prints, which are readily available at fair prices. Nonetheless, a legion of phonies is floating around out there.

✔ **Contemporary art:** Contemporary art means the artist is living. At least you know that you're not getting a fake, but the most minuscule percentage of living artists will be remembered in a decade. Yet, so what? You aren't buying art as a hedge, so purchase what you love.

✔ **Crafts:** Crafts include artistically inventive textiles, jewelry, glass, and pottery. Crafts are always most highly recommended. The prices are right — and the creators are dedicated (in general) to making honest and solid pieces, the manufacture of which is normally impeccable, making such pieces last for centuries. In a few decades, pieces slightly looked down on today as "mere crafts" may be considered the fine and expressive art.

Asking questions

Don't expect to be treated like a mall customer when you're in an art gallery. Art dealers are in love with their merchandise and deep down they don't really want to part with it. Not that you have to arm wrestle them to allow you to buy, but they do appreciate enthusiasm and a willingness to learn.

The best approach is to ask for a lesson or ask a few probing questions. Good, passionate dealers don't hedge on questions of price and authenticity — and typically they teach you a lot about a style of art or a particular artist in the process.

Don't forget to ask about price directly. In fact, if a dealer doesn't quote the price, doesn't bargain a little, doesn't hand you a guarantee of genuineness, balks when you ask for a detailed condition report or a solid provenance, and fails to spell out clearly the terms of getting your money back, make for the door. And spread the word around.

Taking your chances at an auction

Buying at auction is more of a gamble, and the business, although cleaned up in recent years, is still a let-the-buyer-beware, read-the-small-print operation. Auction houses certainly allow you to examine a work that you're interested in, but far less easily than at an art gallery. Your best protection is to read very carefully the qualifying language printed in the front of every sales catalogue.

If you're going to place bids yourself, settle on a final, hard price and never waver. Sit so that the auctioneer can see you. Bid with the paddle or with an articulate voice — no winks or touching the right jacket lapel or some other arcane and confusing gesture. It's okay to ask the auctioneer right in the middle of the fray to split the bid and to indicate to you where the last bid came from. It's also okay to make the auction house prove that the chap on the telephone is or was really on the line.

Chapter 22

Getting Away: Traveling Near and Far

* *

In This Chapter

▶ Picking the perfect destination

▶ Finding a fantastic time to travel

▶ Protecting yourself abroad

* *

*T*ravelers today are lucky. Not only do you have, high-speed transportation, but you also have access to boundless information and services on the Internet. Gone are the days when you booked way-too-expensive transportation to a place you knew nothing about, arriving only to realize that you packed all the wrong clothes.

Choice Travel Destinations for Every Interest

With so many great places to visit in the U.S. and abroad, the following material is merely a sampling of some of the top destinations, whatever your favorite leisure activity:

Must-see U.S. sites for wine lovers

You don't have to go to France to sample some of the world's finest wines. Wonderful wineries exist all across the U.S., and wine aficionados will thrill to visit the following top vineyards.

> ✔ **Napa Valley, California:** Many of California's most prestigious wineries are located throughout the small Napa Valley, where nearly 300 wineries have managed to find space.

✔ **Sonoma, California:** Whereas many of Napa's wineries are showy, most of Sonoma's are rustic, country-like, and laid back.

✔ **Mendocino and Lake Counties, California:** Drive up the coastline to the quaint, old town of Mendocino — perhaps with a side trip to view the magnificent, giant redwoods. Tourists are more scarce than in Napa or Sonoma.

✔ **Santa Cruz, California:** Standing atop one of the isolated Santa Cruz Mountains, the rugged, wild beauty of this area has attracted some of the best winemakers in the state.

✔ **Monterey, California:** Monterey County has a little bit of everything — a beautiful coastline, the chic town of Carmel, a few gigantic wine firms, and lots of small ones.

✔ **Willamette Valley, Oregon:** Directly south of the city of Portland in northwest Oregon, the cool Willamette Valley has established itself in the last 25 years as the most important wine region in Oregon.

✔ **Finger Lakes, New York:** This scenic region in western New York produces approximately 85 percent of New York's wines.

Great golf courses for golf nuts (and the spouses who love them)

Golfers love new challenges. Non-golfing spouses just love getting away! Try sampling some of the finest public courses across the U.S.

✔ **Bethpage State Park Golf Course, Long Island, New York:** This course is a treat to play, it's a real challenge, and the greens fees won't bust your credit line.

✔ **Cog Hill No. 4, Lemont, Illinois:** Cog Hill has a great layout and can host a major event without doing much to the course. If you want to really find out how your game is, show up and go to the back trees.

✔ **Grayhawk Golf Club (Talon and Raptor), Scottsdale, Arizona:** Located up in the higher desert of north Scottsdale, this beautiful public facility has it all: a great clubhouse, two championship golf courses, and a great practice facility.

✔ **The Homestead (Cascades Course), Hot Springs, Virginia:** This old golf facility — built in 1892 — has one of the most peaceful settings you will ever behold. Grandeur is everywhere, and the course is fantastic. Settle in and enjoy the lifestyle.

✔ **Torrey Pines Golf Course, San Diego, California:** Torrey is well maintained and offers many demanding holes that are tougher than the winds kicked up by the Pacific Ocean. (During the right time of the year, you can see whales migrating to Mexico.)

✔ **Tournament Players Course (TPC) at Sawgrass, Ponte Vedra, Florida:** Carved out of the trees and swamps near Jacksonville, this course plays host to one of the biggest tournaments of the year — The Players Championship.

✔ **Whispering Springs, Fond du Lac, Wisconsin:** Whispering Springs is one the most beautiful courses in the Midwest and a good deal at less than $30 per person.

Six favorite cruise destinations

You can find a cruise package that fits in just about any budget or special interest. The following are some the best ports of call:

✔ **Cozumel, Mexico:** Ancient ruins, great shopping, snorkeling, and fun bars — Cozumel has something for everyone.

✔ **Bermuda:** If the gorgeous pink sand and mild temperatures don't grab you, the very proper British atmosphere of this island nation will — it's a place that's genteel, orderly, and downright romantic.

✔ **Nice, France:** The gateway to the French Riviera, Nice offers wonderful museums, an impressive beachside boulevard and beaches, outdoor cafes for people-watching, great restaurants, friendly locals, and a casual atmosphere.

✔ **Juneau, Alaska:** Alaska's capital city is surrounded by water, glaciers, mountains, and wilderness — all of which make one of the prettiest settings for a city you can find anywhere.

✔ **Key West, Florida:** Funky, barefoot, and casual, the city "Papa" Hemingway helped make famous is great fun. Key West features a colorful cast of characters and offbeat museums.

✔ **Santoríni, Greece:** Looking picture-perfect, the cliff-top towns impress you with their whitewashed houses against a usually blue sky. From the port, you can take a donkey or cable car up 1,000 feet to Fira, where shops, cafes, and art galleries abound.

Top spots for kicking back in the Caribbean

The main reason most folks go to the Caribbean is to relax on the beach. You can find many different kinds of beaches to suit almost anything you want to do. Some favorites:

✔ **Bathsheba, Barbados:** Giant boulders and crashing waves make for a perfect spot to watch the sunrise. The beach isn't for swimming, but you'll love the view.

✔ **Chenay Bay, St. Croix, U.S. Virgin Islands:** In a calm, protected bay, local moms bring their kids to splash in the placid sea along with visiting children. It's a relaxed atmosphere on the white sand beach where sea grapes and palms offer shade.

✔ **Condado, Puerto Rico:** One of the most famous Caribbean beaches (though not the prettiest), the Condado throbs with energy.

✔ **Loblolly Beach, Anegada, British Virgin Islands:** Known for its famed Caribbean lobsters caught just offshore, this beach offers great snorkeling while your lunch is being grilled.

✔ **Magen's Bay, St. Thomas, U.S. Virgin Islands:** This beach is the don't-miss attraction on St. Thomas. An ideal spot for swimming and sunning, this half-mile stretch is protected by two peninsulas.

✔ **Palm Beach, Aruba:** This gorgeous, palm-lined wide white strand is the quintessential Caribbean beach, plus it's clean and safe. Arrive early to snag a cabana. During the evenings, go from hotel to hotel enjoying the beach parties.

✔ **Seven Mile Beach, Grand Cayman:** Despite the crowds, you can't beat this beautiful white strand for every kind of water fun.

Of course, not everyone enjoys the beach, so here are two great vacation spots in the Caribbean if you hate getting sand in your shoes:

✔ **Blue Mountains, Jamaica:** At Strawberry Hill, high above Kingston, you can relax at the Aveda Spa, hike the coffee plantations high in the Blue Mountains, and linger over the wild flowers that dot the mountainsides.

✔ **Old San Juan, Puerto Rico:** Cobblestone streets and gorgeous architecture in this colonial city will remind you of Spain. The bustling art scene, great restaurants, and upscale shopping can keep you thoroughly entertained.

Six great European events

A great way to tour Europe is to plan your vacation around a single large festival or event. Celebrate with the locals, take tons of pictures, and make some unforgettable memories at any of the following events:

✔ **Carnevale, Venice, Italy (and just about everywhere else):** Venice is famous for its elegant-yet-drunken masked balls, but anywhere that you see Carnevale is an experience in itself:

Madrid, Spain; Livorno, Italy; and Nice, France. Carnevale starts two or three weeks before Ash Wednesday (usually in late February) and culminates on the final Tuesday ("Mardi Gras") that immediately precedes Lent.

✔ **Shakespeare season, Stratford-upon-Avon, England:** Fans of great theater will relish this experience. The Royal Shakespeare Company performs its season here, where Shakespeare was born and where he also retired. The season runs from April through January.

✔ **Palio, Siena, Italy:** One of the highlights of the Italian summer is this breakneck, bareback, anything-goes horse race that goes around the sloping, dirt-covered main piazza of medieval Siena. The parties held before and after the horse race are street feasts to behold, no matter who wins. The race occurs twice each summer, July 2 and August 16.

✔ **Bastille Day, Paris, France:** France celebrates its nation's birthday with street fairs, parades, feasts, and pageants, starting with a procession along the Champs-Elysées and ending with fireworks over Montmartre. Bastille Day is July 14.

✔ **Bloemencorso, Amsterdam, the Netherlands:** In a country obsessed with blooms, you can experience one of the major flower festivals. The event (the first Saturday in September) begins with a colorful parade of floral floats in the nearby flower market towns.

✔ **Oktoberfest, Munich, Germany:** This festival attracts tens of thousands of people who listen to brass bands, roast whole oxen, and sit under giant tents drinking liter-sized mugs of beer. Oktoberfest actually begins in mid-September. The first weekend in October is the final flourish.

Book your accommodations as soon as you can if you're traveling to a location where a major festival or cultural event is taking place. Accommodations book quickly, sometimes months in advance. Also, consider booking a room in a neighboring town.

Travel Planning

A little bit of planning can go a long way — especially when you're away from home. The following sections help you cover your bases for a variety of trips — from weekend getaways to major international holidays. So, before you get packin', get plannin'!

Choosing less-crowded times

Just about any destination isn't necessarily the busiest when it's at its best; it's the busiest when people have the time to come. Always expect high-season prices, the fewest available deals, and the biggest crowds during peak months — especially on weekends. Here are few other trip-booking tips:

- ✔ If you're planning a weekend trip to a hot destination, book as far in advance as possible — no matter what time of year you visit.

- ✔ If you're planning a one- or two-week vacation throughout a region or state, try to land in touristy areas midweek rather than on the weekend, when those otherwise restful spots become human zoos.

- ✔ Schedule your city visits on weekends — any excess of vacationers in the city is often nicely counterbalanced by the business travelers who've headed home for the weekend, and hotel rates are often lower.

Eight ways to fly cheap

Because you usually shell out more for airfare than anything else when planning a trip, knowing how to get the best ticket prices from airlines literally pays off. You can use the following tips both when purchasing online and at your neighborhood travel agency.

Buy your tickets well in advance

Airlines know that a traveler who really needs to get somewhere on short notice doesn't have much of a choice about routes and ticket prices and thus will pay a higher fare. To avoid the high-ticket prices you get when purchasing close to departure time, buy your tickets at least 21 days before the flight. (Calling more than 21 days in advance may get you an even better deal.)

The 21-day rule isn't set in stone; some airlines require more or less notice. To be on the safe side, call any airline you consider flying with and ask about their advance-purchase schedule.

Buy your tickets at the very last minute

Airlines can usually estimate the number of empty seats on a weekend flight (a flight that leaves on a Friday, Saturday, or a Sunday) by the Wednesday preceding the weekend. Airlines prefer to sell cheap tickets rather than to have empty seats. To fill empty seats in a hurry, the airlines offer last-minute fare sales.

How to spend your time on a European tour

The following info gives you an idea of the minimum amount of time to spend in Europe's major cities.

"Seeing" a city includes settling in, seeing the major sights, getting a taste for the place, and maybe going on one daytrip. You'll definitely miss important sights if you spend less time than recommended here.

Also remember to add on at least an extra day for each side trip or major excursion you want to take.

Amsterdam	2 to 3 days	Madrid	2 to 3 days
Athens	1 to 2 days	Munich	1 to 2 days
Barcelona	2 to 3 days	Paris	3 to 4 days
Bern/Alps	1 to 3 days	Prague	2 to 3 days
Florence	2 to 3 days	Rome	3 to 4 days
Edinburgh	1 to 2 days	Venice	2 to 3 days
Dublin	1 to 2 days	Vienna	1 to 3 days
London	3 to 4 days		

Of course, you must have a flexible schedule in order to take advantage of these great deals. If you have breathing room in your travel time, you can save an incredible amount of money, sometimes more than 50 percent off the published fare. Signing up for e-mail fare alerts with ticket agents and the airlines is the best way to find out about last-minute deals.

Fly on Tuesdays, Wednesdays, and Saturdays

Because of the traffic patterns of travelers, flying on some days of the week costs more than others. On most major airlines, Tuesdays, Wednesdays, and Saturdays are the cheapest days on which to fly.

Forget about this tip if the Tuesday, Wednesday, or Saturday you want to fly happens to be a holiday.

Expand your options

Don't expect the first combination of dates, airports, and flights to result in the cheapest fare. Getting good fares requires persistence and willingness to try many combinations and permutations.

When you use an online travel agency to check fares, most give you an option of how many choices you want returned from each flight query. Set this feature to a maximum number of choices, allowing you to view a wide range of available flights. You have to sift through some chaff to find the wheat.

Try all, great and small

Don't be afraid to fly smaller airlines. The little guys often have lower fares with fewer restrictions. In addition, when looking for a low airfare, you can't afford to play favorites with certain airports. If you live in a city with more than one airport, check the fares going through each.

Look for flights with plenty of empty seats

The inexpensive, less-restricted fares on a flight usually get snatched up pretty quickly. If you find a flight with just a few seats remaining, the seats you have to choose from are bound to be the expensive and restricted ones. Most online travel agencies have features that show the number of seats remaining in each class.

Visit travel agents in many neighborhoods

This tip really applies only to those who live in cities or regions that have diverse ethnic neighborhoods or large immigrant communities, such as New York or Los Angeles. If you're really going for a cheap fare, travel agents that service a Vietnamese or Polish community, for instance, are bound to have the best fares to Saigon or Warsaw.

These agents know that they can sell lots of seats on flights to their constituencies' country of origin, so they negotiate low fares from the airlines. It's a little bit sneaky, but the agents are happy to sell to anyone.

Talk to a travel agent

Even though the Internet is great for travel planning, you can still use online booking in conjunction with living, breathing travel agents. After you scout the Web for the best fares, call up your favorite travel agent and see what he can come up with. Who knows — he may make better the deals you find online.

Seeing it all without going nuts

The idea of planning a large-scale trip can seem overwhelming. Here are six ways to maximize your time and still see as much as you'd hoped.

✔ **Don't duplicate types of sights.** Every sight and city is unique and worth seeing in its own right, but let's face it: Visit several wineries, Gothic cathedrals, or amusement parks, and they all start to look the same. Pick one and move on.

✔ **Stay centrally located.** Use your limited time to see as much of an area as you can, rather than taking days to travel to all the peripheral corners, especially on your first trip. For example, if you're visiting Europe, think about skipping some of the more geographically remote countries, such as Scandinavia, Portugal, Spain, and especially Greece, because it takes forever to travel to them.

✔ **Select side trips prudently.** Daytrips are great because they add variety to your travels. Pick your excursions wisely and make sure these trips do not take time away from the major city you're visiting. Reserve a full day to see any destination that's more than a city bus ride away.

✔ **Go your separate ways.** If you plan six days in one city to accommodate the sightseeing wishes of each member of your family or travel group, you're wasting time. You don't have to spend every moment of a trip joined at the hip. Setting aside a single afternoon and letting three people go their own way can save a whole day and a half of travel time.

✔ **Practice extreme time-saving techniques.** No matter how pretty the countryside en route is, you can save a lot of precious vacation time by taking evening flights, night trains, or driving at night.

✔ **Know that you will probably come back to some locations.** Europe, Florida, California, and the Caribbean (to name a few popular travel destinations) have a lot left to see after one visit. No matter how much you pack in, these destinations will wait for you to return someday.

Easy itinerary-planning tips

When planning your trip, both the whole trip and the daily schedule, add some spontaneity to your itinerary. Leave some elbow room in the agenda, allowing both for relaxation en route and for changes in your plans.

Plan at least one day for doing little or nothing for every five to six days of rigorous sightseeing. You never know when you'll want to take advantage of unexpected opportunities like a day trip or a festival, or when you may want to spend more or less time in a place after you get to know it.

Finding the best online travel information

Web sites are great sources of information — and it's almost always totally free! No matter where you want to go, you can find out about the city or region, identify top attractions, ascertain lodging and rental prices, and even book your flight or room.

Online city guides

A new and unfamiliar city can be one of the most daunting places to navigate for a traveler. Unless you have a friend or relative living in each city you visit, you're dependent on your wits and a city travel guide for all the decisions you make. The city guides you find on the Internet can save you from buying three or four different (heavy) books about your destination. However, the Internet won't save you from visiting your relatives if they've promised to "show you the town."

A quality online city guide directs you to all that a city has to offer, including places to eat, neighborhoods, sights, nightlife options, sporting events, art galleries, festivals, and theater performances. Plus, a good online city guide is frequently updated. The city information you find on the Web is often the most current available.

Dozens, and in many cases hundreds, of guides for every city on Earth are on the Web. In order to save your sanity, here are the top commercial city guides:

- **CitySearch** (www.citysearch.com) covers more than 75 cities worldwide. For most of its listings, editors visit the place they're writing about and then relay the ambiance, the prices, the type of people that go there, and other relevant information to you.

- **Digital City** (www.digitalcity.com) currently covers more than 60 American cities. Their guides generally act as comprehensive Yellow Pages-type directories, with more advertisements and user-generated content than actual editorial listings.

Online travel agency Sites

Without further ado, the Big Four travel agency sites are

- **Expedia** (expedia.msn.com): This site is owned by Microsoft and gets high marks for its ease of use and design.

✔ **Internet Travel Network** (www.itn.net): ITN has carved a niche for itself by becoming the booking site for many of the most popular travel sites on the Web, including CNN and Rough Guides.

✔ **Arthur Frommer's Budget Travel Online** (www.frommers.com): Frommer's offers expert advice and travel discounts for U.S. and international vacations.

✔ **Travelocity** (www.travelocity.com): Travelocity ranks as the biggest online agency on the Web in terms of sales.

Of course, there are other online booking sites out there, but you can feel confident that when you use one of the Big Four sites, you're dealing with online agents who are highly professional and reputable.

Traveling like a Pro

This section offers some hints and tips to make you look and feel like a professional, world-wide traveler (even if you're just spending a weekend out of town).

Practical packing advice

To start packing for your trip, lay out on the bed everything that you think you'll need. Now get rid of half of it. Not only do the airlines have limits, but why would you also want to get a hernia from lugging half your house around with you?

Keep formal wear to a minimum, if possible. Instead, take classic, casual clothes, including some comfortable walking shoes (a must) and airy shirts, blouses, shorts, skirts, or pants. Packing a light jacket or sweater and a thin rain poncho is smart, regardless of where you're headed. Layering your clothing is always a good idea if you're unsure of the weather in your destination.

And don't forget all the necessary toiletries, medications (pack these in your carry-on bag so that you have them if the airline loses your luggage), and a camera.

Use carry-on bags for valuables, medications, and vital documents first. You can then add a book, breakable items you don't want to put in your suitcase, and a snack if you have room. Also, carry the sweater or light jacket with you — cabins can feel like the Arctic one minute and a sauna the next.

Saving a buck or two while traveling

Vacationing frugally does *not* mean you must cut out the fun. Think of it this way: The less money you spend while traveling, the closer you get to experiencing the real people and culture. While you can't realistically manage a trip on just $5 a day anymore, you can go for $60 to $90 a day, plus transportation costs, which is still a great value.

The following sections suggest easy ways to maintain the quality of your trip while stretching every dollar along the way.

Planning a trip budget

Plan out a rough trip budget. Your total cost depends greatly on your means and taste. If you look through the hotel listings in the online or print travel guide, you can easily figure out what price level of hotel and restaurant appeals to you. Just plug the average cost for these accommodations into your expected daily expenses. Remember to budget for:

✓ **Lodging:** Hotels range in price from around $60 per double for a budget hotel to $100 and up (into the thousands!) for a luxury room.

✓ **Dining:** For many folks, sampling an area's local cuisine plays a large role in a vacation, so allow a generous meal budget. A good plan may be to spend $12 per person on lunch. For dinner, assume you'll indulge in a big meal every night and budget around $22 per dinner per person. Don't worry about paying for breakfast because most hotels offer a roll and coffee along with a room. If not, buying a small breakfast costs $2 to $3, which can come out of the lunch allowance.

✓ **Attractions/Shopping:** Museum hounds and sightseeing fanatics should figure enough cash into their budgets to cover the rising costs of admission. Don't be chintzy here. Estimate an average of $5 per sight ($7 to $10 for biggies and $2 to $3 for smaller sights). Therefore, stopping at four major sights per day adds up to $20 per person. Budget at least $5 a day for postcards and other minor souvenirs, more if you're an major shopper.

✓ **Transportation:** Add up the cost of tickets, passes, public transportation, vehicle rentals, gas, and any other expenses related to getting there and back.

As long as you round up all dollar amounts to allow for some padding, you should get a good idea of your costs. As always, overestimating is wise. End your trip with some surprise leftover cash, rather than a disastrous shortfall.

Keeping a lid on hidden expenses

No matter how carefully you plan out a budget, you may find that you always end up shelling out for expenses that you didn't bargain for. The following is a list of common travel expenses and ways to keep them from putting a dent in your vacation fund.

- ✔ **Find out what your rental covers.** When shopping for car rentals, always make sure you know the quoted rate. Some charges that the rental agent may or may not mention to you are the airport pickup/drop-off surcharge, the drop-off fee for renting in one city and dropping off in another, CDW (collision damage waiver), local taxes, mileage (limited or unlimited?), and a tank of gas.

- ✔ **Find out if taxes are included.** Some hotels may quote you room prices without sales and tourism taxes (especially in foreign countries). Always ask to be sure.

- ✔ **Be careful about phone calls.** Some places charge a fee for any long-distance call — even if you use a calling card. Always ask about phone charges when you check in. When in doubt, use a pay phone.

- ✔ **Look before you tip.** Many restaurants include a service charge in your bill, so tipping another 15 percent is tossing your money out the window. Always ask if service is included. If not, tip 10 to 15 percent. If service is included and you felt that your server did a good job, leave a bit extra on the table anyway.

Painless cost-cutting

The following list gives you a taste of the best budgeting strategies that exist.

- ✔ **Go in the off-season.** During nonpeak times, hotels slash their prices by as much as half. Obviously, if you can travel at nonpeak times, do so!

- ✔ **Try a package tour.** By making one simple call to a packager or travel agent, you can often book airfare, hotel reservations, ground transportation, and even some sightseeing for many destinations for a lot less moolah than if you tried to put the trip together yourself.

- ✔ **Reserve your rental car before you leave.** If you know you want to have a car for some or all of your trip, rent it before you leave through a U.S.-wide company to save some money over the cost of renting on the spot.

- ✔ **Invest in a rail or subway pass.** Many cities have extensive subway and train systems that are great transportation assets.

✔ **Take a room without a bathroom.** When traveling in a foreign country or staying at a U.S. bed and breakfast, you can often get a room that shares a bathroom down the hall for about two-thirds as much as you pay for a virtually identical room with its own plumbing.

✔ **If you have kids, get a triple or some cots, not two rooms.** At most hotels, kids stay for free in their parents' room. At the worst, a hotel may charge a nominal fee ($5 to $15) for the extra bed.

✔ **Opt for a double bed instead of two singles.** Fewer sheets for the hotel to wash equals savings for you.

✔ **Do your own laundry.** To avoid laundromat fees, wash a few pieces of clothes in the sink each night, roll them in towels to sop up the dampness, and hang them on the radiator or heater to dry. Never allow the hotel to handle your laundry unless you enjoy being taken to the cleaners, so to speak.

✔ **If your room rate includes breakfast, stuff yourself.** Don't be shy about loading up on the food that comes with your room. Have three rolls and a big bowl of cereal — after all, you're paying for the food. To avoid an expensive lunch, stick an orange and an extra roll in your pocket for later.

✔ **If you can find a room without breakfast for less money, take it.** You can get the same food for which the hotel charges around $10 for about $3 at any cafe on your way out the door.

✔ **Reserve a room with a kitchenette.** Doing your own cooking and dishes may not be your idea of a vacation, but you save a lot of money by not eating in restaurants three times a day. Even if you only make breakfast or cook an occasional dinner, you save in the long run.

✔ **Get out of town.** In many places, big savings are just a short drive or taxi ride away. Hotels outside the historic center, in the next town over or otherwise less-conveniently located, are great bargains.

✔ **Eat at the expensive restaurants at lunch instead of dinner.** Lunch menus often boast many of the same specialties but at a fraction of the dinnertime cost.

✔ **Try picnicking.** For well under $10, you can dine like a king wherever you want — on a grassy patch in the city park, in your hotel room, or on the train.

✔ **Visit the free or near-free sights.** You can experience a heaping help of culture for the price of a cup of coffee at a local café or diner. Tour the town by taking a city-wide bus route. Other free sights and experiences include many museums, most churches and cathedrals, lively public squares, church services, sidewalk performers, fountains, city parks, and street markets.

✔ **Take advantage of free or reduced-price museum days.** Plan ahead. Read your guidebooks carefully and take advantage of the free days and hours of reduced admission, but remember that other people have the same idea — the museums will be crowded during free times.

✔ **Walk as much as possible.** You can save lots of taxi and parking money by strapping on a comfortable pair of walking shoes. Exploring on foot at a slower pace also grants you the opportunity to know your destination more intimately.

✔ **Pass over the souvenirs.** Ten years down the road, you won't care about the T-shirts, key chains, and the like. Your photographs and memories serve as the best mementos of your trip.

✔ **Always check for discounts.** You may be pleasantly surprised to discover that you're eligible for discounts on sights, transportation, hotels, you name it. Members of AAA, trade unions, or AARP; frequent flyers; teachers; and members of other groups sometimes get discounted rates on car rentals, plane tickets, and some chain hotel rooms. Ask your company whether employees can use the corporate travel agent and corporate rates even for private vacations. You never know until you ask.

Are traveler's checks for dinosaurs?

Traveler's checks and the local American Express or Thomas Cooke office used to be your only means of obtaining local currency abroad. Nowadays, however, traveler's checks are the dinosaurs of travel. ATM cards and credit card cash advances are much cheaper and easier. The inconvenience of waiting in line at banks or exchange booths, digging out your passport, and getting charged sometimes high commissions has led most frequent travelers to abandon traveler's checks in favor of a trip to a street-corner ATM or a charge to your credit card (Visa and MasterCard are now almost universally accepted — and in many places, preferred).

Traveler's checks, however, still remain popular because you can sometimes find the ATMs of an entire town evilly disposed to your bank card or Visa (perhaps there's a computer glitch or the phone connections to check your PIN are down). A handful of traveler's checks in your money belt can save your day, and they still remain the safest way to carry your dollars.

Dealing with traveler's burnout

Wherever you're visiting, you may become irritable and tired, catch a cold, or just stop caring whether you see another brilliant oil painting. You can really start to wear down after a few days of full-steam-ahead sightseeing.

Check out these hints for remedying traveler's burnout:

✔ **Just because something's famous, don't feel obligated to do it or see it.** If you're going to wear yourself out, do so on the stuff you like. Feel free to skip what doesn't interest you and go see what really floats your boat.

✔ **Pace yourself.** Don't pack too much into either your trip itinerary or your daily sightseeing agenda. Go a little bit at a time and schedule in rest periods.

✔ **Put variety into your sightseeing.** Visit a church, ruin, or park, or relax in a cafe or restaurant in between sights. Don't hit one big museum after another. Give other areas of your brain a workout for a while.

✔ **Do the siesta thing.** In Mediterranean countries, almost all businesses are closed in the early afternoon — so why not do as the Europeans do (regardless of what continent you're visiting). A nap in the middle of the day can do you a world of good, both physically and mentally.

✔ **Take a break when the sightseeing starts getting to you.** Whatever it takes to bring you back from the brink, do it. Take a day to get off the beaten path. Go shopping. Go to a sporting event. But stop trying to rack up sightseeing points. Sit down and write out all those postcards you've been meaning to send.

Carrying money

After you plan your trip and create a budget, you need to decide how to carry and access your money: traveler's checks, ATM cards, credit cards, cash, or local currency (if you're traveling abroad). The following information weighs the benefits and annoyances of each method and shows you how to get the most out of your dough.

Sniffing out the best exchange rates

Make sure that you do some research before you change your money while traveling abroad, or you risk getting ripped off. Exchange rates are the best and easiest way small-time financiers can take advantage of inattentive tourists.

✔ Avoid exchanging your money in the branch offices of banks you see in airports (and, to a lesser extent, train stations). Instead, exchange your money in a bank or at one of its ATMs if at all possible.

✔ Shop around for the best exchange rate. If you do, you often notice that exchange rates at banks right next door to each other can differ by 40 percent. The business section of major newspapers lists the current rates for currency exchange. The figures published are prime rates, so although you won't find a street price that's as attractive, they're a good guide to follow when shopping for rates.

✔ Remember that rates can fluctuate wildly over even brief periods of time, although they're more likely to rise or fall slowly over the course of months. You can't control rate fluctuations, but they can affect your trip.

✔ For up-to-date rates, look in the business pages or travel section of any major U.S. newspaper or check online at the Universal Currency Converter (www.xe.net/currency) or Oanda (www.oanda.com/converter/classic).

Buying foreign currency before you leave

Before you leave home, consider purchasing about $50 worth of local currency for each country that you plan to visit. Doing so gets you from the airport or train station to the better exchange rates of a downtown bank. Likewise, this money can tide you over until you get your hands on some more, if you arrive in town late at night or on a bank holiday.

Tell your bank when you're vacationing

Consider informing your debit card or credit card's issuing bank that you're taking a trip. Most companies use computerized watchdogs (which look for radical changes in the frequency or location of charges) to monitor your card's use. When the watchdog finds these types of changes, it may automatically freeze your account. Ideally, this system alerts issuing companies if someone steals your card and goes on a shopping spree, but it also has the unfortunate side effect of leaving you without access to your cash, because on a typical vacation, you charge more than usual and you charge from strange places.

Travel insurance: Good idea or bad?

You'll find three primary kinds of travel insurance:

✓ **Trip cancellation insurance:** This type of insurance is a good idea if you've paid a large portion of your vacation expenses up front.

✓ **Lost luggage insurance:** Your homeowner's insurance should cover stolen luggage if your policy encompasses off-premises theft, so check your existing policies before you buy any additional coverage. Airlines are responsible for $2,500 on domestic flights, but that dollar amount may not be enough to cover your sharkskin suit. Best advice: Wear the suit on the plane, and if you're carrying anything else of substantial value, stow it in your carry-on bag.

✓ **Medical insurance:** Your existing health insurance should cover you if you get sick while on vacation. However, if you belong to an HMO, check to see whether you're fully covered when away from home.

AAA offices in the United States sell ready-to-go packs of several currencies at relatively reasonable rates, though you can get better ones at any bank (call ahead — usually only a bank's main, downtown branch carries foreign cash). Shop around for the best rate and ask the teller to give you small bills (close to $10 denominations) because you need the cash primarily to buy inexpensive items like maps, bus tickets, and maybe food.

Street smarts: Avoiding theft

For the most part, the biggest thing you need to worry about when traveling are pickpockets and other petty thieves. Follow these tips to theft-proof yourself:

✓ **Be smart, safe, and have fun.** Stick to populated streets after dark and know the locations of bad neighborhoods.

✓ **Don't tempt thieves.** Leave your jewelry at home and don't flaunt your wallet or valuables.

✓ **Keep all your important stuff in a money belt and wear it at all times.** That way, if someone steals your wallet, all you've lost is a day's spending money (and a wallet).

✓ **Carry your wallet in a secure place.** Place your wallet in a back pocket that buttons or in a front pocket. When riding buses, casually keep one hand in your front pocket with your wallet.

✓ **Don't hang your purse strap off one shoulder.** Instead, hang your purse across your chest. If your purse has a flap, keep the flap and latch side against your body, not facing out where nimble fingers have easy access. When on the sidewalk, walk against the wall rather than close to the curb and keep your purse toward the wall.

✔ **Don't leave your camera bouncing around on your belly when you aren't using it.** Instead, stow your camera in a plain bag (a camera bag announces "steal my camera" to thieves).

✔ **Travel in a trench coat.** A large coat is good for warmth and rain and fits into almost any crowd. You can fit all your valuables inside your coat or pants pockets — and with the trench coat wrapped around you, you can feel pickpocket-proof.

✔ **Make copies.** Make two copies each of your itinerary, plane tickets, and your vital information — the latter featuring the information page of your passport, your driver's license, and your student or teacher's identity card. Also, include your traveler's check numbers, your credit card numbers (write the numbers backward to "code" them), and the phone numbers for the issuers of your bank cards, credit cards, and traveler's checks. Leave one copy of each of these items with a neighbor or a friend at home and carry the second copy with you in a safe place (separate from the originals) while you travel.

When traveling abroad, you're a nonentity without your passport. If you lose your passport, go immediately to the nearest U.S. consulate. Make sure that you bring a photocopy of the information pages (the two pages facing each other with your picture and vital information) of your missing passport, passport-sized photos that you brought with you, and any other form of identification that wasn't lost.

Combating illness away from home

Finding a doctor you trust when you're out of town is difficult. Getting a prescription refilled is no piece of cake, either. So, here are some travel tips to help you avoid a medical dilemma while you're on vacation:

✔ If you have health insurance, carry your identification card in your wallet.

✔ Bring all your medications with you, as well as a prescription for more, if you think you may run out.

✔ Bring an extra pair of contact lenses or glasses in case you lose the ones you wear.

✔ Don't forget to bring over-the-counter medicines for common travelers' ailments, like diarrhea or stomach acid.

✔ If you suffer from a chronic illness, talk to your doctor before taking your trip. For conditions such as epilepsy, diabetes, or a heart condition, wear a Medic Alert identification tag to immediately alert any doctor about your condition and give him access to your medical records.

If your ailment isn't a life-threatening emergency, use a walk-in clinic. You may not get immediate attention, but you only pay around $60 rather than the $300 for just signing in at an emergency-room counter.

You can get a reputable referral from Ask-A-Nurse. You can fill your prescriptions at pharmacies such as Eckerd, Walgreen's, Kmart, or Target. You can find stores such as these in the White or Yellow Pages of the phone book. To find a dentist, call Dental Referral Service (800-917-6453). They can tell you the nearest dentist who meets your needs.

Weighing your rental-car options

Car-rental rates vary even more than airline fares. The price depends on the size of the car, the length of time you keep it, where and when you pick it up and drop it off, where you travel with it, and a host of other factors. Asking a few key questions can save you hundreds of dollars.

✔ **Is the weekend rate lower than the weekday rate?** Ask whether the rate is the same for pickup Friday morning as it is Thursday night. If you're keeping the car five or more days, a weekly rate may be cheaper than the daily rate.

✔ **Will I be charged a drop-off fee if I return the car to a location that's different from where it was rented?** Some companies may assess a drop-off charge; others, notably National, do not. Ask whether the rate is cheaper if you pick up the car at the airport or a location in town.

✔ **May I have the price I saw advertised in the local newspaper?** Be sure to ask for that specific rate; otherwise you may be charged the standard (higher) rate. Don't forget to mention membership in AAA, AARP, frequent-flyer programs, and trade unions. These usually entitle you to discounts ranging from 5 to 30 percent. Ask your travel agent to check any and all these rates.

Special traveling concerns

Ya got 'em. Here's how to handle 'em . . .

Kids

Prepare yourself to take things more slowly with younger folks along for a trip. Intersperse heavy-duty cultural sights like museums and historical landmarks with some fun activities (which can be a welcome respite for everyone).

When you travel with a child, you can usually expect lower rates. Most sights offer reduced-price or free admission for children under a certain age (which can range from 6 to 18). Always ask about discounts on plane and train tickets for kids, too.

Here are a couple of resources you may find helpful:

- ✔ **Families Welcome!,** 92 N. Main St., Ashland, OR 97520; phone 800-326-0724 or 541-482-6121, is a travel company that specializes in worry-free vacations for families.

- ✔ **Smithsonian Study Tours** (highly regarded — albeit expensive) has inaugurated a "Family Adventures" division, phone 877-338-8687 or 202-357-4700; Internet www.si.edu/tsa/sst, that runs escorted educational and adventure trips specifically designed for the whole clan.

Older travelers

People over the age of 60 are traveling more than ever before. If you're a senior citizen, you can discover some terrific travel bargains. You can get discounts on some car rentals and chain hotels if you're a member of the AARP (American Association of Retired Persons), 601 E St. NW, Washington, DC 20049; phone 800-424-3410; Internet www.aarp.org. Membership has its privileges.

Make sure to ask about senior discounts whenever you book your flight. People over 60 or 65 also get reduced admission at theaters, museums, and other attractions. Additionally, they can often get discount fares or cards on public transportation. Make sure to carry identification that proves your age.

Besides publishing the free booklet, *101 Tips for the Mature Traveler,* Grand Circle Travel, 347 Congress St., Boston, MA 02210; phone 800-221- 2610 or 800-597-3644; Internet www.gct.com, specializes in vacations for seniors (as do hundreds of travel agencies).

Beware of the tour-bus style of most of these packages, however. If you're a senior who wants a more independent trip, you should probably consult a regular travel agent. SAGA International Holidays, 222 Berkeley St., Boston, MA 02116; phone 800-343-0273; Internet www.sagaholidays.com, has 40 years' experience running all-inclusive tours and cruises for people 50 and older.

Travelers with disabilities

A disability needn't stop anybody from traveling.

The worldwide organization known as Mobility International, P.O. Box 10767, Eugene, OR 97440; phone 541-343-1284 V/TDD, or fax 541-343-6812; Internet www.miusa.org, promotes international disability rights, provides reference sheets on travel destinations, and hosts international exchanges for people with disabilities.

Some guided tours cater specifically to travelers with disabilities. Flying Wheels Travel, phone 800-535-6790; Internet www.travelexplorer.com/f/flying, is one of the best. The company offers various escorted tours and cruises, as well as private tours in minivans with lifts.

Chapter 23

Ah, Wilderness!: Enjoying Nature

*H*iking, camping, or just visiting your favorite national, state, or local park is a wonderful way to connect with your wild side. With a little planning and preparation, you can ensure your safety and comfort while spending time in the great outdoors.

Hiking

Hiking is as easy as putting one foot in front of the other. No matter how long or short your hike, always remember the axioms, "Plan your hike and hike your plan" and "Be prepared." Planning and preparation simply mean this: Cover the basics to ensure your safety and comfort while you're away from camp, your vehicle, or home.

Choosing a hiking destination

On a hiking trip, deciding how far and how fast to go often becomes a guessing game contingent on your mood, the weather, the difficulty of the terrain, and the interest of the terrain. You really can't do much about your mood, short of keeping an excellent sense of humor. You also can't do much about the weather except to be prepared for anything with the appropriate clothing and gear. However, you can plan and control the difficulty of terrain as well as the visual interest of the terrain to be traveled through.

Dealing with bear encounters

If a bear should approach you while you're camping or hiking, yell, wave your arms, bang pots — anything to alert the bear to your presence, which should encourage it to retreat.

If the bear chooses not to retreat, you should! Move away from the bear slowly and methodically with your eyes to the ground and making no outward appearance of being aggressive. Speak to the bear in calm but firm tones to help it recognize that you are human and not a threat. If the bear attacks, don't run! Ball up, protect your vitals, and lie still.

When traveling through bear country, your best defenses are good ears and alert senses. Look for signs of bear such as fresh tracks, fresh scat (animal poop, silly), and so on. Listen frequently for noises. Try to see a bear before it sees you. If you're traveling in bear country, realize that each district has its own rules and guidelines for you to follow. Be sure to find out what they are.

Three types of trails exist. The type of trail you take depends on your resources and how much variety and effort you want to put into a hike.

- ✔ **Loop trails** are easy. You start hiking, wander around the loop, and end back where you started, assuming you read the map correctly and stayed alert at trail intersections.

- ✔ **Out-and-back trails** take you out one way until you have to turn around and return the way you came. These trails have a certain pleasure to them and are ideal if the time is short and you want to speed your return trip. Keep in mind, however, that very often a trail does look decidedly different when viewed from another direction, so staying alert is still important.

- ✔ **One-way trails** are a lot of fun and often run along riverbanks and through canyons where loop trails are not possible. With proper planning (placing a vehicle at one end of the trail and then getting a ride, or driving another vehicle back to the start), you can enjoy a wonderful hike that's full of variety. Just remember to factor driving time as well as hiking time into your trip planning.

How to avoid getting lost in the wilderness

Anyone can get lost. All it takes is a dense mist, a few unplanned turns in the woods, nightfall, or a storm to disorient most people outdoors.

A good "sense of direction" comes from keeping your senses wide open to all sources of information — sights, sounds, smells, and even touch. Individually, each of the senses contains a fragment of information that can help you from getting lost:

✔ **Sights:** Teach yourself to be aware of significant landmarks such as a tall tree, a prominent rock, or a large meadow. Learn to look in 360-degree sweeps — look at the route you're traveling from the front, side, and back. Quite often, a tree that looked so unique and significant in one direction looks completely different when viewed from another.

✔ **Sounds:** Sounds like a river, cars on a road, and a foghorn on a lighthouse are also important bits of information.

✔ **Smells:** Don't overlook the smell and feel of an area. A valley may feel damp and smell a certain way. Even water can often be smelled from a distance.

Knowing what to do if you become lost

I'm lost! That initial moment of panic surges through the human mind and body like a runaway train. If not controlled, your body soon follows the urge to act like a runaway train and very often takes off plowing through bushes, trees — anything — in a desperate effort to be found. This type of panic is all too common and can lead to complete exhaustion, dehydration, injury, and even death.

Sit and think

You *must* sit down and think quietly if you believe that you're lost. When people panic and begin to frantically attempt to find their way back to home or camp, they usually get into deeper trouble. If you just sit down and think carefully, a solution usually becomes evident. Look around painstakingly and retrace your steps *in your mind.* Very often, after some calm thinking, you can discover the route home.

Explore methodically

Sometimes, the route home isn't clearly evident, and you may feel a need to get up and explore the surrounding area in search of a trail.

Doing so is okay if you can accurately mark the area you're starting from so that you can return to it after your initial search. From that original sit-down point, you can begin working your way outward in a circular pattern until you discover a familiar piece of ground or terrain. While working your way out in this circular fashion, always keep your original starting position in sight.

From each familiar point that you discover, establish another landmark that then identifies the area, and repeat the process. Essentially, you move from familiar point to familiar point and mark your progress along the way. After you discover a trail or a road that's recognizable, you can then head out in a straight line toward home or help.

Predicting Weather Changes

Being aware of the weather and atmospheric conditions can keep you safe and sound while you're enjoying nature.

Keep your head in the clouds

You can make some general predictions about the weather without even knowing a cirrus cloud from a stratus cloud.

- ✔ If clouds are massing and generally increasing in size and density, the weather is possibly changing for the worse. Clouds moving more quickly across the sky indicate a change in wind velocity and also a change in pressure, indicating an approaching storm.

- ✔ Cloud formations that are moving in separate directions and at different altitudes often announce an impending storm.

- ✔ Finally, observe cloud movements and wind direction together. If both the cloud movement and the wind direction are the same, any weather will come from the direction that the wind is blowing.

Turning to Mother Nature for the forecast

Mother Nature provides a lot of weather clues (some in the form of rhymes) but all fairly simple and easy to remember.

✔ **Morning or evening sky:** "Red sky at night, sailor's delight. Red sky in morning, sailors take warning." This weather proverb means that if the clouds take on a reddish hue in the morning, you can expect rain by the end of the day. If the evening sky is red, the weather will probably remain clear the following day.

✔ **Geese and seagulls:** Geese and seagulls have a reputation for not flying before a storm. Biologists theorize that this is because they have a harder time getting airborne in low-pressure conditions. Or maybe they're just a lot smarter than humans give them credit for.

✔ **Mosquitoes and black flies:** The feasting frenzy of bugs usually subsides about an hour before the weather turns.

✔ **Frogs:** Frogs have an uncanny tendency to increase their serenading several hours before a storm arrives. The reason they do this is not so much that they're reliable weather forecasters but that the increased humidity in the air from an incoming storm allows them to stay comfortably out of the water for longer periods.

✔ **Halo around the sun and moon:** In the summer, the sight of a hazy halo or corona around the sun or moon is a good indication that a change in the present weather pattern is in the forecast — most often rain.

✔ **Frost and dew:** The presence of heavy frost or dew early in the morning or late in the evening is a fairly reliable indicator that up to 12 hours of continued good weather can be expected.

✔ **Wind:** "Wind from the south brings rain in its mouth." Low-pressure systems create cyclonic winds that rotate in a counterclockwise direction. Since low-pressure systems are frequently associated with rainstorms, the rhyme proves quite accurate. Counterclockwise wind rotations create wind that blows from the south — wind that brings in the rain.

How far away is that thunderstorm?

You can roughly judge the distance of an approaching storm by observing the lightning's flash followed by the resounding boom of thunder. For this method, count slowly, "one-one thousand, two-one thousand, three-one thousand" and so forth. This method approximates one second elapsed for each thousand counted.

After the lightning has flashed, begin to count. When you hear the thunder, stop counting. Every five seconds of elapsed time indicates one mile of distance.

✔ **Campfire smoke:** By observing the smoke from a campfire, you can tell what pressure system is in the area, low or high. If the smoke from the fire hangs low to the ground and dissipates into the branches, that means a low-pressure system is present, and rain is possible. If the smoke rises in a straight, vertical column, high pressure rules, which means you can anticipate fair weather.

✔ **Crickets:** You can estimate the air temperature in Fahrenheit degrees by counting the number of chirps a cricket emits over a 14-second period and adding 40 to the number. So, if a cricket chirps 25 times over 14 seconds, you add 25 to 40 and arrive at 65 degrees Fahrenheit. Scientific studies have proven that crickets are correct within a degree or two over 75 percent of the time.

Various Vistas for Nature Lovers

Whether your passion is walking, hiking, camping, taking pictures, or just watching a gorgeous sunset, the following destinations are guaranteed to answer your call for the wild:

✔ **Lightning Lakes, British Columbia:** For scenic value alone, this park is worth a visit. Four lakes are linked by a trail system that meanders along the eight-mile-long Cascade Mountain valley floor. Fishing in the lakes is memorable, and the backdrop of jagged, towering peaks is unforgettable. The best time to visit is June through September.

✔ **Glacier National Park, Montana:** Located along the Canadian/U.S. border, this park is full of grizzlies, glaciers, alpine meadows weighted down with colorful blooms, and mountain peaks that seem to reach for the sky.

✔ **All 'Round Ranch, Utah:** Located in Jensen, Utah, this ranch specializes in backcountry trips to the wilder parts of Utah, with a twist — you're assigned a horse as your partner and become a working cowpoke for the week. The ranch is open to guests April to October.

✔ **Cumberland Island National Seashore, Georgia:** Cumberland Island is the largest and most southerly of Georgia's 15 ocean islands. You can wander through live-oak forest adorned with curtains of Spanish moss. The only way to reach the island is by private boat or ferry.

Chapter 24

Entertaining (and Maintaining Your Sanity)

Do you want to throw a holiday cocktail party but don't know where to start? Would you like to entertain the office crowd, but you're not sure what kind of food to serve? Don't stress! This chapter offers you suggestions on entertaining basics: issuing invitations, creating the atmosphere you want, making menus, planning parties for the whole family, and entertaining coworkers.

Invitations that Solicit a "Yes" Response

Not only does an effective invitation arouse curiosity, stir interest, or create excitement, but it also solicits a *yes* response from the people who look forward to coming to your party.

Invitations by phone

The telephone may be your most valuable tool if you want an easy, relaxed, and friendly way to issue invitations. You can use the enthusiasm in your voice to get people excited about your party. Verbal invitations are great for the following situations:

 ✔ Spur-of-the-moment gatherings

 ✔ Casual parties or semiformal events

 ✔ The guest list is subject to change

 ✔ You want to create immediate excitement

Using one guest to entice another

A smart telephone strategy is to entice guests with other guests. First, call a few people who you're dying to entertain to verify that they can come. Then, pique the interest of other guests by mentioning who is coming and that you want them to meet this person or vice versa. Most likely, your invitees will accept your invitation, even if they have to rearrange their social calendar, cancel their vacation plans, and take a taxi to get there.

Planning the right time to call

The type of party that you're planning determines when you need to call with your invitation.

 ✔ For a well-planned large party, call 2 to 3 weeks in advance.

 ✔ If you're hosting a luncheon or small dinner, call 7 to 14 days ahead.

 ✔ For a last-minute get-together, you can call as late as that afternoon.

Advance calling allows you to find out immediately who cannot come and gives you time to invite someone else.

Invitations by mail

An invitation that arrives by mail is like the entryway of your party. The invitation is the first thing people see and the first impression they have of your party. Written invitations are preferable

 ✔ For parties planned far in advance

 ✔ For formal affairs (dinner, luncheon, tea)

 ✔ When you have a definite guest list (a dinner to honor someone or a business party)

 ✔ When you want to establish a tone or theme (bridal and baby showers and ceremonies, such as bar mitzvah's and weddings)

Addressing invitations properly

To prevent misunderstandings, address your party invitation to whomever you're specifically inviting. If you're inviting a husband and wife, address the invitation to "Mr. and Mrs." If you're inviting their children as well, add "and family." If you're having a ladies-only luncheon, then say so in the invitation so that someone doesn't show up with spouse in tow. In other words, do everything you can to make crystal clear whose presence you're requesting.

Give an unmarried person the option of bringing a guest, unless you're inviting him or her to fill a specific place in your guest list. Otherwise, the person may assume that it's okay to bring a date anyway. Or they may wonder if it's okay but hesitate to ask. Extending the courtesy to bring a guest is especially important if you know that the individual you're inviting is seeing someone regularly.

All written invitations must include the same basic information:

- ✔ Hosts' names
- ✔ Type of event
- ✔ Date (you may want to include a rain date)
- ✔ Time
- ✔ Location (you may want to include a map)
- ✔ Reply telephone number

Your time schedule can be a major determining factor in the type of invitation you choose to send. Mail your invitations

- ✔ Four weeks ahead for a formal dinner or big bash
- ✔ Two to three weeks ahead for an informal dinner, luncheon, or tea
- ✔ Three weeks ahead if you're hosting a cocktail party
- ✔ Eight weeks ahead for a wedding

Choosing the right invitation

Choose written invitations that best fit the type of party you're having, the guests you're inviting, the time you have to write out the invitation, and your budget.

✔ **Formal engraved.** This style is appropriate for formal events such as weddings, graduations, black-tie galas, and so on. Allow four weeks for engraving.

✔ **Prepared by a calligrapher.** To relay a feeling of elegance, hire a calligrapher to write the invitations. Card shops and stores that sell invitations can refer you to a calligrapher. Be sure to get started early.

✔ **Specially printed.** Appropriate for semi-formal to casual parties. Use a print company or design your own. Allow two to four weeks for printing.

✔ **Fill-in invitations from the card shop.** A compromise between custom printing and handwritten, this is an easy way to announce birthday parties, holiday get-togethers, open houses, picnics, potlucks, and showers.

✔ **Handwritten on blank cards or on your stationery.** Most appropriate for small parties, formal or informal, when you want to make the invitation personal.

✔ **Computer-designed on your PC or at your local card shop.** Customized invitations are great for casual parties and especially for friends. Use a home computer or computer-generated card services available at many greeting card stores.

✔ **E-mail:** Use this method for casual parties and only if you're certain the recipients check their electronic mail regularly.

Getting responses

Most modern invitations include a reply line at the bottom with a telephone number to which guests can respond. Include more than one number to improve your chances of getting a response.

Avoid using a reply line that says "Regrets only." That term technically means, "call if you can't come." A better option is to use RSVP, which technically means, "the favor of a reply is requested." Unfortunately, many people forget to respond. In order to finalize your guest list, go ahead and call those who haven't responded and ask whether they're coming.

Creating a Party Atmosphere

Give dazzling parties — by creating the right atmosphere and ambiance to make your party unforgettable. The key here is to use your own imagination and focus on your guests' five senses:

Using the sense of touch

If you're a natural toucher, go ahead and greet your guests with a hug, squeeze, or kiss. If, however, hugging and kissing aren't your style, you can touch the small of a guest's back, touch his sleeve, or put your hand on his elbow — any gesture that lets that person know you're delighted to be with him.

Following are a few ways to add touching and feeling to your party:

- ✔ Seat guests close to one another so elbows and shoulders touch. (Only do this at a casual party, not a formal affair or business dinner!)
- ✔ Put on some music that makes people feel like dancing. Watch all the senses go wild.
- ✔ Let guests help make drinks, pour cocktails, or mix up their own concoctions.
- ✔ Solicit someone to pass hors d'oeuvres.
- ✔ Choose someone to stir a sauce.
- ✔ Ask a guest to help put food on a plate.
- ✔ Let guests serve themselves (from your kitchen or a buffet).
- ✔ Serve food that must be attacked with a fork and knife, slurped with a spoon, or eaten with the hands.

People love to get involved in creating the meal. Let guests make homemade pizzas or pasta. You may end up with a migraine and a huge mess, but everyone will be best friends at the end.

Appealing to the sense of sight

Bewitch guests' eyes with the total surroundings. Use everything around you as a possible attraction: candlelight, centerpieces, food arranged on plates, a sunset, a view, and your clothing.

You can soften the atmosphere by lowering the lights, which is one of the easiest and most powerful ways to affect the sense of sight. Lowering the lights calms nerves, softens appearances, and makes almost any room look more beautiful. Fine-tune your lighting with dimmers, rheostats, or by simply buying colored or low-wattage (25-40 watt) bulbs.

For an atmosphere of mystery, intrigue, or romance, dine outside under the stars. Use glowing candles to illuminate the tables and a few flares to define the space. Let the full moon work for you. You save electricity, but your party is fully charged.

Engaging the sense of hearing

The most effective way to enchant guests' ears is by inviting interesting people so that stimulating conversation becomes the main attraction.

Other sounds that can enhance your atmosphere include

- ✔ The pop of the cork from the champagne
- ✔ Meat searing in a hot pan or on a hot grill
- ✔ Wood crackling in a fireplace or a bonfire

Of course, music can be a wonderful addition to a party because you can use it as entertainment or as a simple background effect. Consider your guests and the atmosphere you intend to create when choosing your music. For example, classical music is lovely for a special dinner party, and you can't go wrong with jazz for a cocktail party.

Delighting the sense of smell

Tantalize with the sense of smell from the moment your guests walk in the door. For example, get something in the oven as your guests are arriving, so that they'll start to inhale the mouth-watering aromas.

- ✔ Open the kitchen door.
- ✔ Let guests hang out in the kitchen so the aromas excite them.
- ✔ Bake dessert while guests eat dinner.
- ✔ Reheat cookies during the meal to serve with coffee after dinner.

Aromas are especially important when serving fine wines. The nose (smell) of a fine wine unfolds throughout the meal as it changes temperature. You really want guests to get a good whiff of a great wine.

Use extreme care with any scents other than the food and wine. Flowers and scented candles can be delightful, but too much of a good thing can make a dining room smell like a funeral parlor. Therefore, choose unscented candles and flowers for the table. And be extra cautious when using artificial fragrances.

Bombarding the sense of taste

A common saying is "the fastest way to the heart is through the stomach." You can choose from many methods to awaken taste buds.

- ✔ Excite the mouth with something spicy or exotic.
- ✔ Surprise the throat with cold and hot foods.
- ✔ Soothe the palate with down-home comfort food.
- ✔ Arouse the taste buds with a sensual meal.

Dreaming Up the Perfect Menu

If you're giving a large or elaborate party, start thinking of your menu when you invite your guests. If you're giving a small, casual party, or if you're a relaxed, laid-back person, you may be able to throw together a menu at the last minute.

Any one of the following times may be perfect for making your menu:

- ✔ When you invite your guests and are thinking about what they like
- ✔ When you stop at the food store and see what looks good
- ✔ When you see a recipe that you want to try

Suiting the occasion

The following tips can help you evaluate the occasion and the role you may want the food to play:

- ✔ **Family gatherings** (such as Thanksgiving dinner) place food as the focus of the event.
- ✔ **Business meals** are about communication, not pretentious or fancy food (which can distract from conversations). Keep the menu simple by choosing food that's easy to manage and doesn't require an array of utensils.
- ✔ **Special occasions** celebrate and honor the people and events that have meaning in your life, so choose foods that are special, luxurious, or favorites.
- ✔ **A gathering of friends** means you can do anything with the menu — serve sloppy food, finger food, or attention-getting food.

If cooking isn't your thing, serve sandwiches and beer. True friends don't care. The point of having a party is getting together and having fun.

If you're still stuck for a menu idea and just can't seem to get started, read on for more inspiration.

Considering the season and the weather

Climate affects attitudes and appetites, so why not use it as a starting point for your menu? You can either match the food to the weather or add an element of surprise by contrasting it.

Ask yourself the following questions and build the menu around your answers:

- ✔ What does the weather make me feel like eating?
- ✔ Which foods are associated with the current season?
- ✔ What foods are freshest this time of year?

You can never go wrong choosing foods appropriate for the season, because that's when they're available, ripe, fresh, and beautiful. The following are some examples of seasonal foods:

- ✔ **Spring:** Lamb, salmon, artichokes, asparagus, sweet peppers, zucchini, rhubarb, raspberries, strawberries
- ✔ **Summer:** Lobster, grouper, arugula, scallions, watercress, eggplant, tomatoes, squash, peas, basil, corn, watermelon, peaches, apricots, blackberries, cherries
- ✔ **Fall:** Steak, game, cabbage, garlic, cauliflower, mushrooms, pumpkins, apples, chestnuts, cranberries, figs, grapes, pears, walnuts
- ✔ **Winter:** Beef, pork, ribs, clams, scallops, broccoli, Brussels sprouts, potatoes, oranges, grapefruit, pineapple, collard greens, fennel, parsnips, radishes, spinach, turnips, dried fruits, kiwi

Different seasons conjure up not only different foods, but different cooking methods as well. In cold weather, warm up by roasting, baking, and slow simmering. In warmer months, cool off by chilling, grilling, and poaching.

No-hassle and no-cooking menu approaches

Thousands of menu items are available for the totally hassled or non-cooking host.

- **Mail order:** Call your favorite restaurants around the country or favorite mail-order food suppliers. Have gourmet items delivered overnight. (Mail order suppliers are often listed in the back of food magazines.)

- **Caterers:** Contact someone you've heard of or who catered a party you attended. Know your budget and be explicit about what you want. If you're unsure about your menu, some caterers offer taste tests for a minimal fee.

- **Take-out and delivery:** If you have an impromptu party to prepare for, call your favorite local restaurant or restaurants that prepare take-out or delivery orders on request. Choose to pick up your order on your way home from work or have it delivered. Transfer the food to your dishes and no one will ever have to know that you didn't cook.

- **Convenience foods and grocery store services:** Prepare an impressive meal straight from the freezer case. Add fresh fruit, prepackaged salads, or cut vegetables from the produce department to round out the meal. Or, check out your grocery store deli to supplement your home-cooked meal or pick up an entire meal.

- **Home and dining out.** If you're super short on time, invite friends over for drinks and hors d'oeuvres, followed by a restaurant meal. Or do it the other way around: Have the meal in a restaurant followed by dessert and coffee at your house.

Being a Thoughtful Host

If you want to bring out the best in your guests, start with a warm welcome — a firm handshake or a hug — and tell each person how happy you are that they could come. When guests feel that you're thrilled to see them, you'll get the most out of their personalities.

Entertaining questions and answers

Q. What should I do if a guest arrives early?

A. Take the guest to an area where you feel comfortable — perhaps the kitchen, the living room, or your garden. Offer a drink.

Q. What should I do if a guest is late?

A. If you're serving a meal, start the meal as planned. The late guest can either catch up or start with the course being served when he or she arrives.

Q. What should I do if a guest shows up with a date, and I haven't planned for the extra person?

A. Act like you're thrilled and go out of your way to be gracious. You can always squeeze in an extra place setting and divide the food in smaller portions.

Q. Is it okay to ask a guest to help with something?

A. Yes. Ask guests to pass a platter of hors d'oeuvres, mix a drink, help you carry something to the table, and so on. Just don't ask them to stay and clean up.

During the first ten minutes of your party, make each guest feel like a VIP:

✔ Greet each person enthusiastically.

✔ Put guests at ease by offering drinks.

✔ Introduce guests to each other.

✔ Initiate conversations and find common ground so that guests can continue talking without you.

If guests don't know each other well, they need you to keep conversations started and flowing.

After all the guests have been greeted and are engaged in conversations, refill drinks and pass hors d'oeuvres. Even if you've hired help, passing something yourself is a good way to ensure that you get around to talking with all the guests and a way for you to gauge how conversations are faring.

If you serve it, will they come?

Try one of these people-moving strategies in order to get people to the table:

✔ At a small dinner party, ask a friend or two to take another guest and lead them to the table. Or, ask them to pour wine or light the candles.

✔ At buffets or cocktail buffets, ask a female guest (the guest of honor, the oldest woman, or a close friend) to start serving herself. Then gather up some more guests.

✔ At large parties, moving 50 to 75 people to their tables can take 30 to 45 minutes. You and your help can tell guests, "Bring your drinks; it's time to go in; dinner's ready."

On other occasions, moving people away from the table can be desirable:

✔ If conversation is fading and you want to inject new energy into your party.

✔ If you want to create a transition between the dinner and the time to leave. (Some guests may be uncomfortable leaving the party directly from the table.)

✔ If you've hired help and want them to begin cleaning up.

The most effective and polite way to get guests moving is to say, "Dessert and coffee will be served in the living room." If the dessert and coffee have already been served, say, "Let's move into the living room to talk."

Getting people to go home

After dessert and coffee, guests usually linger a while longer and start their good-byes. If you're tired and ready for guests to leave, however, you must send the right signals:

✔ Stop serving drinks.

✔ Turn off the music.

✔ Let the conversation gradually subside — don't initiate new topics.

✔ If you're sitting down, stand up.

✔ Tell guests how much you enjoyed having them.

✔ Don't say "no." If someone suggests that it's late and they really must go, agree with them and usher them to the door.

For some reason, usually one or two guests don't get the hint. If you can barely keep your eyes open, you have every right to say that you're tired. You don't need to apologize.

Don't start cleaning up until the guests have left. It makes them feel uncomfortable and ruins the atmosphere of the party.

Being a Courteous Guest

As an invited guest at someone else's party, you're expected to behave in a certain way, starting with the invitation. Your first responsibility is to respond with a "yes" or "no," not "maybe," preferably within a day or two of receiving it. Unless the host is a very close friend, don't ask to bring a date or a friend to a small-seated dinner, especially if the invitation is addressed only to you. If you're invited to a cocktail buffet or a large informal party — you may ask — but the host can always say no.

Gifts for the host and hostess

Besides yourself, the one other item you may want to take with you to a party is a small gift for the host or hostess. Think of something that the person would enjoy. If the host is a close friend, you can choose something personal like bubble bath, a book, a favorite brand of cigars, a flat of pansies, and so on. If your host is a business associate, choose something less personal: a bottle of wine, a special coffee or tea, homemade bread, fine chocolates, and so on.

Following are a few tips on what *not* to bring:

- Don't put the hosts on the spot by bringing wine you insist on opening or food you expect to be served.

- Don't show up at the door with flowers that must be arranged. Flowers are a lovely gift but are best sent the day before or the day after the party.

- Never bring a permanent decoration for the host's house. Doing so may be embarrassing for the host if he or she hates the gift but feels compelled to display it.

Coming and going: Being on time is fashionable

For a dinner party, forget about being "fashionably late." However, in some areas of the country and in certain social circles, guests know that they're not expected to arrive at the designated time. In this case, use what you know about the customs of the area and the people with whom you're socializing to help you determine the appropriate arrival time.

Perhaps even more important than arriving on time is leaving on time. Never overstay your welcome.

Planning Parties for Children

In some ways, children's parties are just like any other party you may give. However, some important differences can occur in the way you plan the guest list, the menu, and the activities. With a little knowledge and a lot of planning, you can save your sanity, have some fun, and create a lasting memory.

Special considerations

Develop a complete plan with lists of all the things you need to buy and do. (Allow yourself two to four weeks.) The following are some other thoughts to consider when planning a children's party:

- ✔ **A time limit for the party:** Give yourself enough time to feed and entertain the guests with no time left over for idle hands to get into trouble. (Two hours is average.)

- ✔ **Photography:** Photographs are important, not only for your own memory book, but to send to relatives and other parents. Since you'll be busy, ask someone else to take candid shots throughout the event.

- ✔ **Discipline:** If a child gets out of hand, don't let that child ruin the party for everyone else, but do be careful how you discipline someone else's child. Try diverting the child's attention or channeling his energy somewhere else.

- ✔ **Breaks and spills:** If a child breaks or spills something during the party and it's purely accidental, chalk the mishap up to experience and forget about it. If the item is valuable and the cause of the accident is unruly behavior, whether or not you approach the child's parents is entirely up to you.

✔ **Themes and schemes:** You need a definite theme when planning a party for a child. The key is to know your child's favorite things whether that's an action figure, superhero, toy, or activity such as fire trucks or painting. Then, you can coordinate everything from the invitations to the activities around that central idea.

Guest lists and invitations

If your child is between the ages of 1 and 3, limit the guest list to family only, or invite whomever you want. By age 4, however, many children want to be involved in determining the list of invitees.

When children reach their teens, you probably know who their friends are and can ask your teen to participate in the planning. If the party's a surprise, you can make out the guest list or enlist help from one of your teen's best friends.

Written invitations are a must for children's parties. Locate your guests' addresses in the telephone directory or ask friends or neighbors.

Some children like to take invitations to school to distribute. That's okay, but you need to follow-up with a phone call to the parents. Most of the time, you're better off putting the invitations in the mail.

Kid-friendly food

Choose age-appropriate food, such as finger food for very young children and pizza for teens. Remember, most children don't care what the food is as long as they know what it is and that there's plenty of it.

Older children may like to be involved in preparing the food. As a part of the entertainment, let them make their own banana splits, build their own tacos, top their own pizzas, or share a long submarine sandwich.

Activities and entertainment

For a child's party to be a success, each child must be interested and active. Plan two different kinds of activities for young children, balancing active activities with calming activities. For example, start with a series of active (or physical) activities: games, relays, contests, and so on. Then move to calming activities: sitting down drawing or making something. If you need more help with ideas, details, and directions for activities, go to the library or buy a book on children's games.

You may have times when you want to hire entertainment for your child's party. Look in the Yellow Pages under "Entertainment" or "Entertainment Bureaus" to find professional services. Performers you may want to hire include a juggler, magician, clown, storyteller, puppeteer, face-painting artist, balloon sculptor, or the mascot from a local sports team.

Teenagers need activities, too. Try surprising teens with something they can enjoy without too much parental interference:

- ✔ Stage a murder mystery for them to solve.
- ✔ Let them produce a movie.
- ✔ Organize kite making and flying.
- ✔ Hire a disc jockey, fortune-teller, or line-dance instructor.
- ✔ Take them bowling, skating, skiing, or river rafting. (Get someone younger and cooler than you to help supervise.)
- ✔ Drop them off at a place where they can just hang out, such as their favorite pizza parlor or hamburger joint.

Entertaining for Business

Whether you're hosting or attending a business affair, your primary purpose isn't eating a great meal, sipping a superb wine, or having fun. All business entertaining is entertaining done for a purpose, including

- ✔ **To establish a personal relationship with a potential client, customer, boss, or coworker:** Establish common ground, relax, and let business associates see the personal side of you.
- ✔ **To disarm people:** Improve relationships by entertaining a jealous coworker or a client who thinks you're always after something for yourself at work. Make her feel more comfortable with you.
- ✔ **To increase productivity:** Entertain existing clients to gain new clients. Another way to increase productivity is by entertaining potential clients or customers.
- ✔ **To show appreciation:** Take the time, go to the trouble, and exert the energy to entertain employees, clients, or bosses — show your appreciation for them in a personal way.

 ✔ **To get your spouse involved:** Include your spouse so that he or she gains a better understanding of your work, and your business associates will see that you and your spouse are a team.

 ✔ **To set yourself apart from the crowd:** Take the opportunity to demonstrate your personal skills (organization, communication, family values, and stress management), which are obvious assets at the office.

Thinking food for thought

Choose foods that are simple, delicious, and easy to handle. Avoid huge hunks of meat that require major surgical skill to dissect or dishes with the potential to drip all over a guest's blouse or tie. Serve a meal that's easy to eat.

For your guests' sake and your own, beware of foods such as:

 ✔ Spaghetti and French onion soup, which are easily worn down the front of your shirt

 ✔ Fried chicken, corn on the cob, spare ribs, and other foods that must be picked up with the hands and can end up all over your face

 ✔ Lobster, crab claws, or anything that must be dislodged from its shell

 ✔ Whole artichokes, quail, or other foods that require undivided attention

 ✔ Cherry tomatoes or other foods that may squirt or fly off the plate when cut

 ✔ Parsley and other herbs that are roughly chopped instead of finely minced, which can cause the pieces to cling to your teeth

 ✔ Blueberries, which can turn your teeth purple

Inviting the boss

Even if you know the boss well, don't invite him for a one-to-one dinner, or even a dinner that includes the two of you plus your spouses or companions. Keep in mind that business relationships are highly individual and use your common sense. If you and your boss have a close relationship, you may consider inviting him to a small dinner party with six or more guests. Otherwise, you're better off inviting your boss to a large dinner party or cocktail party so that he feels less obligated or pressured to attend.

Dressing for the occasion

Many companies have dress-down Fridays or allow relaxed clothing every day. But, casual dress codes don't translate to business entertaining. That doesn't necessarily mean you have to wear a business suit at your party, but you are wise to select something conservative.

For women, the rule for dressing is to ask yourself how you want to be remembered — for your earrings or your ideas? For your cleavage or your intelligence? When you get dressed, find a full-length mirror. As you walk away, notice if anything stands out about your appearance that shouldn't (dress too clingy, slip hanging out, makeup too heavy, hair overdone, and so on). A wise choice is to select something conservative to wear.

If you're not the host but are an invited guest, your best bet is to research what to wear. If the invitation says "formal," find out exactly what that means. If there's no one to ask or if you're still unsure, you're best to err on the side of being overdressed.

Choose a menu that's elegant but not beyond your means. Don't experiment with new recipes or serve exotic, unusual food. Prepare foods that don't require too much last-minute attention, as you don't want to be toiling in the kitchen all night.

Entertaining in restaurants

Sometimes, business entertaining somewhere other than in your home is simply more convenient. Restaurant entertaining has its own special advantage for the host: By having someone else tend to the cooking and serving, you can relax and concentrate on the business at hand.

The restaurant you choose says a lot about you. Don't invite business associates to a loud and smoky place. Unless you know your guests' food preferences, don't choose a restaurant that specializes in exotic food or a particular ethnic cuisine. To be safe, stick with a restaurant that offers broad menu selections.

Here are a few more tips for successful restaurant entertaining:

- ✔ Frequent one or two restaurants so that the staff gets to know you. You can improve your chances of getting a good table and service.
- ✔ Remember to call the restaurant in advance to make sure that the restaurant is open and to make a reservation, if needed.

✔ Request a table that's conducive to conversation — out of the mainstream of traffic, away from the kitchen, restroom, or telephones.

✔ Inform your guests how to find the restaurant and the best place to park. Provide a map for guests who may be unfamiliar with the area.

✔ Arrive early so that you can check the table, arrange for hat and coat check, and make arrangements to pay the check and take care of tips.

✔ If the party is large, ask for a private room and consider a limited menu that offers three choices: red meat, seafood, and pasta. Distribute place cards or provide the maître d' with a seating chart.

✔ Do not start eating bread, drinking (except water), or ordering before your guests arrive.

✔ Be a gracious host. Make sure that guests have what they need in terms of food and drink. Don't grill them with so many questions that they never get a chance to eat.

So who coughs up the cash? Well, if you're the person doing the inviting, you should arrange to pay the bill. When a meal is mutually arranged between two business associates within the same company, both parties should offer to pay. If you're the senior person who's invited to lunch by a subordinate, you should offer to pay; however, since the subordinate did the inviting, that person is obligated to pick up the check. Never attempt to split the bill by deciding who ate what. If a group of business peers agree to split the bill, divide it evenly.

Making your conversations count

Whether hosting or attending a business event, you will be involved in conversations with people who can influence your career. Sometimes what you *don't* say is more important than what you do say:

✔ Let nothing negative enter your conversation, particularly if the company has had bad news (like disastrous third-quarter earnings).

✔ Never gossip about the boss's spouse, or anyone else, for that matter.

✔ Don't bring up any subject that can be controversial.

✔ Stay away from the forbidden topics of sex, religion, and politics.

Chapter 25

Etiquette and Manners

• •

In This Chapter

▶ Using the telephone

▶ Conversing graciously

▶ Displaying good manners when dining

▶ Honoring major life events

▶ Visiting another culture

• •

*I*n a world where people are often hurried and stressed, being courteous isn't always easy. But that's when extending courtesy is most important and most appreciated. This chapter offers suggestions for ways to easily incorporate etiquette and manners into your daily routine.

Telephone Etiquette

Today, technology not only has multiplied our communication options, but it's also made the number of opportunities for making an etiquette faux pas greater.

Making calls

Follow these steps for making a successful phone call:

1. **Think ahead about what you want to achieve before you place the call.**

   Will you actually reserve a flight if the price is right and the schedule is convenient? Will you agree to make reservations if the other party approves of your restaurant recommendation? If you decide *before calling* what you want to settle on, your phone conversations will be brief, effective, and satisfying to both parties.

2. **Adopt a pleasant tone with the person who answers the call.**

   Make sure that your voice sounds warm, cheerful, and upbeat and that your pronunciation is clear. Even if the purpose of your call is unpleasant (such as to make a complaint to a store), sounding pleasant gets the conversation off on the right foot and makes the recipient of the call more inclined to help you in an equally pleasant manner.

3. **Establish the identity of the other party.**

   When you get another person on the line, establish the identity of the other party before moving to the business at hand: "Good morning. Is this Mr. O'Malley?" If the answer is a flat "No," say, "My name is Ed Anderson. To whom am I speaking?" Have a piece of paper nearby and write down the person's name. That information may come in handy during the remainder of the conversation, or perhaps later, when you speak with someone else.

   Once in a while, you reach someone who hasn't adopted good manners as a way of life. At your first opportunity, ask for that person's name. If you get a generic answer like, "This is the floor nurse," say, "That's wonderful. I understand there are many nurses on the sixth floor. May I have your name?"

4. **Identify yourself and your reason for calling.**

   Just as you want to know whom you're speaking with, the other party wants to know who you are and what you want. Settle this issue before you're asked.

5. **Inquire considerately whether the timing of the call is convenient.**

   No matter whom you call or what time of day it is, begin your conversation by asking, "Is this a convenient time to talk?" If it isn't, volunteer to call back at a better time. Folks who have call waiting appreciate this little courtesy.

6. **Take notes during the conversation.**

   You can exchange a great deal of information in the course of a telephone conversation. Get in the habit of keeping a notepad near every telephone and making notes as you chat. Don't trust your memory. Jot it down.

7. **Achieve closure.**

   When you finish the business at hand, say so: "Thanks for helping me. I really appreciate it" or "Thanks for changing my appointment. I'll see you next Tuesday at 11 a.m." Then end the conversation. Just say "Good-bye" and hang up.

Receiving calls

Receiving calls is the delicate flip side of making calls. The human relations skills that you can bring to bear may cheer up a grouch or deal effectively with a nuisance.

If at all possible, answer your home telephone before it rings a fourth time. If you pick up the phone after four rings, the caller may expect to be transferred to an answering machine or voice-mail system or worry that you're in the middle of something and don't have the time to talk.

If you get a call from an unknown voice and you hear, "Hello, who's this?" you can say, "This is Charlie. To whom would you like to speak?" Give enough information for a genuine friend to verify that he or she dialed the right number, but no more. For safety's sake, never give out your number if someone asks, "What number is this?" Instead, ask what number the person is trying to call.

If you have call waiting and must pick up another call, be conscious of how long you leave the other person on hold. If you'll be any longer than a few seconds, offer to call the second caller back and resume your first conversation.

Ridding yourself of nuisances

Phone nuisances come in several guises. The following tips can help you deal with them.

Dinnertime sales calls

You don't owe any consideration to sales solicitations made during the dinner hour or later in the evening. However, as a polite person, you may not be able to bring yourself to be unmannerly. Just wait for the first opening and say, "Thanks, but I'm not interested. Good-bye." And with that, hang up the telephone.

Truly obnoxious sales callers don't require any conversation. If a caller is rude or harassing to you, you're within your rights to hang up the phone without a single word of explanation. However, you may want to ask to be removed from the calling list before you hang up so that you don't have to deal with callers from that organization again. What you may *not* do is curse the caller and slam down the phone angrily. This behavior sets a terrible example for your children and others.

Repeated wrong numbers

If you frequently get wrong-number calls, discuss the problem with your phone company. The cause may be a typo in the phone book. The ultimate solution is to request a new telephone number, but if all the mistaken calls seem to be connected to the same voice, try letting your answering machine take over for a week or so.

Prank calls and other nuisances

The easiest way to deal with nuisance calls is to let your answering machine or voice-mail system do the work. Nuisance callers are quickly discouraged when they can't reach an actual human being. If you happen to pick up a nuisance call, just hang up the phone without comment.

Every telephone company has a department that deals with nuisance calls and other telephone offenses. By all means, call the phone company, ask for the appropriate department, and describe your problem. The phone company has many resources to help you.

Tussling with technology

For better or worse, voice mail, answering machines, beepers, and cellular phones are a part of the modern world. When used properly and with consideration, technology can save you time. The following shows you how to get the knack of the latest communication technologies.

Voice mail and answering machines

When confronted with complex voice mail systems, especially in business, keep in mind that the person you called probably didn't have anything to do with creating the system. Don't take out your frustrations by leaving a nasty message. Just go with the flow — leave a pleasant message and wait for a callback.

Dealing with threats

There's absolutely *no* difference between a telephoned threat and an in-person threat. Never take it upon yourself to decide that a telephoned threat is just a prank. If you receive a threatening call, write down all the details, keep the caller on the line by asking how you can eliminate the threatened action, and then, immediately after the conversation ends, alert your supervisor (if you're at work) or the police. If you're in charge at work and others are at risk, alert the police at once and take the necessary action to protect everyone's safety.

When you get connected with voice mail or an answering machine, leave a simple message. Speak distinctly and clearly. Don't mumble or say "ummm" repeatedly. Identify yourself, slowly give a phone number where you can be reached, say why you're calling, wish the person well, and say good-bye.

If you own an answering machine, make your message as brief as possible. A simple "You've reached the Jones residence. We can't come to the phone right now, but if you leave a message at the beep, we'll get back to you" will do. Make sure that your voice sounds pleasant and cheerful (try smiling as you're recording the message).

Cellular phones

Although most people don't mean to be rude, they can get into a sort of bubble while talking on cellular phones and may seem to forget the people around them.

Here are some tips for using a cellular phone with the best of manners:

- ✔ **Turn off the phone before entering any place where people gather to listen to each other or to enjoy paid entertainment.** If you forget to turn off your phone and it rings, leave the area and talk in the lobby or immediately turn off the phone and don't answer the call. Believe it or not, humanity survived back in the days when folks called their babysitters from pay phones during the intermission or between courses.

- ✔ **Understand that walking down the street while engaged in a lively discussion — business or personal — looks ridiculous.** If the communication is essential, be like Superman and duck into a nearby doorway or phone booth.

- ✔ **Never initiate a cellular phone conversation while seated in a reasonably quiet restaurant.** Do your communicating before cocktails or after coffee — and do it outside the restaurant. Many restaurants are taking a stand against patrons who insist on talking on cell phones at the table by having customers check their phones at the door.

Caller ID

A Caller ID box displays the number and the name of the person calling; it also records the date and time. One of the main etiquette challenges that Caller ID presents is people who check their Caller ID and then track down the poor souls who may have called their number by mistake and demand to know who they are and why they called. The following list answers some commonly asked etiquette questions about Caller ID:

- ✔ **Should I tell people that I have Caller ID?** Yes, the polite thing to do is to notify close friends and relatives that you have Caller ID. Tell them how it works and what the features are. Doing so can eliminate hurt feelings and embarrassment in the future.

- ✔ **If someone, even a friend, fails to leave a message, is it okay to call and see what he or she wants?** Yes, it's fine to call your friend back. Just let your friend know that you saw from your Caller ID unit that he or she called.

  If you don't recognize a name or number, don't call the person back. The person may have dialed a wrong number and hung up upon hearing the voice-mail message.

- ✔ **If your Caller ID box tells you that, say, your neighbor is calling, is it okay to answer the phone "Hi, Scott" instead of the standard "Hello"?** Yes, that's fine. Again, announce to the caller that you have Caller ID, because people may be surprised that you know who's calling.

- ✔ **What's the polite response when someone tracks you down after you make an errant phone call or fail to leave a message?** Common sense and courtesy should prevail. Scolding someone for not leaving a message is rude. If someone calls you to ask why you called, just tell the truth: Explain that another call came in or that you simply decided to call back later. If the person is polite to you, be equally polite to him.

- ✔ **Are there times when you shouldn't reveal that you even have Caller ID?** The situation can get tricky if someone lies and tells you that he called you all day but you weren't home. You probably wouldn't want to let the person know that you have Caller ID at that point, unless the person is a very close friend or relative whom you can tease or joke with.

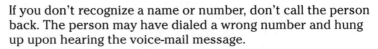

Safety issues for children at home alone

If your older children are home alone and a stranger calls and asks, "Is your mother home?" the child should always answer, "I'm sorry, but she's unable to come to the phone right now. May I have your name and number? I'll have her call you as soon as she's free." No further answers are necessary, even if the stranger presses for further information about what the mother is doing or when she will be free.

Developing the Art of Conversation

Although times change, the basic human need to interact with other humans does not. Those people who have been able to cultivate the skill of conversation have a leg up on others who are stuck behind a computer or buried beneath a stack of paper. Keep these three principles in mind:

> ✔ You want to put the other person at ease and avoid saying anything that may cause discomfort.

> ✔ You want to show that you really care about what's on the other person's mind.

> ✔ You want to engage in a genuine exchange of information and opinions.

If your personality is sparkling and outgoing, you'll find these suggestions easy to follow. On the other hand, if you're shy, you may need to work a little harder. The best way to do so is to attend social functions more frequently and make an effort to circulate among acquaintances and new faces. In conversation, as with other skills, practice makes perfect.

Initiating a conversation

Good conversation starters pull everyone in a group into a lively discussion. A talented conversationalist understands who is in the group and what is appropriate for the occasion. For example, it's not good to introduce the topic of baseball and then go on and on about statistics with the one other person in the circle who's a fan of the sport. The other people will feel left out and distressed. Bringing up an interesting story that you heard earlier that day is, however, a good way to involve the group in a lively conversation.

Asking beats telling

A good way to break the ice with someone is to ask a question. Make a resolution on your part to say something when you find yourself making eye contact with another person. Here are a few ideas to get you started:

> ✔ **At a wedding reception:** "Hello. Are you a friend of the bride?"

> ✔ **At a company party:** "My name is Howard. Do you work in the headquarters building?"

> ✔ **At a dinner party:** "I heard our host introduce you as Captain Lawrence. My name is Judy Jones. Are you on active duty?"

When the answer comes back to you, you need to respond with a reasonable answer in turn. A simple yes or no stops the whole conversation. Remember the power of question-and-answer and keep the ball rolling.

Some questions, however, are simply too corny to use as ice-breakers. No matter how strong the temptation, stay away from "What's your sign?", "Do you come here often?", and "What's a nice person like you doing in a place like this?" A little creativity goes a long way in the initial stage of a conversation. You're more likely to get a good response if you think of a good question to ask.

Complimenting someone

You're always on safe ground when you start the ball rolling with a genuine compliment. To be successful, a compliment should be sincere and specific. For example, say you notice someone's accessory — earrings, eyeglasses, a button — and admire it:

- "Those are lovely earrings — and so unique! Do they have a story?"
- "I've never seen eyeglass frames like that. Where did you find them?"
- "That's an interesting button on your lapel. What does it mean?"

Finding something to talk about

Every kind of conversation has a time and a place. If you're casually having a drink at a close friend's home, you can share almost without limit. On the other hand, many situations call for a careful selection of topics and a reasonable use of the other person's time.

After the initial greetings and pleasantries, what do you say next? The etiquette of conversation is governed by your sensitivity. Topics that seem perfectly reasonable at a backyard barbecue may be totally out of place at a bar mitzvah. If you're at a funeral, discussing the latest news about the breakup of your favorite star's marriage will be seen as disrespectful to the occasion and frivolous; whereas at lunch with a couple of close friends, celebrity news may be completely acceptable as a light topic of conversation. Make sure to give yourself a second or two of time to think about the situation before opening your mouth.

In addition to an appropriate subject, timing is also of the essence. At a cocktail party, a five- or ten-minute conversation may be the maximum in order to allow everyone to circulate. At a dinner party, however, you may converse with the people to either side of you for the duration of the meal.

The most explosive conversational subjects are sex, politics, money, and religion. People tend to have strong emotions and can be highly opinionated about these troublesome topics.

Keeping your personal life personal

Good friends can discuss almost anything, but people you meet at social gatherings aren't entitled to the deeply personal details of your life. Moreover, something that you think is interesting may bore another person. For example, if you've recently been sick and a friend asks you at a dinner party, "How are you feeling now?", give a simple answer. You don't need to go into a detailed explanation. Likewise, details about relationships or raises or grades that your children have received are more information than most pleasant conversations require.

The question "How are you?" is a formal artifact of our society and isn't meant to elicit a detailed response. Keep it brief.

Good manners start to overlap into self-defense when strangers start probing into your personal affairs. You don't have to answer questions about your finances, your marital history, or anything you'd rather not discuss. Deal with a Nosy Nellie by looking her in the eye and asking, "Why do you ask?" or stating "I'd rather not talk about that right now."

Finding successful conversation topics

Successful conversationalists know how to introduce topics that interest just about everyone. Here are some topics that usually spark lively conversation:

- ✔ **Current events:** Scan a news magazine, Web site, or newspaper before heading off to a social event to find upbeat, interesting, or unusual news.

- ✔ **Congratulations:** Offering congratulations to someone on an accomplishment, such as a graduation, promotion, or new baby, can get the conversation rolling on a pleasant note.

- ✔ **Good news:** Providing happy news about mutual friends is an upbeat topic that puts people in a good mood.

- ✔ **Cultural events:** Talking about the latest play, musical perform-ance, or art show interests almost everyone.

✔ **Sports:** If a sporting event is of national interest, such as the Olympics or the Super Bowl, everyone should be able to participate.

Listening: More than merely not talking

Listening well is an act of generosity. To truly listen to someone is an unselfish act. How do you learn to listen? Ask a question of someone, and then let that person answer. Concentrate on what the person is saying. Don't interrupt or interject comments that shift the attention to you. All these signals show the depth of your attention. Beyond that, here are some special ways to be a good listener.

✔ **Staying eyeball to eyeball:** Eye contact is the glue of a conversation. When you look directly at a person and pay attention to the conversation, you give a signal that, for the moment at least, the person you're talking to is the most interesting person imaginable. Looking away, especially at your shoes or the ceiling, indicates your wish to be far away.

✔ **Utilizing the well-placed "Hmmm":** Keep your conversation partner going with little prompts. A well-placed "hmmm" here and there indicates your understanding of what is being said and shows that you're following along. Failing to respond and keeping your face neutral have the opposite effect — and may even bring the conversation to a halt.

✔ **Maintaining a sense of curiosity:** The best way to learn is to listen — not to talk. If you maintain a lively curiosity about life, people, why things happen the way they do, how things work, and what people do in their jobs, for example, you'll always be at the center of good conversations. People are flattered when you ask questions about their life and work. Be curious. The more you learn, the more interesting you become.

Ending a conversation

Say that you've been conversing with a person at a cocktail party for 15 minutes. This person won't get off the subject of his job, his health, or his children — three of the topics that are most likely to bore other people. No rule says that you have to remain trapped in a conversation you'd rather end. How you extricate yourself is just one more measure of your mastery of good manners. Here are some polite exit lines:

> ✔ "I didn't know that quantum electrodynamics was such a fascinating subject. Perhaps you can tell me more after I finish saying hello to my cousin, who just arrived."
>
> ✔ "You know, that cat of yours sounds like a real character. I'll be thinking about her while I powder my nose."
>
> ✔ "Oh, for goodness sake! The time passed so quickly that I forgot to call my babysitter. Please excuse me."

A polite person is never cruel to another — no matter how bored you are. Smile, shake hands, and part graciously.

Minding Your Manners at Dinner Time

Nowhere else is man's difference from beasts more evident than in our eating manners.

Formal seating

Certain rules govern where guests sit during a formal meal:

> ✔ Almost every meal has a *host* — the person in whose home you're dining or who invited you out to a restaurant. The host sits at the end of the table. If a couple is hosting, the man sits at one end, and the woman sits at the other.
>
> ✔ The male guest of honor sits on the hostess's right.
>
> ✔ The next most important man sits on the hostess's left.
>
> ✔ The female guest of honor sits to the host's right.
>
> ✔ The second most important woman sits to the host's left.
>
> ✔ Whatever the shape of the table, try to separate couples and seat men and women alternately.
>
> ✔ Consider using placecards for larger parties or more formal affairs.

> ✔ If placecards are used, never move them or change your seat; your host probably put some creative logic into seating you there.

Coming to the table

Whether you're having cocktails and conversation in a restaurant lounge or in your living room, at some point you must go to the table with your family or group. Follow these very specific ways to offer and take a seat:

- ✔ In formal situations, the men individually escort the women by the arm to their seats and assist them in being seated.

- ✔ In informal situations, the men allow the women to approach the table in a group and then assist them in taking their seats.

Taking a seat

Here's how you take a seat, step by step: The woman approaches her chair and waits to be seated. The man stands behind the woman's chair and draws it back for her. The woman then begins to sit. When she is halfway down, the man pushes the chair gently beneath her. After she's seated, the woman can move the chair closer or farther from the table by holding the sides of the seat and scooting it forward or backward. The man then seats himself to the left of the woman he just seated.

In a formal dining situation, no one sits down until the host(s) or guest of honor is seated.

Everyone is seated — now what?

After you're seated, wait for your host or guest of honor to pick up the napkin and place it on his or her lap and then gently put your own napkin in your lap. (*Note:* In more upscale restaurants, your waiter may place your napkin on your lap for you.)

No matter what the occasion, do not flap your napkin around like a flag before placing it in your lap. Men are not to tuck napkins into their shirts like a bib. And remember, the purpose of a napkin is to dab the corners of your mouth. Never use it to wipe off lipstick or to blow your nose!

Knowing when to eat

Start to eat when your host begins to eat. If a course is brought to the table in twos or threes and not everyone has his or her food, wait until everyone has been served the course, and then begin to eat together.

In this situation, the host may encourage you to go ahead and begin eating. If he or she does so, it's perfectly fine to begin eating. If you wish, though, you may continue to wait until everyone has his or her meal before you begin, chatting with the other guests in the meantime.

Minding your posture

During the meal, keep both feet flat on the floor or cross your feet at your ankles. Don't cross your legs at the knees and don't prop your feet on chair rungs or table legs or wrap them around anything under the table.

You can rest your hands up to your forearms on the table but don't prop your elbows on the table. Keep your elbows close to your body so that you don't bump into others and so that you can generally control your arm movements better. Between courses, or anytime you want to rest, you can place both hands in your lap or place one hand in your lap and the other on the edge of the table at the wrist.

As you eat, sit up straight on the front three-quarters of your chair. This way, you don't have to bend over your food; you can simply bring your utensils to your mouth. Don't rush when you lift your food from the table to your mouth. Don't bend closely over your plate or try to meet your utensils halfway.

Excusing yourself

If you must leave the table during a meal for any reason, do so with as little interruption to others as possible. Politely and quietly excuse yourself, lay your napkin on your chair, and leave without fanfare.

If you have to cough or sneeze while dining, simply turn your head toward your shoulder and cover your mouth and nose with a tissue or your handkerchief (or in an emergency, your napkin). If you have a fit of sneezes or hiccups or you must blow your nose with force, excuse yourself, go to the restroom, and take care of your business. Take medication in the restroom as well.

After you finish your entire meal and you're leaving the table, place your napkin to the left of your plate. You don't have to fold your napkin again but leave it sitting neatly, with no soiled areas showing.

Figuring out a table setting

Unlike Julia Roberts in *Pretty Woman*, you don't need to freak out when confronted with a dinner table setting. Figure 25-1 shows a standard table setting, while Figure 25-2 shows a very elaborate setting.

Figure 25-1: A basic place setting.

Figure 25-2: A formal place setting.

Bottom line: Whatever the place setting:

✔ Liquids are to the right and solids to the left.

✔ You start from the outside utensils and work inward with each course.

The following information gives you a few more hints for using specific items in a place setting:

- **Plates and bowls:** The place plate, or main dinner plate, is in the center in front of each chair setting. In formal dining, an underplate or charger is usually included as well. The bread plate is always to the left, slightly above the forks.

  If soup and salad courses are served, the soup bowl and salad plate are brought to the table and later removed. The soup bowl is placed on a service plate, which sits on the dinner plate. The salad plate is also placed on top of the dinner plate.

  Note: Sometimes a small bowl and a small plate with a doily, a small fork, and a small spoon rest above the dinner plate. These dishes are the finger bowl and the dessert plate, respectively.

- **Utensils:** Forks are placed to the left of the plate, and knives and spoons to the right (with the exception of the cocktail fork, which is placed on the soup spoon or to right of the soup spoon). The dessert fork and spoon are placed above the dinner plate.

  Depending on the course, the salad fork, which is smaller than the dinner fork, is normally farthest to the left. Next is the dinner fork, which you use for the entree. Salad is sometimes served as the third or fourth course, in which case the salad fork is closest to the plate. The butter spreader is placed on the bread plate, on the left above the forks.

  To the right of the plate, starting from the outermost utensil, are the cocktail fork, the soup spoon, the fish knife (if fish is being served), the dinner knife, and then the salad knife nearest the plate. The cutting edge of each knife is turned toward the plate.

  Finally, the dessert fork or spoon is placed horizontally above the place plate, tines facing to the right or spoon bowl facing to the left.

- **Glassware:** In a formal setting, you usually have five glasses at the table. The glasses are always to the right, above the knives, because most people are right-handed. To suit the beverage with which it is filled, each glass is slightly different in shape and size:

  - The glass farthest to the right is a sherry or aperitif glass. This glass is the first one you use, because sherry is poured during the soup course.

  - Next comes the white wine glass, which is used during the fish course or appetizer.

  - Behind the white wine glass is the red wine glass. This glass is larger, with a fuller bowl that allows the red wine to "breathe."

- The largest glass is the water goblet, which usually sits just above the dinner knife.

- Behind and to the right of the water goblet is the Champagne flute. This glass is not used until dessert is served.

You hold most stem glasses by the bowl, except for a white wine glass or a Champagne flute. Because white wine and Champagne are served chilled, you don't want to warm them with your hand. Also, you don't want to shake hands with a chilly hand.

Consuming each course of a meal

The following information walks you through a typical meal, course by course, giving you suggestions for what to do and not to do.

Bread

Bread is placed on the table or passed around the table. If a bread basket or bread plate is sitting in front of you, it's your responsibility to begin passing the bread. If the table is round, offer the bread to the person on your right and don't help yourself until the bread comes back around to you. If the table is rectangular and you can see that the bread may not come back your way, help yourself and then pass to your right.

When bread is served half-sliced in a basket with a napkin, take a portion of the napkin in your left hand and hold a section of the bread in the napkin, without touching the bread, and then with your right hand tear off a piece. The napkin is placed in the basket to cover and protect the remaining bread.

If you'd like some butter for your bread, take the butter from the serving dish and place it on your bread-and-butter plate, not directly on the bread. Never use the knife that accompanies the butter dish to butter your bread. If no knife rests on the butter dish, you may use your own butter spreader.

Dipping, dunking, or wiping sauces with your bread is not polite, except in the most informal gatherings or with certain dishes that are designed to do just that — such as fondues, certain au jus dishes, and olive oil. If you're dipping your bread into a communal sauce, never double-dip!

Soup

You eat all soups the same way: By holding your soup spoon the way you hold a pencil, between your index and middle fingers with your thumb up. Spoon the soup away from you toward the center or top of the bowl, and then sip the soup from the side — not the point — of the spoon. Rest the spoon in the soup bowl while you pause. After you finish, place the spoon on the saucer or plate beneath the cup or bowl; do not leave the spoon in the bowl or cup.

Blowing on your soup to cool it down is not polite. If you're worried that your soup is too hot, gently stir it or spoon soup from the edge of the bowl first.

At a formal meal, a sherry or aperitif may be served with the soup course.

Salad

Salad may be served before or after the main course; the placement of the fork will tip you off. However, in a basic table setting, you usually have only one knife. For this reason, some Americans seem to think that this knife is for the main course and that they cannot use it for the salad. Not true! A fine restaurant or a considerate host always serves salad with the lettuce in bite-sized pieces. However, if you're served large pieces, cut one bite at a time by using the knife that's provided. Using your knife to cut lettuce is perfectly fine — just request a clean knife when the main course arrives.

If a salad is the main course, such as at a luncheon, use the entree fork. If a salad is served prior to or after the main course, use the smaller salad fork. When a salad is served during a formal meal, you always have a salad knife, which is usually smaller than the dinner knife.

After you finish your salad (or any course, for that matter), never push your plate or bowl away from you. The placement of your cutlery informs the wait staff that you have finished.

Sorbet or intermezzo

A sorbet or intermezzo may be served between the appetizer and entree to cleanse the palate. You need to have only a small taste; you don't need to finish the entire dish.

Entree

The main course is normally beef, chicken, duck, or lamb, and you eat these foods with a knife and fork. Finger foods, such as fried chicken, are usually served at informal occasions and not in formal dining situations.

If you're served a large steak, you may cut it into two or three sections, but not into many small pieces. (You may be given a special steak knife to help you cut the meat without sawing.) Otherwise, continue to cut one or at most two bites at a time.

Finger bowl

A finger bowl is presented after the main course and before dessert arrives. Your server places it in front of you on a plate, usually with a doily under the bowl. The bowl contains warm water with a slice of lemon and occasionally a small flower. A small dessert fork and spoon are also on the plate; you bring these utensils down and place them to the left and right, respectively, of where the dessert plate will go.

Dip just your fingertips in the water and dry them on your napkin. Remove the doily and bowl and place them to the left. A waiter then removes them.

Dessert

Dessert is normally served to you along with a dessert wine or Champagne. If you're served ice cream, use your spoon; if you're served cake with a sauce, use both the spoon and the fork. Fresh fruit and cheese are sometimes served as dessert. You eat these foods with a knife and fork.

Chopsticks

Using chopsticks does require a technique; however, it's easy to master with just a little practice. Here are a few pointers for eating with chopsticks:

✔ Hold the chopsticks between your index finger and thumb.

✔ Rest the lower chopstick in the web of your hand and remain still.

✔ Hold the top chopstick as you would hold a pencil; the top chopstick does most of the moving, and you use your two middle fingers to maneuver it.

✔ Do not hold chopsticks too tightly; mobility is easier if you hold them loosely.

✔ Do not hold chopsticks too close to the tip, because doing so makes you lose leverage, which makes picking up food difficult.

✔ If a piece of food is too big, you may cut it with your chopsticks or hold it with your chopsticks while you take a couple of bites.

✔ As with Western eating tools, never point, gesture, or talk with your chopsticks.

✔ Between bites, place your chopsticks on the rest provided or lay them across the lower dish or plate. Don't leave your chopsticks pointed upright in your rice or soup bowl.

✔ Never take food from another person's chopsticks.

Most importantly: If you're not ready to try using chopsticks, you're perfectly fine requesting a knife and fork.

Avoiding distressing mealtime moments

Eating in any social setting may result in mishaps. Use the following tips to steer yourself out of common accidents that can occur:

- ✔ **You drop a utensil onto the floor.** Never lean over and pick up the utensil (unless, of course, you're at your mother's dinner table and no waiters are present, in which case you may use your napkin to retrieve the wandering fork, walk it out to the kitchen, and get yourself both a clean napkin and a clean fork). In any situation where servers are present, beckon a server and explain what happened. The server will pick up the utensil and bring you a clean one.

- ✔ **You're served a piece of food that isn't cooked properly.** This situation can be especially dangerous with meat. If you encounter such a situation, call over a server and quietly explain what's happened. Trust the waitstaff to reappear with a different plate of food for you.

- ✔ **You find a foreign object in your food.** Find your server and very discreetly tell him or her about the problem. Rest assured that your meal will be replaced quickly and may even be complimentary.

- ✔ **You dislike the food that's being served, or you're allergic to it.** The polite thing to do is try a little of everything; however, if you're allergic to a food, just smile and say "No, thank you." You don't need to say anything critical.

- ✔ **You have bone, gristle, or some other unwanted food item in your mouth.** Discreetly remove the food onto the tine of your fork and place it on your plate. If possible, hide it under a garnish or other food on your plate so that the people around you can't see it. Never spit anything into your napkin!

Using salt and pepper judiciously

Although you find salt and pepper on nearly every table, good manners call for you to thoughtfully taste your food *before* you add any seasoning. The chef (whether your host or the chef at a restaurant or banquet facility) tried to achieve perfect seasoning, and when you reach for the salt and pepper, you indicate that perfection was not quite achieved.

If you're asked to pass the salt or the pepper, always pass them together, as they should stay together on the table throughout the meal.

Dealing with Difficult Foods at Formal Dinners

Foods such as pot roast, mashed potatoes, broccoli, and blueberry pie are relatively easy to eat, but real life is full of surprises. The following list offers a few words of advice on difficult foods you may encounter:

- ✔ **Asparagus:** In a more casual setting, eating asparagus as a finger food is acceptable. But at a formal dinner, you're best to use a fork and knife, cutting one bite at a time.

- ✔ **Bacon:** When bacon is cooked crisp, you can consider it a finger food. When it's soft, however, use your fork and knife to cut one bite of bacon at a time.

- ✔ **Fish with bones:** You can remove small fish bones with your fork or your forefinger and thumb — as always, try to be discreet.

- ✔ **Peas:** You can get peas onto your fork any number of ways. Either move the peas against the meat and scoop them onto your fork, or use a crust of bread to help push the peas onto the fork. Or, you can use your knife or food on your plate and push or smash the peas onto the backs of the fork tines.

- ✔ **Olives and other pitted foods:** Pitted foods are finger foods after they're on your plate, so you may pick them up with your fingers. Large stuffed olives are best eaten in two bites. Discreetly remove the pits with your forefinger and thumb.

- ✔ **Poultry:** If you're lucky, the kitchen crew or the server will debone or cut most birds into manageable pieces that you can then handle with your knife and fork. Otherwise, try these approaches (listed in order of mannerly preference):

  - Ask your waiter for help in disjointing the bird.

  - Ask for a sharp knife if you don't have one.

  - Do your best to separate the bird at its major joints.

  - Pick up tiny legs and wings by a protruding bone and then eat the meat as finger food.

  Place all bones to one side on your dinner plate.

- ✔ **Lobster and crab:** Lobster and crab are almost always served in informal situations. The host provides bibs, and everyone generally accepts that a lot of finger work is proper behavior. If you're unfamiliar with the procedure for eating a whole lobster and you find yourself confronted by one, the other guests are likely to have plenty of good advice.

✔ **Mussels:** Steamed mussels may be eaten with a fork and spoon or a cocktail fork. Spear the mussel, dip it into the sauce provided, and eat it whole.

✔ **Oysters:** Oysters on the half shell remain attached to the bottom shell by a slender little membrane. To free the meat from the shell, slip your oyster fork underneath the meat and wiggle it back and forth. Use your cocktail fork to spear the oyster and dip it into the sauce. At an informal setting, it's acceptable to pick up the shell with your fingers and suck the oyster right off the shell.

✔ **Shrimp:** If shrimp is served ready-to-eat in a cocktail appetizer, pierce the shrimp on a cocktail fork and bite off a succession of manageable pieces. If the shrimp are large, place them on your plate and cut them with the fork provided before dipping them into the sauce. Steamed shrimp served in their shells, however, are definitely a finger food. If you don't receive a bowl for empty shells, just accumulate the shells in a neat little heap on your plate.

✔ **Snails (Escargot):** Pick up one escargot at a time, using the escargot tong that's provided to secure the snail. Remove the snail with a cocktail fork prior to dipping the meat into butter sauce.

✔ **Spaghetti:** Eating spaghetti may look difficult, but really it's easy. You normally twirl spaghetti on the edge of your plate with your fork. However, you may use your fork and a place spoon as well. You can also use your fork to cut the spaghetti into bite-sized portions, although you rarely see this method used in Italy.

✔ **Sushi and sashimi:** You can use chopsticks or a fork to eat sushi, but many aficionados prefer to use their fingers. No matter how you choose to eat sushi, eat it in one or two bites. Sushi is served with soy sauce and various condiments for dipping, with ginger provided as a refresher for the palate between courses.

Marking Many of Life's Major Events

Life's major events are often a challenge: They call on you to stop what you're doing, take pause, and give of yourself to others — whether it's taking a weekend to travel to a high school graduation or spending time with your sister at home after the birth of her baby. What counts most is that you're there for your friends and family and that you care.

Baby showers

Traditionally, a woman only had a shower with her first child. But times are changing, and Mom can have a shower for every child who joins her family. This is especially true if the new baby is a different gender or if multiples are expected. If Mom already has everything she needs for the baby and you just want to do something nice, a little get-together in her honor is a lovely idea. For example, you can host an afternoon tea and ask each guest to bring a small item related to tea for the mom-to-be.

The shower is usually held two to three months before the baby's due date. That way, the mother has time to evaluate what she's received at the shower and decide what she needs to purchase or borrow herself.

Who attends/Who's invited: Traditionally, only women attended showers; however, many showers today also include men. If you're going the traditional route, immediate female family members of both the mother and father-to-be's families are to be invited, as well as close friends of the mother-to-be. Consult with the parents-to-be when making up the invitation list. If the shower is to be a surprise, make sure to check with the parents-to-be's families when making up your guest list.

Showers usually have between 6 and 25 guests. If the number of guests seems too large, consider having two showers — one for family and relatives and one for friends. Usually, a shower is held in the host's home, but it can also be held in a restaurant, a tearoom, a community room, or a church social hall. The shower should last about two hours.

Dress: Dress at a traditional baby shower held on a weekend afternoon is relaxed, but nice. A pantsuit, dress, or long skirt and sweater are all good choices. If the shower is themed, it may call for special dress. When in doubt, ask the host for advice.

Flowers/Gifts/Donations: The host is responsible for guiding the guests to presents that are needed and will be appreciated. If possible, the host should sit with the mom-to-be and make a list together. If she hasn't already done so, suggest that she register at one or two baby stores. You can then advise individual guests about her wish list.

Baptisms

Baptisms (also commonly called "christenings," although the proper term is "baptism") usually take place in a child's first six months.

Catholic children are sometimes baptized very early, within the first six weeks of life. Protestant children are usually baptized during their first six months, although baptism can take place at any age.

Notices/Announcements/Invitations: Invitations to a baptism are usually issued over the telephone. Usually, the parents or grandparents have a small gathering afterward. Invitations to a baptism should be informal.

Who attends/Who's invited: Close family members attend the baptism, as well as the godparents, if there are any.

Dress: Dress for a baptism as you would for a religious service.

Flowers/Gifts/Donations: Gifts for the baby are usually brought by the guests, as the guests are presumably very close relatives. For a girl, godparents may give a small piece of jewelry to be worn when she is older or an engraved silver frame, small cup, or baby spoon.

B'rith Milahs

A circumcision and naming ceremony takes place eight days after a Jewish baby boy is born. The boy is also given godparents at this time. The ceremony can take place in the parents' home or in a special room in the hospital.

For a girl, the naming ceremony is on the first Sabbath after she's born, in a service at the temple. Her father is called up to the Torah, where he recites a short prayer and states his daughter's name. The rabbi then recites a special blessing. A reception is hosted afterward by the baby's mother.

Notices/Announcements/Invitations: Invitations are usually issued over the telephone.

Who attends/Who's invited: Only a few family members and close relatives attend the ceremony.

Dress: Dress as you would for a religious service.

Flowers/Gifts/Donations: Gifts are sometimes presented for the baby on the occasion.

Bar and bat mitzvahs

Jewish tradition celebrates the attainment of age 13 for boys (bar mitzvah) and age 12 for girls (bat mitzvah). At this milestone, the community considers the young person to be capable of participating in religious observances as an adult. To commemorate this event, families usually allow the celebrant (the boy or girl) to lead the congregation in a regular weekly prayer service, including the reading of a passage from the Torah in Hebrew.

After the ceremony, the immediate family may gather in a private room in the temple to greet members of the congregation who want to offer congratulations. Often, this is followed by a lavish reception, which may be held in a temple reception room, a hotel, or other public hall. The reception often includes a seated luncheon or dinner and may include dancing, flowers, and decorated tables.

Notices/Announcements/Invitations: If the reception is to be a large one, issue written invitations. If it's a small affair with family and a very few friends, you can make your invitations by telephone.

Who attends/Who's invited: Proud parents invite friends to participate in and witness the proceedings. Non-Jewish well-wishers may also be invited to sit among the congregation. All congregations welcome non-Jews and don't expect them to know the details of the ritual. What counts is your presence. After the ceremony is over, generously congratulate the celebrant and his or her parents.

Dress: In some congregations, men are asked to wear a small, symbolic head covering. In Orthodox congregations, women also cover their heads and sit apart from the men. Otherwise, wear whatever types of clothing you would normally wear to attend a religious service.

Flowers/Gifts/Donations: Gifts should not be brought to the temple or the reception but should be sent to the child's home. Gifts are wonderful, but most children also appreciate checks. Gift ideas include a good book, a magazine subscription, or a gift certificate.

Confirmations

Confirmations are a rite of passage for Christians that means that the confirmands are capable of participating in the religious life of their congregation as adults. The ceremony usually takes place when the child is in the seventh or eighth grade.

A quiet family occasion, usually only the godparents and close relatives attend. If a social gathering takes place after the confirmation ceremony, it's appropriate to bring a small gift — a book that is inspirational in some way is very appropriate, for instance.

You should dress as you would to attend a service in a house of worship. The confirmand is usually dressed in his or her very best clothes.

Graduations

High-school and college graduations are some of the proudest occasions in a young person's life — and in the life of their proud parents. They mark completion of a stage of life, and the start of an exciting new life.

Notices/Announcements/Invitations: Graduation ceremony invitations and announcements are normally given out by the school, which means that immediate families only are able to attend. Parents usually plan a party or afternoon reception after the graduation ceremony. The setting can be elaborate or simple, and depending on the nature of the party, invitations can be printed, handwritten, or telephoned. Often, graduates spend time at their own party and then late in the day begin circulating among their friends' houses to greet them and visit their graduation parties as well.

Parents often mail out announcements of a child's graduation, especially to out-of-town friends. (This announcement differs from an invitation to attend a graduation ceremony or reception.) The announcement should be mailed two weeks prior to graduation. If you receive a graduation announcement, you're not obligated to attend or send a gift.

Who attends/Who's invited: If you've attended a high school or college commencement recently, you know that seating is often limited. Tickets to graduation exercises are often rationed among the participants, so if you're invited to attend a graduation and you accept the invitation, go. Usually, there are just enough tickets for the parents and siblings of the graduates, and the grandparents. If you're allowed to invite more guests, other close relatives or family friends should be invited. If you cannot invite everyone you'd like to the graduation ceremony, you should tell them why. Most people will understand. However, everyone should be invited to a gathering honoring the graduate after the ceremony.

Dress: A graduation ceremony and party are an opportunity to look your festive best. Suits and ties for the men and nice dresses or long skirts and matching tops for the women are in order. Graduates often wear a new outfit, whether it's a suit or a special dress, which they can then use in their new life at college or out in the working world.

Flowers/Gifts/Donations: Even if you can't attend the party, as a close friend or relative, it's thoughtful to send a gift to the graduate. Depending on your preference and price range, welcome gifts may include a book, a diary or journal, a calculator, dorm supplies, tickets to a sporting event or a rock concert or a play, or gift certificates.

Funerals and memorial services

Most cultures and religions have some type of memorial when a person passes away. These services provide a sense of completion, a process for mourning, and comfort for the living.

Notices/Announcements/Invitations: Notices should be placed in newspapers where family and friends of the deceased person live or have previously lived.

A notice can include the following information:

- ✔ Name and address of the person who died
- ✔ Date and place where he or she died
- ✔ Cause of death
- ✔ Name of spouse
- ✔ City of birth and date of birth
- ✔ Company where the person worked and his or her title
- ✔ Education, military service, or major awards or distinctions
- ✔ Names of survivors and their relationship to the deceased
- ✔ Information on the funeral or memorial service and whether it is private or for the public
- ✔ Where to send donations as memorials

Who attends: A funeral or memorial service may be a very public event, attended by family, friends, colleagues, neighbors and even acquaintances. The gathering held after the event usually includes only family members, the minister or priest, ushers, pallbearers, close social and business friends, and anyone who came from out of town for the service. If the service is private, those attending will be notified personally, usually by telephone.

Attending the events: In many cultures, the first event that follows a death is a *visitation* — a courtesy call at the funeral home prior to the funeral. The casket is present (open or closed), with flowers on display, and the family receives visitors who come to greet them and offer words of comfort and support.

Funerals are often held in a chapel or a house of worship. Because the immediate family may be overwhelmed, you need only to greet the mourners and briefly offer condolences. Most important for the family is the knowledge of your presence.

Burials usually follow funerals. Some cultures consider it a sign of respect to deposit a ceremonial shovel of earth into the grave. This ceremony is initiated by a member of the family and followed by others. If you were close to the deceased, you may take your turn.

You usually exchange expressions of support at the residence of the deceased, a reserved social hall, or a room at the house of worship immediately following the burial or memorial service. In almost all cultures, taking a meal in the company of friends and family is a symbol of the continuation of life and a moment of separation from the intense details of the death, funeral, and burial. Recalling fond memories of the deceased may inspire smiles and even laughter at this gathering — this behavior is perfectly acceptable.

In the days immediately following a funeral, custom calls for neighbors and close friends to visit the bereaved family on a daily basis. Bringing prepared foods that the mourners can eat and share with visitors is a nice gesture.

Dress: Black has long been the traditional color for mourning. However, black is no longer required and it isn't considered a sign of disrespect to wear a color other than black, as long as the color isn't a bright one. Hats may be worn by women, and at Orthodox Jewish services, yarmulkes will be worn by the men. Dark suits and ties for men and dresses or suits for women are appropriate.

When in doubt, go

Funerals can be difficult occasions. Many otherwise well-mannered people avoid funerals because they're sad and often emotional. The same goes for visiting a hospital patient who is seriously ill and may be connected to monitors and life-support equipment.

As a general rule, you can assume that the more difficult the situation, the more the family will appreciate your presence and your words of support. You don't need to remain on the scene for a long time; hospitals may limit visits with patients to just a few minutes. But your willingness to go out of your way to say a word or two of comfort will be very much appreciated.

Flowers/Gifts/Donations: During this period, you may send flowers to the funeral home. Donations may be made to the house of worship or made in the deceased person's name. Out-of-town friends and relatives who are not able to attend the funeral may send flowers and messages of condolence.

Four Hints for Good Manners While Visiting a Foreign Culture

You will find no tougher test of your manners than traveling. Being away from home does not give you permission to abandon politeness. Particularly when you're a guest in another state or another culture, you need to be *extra* mannerly.

If you happen to make an etiquette faux pas, don't panic. Most local residents are impressed by travelers who are as interested in their outlook and way of life as they are in their monuments and museums.

Know your destination

When you step onto foreign ground, you can no longer assume that you know what behavior is acceptable. Try to be at least twice as courteous and tactful in a foreign country as you are at home. Respect differences in cultures, be patient, practice good listening skills, and remain flexible.

Perhaps most important, keep your sense of humor. If you can laugh at yourself in an awkward situation or alleviate a fellow traveler's embarrassment at making a mistake, people will appreciate it.

Foreign beaches

You may be surprised to discover that beach manners are generally more relaxed abroad than at home. Europeans everywhere are more casual than Americans are about changing clothes and the size of their swimwear.

Beach rules can be completely different from one neighboring country to another. Regardless of how socially protected the women of certain countries are, as a visiting foreigner you can get away with wearing a bikini in most cosmopolitan resorts. To be on the safe side, pack a conservative bathing suit and check with your hotel's concierge about local customs and beach wear before venturing out.

Dress appropriately

You can utilize a few general guidelines when you pack for a trip and select your outfit for each day of travel activities:

- ✔ **Less flash is better when it comes to travel clothing.** Lean toward the inconspicuous instead of standing out in garish garb. Although college students on a backpacking tour can get away with more casual clothing, make an effort to look neat and well put together.

- ✔ **Your clothes should be natural to the surroundings you're visiting.** In other words, no sarongs and bikini tops on the streets of London, and no stiletto heels or black pantsuits at a Caribbean beach!

- ✔ **Skin can be a sin.** Religious establishments, in particular, impose strict modesty rules, especially for female visitors. Depending on the religion and the place, women may be required to cover their shoulders, arms, heads, legs, and/or feet. In general, dress rules are not strictly enforced for tourists, but you show your good manners when you show less of yourself.

- ✔ **Casual business dress doesn't translate.** Corporate officers may put in a productive day in California while wearing blue jeans, running shoes, and open-neck shirts, but the rest of the world hasn't quite caught up with casual business attire. When conducting business abroad, dress conventionally, conservatively, and appropriately.

- ✔ **Baubles inspire bandits.** Play it safe by leaving your precious jewelry locked up at home and make do with costume jewelry and timepieces that you can bear to lose.

Communicate like a local

Language barriers are the biggest potential pitfall of etiquette-conscious travelers. You can't be courteous if you can't communicate. If you plan to travel to a country where the language is not your own, learn a few of the most polite phrases in the local language. At a bare minimum, you need to know how to say hello, good-bye, please, thank you, where?, how?, when?, how much?, yes, and no. Every large bookstore sells small, pocket-sized phrasebooks and audio tapes in just about every language you'll ever need.

English is taught as a second language in many countries, and you may find your verbal exchanges easier if you begin a new contact by asking, "Do you speak English?" More often than not, the answer will be, "A little."

Smoking

Although Americans have cut down on smoking and have outlawed it in many public places, the same rules do not necessarily apply in the rest of the world. Be prepared to find smokers in public, in private, and in transit. Smokers in public places in many foreign countries are within their legal rights, so you should either move away or put up with it. If you're highly sensitive to smoke, avoid bars and café areas that are frequented by smokers.

A few other useful communication tips include

✔ **Don't use English as a secret code.** You may be tempted to use English to exchange private comments with your travel companion. However, doing this is almost always a mistake. Most non-U.S. citizens know at least a few words of English.

Never say anything in English to your companion that you don't want others around you to overhear. Your inability to speak the language of your host country is no excuse to abandon everyday good manners.

✔ **Use polite expressions as much as possible.** Phrases such as "good morning," "good evening," "please," and "thank you," when spoken in the native language of the country you're visiting, go far in making you appear to be a polite and courteous traveler.

✔ **Watch your gestures.** Contrary to what you may think, gestures don't have universal meanings. For example, in many parts of the world, a thumbs-up is an obscene gesture and pointing is considered rude. Study a guidebook for the country you're visiting to find out which gestures and body language to avoid while you're there.

✔ **Body language can say as much about you as the words that come out of your mouth.** The appropriate level of physical contact varies greatly from culture to culture. A guidebook for the country you're visiting should help you figure out what's appropriate.

✔ **Every culture has its own rules for how to show various emotions.** Some cultures frown upon public expressions of sorrow or joy, and others encourage it. When you travel, understand what is acceptable by observing the natives. You don't need to change who you are when you're traveling but do accept others' manners while you're among them and try to blend in.

✔ **Mind your conversations.** Although Americans find it perfectly acceptable to ask what people do for a living and whether they are married, citizens of other countries often consider these questions rude. Food, the arts, and sports are generally good, safe conversation topics. Unless you're speaking to a close friend of many years from another country, avoid personal questions, jokes, and intimate topics. And never criticize the person's country or city!

Eat, drink, and be merry

When the term "When in Rome" was coined, it not only meant to embrace the customs and culture, but it also included trying the food and drink! If you're adventurous, food can be one of the best parts of traveling.

The following information can help steer you around the gastronomical glitches that often trip up international travelers:

✔ **Hearty breakfasts are virtually unknown in most foreign countries.** Europeans tend to drink a glass of fruit juice, eat a croissant or roll, and follow it with a cup of coffee. Some even skip the bread. Try carrying a piece of fruit, some crackers, or some trail mix as a mid-morning snack on your first few days to get you to lunch.

✔ **In some countries, all the retail stores close a few minutes before noon and don't reopen until mid-afternoon.** Therefore, if you want to have an impulsive picnic, you must put your plans into action by 11:00 or 11:30 a.m. at the latest. Buy your sandwich makings and other goodies at a deli, pick up some bread, and head for a quiet spot.

✔ **Try your best to grit your teeth, swallow, and smile if you encounter unappealing foreign food.** You won't offend your host if you leave something on your plate because it disagrees with you, but you may offend your host if you don't try the food because it's strange to you.

✔ **Adjust your table manners as appropriate.** If you follow proper American dining etiquette, you'll do passably in most countries. However, many other subtle differences in table manners exist. Ask your host what to do if you're uncertain.

✔ **Being intoxicated is never good manners.** In many countries, the drink you're served with lunch or dinner may well be alcoholic. Be careful with beer as well as wine. Beer in other countries is much stronger than American beer.

Part VII
Connecting to the World with Technology

"You know, I liked you a whole lot more on the Internet."

In this part . . .

*W*hether you're cruising the Internet in a slick sports car or puttering along in a slow-but-steady station wagon (with wood paneling, of course), this part has all the information you need to survive and start to thrive in the ever-expanding online universe. Although technology and the World Wide Web can be overwhelming, the following chapters can help you easily — and dare we say, painlessly? — do any and all of the following things:

- ✔ Catch up with friends and family online.
- ✔ Make new friends who share your hobbies and interests.
- ✔ Find the perfect gift without leaving the comfort of your home.
- ✔ Get answers to just about any question or concern with the click of your mouse.

Yes, you *can* do all these activities online. And in this part, you find out *how* to do them the quick and easy way.

Chapter 26

Getting to Know the Internet

● ●

In This Chapter

▶ Getting online

▶ Keeping your personal information and finances private

▶ Surfing the Web like a pro

▶ Chatting it up in chat rooms

● ●

*T*he Internet — also known as the *Net* — is the world's largest computer network. The Internet connects all sorts of computers, ranging from the big and formal (such as the corporate networks at AT&T or Hewlett-Packard) to the small and informal (the one in your back bedroom) and everything in between. And, in the past few years, Internet usage has been increasing at an astonishing 40 to 50 percent per year with more than 300 million users worldwide.

If you're new to the Internet, and especially if you don't have much computer experience, *be patient with yourself.* Think of the Web as a brand-new world with its own language. And even if you're an experienced computer user, you may find the Internet unlike anything you've ever tackled. The Internet is not a software package and doesn't easily lend itself to step-by-step instructions.

Leading a Satisfying (and Safe) Online Life

As the Internet becomes a more prominent part of everyday life, having a good time and protecting yourself are becoming even more important issues. The following sections offer advice for getting more out of the Internet, building genuine online relationships, and ensuring your safety.

Four tips for connecting to the Web

Although getting online is becoming easier with every passing day, setting up your first connection to the Internet can still be tricky work. Don't stress. Don't fret. The following hints are geared for making the process as painless as possible:

✔ **Some setup programs are easier to use than others.** AOL, MSN, AT&T WorldNet, and a slew of other online service providers offer good, automated sign-up software programs that can get you connected to the Internet with no fuss, no muss.

✔ **Consider local Internet service providers.** Your town or surrounding area probably has a few local providers offering online access. Look in your Yellow Pages or ask anyone with a computer (teachers, librarians, and other technically savvy friends) what are the best local providers in your area.

✔ **If you choose a local online service provider, make sure that they're helpful and available.** You should be able to talk to a human via phone. If you can't get good customer service, choose another ISP.

✔ **Use bribery.** If you can bribe or coerce a friend or relative into helping you get online, do so. *Hint:* Look for someone roughly between the ages of 12 and 16, who can be very knowledgeable and very patient — after you get past your humiliation. Chocolate chip cookies always help.

Keeping credit card information safe and secure

If you're comfortable using a credit card for other uses, you don't have to get really scared about using it over the Internet. Every day, you probably hand your actual physical credit cards with your handwritten signature to sales clerks, waiters, and cashiers. Do you know what they do with the card before they give it back to you? Do you worry about it? Probably not.

If you use a credit card, remember that credit card companies are even more concerned than you are about the idea of any kind of credit card fraud, on or off the Internet. All cards have a limit on the amount of fraudulent use for which you're liable; if you're a U.S. resident, the limit is $50 or less.

Take the following sensible precautions with your credit information and you'll have a great time online:

Stop hating call waiting

Make sure that your phone line doesn't have call waiting. If it does, you (or your Internet connection program) have to type *70 or 1170 at the beginning of your provider's phone number to tell your phone company to turn off call waiting for this phone call; otherwise, an incoming phone call will disturb your Internet connection.

✔ **Look for the little padlock on Web pages that ask for your credit information.** The padlock tells you that you're running in *secure mode,* which means communication between your computer and the stores' computers is encrypted with special coding that ensures greater privacy and protection.

✔ **If possible, use credit cards rather than debit cards or checks when ordering online.** If you have a dispute with an online vendor, you can ask your credit card company to reverse the charge or to refuse charges from that company. However, debit cards and checks aren't the same as credit cards and aren't protected in the same way.

✔ **Remember that you don't *have* to use a credit card online.** If you don't want to send your plastic over the Net or you're one of the fiscally responsible holdouts who doesn't do plastic, most reputable online stores are happy to have you call in your card number or send them a check.

Protecting your privacy

The Internet is a funny place. Although it seems completely anonymous, it's not. People used to have Internet usernames that bore some resemblance to their true identity — their name or initials or some combination in conjunction with their university or corporation gave a fairly traceable route to an actual person. Today, with the phenomenon of screen names and multiple e-mail addresses, revealing your identity is definitely optional.

Depending on who you are and what you want to do on the Net, you may, in fact, want different names and different accounts. Here are some legitimate reasons why:

✔ You're a professional — a physician, for example — and you want to participate in a mailing list or newsgroup without being asked for your professional opinion.

✔ You want help with an area of concern that you feel is private, and you wouldn't want your problem known to people close to you who may find out if your name is associated with it.

✔ You do business on the Net, and you socialize on the Net. You may want to keep those activities separate.

If you abuse the anonymous nature of the Net, realize that most online activities can be traced. If you start to abuse the Net, you soon find that you're not so anonymous.

You have no "right to privacy" at work, even though most people find the idea creepy. Courts have repeatedly ruled that companies own their computers and their contents. Companies can eavesdrop on phone calls, read your e-mail (going and coming), and read anything on your computer, which can be problematic if you do a little unofficial surfing at lunchtime.

Safety first

To keep yourself as safe as possible online, remember the following simple things:

✔ Don't use your full name or ever provide your name, address, and phone number over the Net to someone you don't know.

✔ Never believe anyone who says that he's from "AOL tech support" or some such authority and asks you for your password. No legitimate entity will ever ask you for your password.

✔ Be especially careful about disclosing information about kids. Don't fill out profiles in chat rooms that ask for a kid's name, hometown, school, age, address, or phone number, because they are invariably used for "targeted marketing" (a.k.a. junk mail).

Meeting online friends in the real world

The Net is a wonderful place, and meeting new people and making new friends is one of its big attractions. You just want to make sure that you're being careful.

Though relatively rare, horrible things have happened to a few people who have taken their Internet encounters into real life. Many wonderful things have happened, too. Many folks have become fine friends, business partners, or spouses. If you do choose to meet an online friend in person, use at least the same caution that you use in meeting someone through a newspaper ad:

- ✔ **Don't arrange a meeting until you have talked to a person a number of times, including conversations at length by telephone over the course of days or weeks.** If you don't like the sound of the person's voice or something makes you nervous, don't do it.

- ✔ **Depending on the context, try to check out the person a little.** If you've met in a newsgroup or chat room, ask someone else you know whether they know this person. (Women, ask another woman before agreeing to meet a man.)

- ✔ **Meet in a well-lit public place.** Consider a daytime meeting for additional safety.

- ✔ **Bring a friend along, if you can.** If you can't, at least let someone know what you're doing and agree to call that person at a certain time (for example, a half-hour) after the planned meeting time.

- ✔ **Arrange to stay in a hotel if you travel a long distance to meet someone.** Don't commit yourself to staying at that person's home.

An online shopper's checklist

Keep the following questions in mind when you're shopping online. An astute shopper will notice that these questions are the same ones you should keep in mind no matter where you're shopping.

- ✔ Are the descriptions clear enough to know what you're ordering?

- ✔ Are the prices competitive, both with other online stores and with mail-order and regular retail?

- ✔ Does the store have the products in stock; does it offer a firm shipping date?

- ✔ Does the store have a good reputation?

- ✔ Can you return unsatisfactory goods?

- ✔ Does the store have a clear, understandable, and posted policy about how it protects and uses your personal financial and credit information?

If you cannot answer "yes" to each of the preceding questions, keep searching for another store — online or in the real world — to shop.

Cookie alert

You may have heard horrible stories about things called *cookies* that Web sites reputedly use to spy on you, steal your data, ravage your computer, and otherwise make your life miserable. In truth, most cookies aren't all that bad. (And if you shop online, cookies can be downright helpful because they let the online store track the "shopping cart" of items you've selected but not yet bought, even if you log out and turn off your computer in the interim.)

A *cookie* is no more than a little chunk of text that a Web site sends to your PC with a request (not a command) to send the cookie back during future visits to the same Web site. The cookie is stored on your computer in the form of a tiny file. That's it. Contrary to rumor, cookie files cannot get other information from your hard disk. Cookies collect only information that the browser tells them about.

Cruising the Internet like a Pro

When you first venture out onto the Internet, you may feel like you're riding with training wheels. Never fear — you'll get the hang of it. And you can get up to full speed even faster when you keep the following information in mind.

Browser basics

A *browser* is the software tool that you use as your vehicle as you tour online. Popular browsers include Netscape Navigator, Internet Explorer, AOL, and others.

Although each browser is unique, the following paragraphs contain hints for using them efficiently and effectively.

Getting around

Moving from page to page is easy: Click any link that looks interesting. That's all. Underlined blue text and blue-bordered pictures are links to other pages. Anything that looks like a button is probably a link also. You can tell when you're pointing to a link because the mouse pointer changes to a little hand. If you're not sure whether something is a link, click it anyway because, if it's not, clicking doesn't hurt anything.

As you move the mouse cursor around a Web page, whenever you're pointing at a link, the URL of the place it links to appears in small type at the bottom of the screen, or in a little box that "floats" over the mouse pointer.

Backward, ho!

Web browsers remember the last few pages you visited, so if you click a link and decide that you're not so crazy about the new page, you can easily go back to the preceding one. To go back, click the Back or Previous button on the toolbar (you'll see a picture of an arrow pointing to the left).

Visiting a specific place

These days, everyone and his dog has an Internet home page. A *home page* is the main Web page for a person or organization. Companies advertise their home pages, and people are sending e-mail talking about cool sites.

All you need to visit a specific place online is a *URL,* or Internet address. When you see a URL you want to check out, here's what you do:

1. **Click the mouse in the Location or Address box, near the top of your browser window.**

2. **Type the URL in the box. Most browsers let you leave off the** `http://` **part.**

   The URL is something like `http://net.gurus.com` — or you can just type **net.gurus.com**.

3. **Press Enter.**

If you receive URLs in an e-mail, word-processing document, or anywhere else on your computer, you can use a *cut-and-paste technique* and avoid retyping:

1. **Scroll across the URL in whatever program is showing it while holding down the mouse button.**

2. **Press Ctrl+C (Command Key+C on the Mac) to copy the information.**

3. **Click in the Location or Address box in the browser to highlight whatever appears there.**

4. **Press Ctrl+V (Command Key+V on the Mac) to paste the URL into the box, and then press Enter.**

This page looks funny

Sometimes a Web page gets garbled on the way in or you interrupt it (by clicking the Stop button on the toolbar). You can tell your browser to get the information on the page again: Click the Reload or Refresh button.

Saving favorite pages

The Web has some really cool places that you may want to visit over and over again. Fortunately, almost all browsers provide a handy way for you to remember your favorite spots so that you don't have to write down those nasty URLs just so you can type them again later.

Although the name of this process varies, the idea is simple: Your browser lets you mark a Web page and adds its URL to a list. Later, when you want to go back, you just go to your list and pick the page you want. Netscape calls these saved Web addresses *bookmarks;* Internet Explorer and AOL call them *favorites*.

✔ **In Netscape Navigator,** choose Bookmarks⇨Add Bookmark from the menu. The bookmarks appear as entries on the menu that appears when you click the Bookmarks Quick File button.

✔ **In Internet Explorer,** choose Favorites⇨Add to Favorites from the menu. To see your Favorites folder, choose Favorites⇨ Organize Favorites from the menu. Internet Explorer also has a Favorites button on the toolbar that displays your list of Favorites down the left side of your Internet Explorer window.

Keeping in touch with e-mail

In the fast-paced world, e-mail is a great way to communicate with people scattered around the world. Get more out of your e-mailing by the keeping the following tips in mind.

Chain letters

Sending a chain letter on the Net is easy: Just click the Forward button, type a few names, and send off your letter. Although it's easy to do, it's a lousy idea. A bunch of classic chain letters (phantom viruses, nonexistent modem taxes, overpriced recipes, and ways you *won't* make money fast) have been circulating around the Net for more than a decade. Regardless of where these messages come from, and even if they seem to be for a good cause, throw them away.

Spammity spam, horrible spam

One of the least pleasant online innovations is *spamming,* or sending the same message — usually selling something that was rather dubious in the first place — to as many e-mail addresses as possible. This practice is annoying, illegal in some places, and the spammer is usually liable for her ISP's costs in cleaning it up.

The Internet tries to be self-policing, and the community of people who make up the users and inventors of this marvelous medium don't want the Internet to fall under the control of short-sighted governments or gangsters. That said, an increasing number of Internet service providers offer e-mail filtering help.

Check out these Web sites for information about spam and how to fight it, technically, socially, and (increasingly) legally:

- ✔ spam.abuse.net (a spam overview)
- ✔ www.cauce.org (anti-spam laws)
- ✔ www.abuse.net (a complaint forwarding service)

Flaming

For some reason, people find it easy to get VERY, VERY UPSET ABOUT SOMETHING SOMEONE SAYS ON THE NET. You may be tempted to shoot a message right back (or *flame* someone), telling that person what a doofus he is. Guess what? He will almost certainly shoot back.

Now and then, flaming is fun if you're certain that the recipient will take it in good humor, but it's always unnecessary. For one thing, e-mail messages always come across as crabbier than you intended; for another, crabbing back hardly makes the recipient more reasonable.

A helpful technique for not flaming is to write the strongest, crabbiest response possible, full of biting wit and skewering each point in turn. Then, wait for an hour or two and rewrite the message. Or just throw out the flammable message rather than sending it at all.

Sending attachments

Attachments are a useful way to send files by e-mail. But they work only if the person on the receiving end has a program that can read the files you are sending. Indeed, some older mail systems can't handle attachments at all. Always ask *first* before sending an attachment.

I think I've got a virus!

Viruses have been around the Internet for a long time. Originally, they lived in program files that people downloaded to their computers. Now, most viruses are spread through files that are sent via e-mail, as attachments to mail messages.

The text of a plain text message can't contain a virus, because it's only text, and a virus is a (rather sneaky) program. But attachments can, and sometimes do. For the virus to work (that is, for it to run, infect your computer, and send copies of itself out to other people via e-mail), you need to run it.

In most e-mail programs (including Netscape Messenger and Eudora), programs contained in attachments don't run until you click them — so *don't* open programs that come from people you don't know. Don't even open attachments (especially those that end with extensions like .vba or .exe) from people you *do* know if you weren't expecting to receive them.

The same rule applies for sending formatted e-mail. Newer e-mail programs let you use boldface, italics, and other formatting, but formatted messages are readable only if you have a matching e-mail program. On older programs, formatted messages contain so many formatting characters that the text is unreadable. Send a tester message first to see whether the recipient's e-mail program can handle formatting.

Chapter 27

Web Searching

● ●

● ●

Someone once called the Web "the world's biggest library" — ah, if only the Web were as orderly and logical as a library! Another favorite metaphor for the online world is "a shopping mall after an earthquake" — go in expecting chaos, and you'll be pleasantly surprised when you stumble across a section that still bears some semblance of order and rationality.

Nevertheless, the Web is fast becoming the preferred route for information of all kinds, so you need to know how to get from it the stuff you want. You *can* become an effective online researcher, by using your own logic and creativity to track down systematically the information that you're looking for.

Search Engines and Search Strategies

No single search tool or strategy works throughout the online universe.

Search engines are the remarkable online tools that help you find what you're looking for on the Web. General search engines make sense when you're looking for the proverbial needle in a haystack, or when you need to gather a great deal of information on a topic.

Tons more at Yahoo!

Although Yahoo! is primarily a directory of resources that are available on the Web, it's now a *portal*, which means that it has lots of other databases available to encourage you to stick around inside Yahoo!. Each database has a link you can click that's located just under the box in which you type search terms. Here are just a few:

- ✔ **Auctions:** Web-based auctions, not unlike eBay.

- ✔ **Classifieds:** Lets you read and submit ads for automobiles, apartments, computers, and jobs.

- ✔ **Maps:** Gets a more-or-less accurate map of a street address that you type.

- ✔ **Yellow Pages:** A business directory.

- ✔ **Today's News, Stock Quotes, and Sports Scores:** News from Reuters.

- ✔ **Chat:** Gets you into online chat through the Web.

- ✔ **Mail:** Free Web-based e-mail service.

- ✔ **People Search:** Finds addresses and phone numbers, like a white pages directory (see the "Finding People" section).

- ✔ **My Yahoo:** A customized starting page just for you, with headlines, sports scores, and other news based on your preferences.

- ✔ **TV:** Impressively complete TV and cable listings, by area.

- ✔ **Travel:** A link to the Travelocity reservation system, as well as a variety of other resources.

- ✔ **Health:** Click "more" to explore this topic with research, recipes, and tips.

Choosing a search engine

Three of the most popular search systems are Yahoo!, AltaVista, and Google. You may find one of these search engines or another most comfortable, but don't get in a rut by always using the same one. Because every search engine searches differently, using several of them usually gets the best results.

Yahoo!

Yahoo! (www.yahoo.com) is a popular Web directory that categorizes millions of Web pages into handy topics for your perusal. Yahoo! also has many other nifty search options.

You can find stuff in Yahoo! in two ways. The easier way is just to click from category to subcategory until you find something you like.

At the top of each Yahoo! page is the list of categories, subcategories, and so on, separated by colons, that lead to that page. If you want to back up a few levels and look at different subcategories, just click the place on the list to which you want to back up. After a little clicking up and down, you'll soon have the hang of it.

You can also search the Yahoo! index. Near the top of every Yahoo! screen is a search box in which you can type words, known as *keywords,* for any interests that you have. In fact, if you have some idea of the title of the page that you're looking for, this kind of keyword search is your best way to use Yahoo!.

Above each entry that it finds with your keyword search, Yahoo! reports the category in which the entry is located. Even if the entry isn't quite right but you click the category, you find other related titles — some of them often do the trick.

Google and AltaVista

Google (www.google.com) and AltaVista (www.altavista.com) rank highly among favorite Web indexes. *Indexes* have little robots that spend their time merrily visiting Web pages all over the Net and reporting back what they saw. Each search engine makes a humongous index of which words occurred in what pages. As you search either engine, it picks pages from the index that contain the words you asked for.

Type some search terms (keywords) in the search box, click the Search button, and AltaVista or Google finds the pages that best match your terms. Remember, that's "best match," not "match" — if an index can't match all the terms, then it finds pages that match as well as possible. The trick for you is thinking up good search words (see the "Narrowing a search with keywords" section later in this chapter).

Regardless of what you ask for, you're likely to get about 15,000 pages on your first try — although the first pages found are usually the most relevant. However, be sure to look at the next couple of screens of matches if the first screen doesn't have what you want. The page numbers for your results appear at the bottom of the index screen's results; click Next to go to the next page.

Other search engines

After you surf around Yahoo!, Google, and AltaVista for a while, you may want to check out the competition as well.

- ✔ **Go.com** (www.go.com) provides both an index and a directory. For general searches, this site's okay, but it's less reliable for more obscure topics.

- ✔ **Lycos** (www.lycos.com) is an automated index that offers both a Web search engine and a directory of selected sources, organized by category.

- ✔ **Northern Light** (www.northernlight.com) contains an automated index of both the Web and its Special Collection, in-depth articles from various sources for which you must pay if you decide to read them. If you would rather stick with the (free) Web, you can choose to do so. Also, the Northern Light search engine automatically and categorically puts the pages it finds in folders for you to choose from.

- ✔ **WiseNut** (www.wisenut.com) is a relatively new index with a deserved reputation for highly relevant returns.

Still more Web guides

Lots of other Web guides are available, including many specialized guides put together for particular interests (Femina, for example, is a feminist guide, at femina.cybergrrl.com).

Index, directory — what's the dif?

A *directory* works rather like an encyclopedia, including named categories with entries that are assigned to categories partly or entirely by human catalogers. You look up things by finding a category that you want and seeing what it contains.

An *index*, on the other hand, simply collects all the items, extracts keywords from them, and makes a big list. You search the index by specifying some words that seem likely, and the index finds all the entries containing that word.

Each tool has its advantages and disadvantages. Directories are organized better, but indexes are larger. Directories use consistent terminology, whereas indexes use whatever terms the indexed Web pages used. Directories contain fewer useless pages, but indexes are updated more often.

Some overlap exists between directories and indexes — Yahoo!, the best known Web page directory, lets you search by keyword, and the index Northern Light divides its entries into general categories that let you limit the search.

Yahoo! has a directory of other guides: Starting at the Yahoo! home page (www.yahoo.com), look under the Computers and Internet heading, click WWW, click Searching the Web, and then click Search Engines and Directories. You can even find search engines for images on the Web.

Conducting a basic Internet search

When you're ready to surf the Net for a topic of interest, begin with one of the general indexes or directories discussed in the preceding section. You use them all in more or less the same way:

1. **Start your Web browser, such as Netscape or Internet Explorer.**

2. **Pick a directory or index that you like and type the Web address of its home page in the browser's search box.**

   The URLs (Web addresses) of the home pages for various search engines are listed in the preceding section.

   After you get to the Web site, you can choose one of two approaches.

3a. **If a Search box is available, type some likely *keywords* in the box and click Search.**

   After perhaps a long delay (the Web is pretty big), an index page is returned with links to pages that match your keywords. The list of links may be way too long to deal with — like 300,000 of them. But if your search engine has sorted the list well, your most likely matches will be toward the top.

   or

3b. **If you see a list of links to topic areas, click a topic area of interest.**

   With this approach, you begin at a general topic. Each page then provides links to pages that get more and more specific until they link to actual pages that are likely to be of interest.

4. **Adjust and repeat your search until you find something that you like.**

   See the following section for tips on refining your search process.

Time-saving global searches

You may feel a wee bit overwhelmed with all these search indexes and direc-tories. Wouldn't it be great if you could type a few keywords and search five or ten search engines at once? You can!

Meta-search engines provide the top results from multiple search engines, more or less simultaneously. If you don't need super-specific results, you may want to try one of these popular meta-engines as a starting point:

✔ Dogpile (www.dogpile.com)

✔ Ixquick (www.ixquick.com)

✔ Mamma (www.mamma.com)

Narrowing a search with keywords

"Yikes! 42,178 hits! What do I do now?" What you *don't* do is look at all 42,178 of them. Most search engines are pretty dumb; *you* have to add the intelligence. If your search finds hundreds of pages or cate-gories, then refine your search.

One way to refine a search is to add extra words to make more spe-cific what you're looking for. Ask yourself two questions:

✔ **What, exactly, is your topic?** Keywords or phrases, such as *internal combustion engine*, are just a starting point. Do you want a basic description of how an internal combustion engine works or technical information about the kind and quantity of emissions it puts out? In other words, what's the *angle,* the aspect of the subject you really want to know about?

✔ **How else can you describe your topic?** The English language is rich with synonyms, jargon, and figures of speech. You can usu-ally find more than one way of expressing the same concept. For example, a dip in *employment* is the same as a rise in *unem-ployment*. If you're looking for statistics on one or the other, search for both.

With many search engines, including Yahoo!, Google, and AltaVista, you can click an "advanced search" option next to the Search button to get a slightly more focused search page. This feature may let you limit how far back you want to see pages, in what languages you want to see pages, or what kinds of sites you want (.edu or .gov only,

Getting something from nothing

A zero-hits scenario ("there are 0 matches for this term") doesn't necessarily mean nothing exists on a particular subject. Here are some tips to try when you get no results from a search:

✔ Double-check your search terms. A typo or misspelling will throw off your results.

✔ Think of synonyms for your search term or other ways of expressing the concept you're looking for.

✔ Don't over-restrict at the outset to specific dates or sources.

✔ Make sure that you're in the right database or haven't inadvertently told the search engine to check newsgroups or company directories only, for example, when you intended to do a Web-wide search.

for example). Usually, you can look for all the keywords (try using "AND" between each term) or any of the keywords (try using "OR" between the terms).

Indexes like AltaVista and Google also make it easy to refine your search more exactly to target the pages that you want to find. After each search, your search terms appear in a box at the top of the page so that you can change them and try again. Here are some tips on how you may want to change your terms:

✔ Type most search words in lowercase. Type proper names with a single capital letter, such as Elvis.

✔ If two or more words should appear together, put quotes around them, as in "Elvis Presley".

✔ Click "help" to find out what other techniques the search engine supports. For example, in AltaVista, you can use + and – to indicate words that must either appear or not appear, such as +Elvis +Costello -Presley if you're looking for the modern Elvis, not the classic one.

Most search engines look at the order in which you typed your search terms, assuming that you put the more important terms first. You may get better, more relevant search results if you put the key ideas and most unusual or unique terms at the beginning of your list of search words.

Finding People

Finding people on the Net is surprisingly easy. Two overlapping categories of people finders are available: Those that look for people on the Net with e-mail and Web addresses, and those that look for people in real life with phone numbers and street addresses.

Tapping into White Pages

The real-life directories are compiled mostly from telephone directories. If a person hasn't had a listed phone number in the past few years, you probably can't find him or her in any of these directories. Try one of these sites for the United States or Canada:

> ✔ **American Directory Assistance** (www.abii.com)
>
> ✔ **Canada 411** (www.canada411.sympatico.ca)

Looking up an e-mail address

The process of finding e-mail and Web addresses is somewhat hit-and-miss. No online equivalent to the official phone book that the telephone company produces has ever existed, so directories of e-mail addresses are collected from addresses used in Usenet messages, mailing lists, and other more or less public places on the Net. Because the different directories use different sources, if you don't find someone in one directory, you can try another. Here are some common starting points:

> ✔ **Bigfoot** (www.bigfoot.com)
>
> ✔ **WhoWhere** (www.whowhere.lycos.com)
>
> ✔ **Yahoo! People Search** (www.people.yahoo.com) is the most comprehensive. You can search for addresses, phone numbers, and e-mail addresses. If you don't like your own listing, you can add, update, or delete it.

If you're wondering whether someone has a Web page, use a general search engine to search for his name. If you're wondering whether you're famous, search for your own name and see how many people mention you or link to your Web pages.

Locating Companies

The first way to search for a company is to search for the company name as a topic in a general search engine. If the company has a home page, it's usually among the top sites returned. After you do that, a few other places are worth checking for business-related info.

Hoovering in

Company home pages vary in informativeness, but they often don't tell you much about the company itself. Hoover's (www.hoovers.com) is a business information company that offers free company capsules, stock prices, and other company info. If you sign up for its paid service, Hoover's offers considerably more. Even the free stuff is quite useful.

Asking EDGAR

The U.S. Securities and Exchange Commission (SEC), the people who regulate stock and bond markets, maintains a system called EDGAR that collects all the financial material that publicly traded companies have to file with the government. Although most of this stuff is dry reading, if you can read financial statements, you can find all sorts of interesting information, such as Martha Stewart's salary.

The government EDGAR site (go to edgar.sec.gov and click "Search Edgar Archives") is run directly by the SEC, and the private site, EDGAR Online (www.edgar-online.com), is run by an independent company, Cybernet Data Systems, Inc. Although the two sites have pretty much the same information, the private site offers free, limited access and charges a modest price (about $5 per month) for more complete access and automatic e-mail updates when a company in which you're interested files EDGAR documents.

Bidding at Online Auctions

Most people know how traditional auctions worked in the B.I. era (Before the Internet). A person with something to sell let interested buyers gather to inspect the item and bid on it. The bidders traded offers, and the person willing to pay the highest price won the item, handed over the money, and took the treasure home.

In an Internet auction, merchandise is offered for sale on the World Wide Web. Prospective buyers use their Web browsers to connect to the auction site and submit bids to the site by filling out a Web page form. Millions of sales have been conducted smoothly in recent years, and thousands of satisfied buyers and sellers can attest that the system is usually a good one.

The procedure for participating in online auctions differs depending on the type of auction you use. Each auction service has its own set of rules for bidding and selling. Read these guidelines carefully. They don't make for exciting reading, but they're important. Check out the bidding rules. Some auctions keep track of the time you first bid on an item, and subsequent bids can "bump" someone at the same price whose first bid was later than yours. Also, note the shipping charges, which can be excessive and can raise the actual value of your bid.

Here's the bidding process in a nutshell:

1. **Register.** Typically, you provide the auction service with a username and password that you then use to login or place bids, as well as an e-mail address. You also provide the site with your real name and address in case it needs to contact you. Auction houses that function as the seller (many of which specialize in computer and other electronics equipment) usually require a credit card number when you register.

2. **Shop.** You search the selection of sale items in one of two ways: You can click links that denote categories of merchandise until you find the specific merchandise you're looking for, or you can search for particular brands or models by entering keywords in a search box.

3. **Place a bid.** You fill out a form on a Web page and submit your bid along with your registered username and password to the site. If you're the high bidder (or in the case of a Dutch auction, one of the low bidders), your bid is recorded on the Web page on which the auction item is displayed.

4. **Track your bid.** While the auction is going on, you can find out whether anyone has outbid you. Some sites automatically send you an e-mail message if this happens.

5. **If you're the winning bidder, make payment and shipping arrangements with the seller.** The seller tells you how much to pay (your winning bid plus shipping) and where to send payment.

Part VIII
The Part of Tens

The 5th Wave   By Rich Tennant

"QUIT MOPING—YOU WON FIRST PLACE IN THE MEATLOAF CATEGORY, AND THAT'S GOOD. I'M THE ONLY ONE WHO KNOWS IT WAS A CARROT CAKE YOU ENTERED."

In this part . . .

Who doesn't love a top-ten list?

Well, for list lovers and list makers everywhere, each *For Dummies* book includes a Part of Tens — a collection of chapters that give you great tips and fast solutions in a convenient list format. The following chapters are perfect for a quick scan — or for a jumping off point for more in-depth reading. Whatever you choose to do, the Part of Tens is always easy in and easy out, as well as a whole lot of fun! So dive in to any topic that interests you. Great information on health, personal finance, successful living — even romance — awaits you!

Chapter 28

Ten Keys to Successful Living

In This Chapter

▶ Wasting no time in your life

▶ Evaluating and taking risks

▶ Forming winning habits

*B*ecause every success strategy is different, you have to find the approach that works for you. However, nearly all successful people share more than just a few of the same characteristics — characteristics that you want to incorporate into your own success strategy.

Valuing Hustle

On the way to becoming successful, people who make it and make it big are almost without exception ambitiously dissatisfied with the status quo. They understand that where they are is part of the process of getting where they want to be, and they don't dally around. Successful people have specific objectives in mind, get busy seeking them, and work hard. In other words, they hustle.

The 40-hour work week, in most cases, doesn't suffice for those who want to climb the corporate ladder or build their own business while maintaining a balanced life with family and friends. In addition, these people invariably give up some of the things that are not only counter productive but are also detrimental, such as squandering countless hours sitting in front of the TV. People who are serious about their success show it in the things they do and don't do.

Building Character

Character is one factor that belongs in every success strategy. It's been said that character is "what you do in the dark." Sometimes life throws tough situations at you, but there's a difference between being tough and being hard. You need to be tough, not hard, when you're attacked. You mustn't be a pushover, but you also need to be compassionate, gentle, and flexible, particularly on procedure (as opposed to principle).

Taking Risks

People who refuse to take risks are definitely going to lose. Think about the following situations:

- ✔ If you refuse a new promotion because you're not sure that you have the skills to do the job, you'll probably be passed over when other chances for advancement open up.

- ✔ If you're afraid of rejection, you won't risk being the initiator in friendships, and you'll miss out on one of life's greatest treasures.

- ✔ If you put all your money in an interest-bearing savings account (rather than CDs or stocks), you'll never realize the income that you could have had if only you'd taken a risk.

Becoming a Time Miser

People who enjoy a balanced success — success in their personal, family, business, spiritual, physical, and financial lives — are the ones who most effectively utilize their time.

Proper time management is a must for every person who aspires to be successful. Time is your most important, and certainly your most consistent, commodity; you get the same amount each day. To use your time more effectively:

- ✔ **Record what you do each day for a week.** Break the day into 30-minute segments and note what you do during those 30 minutes. Doing so makes you aware of the incredible amount of time that slips through your fingers in 5-, 10-, and 15-minute increments.

> ✔ **Take advantage of the time you have.** Herbert Hoover wrote a book in the time he spent waiting in railroad stations. Noel Coward wrote songs while caught in traffic. Remember, you have just as much time as Edison had when he invented the light bulb.

People who make and use to-do lists and take advantage of "two-fers" get the maximum benefit from their time. What's a two-fer? Here's one: Always take along something to read while you're waiting in a line or in traffic. You can probably salvage an hour a week of reading time by using this strategy.

Take a look at Chapter 16 for some great suggestions.

Practicing Nonverbal Communication

In addition to speaking and writing, you communicate with your facial expressions and body language. Have you ever been asked by someone, "Are you okay?" and been surprised when they said that you looked worried, tired, sad, unhappy, and so on? When the words that come out of your mouth don't match your facial expression or your body language, you confuse the person with whom you're trying to communicate.

Wearing a Thick Skin

One of the most important success strategies is to wear a thick skin to any barbs that come your way — whether deserved or not. How do *you* deal with criticism? Do you lose your cool, become defensive or angry, or blow off steam? Admittedly, you can go in those directions, but they serve no constructive purpose.

When Jay Leno replaced Johnny Carson on *The Tonight Show,* critics compared him unfavorably to Carson. People said that his stay as host would be short-lived. But Leno never really worried. In fact, he kept a stack of unpleasant reviews on his desk for inspiration. One critic said, "Too many soft questions." Another said, "He's being too nice." But these unkind words didn't bother Leno, because they'd been written in 1962 about Jack Paar's replacement — "an awkward nobody named Johnny Carson."

Anybody who does anything of significance, regardless of the field of endeavor, is going to be criticized. The way that the successful ones handle that criticism is a big part of their success.

Responding with Obedience

You need to incorporate old-fashioned *obedience* into your success strategy. In our society, obedience isn't only a "foreign" concept, but it's also considered demeaning by many people. However, this concept is extremely important. One of the first principles of leadership is to understand that before you can become a leader, you must know how to follow — which means that you must learn to obey.

Think about this: 175 of the CEOs of Fortune 500 companies are former U.S. Marines, and 26 U.S. presidents served in the military. Before they learned to lead, they learned to obey.

Similarly, in the corporate world, somebody is ultimately responsible for final decisions. Those people who play by the rules and learn to obey place themselves in the best position to learn how to command or lead the organization to higher levels.

Demonstrating Courage

Most people have watched with envy as some simple idea produces notable results and brings fame and fortune to its originator. Haven't we all heard somebody say, "I thought of the same thing several years ago and never did anything about it!"

Many people go through life without the courage to stick their necks out to get ahead. When you have courage, you follow through on your vision. Without courage, the vision can never become a reality.

Courage is on display every day, and only the courageous wring the most out of life. The next time you're confronted with a decision, weigh it carefully and consider heavily the right thing to do. Then summon the courage to do what's right. You'll be glad that you did.

Embracing Intolerance

Intolerance (yes, you read that correctly), must be incorporated into a workable success strategy. One of the greatest disasters of modern time is the universal acceptance of the word *tolerance* as a virtue. Tolerance is lauded from the big and little screen to the print press — we mustn't be judgmental; we must be tolerant of other people and their points of view. In reality, everyone needs to be intolerant of many things, such as child abuse or groups that preach hate and violence.

Keeping a Sense of Humor

The health benefits of a good, hearty laugh have been well established. The relief from tension that laughter brings is significant. And humor's impact on others is usually positive because everyone enjoys being around pleasant, optimistic people who get real enjoyment out of life.

Humor also helps to build winning relationships — who doesn't like to be around people who are fun? In the business world, people with a sense of humor are better liked — and, everything else being equal, management promotes people who they like. Individuals with a good sense of humor don't take themselves overly seriously.

Honing Winning Habits

Winning habits are the best friends you can have, particularly in the business world. Good work habits lead to promotions and job security. Arriving at work and completing assignments on time, being courteous and conscientious, returning phone calls promptly, and going the extra mile are all habits that lead to success.

When you do more than you're paid to do, the day will come when you're paid more for what you do.

Good habits must be grabbed firmly and with a strong commitment. That decision, reinforced by your will to take action on your commitment regardless of how you feel at the moment, produces marvelous results in an amazingly short period of time.

Chapter 29

Ten Things You Can Do Today to Improve Your Family's Health

*F*ortunately, boosting the health of everyone in your family doesn't take as much time and effort as you may think. In fact, just a few tweaks to your regular routine can mean better health for your entire family. This chapter covers some of the most import adjustments you can make — right now.

For more detailed health information, check out Part II of this book.

Wash Your Hands Regularly

Having everyone in the family wash their hands on a regular basis — and especially after using the bathroom and before meals — helps prevent the spread of infectious disease. We're not just talking about colds and flu. Chicken pox, measles, mumps, and a host of other conditions spread through hand-to-hand contact. Plus, the bacteria that may cling to the hands after you use the bathroom can lead to especially nasty *E. coli* infections.

Does hand washing work? Experts say yes. One four-month study of elementary school kids found that students who washed their hands four times a day had fewer stomachaches, colds, and flu episodes than kids who were allowed to do as they pleased.

For best results, you need to do more than just run your hands under the faucet. Lather up and rub your hands together for a minute or two. Make sure to get the areas under your fingernails, between your fingers, and on the backs of your hands. Then rinse your hands thoroughly. If you wear rings, make sure to wash well around and underneath them — rings give germs a place to hide. Finally, dry off thoroughly on a clean hand towel. Don't forget to wash your hand towels regularly to keep bacteria from hanging around. To be extra safe, use disposable towels.

When washing your hands, you may want to use antibacterial soap, which is said to kill germs better than ordinary soap and even to inhibit the growth of bacteria after you dry off. However, be aware that some researchers worry that antibacterial soaps actually make the bacteria that it doesn't eliminate even stronger, contributing to antibiotic resistance.

Drive Slower

As the driver of a car, *you* are responsible for the safety of your passengers. And it's a simple fact: Drivers who exceed the speed limit have more accidents than those who obey the law. Speeding is a factor in 30 percent of all fatal crashes, says the U.S. Department of Transportation.

Do yourself and your family a favor by sticking to the speed limit and adjusting your speed to road conditions. You may get there a little later, but you'll get there in one piece.

Take a Breather

Good things happen to your body when you relax. Your muscles become less tense, and your alpha (or relaxed) brain waves increase. Your heart and breathing rates slow down. Your metabolism slows, and your digestive system cuts back on the amount of acid it's secreting. Your brain steps up production of feel-good hormones called *endorphins*.

Fortunately, you don't have to escape to a tropical island to unwind; you can practice a relaxation technique. Granted, a relaxation strategy isn't quite as enticing as a vacation, but it can boost your health with only one or two 10- to 15-minute sessions every day.

Techniques range from mediation and visualization (imagining your-self on that tropical island, for example) to aromatherapy and hydrotherapy (taking a warm, scented bath). For more about these methods and others, check out Chapter 9. Many books with more specifics are available at your local library.

The important thing to remember is that there *is* a distinction between relaxing and doing nothing. The health benefits of these techniques come only when you reach a state of true relaxation — not a state of boredom.

Apply Sunscreen

You may be wondering how sunscreen pops up on a list of daily activities. Isn't it just for days at the beach or the amusement park? Nope. Sunscreen is important all the time. Ninety percent of sun exposure comes from everyday outdoor activity. Sunburns can occur even on cool and cloudy days — and even in the shade if light reflects off water, sand, or snow.

The problem with sunburn, and even suntans, goes beyond the tem-porary pain of lobster-red skin. Sun damage contributes to wrinkles, age spots, and sagging skin, as well as skin cancer.

Both sunblock and sunscreen protect the skin; they just do it in slightly different ways. Sunblock reflects the sun's rays off the skin; sunscreen absorbs the harmful rays. When choosing a product, look for one that's marked *broad-spectrum*. This term indicates that the product repels both ultraviolet A (UVA) and ultraviolet B (UVB) wavelengths of light. At one time, experts thought that only UVB rays were harmful; now, it's known that both forms cause damage.

You also want to read the label if you have sensitive skin. A common sunblock ingredient, para-aminobenzoic acid (or PABA), can trigger allergic reactions. To prevent problems, look for products labeled *PABA-free*. In addition, put the product on a small patch of skin before applying it all over, and then wait an hour or two to see whether a reaction develops. If the sunblock fails this test, switch to another brand.

Apply sunscreen liberally to all exposed skin 15 to 30 minutes *before* you go outside; the delay gives the product time to be absorbed into the skin for maximum effectiveness.

Kids need sunscreen, too. Children and teens who get sunburns or blisters are more likely to get skin cancer later in life. However, don't apply sunscreen to babies under six months of age because the chemicals can be easily absorbed into the child's system. Ask your pediatrician about using sunscreen on young children.

Spend Time with Your Pets

A study by Johns Hopkins Medical Center found that 50 out of 53 people with pets were alive a year after their first heart attack, while only 17 out of 39 people without pets survived the year.

Bottom line? Pets are great stress-relievers; and the more relaxed you are, the better your health tends to be. Stress taxes the body's systems by boosting heart and breathing rates, and it also depresses the immune system, leaving you more open to infection or disease.

So take a few minutes out of your day to spend with your favorite pet. Toss the tennis ball around with the dog, tease the cat with some catnip, or just sit and stare at the graceful tropical fish in your aquarium. If you have an outdoorsy pet, double your relaxation and better your health by taking your pet for a walk or run or by playing an energetic game of Frisbee or the like. Exercise energizes and tones your body and also helps get rid of stressful impulses (clenched teeth, for example).

If you don't have a pet, consider getting one. However, choose wisely: Taking care of a rambunctious puppy could very well cause you more stress than it relieves. See Chapter 4 for more advice on sharing your life with a pet.

Get Your Family on the Move

The family that plays together stays together, right? That family is also probably very healthy, too. Guidelines say that for maximum health, everyone — kids included — should get at least 30 minutes of continuous exercise on most, if not all, days of the week.

Follow these tips to help make family exercise fun:

- **Practice togetherness.** Choose group activities such as hiking, swimming, or cross-country skiing. And don't leave out the older generation: Exercise is especially helpful for seniors.

✔ **Pick something that's satisfying for everyone.** Small children can get frustrated with games and activities that are too complex, and older kids can get bored just as easily with simpler fare. Choose an activity that everyone enjoys.

✔ **Don't exercise just for exercise's sake.** Instead of dragging the family out for a lap around the block, invite them for a neighborhood nature walk. Or teach them to dance instead of pushing an aerobics video.

✔ **Involve friends.** Have your children invite their friends and classmates for a bowling or skating party or for a camping trip to make exercise a social event.

Change Your Perspective on Dinner

The U.S. Department of Agriculture's Food Guide Pyramid (see Chapter 6) is all well and good, but most people don't take the information to heart when preparing meals. Americans have a love affair with protein and prefer to plop down a big piece of meat or fish, beans, or eggs and back it up with a few spoonfuls of potatoes or broccoli or flavored rice.

To boost your family's health, start thinking of your main dish as a side dish and vice versa. Proteins rank high on the food pyramid, meaning that you should eat less of them than of vegetables, grains, rice, and breads, all of which rank in lower, larger tiers.

 To figure out how your plate should be divided, picture it as a typical pie chart. Devote about a quarter of it to your traditional "main-dish" protein. Then fill up the rest with low-fat vegetables and grains.

Turn Off the TV or Computer

A recent study found that boys and girls who watch four or more hours of television each day have greater body fat and a greater body mass index (BMI) than those who watch fewer than two hours per day.

Of course, you don't need rocket science to tell you that if your kids are watching Nickelodeon or surfing the Net, they're not getting the exercise they need. (The same goes for adults!) Another complicating factor is food. In plenty of households, snacking and watching TV are inseparable activities. So if you turn off the tube, you also encourage better eating habits.

Brush and Floss

Brushing and flossing — although widely regarded as chores — prevent the development of tooth decay and gum disease, which can cause problems ranging from bad breath to tooth loss. These activities also take a measly three minutes twice a day. If you don't brush and floss already, start now to make them part of your daily routine.

Encourage (that is, force) your kids to brush and floss, too! Although national statistics show that children's dental heath is improving, 50 percent of kids still get cavities in their permanent teeth.

Go to Sleep Early

Sleep is as important to your health as nutrition and exercise are. Despite the fact that 98 percent of Americans agree with that statement, says the National Sleep Foundation, one out of every three Americans sleeps 6 hours or less a night during the work week.

The average American gets about 7 hours of sleep a night, which is at the low end of the 7-to-9-hour stint that experts say the average person needs. (Babies, by the way, need 18 hours; children need 10 to 12 hours; teens need 10 hours; and seniors need 8 hours.)

To improve your health, stop thinking of sleep as a luxury and make an honest attempt to get a good night's sleep — even if it means not catching the end of a late night television show or waiting until morning to finish the laundry.

Chapter 30

Ten+ Keys to Personal Financial Success

Take Charge of Your Finances

Procrastinating is detrimental to your long-term financial health. Don't wait for a crisis or major life event to get your act together. Read publications that have high-quality standards and that aren't afraid to take a stand. Become financially literate and start implementing sound financial strategies. Don't purchase any financial product that you don't understand. Ask questions and compare offerings.

Prioritize Your Financial Goals

Prioritize your financial goals and start working toward them. Be patient. Focus on your accomplishments and learn from your past mistakes. You are the best financial person that you can hire, so hire yourself first. If you need help making a major decision, hire conflict-free advisers who charge a fee for their time. Work in partnership with your advisers — don't abdicate control. If you're married, make time to discuss joint goals, issues, and concerns. Be accepting of your partner's money personality; learn to compromise and manage as a team. If you can't work as a team, consider separate accounts that each of you can manage according to your own financial priorities.

Use Credit Cards Only for Convenience

Use your credit cards only for their buying convenience and not to carry debt. If you have a tendency to run up credit-card debt, then get rid of your cards and use only cash, checks, and debit cards. Don't buy consumer items (cars, vacations, clothing, and so on) that lose value over time on credit. Use debt only to make investments that gain value, such as real estate, a business, or an education.

Stay Financially in Reach of Your Resources

Live within your means and don't try to keep up with your coworkers, neighbor, and peers. Many people who engage in conspicuous consumption are borrowing against their future.

Save and Invest $1 out of every $10

Save and invest at least 5 to 10 percent of your income. Preferably, invest through a retirement savings account to reduce your taxes and ensure your future financial independence.

Own Your Own Home

In the long run, owning is more cost-effective than renting, unless you have a terrific rent-control deal. But don't buy until you can stay put for a number of years.

Insure against Catastrophe

Purchase broad insurance coverage to protect against financial catastrophes. Eliminate insurance for small potential losses.

Make Sound Investing Decisions

Make investing decisions based on your needs and the long-term fundamentals of what you're buying. Ignore the predictive advice offered by financial prognosticators — nobody has a working crystal ball. Don't make knee-jerk decisions based on news headlines. Research before you buy. Never purchase a financial product or service on the basis of an advertisement or salesperson's recommendation.

Invest the majority of your long-term money in ownership vehicles that have appreciation potential, such as stocks, real estate, and your own business. When you invest in bonds or bank accounts, you're simply lending your money to others and will earn a return that probably won't keep you ahead of inflation and taxes. Consider buying professionally managed, no-load mutual funds.

Don't Buy High-Cost Investment Products

Avoid investing in financial products that carry high commissions and expenses. Companies that sell their financial products through aggressive sales techniques generally have the worst products and the highest commissions.

Avoid Emotionally Based Financial Decisions

Investors who panic and sell their stock offerings after a major stock market change miss a buying opportunity. Be especially careful about making important financial decisions following a major life-altering event, such as divorce, job loss, or death in your family.

Invest in Yourself and Others

Invest in your education, your health, and your relationships with family and friends. Having a lot of money isn't worth much if you don't have your health and people to share your life with. Give time and money to causes that benefit the world.

Chapter 31

Ten Great Ways to Date Your Mate

• •

In This Chapter

▶ Staying connected morning, noon, and night

▶ Breaking the traditional dinner-date routine

▶ Finding time to date even on the busiest days

• •

*N*o couple should expect to be romantic all of the time; after all, you *do* have a life that needs your attention. But the best way to make sure that you do have some romance in your relationship is to continue to date, just the way you did before you began to live together.

The Morning Date

Weekend mornings are a great time for a date. When you first get up, your creative juices may feel drained. But you can get around your grogginess by being prepared. For example, if you want to have a romantic breakfast in bed, fix a breakfast tray the night before.

A morning date needn't take place only in bed. The two of you can take a stroll to watch the sunrise, ride your bikes to a field to pick wildflowers, or put on your snowshoes to make the first tracks in the freshly fallen snow. Keep in mind that men experience the highest levels of testosterone in the morning. So, if your morning date starts out in bed, don't be surprised if it heats up quickly.

Lunch Dates

Lunch dates are a great way to keep your romance going during the week. If your offices are close enough to each other, meet somewhere for lunch. What's important about a lunch date is that you get to see each other during the day, which is not a part of your normal routine.

The menu for a lunch date isn't critical to its success. Because your time is limited, you may find that the most convenient way to lunch is to grab a couple of hot dogs from a street vendor. If the weather's nice, just sharing some unaccustomed sunlight on a workday can seem like a mini-vacation.

Keep in mind that the best-made plans often go awry. Just because you decide in the morning to have lunch, that doesn't mean that both of you can completely control your workday schedule. If your partner has to rush back to the office, don't make him or her feel guilty for needing to cut things short; when that happens, simply try to stretch out your next lunch date.

Avoid surprise lunchtime visits. If your partner is extremely busy, you may get the cold shoulder. That chill can definitely harm a romance-rekindling project.

Phone Dates

When they're dating, many couples spend a lot of time on the phone and develop an intimate phone relationship. Then they move in together and that aspect of their relationship dies. Certainly, being face-to-face with a person is better than speaking with that person on the phone. However, some aspects of a phone relationship can't be replaced. When you talk on the phone, your voice goes directly into your partner's ear. You can keep your voice low and whispery to cultivate intimacy. Your intonations are very different than when you speak to your partner in person, even when your partner is sitting only a few feet away.

Although talking to your spouse on the phone for a half hour before each of you leaves work for the day may seem absurd, sometimes the absurd is just what you need in a relationship. Make phone dates with each other and see what transpires. If you find something uniquely satisfying in this type of date, make sure that you continue to connect in this way.

Traditional Dinner Dates

What differentiates a date from simply being a meal? Well, the time you spend is one factor. If you linger over each course and don't mind that the waiter is taking his time bringing you the bill, that means you're deep in conversation and busy rekindling your romance.

 For couples who eat out a lot and the act of sharing a meal in a restaurant can be downright mundane, try keeping certain restaurants as "date" restaurants. Select from the remaining restaurants on your list when you're merely going out to kill your appetites.

Nontraditional Dinner Dates

A dinner date usually means that two people get together between 6 and 9 p.m. to share a meal. However, you may also spend that time together without eating a thing. If you decide that the meal part of a date isn't that important, you open up a whole world of possible activities. Instead of eating, you can

- Go for a run, stop at a nearby lake, and watch the sunset or the stars twinkle.
- Take a painting or language class together and stimulate your minds.
- Take advantage of stores that stay open late and do your Christmas shopping early; then you won't be so frazzled during holidays.
- Take in an early movie, when the lines aren't so long, and dine on buttered popcorn and Raisinets.
- Give each other massages; then meet some friends at a bar and empty the nut dishes over beers and good conversation.
- Take advantage of the last hours of daylight to work on your garden; then have a salad from the greens you picked in your back yard.

In other words, a nontraditional dinner date means that you set aside your dinner time to do something different together, rather than sit at home, eat leftovers, and watch TV.

Warm-Up Dates

Every date doesn't have to lead to a sexual episode. But what if sex is on your mind? What if you want the evening's activities to be just a warm-up to the main event? If that's your hope, plan a date that charges up your batteries, not one that depletes your energy and short-circuits your libido.

To stay alert on this kind of date, eat very little and limit yourself to one glass of wine. If you're tired already, avoid alcohol altogether. To get your blood circulating, include some exercise on your date. You don't want to tire yourself out, so a brisk walk should do it.

When you get home, head for the showers — a great place to have foreplay while getting squeaky clean. Afterwards, you're primed for some terrific sex.

Pick-Up Dates

How do you overcome the staleness that can stem from familiarity? For starters, each of you can pretend to be someone else. Set a date to meet at a particular bar at a certain time. Start the date as if you were strangers. (You may have played this game before and have favorite characters that you like to play. Feel free to slip into those personalities.)

How far you go with the role-playing is up to you. Your creative juices may run out after half an hour; then you can each have a good laugh and go back to being yourselves. On the other hand, if you can carry your act off for the entire evening, you may even be able to add some variety to your bedroom activities. Use positions that you consider taboo in "real life" but not on these special nights.

Choose your bar carefully as it can play an important role in the proceedings. Make dim lighting, soft music, and a quiet gathering your goal. Then, let the games begin.

If play-acting seems too daring for you, try this game at home the first time. See whether you can pull off your act for a while. If the rehearsal goes well, you can try out your new personality in public the next time.

The Cocoon Date

If you want to have an ultra-romantic date, you need to be able to truly concentrate on each other — like being wrapped in a cocoon where nothing can distract your attentions. To create your cocoon, reserve a room in a hotel that offers room service. Hotel rooms are free of distractions — other than the TV, which you must promise each other not to turn on. After you examine the paltry artwork and check to make sure that the toilet works, you can gaze into each other's eyes to your hearts' content.

You can enjoy sexual interplay while you're inside this cocoon, but the main purpose of such a getaway isn't to have orgasms. Use the time to reconnect, because running in the rat race can easily drive a wedge between you and your partner.

Mini Dates

Sadly, people are often too busy these days to plan dates with their partners. Waiting for an opportune time to meet isn't a viable way to maintain a relationship. You need to make finding time a priority to keep any rifts from developing. Don't limit your dates to large blocks of time; fit some mini dates in whenever you can.

Any time that you spend together focusing on just the two of you qualifies as a mini date. (Having dinner with your children is *not* a mini date.)

Here are a few examples of how to have a mini date:

- ✔ He works late; you go home and eat dinner. Later in the evening, you drive to his office and pick him up. You stop at a bar that serves food and while he has dinner, you sip a beer.

- ✔ You ask the teenager next door to come over at 9 p.m. while the kids are sleeping, and the two of you go out for an ice cream soda.

- ✔ The kids watch cartoons; you tell them that mom and dad are going to be in the garage and that they shouldn't disturb you unless it's an emergency. You pop a pleasant CD in the car stereo, share some fresh fruit, and have a private conversation.

Whatever form your mini dates take, the point is that they require time put aside for just the two of you. Even a half an hour is better than nothing.

Extended Dates

How great would it be if you could hop on a plane Friday afternoon and spend the weekend in Paris? Unfortunately, such glamorous voyages don't mix with most people's budgets; but you can find less extravagant ways of spending an entire weekend together.

Many couples leave the kids with a sitter and take weekend trips that involve picking a place on the map that's a few hours away, driving there, and enjoying whatever that community has to offer.

Don't try to pack too much into these long weekends. For a trip to qualify as a date, you need some time to unwind and get close to one another. That closeness is difficult to achieve if you never remove your seat belts.

Index

Dummies Books™
Bestsellers on Every Topic!

TRAVEL

Title	Author	ISBN	Price
America's National Parks For Dummies®	Kurt Repanshek	0-7645-6204-5	$16.99 US/$25.99 CAN
Arizona For Dummies®	Edie Jarolim	0-7645-6196-0	$16.99 US/$25.99 CAN
California For Dummies®	Cheryl Farr Leas	0-7645-6158-8	$16.99 US/$25.99 CAN
Camping For Dummies®	Michael Hodgson	0-7645-5221-X	$19.99 US/$27.99 CAN
Caribbean For Dummies®	Echo Montgomery Garrett & Kevin Garrett	0-7645-6197-9	$19.99 US/$27.99 CAN
Europe For Dummies®	Reid Bramblett	0-7645-6190-1	$19.99 US/$27.99 CAN
Florida For Dummies®	Jim Tunstall, et al.	0-7645-6361-0	$16.99 US/$25.99 CAN
Hawaii For Dummies®	Cheryl Farr Leas	0-7645-6200-2	$19.99 US/$27.99 CAN
Las Vegas For Dummies®	Mary Herczog	0-7645-6162-6	$15.99 US/$23.99 CAN
New Orleans For Dummies®	Kevin Forest Moreau	0-7645-6159-6	$15.99 US/$23.99 CAN
New York City For Dummies®	Bruce Murphy & Alessandra de Rosa	0-7645-6160-X	$15.99 US/$23.99 CAN
Walt Disney World & Orlando For Dummies® 2002	Jim Tunstall, et al.	0-7645-5388-7	$15.99 US/$23.99 CAN

BUSINESS & PERSONAL FINANCE

Business Etiquette For Dummies®	Sue Fox & Perrin Cunningham	0-7645-5282-1	$21.99 US/$29.99 CAN
Coaching & Mentoring For Dummies®	Marty Brounstein	0-7645-5223-6	$19.99 US/$27.99 CAN
Communicating Effectively For Dummies®	Marty Brounstein	0-7645-5319-4	$21.99 US/$29.99 CAN
Home Buying For Dummies®, 2E	Eric Tyson, MBA & Ray Brown	0-7645-5331-3	$21.99 US/$29.99 CAN
Insurance For Dummies®	Jack Hungelmann	0-7645-5294-5	$21.99 US/$29.99 CAN
Investing For Dummies®, 2E	Eric Tyson, MBA	0-7645-5162-0	$21.99 US/$29.99 CAN
Managing For Dummies®	Bob Nelson & Peter Economy	1-56884-858-7	$21.99 US/$29.99 CAN
Motivating Employees For Dummies®	Max Messmer	0-7645-5327-5	$21.99 US/$29.99 CAN
Mutual Funds For Dummies®, 3E	Eric Tyson, MBA	0-7645-5329-1	$21.99 US/$29.99 CAN
Negotiating For Dummies®	Michael C. Donaldson & Mimi Donaldson	1-56884-867-6	$19.99 US/$27.99 CAN
Personal Finance For Dummies®, 3E	Eric Tyson, MBA	0-7645-5231-7	$21.99 US/$28.99 CAN
Public Speaking For Dummies®	Malcolm Kushner	0-7645-5159-0	$21.99 US/$29.99 CAN
The Complete MBA For Dummies®	Dr. Kathleen Allen & Peter Economy	0-7645-5204-X	$21.99 US/$29.99 CAN
Time Management For Dummies®, 2E	Jeffrey J. Mayer	0-7645-5145-0	$21.99 US/$29.99 CAN

INTERNET/ONLINE

Title	Author	ISBN	Price
The Internet For Dummies®, 7E	John R. Levine, Carol Baroudi, & Arnold Reinhold	0-7645-0674-9	$21.99 US/$32.99 CAN
Internet Auctions For Dummies®	Greg Holden	0-7645-0578-5	$24.99 US/$37.99 CAN

FOOD & BEVERAGE/ENTERTAINING

Title	Author	ISBN	Price
Chinese Cooking For Dummies®	Martin Yan	0-7645-5247-3	$21.99 US/$29.99 CAN
Cooking For Dummies®, 2E	Bryan Miller & Marie Rama	0-7645-5250-3	$19.99 US/$27.99 CAN
Entertaining For Dummies®	Suzanne Williamson with Linda Smith	0-7645-5027-6	$19.99 US/$27.99 CAN
Etiquette For Dummies®	Sue Fox	0-7645-5170-1	$21.99 US/$29.99 CAN
Mexican Cooking For Dummies®	Mary Sue Miliken & Susan Feniger	0-7645-5169-8	$21.99 US/$29.99 CAN
Quick & Healthy Cooking For Dummies®	Lynn Fischer	0-7645-5214-7	$19.99 US/$27.99 CAN

HOME & GARDEN

Antiquing For Dummies®	Ron Zoglin & Deborah Shouse	0-7645-5108-6	$19.99 US/$27.99 CAN
Auto Repair For Dummies®	Deana Sclar	0-7645-5089-6	$21.99 US/$29.99 CAN
Flowering Bulbs For Dummies®	Judy Glattstein & NGA	0-7645-5103-5	$16.99 US/$24.99 CAN
Gardening For Dummies®, 2E	Michael MacCaskey & NGA	0-7645-5130-2	$19.99 US/$29.99 CAN
Herb Gardening For Dummies®	Karen Davis Cutler & Kathleen Fisher	0-7645-5200-7	$16.99 US/$24.99 CAN
Home Decorating For Dummies®	Patricia Hart McMillan & Katharine Kaye McMillan	0-7645-5107-8	$19.99 US/$27.99 CAN
Home Improvement For Dummies®	Gene & Katie Hamilton & the Editors of HouseNet, inc.	0-7645-5005-5	$19.99 US/$26.99 CAN
Home Maintenance For Dummies®	Morris Carey & James Carey	0-7645-5215-5	$21.99 US/$32.99 CAN
Home Remodeling For Dummies®	Morris Carey & James Carey & Dom Deluise	0-7645-5088-8	$19.99 US/$26.99 CAN
Household Hints For Dummies®	Janet Sobesky	0-7645-5141-8	$19.99 US/$26.99 CAN
Lawn Care For Dummies®	Lance Walheim	0-7645-5077-2	$19.99 US/$29.99 CAN
Vegetable Gardening For Dummies®	Charlie Nardozzi & NGA	0-7645-5129-9	$16.99 US/$24.99 CAN

Dummies Books™
Bestsellers on Every Topic!

EDUCATION

| College Planning For Dummies® | Pat Ordovensky | 0-7645-5121-3 | $19.99 US/$26.99 CAN |

CAREERS

Cool Careers For Dummies®, 2E	Marty Nemko, Paul Edwards, & Sarah Edwards	0-7645-5345-3	$19.99 US/$27.99 CAN
Job Hunting For Dummies®, 2E	Max Messmer	0-7645-5163-9	$16.99 US/$25.99 CAN
Job Interviews For Dummies®, 2E	Joyce Lain Kennedy	0-7645-5225-2	$16.99 US/$25.99 CAN
Managing Your Career For Dummies®	Max Messmer	0-7645-5253-8	$21.99 US/$29.99 CAN
Resumes For Dummies®, 3E	Joyce Lain Kennedy	0-7645-5226-0	$16.99 US/$25.99 CAN

THE ARTS

| Art For Dummies® | Thomas Hoving | 0-7645-5104-3 | $24.99 US/$34.99 CAN |

SELF-HELP

Dating For Dummies®	Dr. Joy Browne	0-7645-5072-1	$19.99 US/$27.99 CAN
Feng Shui For Dummies®	David Kennedy	0-7645-5295-3	$19.99 US/$27.99 CAN
Making Marriage Work For Dummies®	Steven Simring, MD & Sue Klavans Simring, DSW	0-7645-5173-6	$19.99 US/$27.99 CAN
Meditation For Dummies®	Stephen Bodian	0-7645-5116-7	$19.99 US/$27.99 CAN
Organizing For Dummies®	Eileen Roth & Elizabeth Miles	0-7645-5300-3	$21.99 US, $29.99 CAN
Parenting For Dummies®	Sandra H. Gookin	1-56884-383-6	$21.99 US/$29.99 CAN
Rekindling Romance For Dummies®	Dr. Ruth K. Westheimer	0-7645-5303-8	$21.99 US/$29.99 CAN
Sex For Dummies®, 2E	Dr. Ruth K. Westheimer	0-7645-5302-X	$21.99 US/$29.99 CAN
Success For Dummies®	Zig Ziglar	0-7645-5061-6	$19.99 US/$27.99 CAN

PETS

Aquariums For Dummies®	Maddy Hargrove & Mic Hargrove	0-7645-5156-6	$21.99 US/$29.99 CAN
Birds For Dummies®	Gina Spadafori & Dr. Brian L. Speer	0-7645-5139-6	$19.99 US/$27.99 CAN
Cats For Dummies®, 2E	Gina Spadafori & Dr. Paul D. Pion	0-7645-5275-9	$21.99 US/$29.99 CAN
Dogs For Dummies®, 2E	Gina Spadafori	0-7645-5274-0	$21.99 US/$29.99 CAN
Dog Training For Dummies®	Jack Volhard & Wendy Volhard	0-7645-5286-4	$21.99 US/$29.99 CAN
Dog Tricks For Dummies®	Sarah Hodgson	0-7645-5287-2	$15.99 US/$23.99 CAN
Puppies For Dummies®	Sarah Hodgson	0-7645-5255-4	$19.99 US/$27.99 CAN

HEALTH

Allergies & Asthma For Dummies®	William Berger, MD	0-7645-5218-X	$19.99 US/$27.99 CAN
Alternative Medicine For Dummies®	James Dillard & Terra Diane Ziporan	0-7645-5109-4	$19.99 US/$27.99 CAN
Aromatherapy For Dummies®	Kathi Keville	0-7645-5171-X	$19.99 US/$27.99 CAN
Arthritis For Dummies®	Barry Fox , PhD & Nadine Taylor-Fox	0-7645-5258-9	$19.99 US/$27.99 CAN
Diabetes For Dummies®	Alan L. Rubin, MD	0-7645-5154-X	$21.99 US/$29.99 CAN
Dieting For Dummies®	The American Dietetic Society with Jane Kirby, RD	0-7645-5126-4	$21.99 US/$29.99 CAN
Family Health For Dummies®	Charles Inlander & Karla Morales	0-7645-5121-3	$19.99 US/$27.99 CAN
First Aid & Safety For Dummies®	Charles B. Inlander & Janet Worsley Norwood	0-7645-5213-9	$19.99 US/$27.99 CAN
Healing Foods For Dummies®	Molly Siple	0-7645-5198-1	$19.99 US/$27.99 CAN
Herbal Remedies For Dummies®	Christopher Hobbs	0-7645-5127-2	$21.99 US/$29.99 CAN
Men's Health For Dummies®	Charles Inlander	0-7645-5120-5	$19.99 US/$27.99 CAN
Nutrition For Dummies®, 2E	Carol Ann Rinzler	0-7645-5180-9	$21.99 US/$29.99 CAN
The Healthy Heart For Dummies®	James M. Ripple, MD	0-7645-5199-X	$19.99 US/$27.99 CAN
Massage For Dummies®	Steve Capellini & Michael Van Welden	0-7645-5172-8	$21.99 US/$29.99 CAN
Vitamins For Dummies®	Christopher Hobbs , Elson Haas , MD	0-7645-5179-5	$19.99 US/$27.99 CAN
Women's Health For Dummies®	Pamela Maraldo, PhD, RN, & The People's Medical Society	0-7645-5119-1	$19.99 US/$27.99 CAN

FITNESS

Fitness For Dummies®, 2E	Suzanne Schlosberg & Liz Neporent	0-7645-5167-1	$21.99 US/$29.99 CAN
Fitness Walking For Dummies®	Liz Neporent	0-7645-5192-2	$19.99 US/$27.99 CAN
Mind-Body Fitness For Dummies®	Therese Iknoian	0-7645-5304-6	$19.99 US/$27.99 CAN
Weight Training For Dummies®, 2E	Liz Neporent, M.A. & Suzanne Schlosberg	0-7645-5168-X	$21.99 US/$29.99 CAN